MW00526475

John Corner's pursuit of his father h
past; truly the stuff of tragedy in the
shattering defeat in the Far East, wh
whole family. It would have been tempt̲i̲n̲g̲ ̲t̲o̲ ̲h̲a̲v̲e̲ ̲d̲u̲c̲k̲e̲d̲ ̲s̲o̲m̲e̲ ̲o̲f̲ ̲t̲h̲e̲ ̲i̲s̲s̲u̲e̲s̲.̲ ̲J̲o̲h̲n̲,
consistently brave, has never done this. The picture is painted 'warts and all'.
   It is surely easier to understand than to forgive; that demands not only balance
but generosity of spirit. The complete absence of bitterness in this book shows that
John has this.

Peter Williams
Brigadier, retd., Welsh Guards

My Father in His Suitcase is much more than a biography of one of the titans of
tropical botany. John K Corner has written a deeply-moving, heartfelt account of his
estranged father. We should all be grateful that John never destroyed the suitcase his
father left him, but instead faced his demons with a 'stiff upper lip' to give us this
remarkable book. Meticulously researched, beautifully written, this is one of the most
riveting biographies ever.

Dr Kevin YL Tan
Past President, Singapore Heritage Society

John Corner has written a riveting but tragic account of his father, Professor
E. J. H. Corner. Behind the achievements of this man obsessed by science lay a
personality totally incapable of coping with the emotional demands of his family.
The consequences were dire.

Dato' Henry Barlow
OBE, MA, FCA
Honourary Treasurer, Malaysian Branch of the Royal Asiatic Society

John has impressed me for his attention to detail and search for the facts. His book is
extraordinary, intriguing, sad, and a fascinating story. I am captivated, more than in
reading a novel. In this documentary, I can feel the author maturing as he writes. It
is surprising to discover that one can receive more insight when finding truth even at
a mature age.
   The story shows that E. J. H. Corner had the trust and respect from the Japanese
scientists and some Japanese administrators during the war. They respected each
other. When I travelled around Japan with him to visit his friends, including
academic ones, I saw that their friendship continued and was deepened.

Prof Mikiko Ishii

The life of Edred John Corner, extensively read and larger-than-life man, who did
not suffer fools gladly, is fully explored by his estranged son, who himself, until this
deeply researched personal journey, knew very little about his father's arduous war-
time experiences and world-acknowledged, academic achievements in botany and
especially mycology. The present book explores these and the many inconsistences
and secrets of his father's life, of which most people only know snippets and not
the full story. My Father in His Suitcase is essential reading as an 'adventure' or
documentation of an extraordinary scientist.

Roy Watling
M.B.E., DSc.,PhD, FRSE., FLS., FSB., C.Biol.

John Corner – irascible, imperious, intolerant to implied criticism, but brilliant – was an inspiration to those Cambridge undergraduates motivated from childhood by an abiding addiction to natural history, and with aspirations for a life in the rain forest. Poised over his erect brass microscope in the tall window beside the door to the Botany School, he could be seen to dedicate more time to science than anyone else we knew; yet he was never a drudge, always alive with some unexpected and exciting observation. His past was only hinted at, a mystery seemingly dark, apparently deserting family, surviving unscathed in Japanese Singapore, succoured by the last Tokugawa shogun and honoured by the emperor: but was he himself entirely honourable? Here, his son who, once adult, never heard from his father again, has asked our questions with more vehemence than we could possibly do, and now recounts the results of his years of enquiry and the conclusions that they have at last elicited.

Dr Peter Ashton
Charles Bullard Professor of Forestry emeritus, Harvard University

E.J.H. Corner was at the Botany Department at Cambridge when I took Part 1 in Natural Sciences. Much later, when I became president of the Rain Forest Club, I invited him as our after-dinner speaker. He lounged over the table and reminisced, impromptu and outrageously, about episodes of his life and colleagues. "Is this man real?" asked my guest. The answer is that he was very real, a true innovator in the field and intellectually, well deserving a biography. When John Corner first approached me, he felt that I knew his father better than he did. Now, thanks to his dedicated and industrious research, through these pages all of us know much more about a great man.

Gathorne Gathorne-Hardy
5th Earl of Cranbrook

I approached John Corner's book expecting to add a few more stories to the EJH Corner compendium. While I did learn fascinating new tales about the author's father, this book works on so many different and more important levels. It documents a key turning point in the histories of several countries, it chronicles the growth of tropical botany, and it documents the beginnings of what would soon become the wholesale, and sadly permanent, transformation of a vast tropical landscape. It is also the story of a daring and iconoclastic scientist, and of his son who comes to terms with a very difficult part of his life, at first reluctantly, and then with the tenacity of someone on a mission. It is a compelling and moving read that deserves a wide audience.

Dr Shawn Kaihekulani Yamauchi Lum
President, Nature Society (Singapore)

Would I have wanted EJHC as my deputy? For his brilliance and tropical forest understanding, yes, but how to manage him, no one his superior? His conservation ethic was before its time and sadly the world continued to destroy. This superbly written biography is as much a work of scholarship as it is an emotional roller coaster, both for writer and reader, but I love the lighter moments too. 'The Frock' is wonderful! Singapore Botanic Gardens is grateful to its illustrious former Assistant Director and equally his son.

Dr Nigel Taylor
Director, Singapore Botanic Gardens

MY FATHER IN HIS SUITCASE

MY FATHER IN
HIS SUITCASE

In Search of E. J. H. Corner
the Relentless Botanist

JOHN K. CORNER

Foreword by
Douglas Hurd,
Rt. Hon. Lord Hurd of Westwell, C.H., C.B.E.

◦LANDMΔRK◦BOOKS◦

Published by Landmark Books Pte Ltd
5001 Beach Road
#02-73/74
Singapore 199588

ISBN 978-981-4189-47-7

Printed by COS Printers Pte Ltd

CONTENTS

LIST OF PLATES

FOREWORD

The British Empire has had its black as well as its splendid days. Query – one of the blackest was 15 February 1942. That was the day on which the British surrendered to the Japanese the colony of Singapore, which had been the proud centre of British dominion in South East Asia. Attacked from the land rather than as expected from the sea, Singapore fell with hardly a fight. Lee Kuan Yew, the future ruler of Singapore, watched as a student of 18, the crowds of defeated British soldiers filling the streets. He wrote afterwards "this endless stream of bewildered men who did not know what had happened, why it had happened or what they were doing in Singapore anyway". One young Englishman was clear why he was in Singapore. John Corner had 13 years earlier accepted the post of Assistant Director of the Botanic Gardens in Singapore. His overriding allegiance was to the cause of science. As his son writes in this admirable book, he was consumed by the relentless drive for knowledge. His duty, as he saw it, was to the cause of science. He had no doubt that it was his duty to look after the Botanic Gardens even under Japanese military occupation. He stayed at his post until the Japanese surrendered in 1945. He managed to steer clear of any political commitment and developed a sound working relationship with the Japanese occupiers, and in particular with the Marquis Tokugawa, a senior Japanese official who had general oversight of the Occupation, and in particular of the relationship with the Malay Sultans and the scientific work in Singapore. John Corner was my uncle, my mother's brother.

After Singapore was liberated in 1945 there was a strong feeling amongst the British who had been detained in the prison camps against those like my uncle who had continued with their jobs and professional lives. John Corner was by nature argumentative, indeed dogmatic. He brushed aside all reproaches and indeed intensified his friendship with the Japanese, going so far as to write a book, *The Marquis,* about his friend, and also about the hobby of Emperor Hirohito as a marine biologist. He paid a price; after years of separation his marriage to an American girl collapsed, and he failed to develop a friendship with her son, the author of this book, and two daughters. His scientific work earned him the reward of a Fellowship of the Royal Society, and he welcomed friendly nephews who rode out from Cambridge to Great Shelford to take tea with their uncle.

I am glad that his son has broken through the barrier, albeit after his father's death. This is a readable and painstaking work of a family that came to grief under the divisive pressures of the war and strain of my uncle's scientific vocation which came to dominate his life. This cannot have been an easy book to write. The author does justice to his parents, shows sympathy and understanding for his father's stubborn determination to follow science wherever it might lead him.

Douglas Hurd
Rt. Hon. Lord Hurd of Westwell, C.H., C.B.E.

ACKNOWLEDGMENTS

Arts Centre Press, WA. Au Jardin restaurant of the Les Amis Group in E. J. H. Corner House. Audrey McCormick. Australian National Botanic Gardens, Canberra: Dr Heino Lepp, Catherine Jordan (Librarian) and staff of the herbarium.

Belinda Corner. Botanic Gardens of Adelaide: The letter from Professor J. B. Cleland to E. J. H Corner in Singapore, dated 21/11/1941 is courtesy of the Board of Botanic Gardens and State Herbarium, Adelaide, South Australia. Brigadier Peter Williams (Welsh Guards, retired).

Cambridge University Library (Rachel Rowe). Casa da Cultura de Itaborai Museum, near Rio de Janeiro, Brazil. Changi Chapel & Museum, Singapore. Charles Chai. COFEPOW. Colorado State University, Archives and Special Collections – The Dana Bailey In Memoriam Testimonials, particularly those of Prof Les Barclay, OBE, FREng, FIEE, Peter A Bradley, Jack W Herbstreit, Col Earl J Holliman, USA (Ret), Takashi Iida (Communications Research Laboratory, Tokyo, Japan), Richard C Kirby, Ernest K Smith, and Noboru Wakai (ex-Director General Radio Research Laboratories, Tokyo, Japan).

Dato' Henry Barlow. Dr David Hill, son of Dr Robin Hill. David Wingate, grandson of Pen Landon. Deborah Holttum. Douglas and Morag Walmsley, she being Colin Fraser Symington's daughter. Dr Barbara Parris. Dr Bruce Bernstein (Executive Director of SWAIA, USA). Dr David J Chivers (Fellow and Tutor at Selwyn College, and University Reader in Primate Biology and Conservation, Cambridge). David Fuller (*Great Shelford Village News* editor). Dr Francis Macnab (Executive Minister, St Michael's Uniting Church, Melbourne, Australia). Dr Godfrey Curtis. Dr Henry Noltie. Dr Beatriz Bernal (lecturer, Rio de Janeiro Rural University who is working on seaweeds and introduced to me by Christine Maggs, Professor of Phycology at Queen's University, Belfast). Dr Ian Turner. Dr Janet Evans. Dr John Dawson. Dr John Hewitson (SAPS, Cambridge). Dr Pam Catcheside (for the Professor J. B. Cleland story). Dr Patrick Petitjean (Laboratoire de Philosophie et d'Histoire des Sciences). Dr Peter Collenette. Dr Peter Tanner. Dr Quentin C. B. Cronk. Dr Robin Blackburn. Dr Ronald (Ron) Petersen. Dr Scott Redhead. Dr Sheila Collenette. Dr Tadamichi Koga's family. Dr Tadashi Kajita (Associate Professor Dept of Biology, Faculty of Science, Chiba University).

Edward Newman. Elizabeth Lewis (née Morley). E. J. H. Corner's research students: Dr Chew Wee Lek. Dr David Frodin. Dr David Mabberley. Dr Engkik Soepadmo. Dr Gordon deWolf. Dr John Dransfield. Dr Peter Ashton. Dr Ruth Kiew. Dr Vernon Heywood. The late Dr Brenda Slade. The late Dr Chang Kiaw Lan. The late Dr Tim Whitmore.

Fitzwilliam Museum, Cambridge.

Gathorne Gathorne-Hardy, Earl of Cranbrook. Gina Murrell (Department of Plant Sciences, Cambridge, retired). Geoff Foster-Taylor of *Tilbury Hall*. Glenn Shelly

(NORPAC Yacht & Ship Brokerage, San Francisco Bay, USA) for Stroma of Mey information. Griselda Hitchcock (née Worthington) for much material.

Hachiro Ikeda (TV producer in Japan, particularly of the 1995 documentary *Do You Know Shonanto, Portraits of Humanity under the Shadow of War*, and director of the 1985 documentary by Japan TV Aichi *The Flower Blossomed in the Battlefield*.) Helen Harwood. Heloisa M. Bertol Domingues. Hiromi Kubota.

IUCN Archives, Switzerland, and Australia.

James Wang Wei. Jean Paton. Jonathan Moffatt. The late John Gullick. Judith Wilson (*Great Shelford Village News* editor). Judy Bryning.

K. S. Pang (Keeper of the Hong Kong Herbarium). Kit Seddon, the daughter of the late Charles Cox MBE, for her father's notes. Kiyose Kazuhiro (Embassy of Japan, Singapore).

Douglas Hurd, Lord Hurd of Westwell. Lord Thomas of Swynnerton, for approval to quote from Brian Montgomery's *Shenton of Singapore*. Lyana Shah.

Malayan Volunteers Group. Mark Wong Wenwei (Oral History Department, Singapore). Marthe Kiley-Worthington, daughter of Barton Worthington. Mary Harris. The late Mary Turnbull. Mayumi Shimizu. Michael Brown. Michael E. Leveridge. Michael Wood who helped with the Cover Note. Mrs April Duck who transcribed the Japan audio tapes. Mrs Etty Saul. Mrs June Wingate, Pen Landon's daughter. Mrs Kiyoko Tanigawa, daughter of Dr Koga. Mrs Margo Ewart for the poem *Zebra* (after that of Gavin Ewart) from *The Learned Hippopotomas* (1986). Mrs Marj Goodhue, my American relation. Mrs Ro McConnell. Mrs Thyra Godber.

National Archives of Australia. National Archives of Singapore. National Archives (UK). Nationaal Herbarium of Nederland. National Parks Board, Singapore.

Oliver Tooley, grandson of the late Frank Kingdon-Ward.

P. K. Nettur (First Admiral, Retd, who attempt to find Yamashita's battle map). Peter Williams, Prof Andrew Smith. Prof Anthony Hopkin who introduced me to Tim Wilson. Prof Bruce Ing. The late Prof C. C. Berg. Prof David Crompton. Prof David Hawksworth. Prof Derek Beales. Prof Duncan Poore. Prof Ho Coy Choke. Prof Jose I dos R Furtado, son of Dr C. X. Furtado from Singapore Botanic Gardens, prewar. Prof Jim Ginns. Prof Kevin Kenneally, introduced by Jean Paton. The late Prof Jeffrey Switzer and his wife, Sheila. Prof Marcos Chor Maio (Sociologist, Senior Researcher, Oswaldo Cruz House/Oswaldo Cruz Foundation, Brazil, June 2007). Prof Mikiko Ishii. Prof Mitsuyasyu Habebe and Mrs Yuki Habebe, his wife. Prof Peter Askew. Prof Peter Austwick. Prof Peter Grubb. Prof Stephen Hopper, FLS, FTSE (Director, CEO and Chief Scientist, RBG Kew). Prof Vincent Demoulin, Institut de Botanique, University of Liege, Belgium. Prof Yoji Akashi (Emeritus Professor of Southeast Asian History – modern times to present – Nanzan University, Nagoya, who has access to the diaries of Marquis Yoshichika Tokugawa).

Ravi Mandalam of the Sabah Society. Richard Morley. Robin Campbell. Robin Miller. The late Roderick MacLean, MCS, OBE. Roger Hicks. Rosemary Fell (Malayan Volunteers Group, UK). Royal Botanic Gardens, Edinburgh: Professor

Roy Watling (former Head of Mycology and Plant Pathology) and Jane Hutcheon (Head of Library Services & Publications). Royal Botanic Gardens, Melbourne: Dr Tom May (Senior Mycologist, RBG Melbourne), Jill Thurlow (Library Technician, RBG Melbourne) and staff of the herbarium. Royal Botanic Gardens, Sydney: Dr Peter Valder, Dr Joy Everett (Botanist) and Louisa Murray (Flora Botanist) National Herbarium of New South Wales, Botanic Gardens Trust.

Sebastian Raboude for his great help with my computer skills. Shelagh Wakely (née Worthington). Sidney Sussex College, Cambridge, The Archives: Nicholas Rogers. Simon Appleby. Singapore Botanic Gardens: Dr Nigel Taylor (Director), Dr Chin See Chung, (immediate past Director), Christina Soh (Manager Library of Botany and Horticulture) and staff of the Gardens. The late Sir Arthur Bryan. Sir Hugh Cortazzi. Sir John and Lady Jean Gurdon. Sir John Whitehead. Sonoo Uetake. Susan Hill, elder daughter of Dr Robert (Robin) Hill. SS *Orion* evacuees: Bridget Kitchin (née Hayward). Eileen Ritson (née Carey). Graem Castell. Ian Richardson. Jane Brighouse via Sheila Stuart. Jill Smallshaw (née Wright). Joan Lardy (née Mulligan). Judy Bryning for the two poems. June Dunnett. Kenneth Miles. Kit Seddon (née Cox). Mary O'Sullivan (née Mulligan). Nigel Killeen. Patricia McEntee. Rita Mason via Dennis Luff. Sandy Lincoln. The late Sheila Corner. The late Lt Col Tom Irlam, MBE. Trish Niblock. Yvonne Heritage (née Spranklin). Morag Walmsley (née Symington). Allan Proctor.

Terry Waite, CBE. The Archives of the Needham Research Institute, Cambridge. The Dandenong Historical Society. The Hon. Stephen Hurd. The Journal *New Scientist Syndication*. The National Diet Library, Tokyo. The National Maritime Museum, Sydney, Australia. The Office of *Who's Who*. The Royal Society, London: Rupert Baker and Gill Jackson. The Sabah Society: Datuk C. L. Chan (past President) and members of the Society. The Singapore General Hospital. The Singapore General Hospital Museum: Dr Lee Seng Teik (Director), Toby Huynh (Curator). *The Whitehorse Leader*, my local weekly newspaper. *Tilbury Hall*. Tim Mahony for pictures from Dana Bailey's collection, and the motor-bike story. Tim Walker, son of Frank and Bobby Walker. Tim Williams, son of Bill and Kate Williams. Tim Wilson, son of the late Bishop of Birmingham and Singapore. Tohoku University, Japan. Tokyo Zoological Park Society, Ueno: Shigeo Nakagawa (Education Manager) and Hiroshi Ohira. Tony O'Dempsey. Twyford School: David Livingstone (ex-headmaster), David Wickham (ex-headmaster), Luke Wordley (Development Officer, retired), Roger Porteous (Archivist), Burser and staff.

UNESCO archives, Paris.

Veronica Appleby. Vytas Levickis, for digital enhancement of photographs and computer help.

Wal Reid. Wendy How, my father's housekeeper and carer in his last years and a very caring friend to him. William Langstaff, my father's gardener in his last years and a good friend to him.

PROLOGUE

Suddenly and unexpectedly a suitcase came into my life. I was angry, irritated, intrigued, and just a little inquisitive. Why? Why did he do it? What was behind it? He never did anything without reason. I had managed to put him at the very back of my mind and thought I was at peace with the world. This risked disturbing everything, bringing back the past of which I so hoped I had rid from my mind.

He was Edred John Henry Corner, my father, yet I hardly knew him. I had left home in 1960, aged 19, never to see him again.

I knew very little about him and his work: what I did know was that he was a botanist, specialising in mushrooms and also did much work on figs. I seem to recall from a conversation in his study over 50 years ago that he had re-named over 10,000 figs in Latin which had been improperly named as far back as Henry VIII.

He was a difficult man with a temper to whom I never felt close.

*

In 1997, my father-in-law was surprised to have a visit from my cousin Stephen Hurd bearing that suitcase, left by my late father in his study, with a note saying that it be given to me 'wherever he may be'. Stephen had asked my wife, Belinda, what he should do with it and they agreed the best thing was to deliver it to Oakington where my in-laws lived, not so far from Great Shelford where my father had lived.

My father-in-law told Belinda it had arrived and she knew I wouldn't be interested. She briefly mentioned its arrival and we agreed it should remain at her parents' house for a while. I quickly forgot its existence, but never really cleared it from my mind. Belinda occasionally reminded me that her parents still had the suitcase and, from time to time reminded by her father, wondered when we were going to collect it. It remained there unopened until they died. When clearing the house in 2002, we found it in the garage and I finally accepted that it must return with us to our home.

Interestingly, my father's housekeeper of his later years noticed a suitcase behind his desk in his study, a most holy of holy place where few dared to tread without invitation. She wondered about it but never asked and just cleaned around it. I thought this was the suitcase bought for me when I first went away to school in 1949. They were not happy times and seeing it again brought many memories flooding back that were not good. I really wanted nothing of it and so it remained untouched in our loft until we came to sort out things to take to Australia late in 2004.

At one point before we left for Australia, I wanted to throw it away, and nearly did. I was frankly angry that after all these years and many fruitless attempts at reconciliation he was reminding me of great unhappiness by bequeathing that damn suitcase. Fortunately, wise wifely counsel prevailed. I did, though, in a moment of anger dispose of some of my father's books which my mother had passed on to me, including a first edition of his major work, *Wayside Trees of Malaya*. How I came to regret the loss of that first edition!

Looking back, I believe if I had opened the case when it first arrived, nothing of this would have happened. It was luck, karma, that I took so long 'to break the seal' and thank goodness I did.

The suitcase travelled with us to Australia and rested on a garage shelf until mid-year 2006. I was under advice to do something about it or put it away somewhere; I had moved it to the floor by my desk so that it was a constant reminder. I knew I had to open it at some point. When I did open it, it was with considerable trepidation and great uncertainty.

The Melbourne winter day was dull and wet. There I was on my own sitting on the floor, Belinda wisely having decided that it was 'my moment' and it might prove difficult. The two locks opened easily, no need for a key, and just as well for there was none. I wondered when they had last been released. The fusty smell which greeted me was the beginning of quite an adventure which, just moments before, I would never in a million years have thought possible. I had, for more than 46 years, managed with some difficulty, and great effort, to put my father and all the unpleasant happenings out of my mind. But now, I was faced with countless envelopes of all sizes and styles, a mix of papers and postcards, and much more. (See Appendix B for a selected list of the suitcase's contents).

I found many letters, old photographs, maps and school books, some from as far back as 1947 when I was at school in Niteroi, across the bay from Rio de Janeiro. Then there were the many school bills of a size (the cost not the paper) which even today surprises me. Some of the photographs, many dating from the 1930s, showed people – but who were they? Nothing was written on the back. There were stories, complete and incomplete, and even some seaweed that my father taught me how to collect and dry when we were in Brazil. The colour was as bright as the day they were dried. Immediately I remembered the collecting – how the memory can recall at a moment's notice something from the distant past and forget something which happened recently.

In that moment I was happy and quickly told myself that that cannot be right… or could it?

I opened the envelopes to find letters from my father to his new in-laws in New York; letters of 1949–1954 from him to my headmaster at my prep school which did not read well, with some replies from the Head which showed understanding of my poor performance. There were letters from my mother to me, and from me to her. How on earth did he get these?

As I read them, I could not contain the emotion even though I had been brought up to have that stiff upper-lip! It was wonderfully difficult and I didn't know how I felt; Belinda noticed and was a great comfort.

I sat back overwhelmed by it all – so many memories flooding back – and wondered what it was all about. What an extraordinary thing for him to do. Why, for heavens sake why, and where did he get some of those things?

I re-packed the case and it rested again by my desk for some days while I came to grips with the enormity of it all, and gradually, I decided what had to be done. The option of suitcase destruction was no more.

I knew my father only up to when I left home; my two children, Andrew (Andy) and Katharine (Katie), never met him and of course neither have their children, and consequently they had no conception of the sort of man he was. I set out to rectify all of this and to determine whether my few memories are right, a little right – or simply wrong.

I resolved to find out all about my father's life and write about it for them, so that the family would know and have a proper record which would remain for family posterity. It was of course for me too. I will always remember being asked about my father by one of my Australian grandchildren; Annabel in her small voice fired me to action. She represented the part of family with no father-in-law, no paternal uncles and aunts and no paternal grandfather or great-grandfather. Only then did I realise what a loss it was and what it means to them, and me. I had thought that by putting it all into the farthest corner of my mind I could forget and no one would ever enquire. I was also determined to find out about my parents' divorce which split the family. I felt to blame.

I found that at this defining moment I bore no malice, which surprised me. Yes, I was angry initially and quite upset but I came to absorb things and determined that the story I write must be even-handed and fair, with my personal feelings only where appropriate.

I decided to call the suitcase Pandora's Box. When Pandora opened the box, it is said that after all the evils of the world like anger, pride and shame had escaped, there was one other creature – very small and very frail – which followed them into the world. Hope.

My Pandora certainly fired my enthusiasm to research and I was even becoming excited about the prospect. I hadn't begun to appreciate the challenge of it all and the emotional rollercoaster it represented.

I completed the story for the family in April 2008 and presented copies to Andy and Katie at her 40th dinner party. It was more a compilation of facts with photographs than a book – things I wanted my family to have on record and not lost to posterity. I called it *In Search of my Father; Quest for the Truth.*

During the research, a number of people suggested I write it as a book. I gave this much thought, for they were responsible suggestions from people of position, took a break from it, and decided, with Belinda's support, to have a go. After all, it did keep me 'out from under' and absorbed for long periods.

I realised that to be a book the material had to be presented differently – a total rewrite which was a very daunting challenge. I have now done the work and here is the story which I want to tell.

It is the story of Professor E. J. H. Corner containing much about his family and my life, much of which would not have been revealed if my Pandora's Box had not been packed – and opened.

My father's views of pre-war Singapore and Malaya are important, and amongst them are amusing moments written when times were very different in that part of the world. His wartime experiences in occupied Singapore must also be told and understood – for good and bad. I knew so little and had never thought of asking, 'What did you do in the war, Dad?' While I am not equipped to write a scientific book, scientific matters are included; indeed they must be, for my father's enormous success as a scientist and botanist must be appreciated just as his equally enormous failure with his family.

Why did he shun the many attempts at reconciliation yet leave Pandora for me?

I believe I now know why he bequeathed that case. It was a challenge, from the grave, to me his 'dullard' son. Would I rise to the challenge of being the son of a brilliant yet impossibly difficult man? Yes.

A book can be considered a mirror of the soul: but who can see the reflection and accept the truth which after so many years has been distorted, denied and hidden? The family traumas had to be put behind, difficult as that must be, so that a better understanding of the family history may be revealed. Long-held beliefs and blame had to be magnanimously put away, the mind opened – and the real truth absorbed, perhaps from a long look into that mirror.

In the pursuit of truth, I have followed the mottoes of Twyford School and The Leys School where I received my education: *Vince Patientia* – loosely translated as it's dogged as does it; and *In fide fiducia* – in faith faithfully. I have striven to find the truth and believe I have.

- I -

EARLY LIFE

Before I find the entry to the trail, rather maze, which I must follow to find my father, I must set the scene with his early years through to university, for this is important to the story and the understanding of E. J. H. Corner.

I knew only very little of what follows. I knew that he was born in London and lived in Harley Street, that he went to Rugby School and had been good at rugby football: that he went on to Sidney Sussex College, Cambridge. I knew that his parents were 'medical' people. I also knew we apparently were 'descended' from Cromwell and that he had re-named possibly 10,000 figs. I learned all of this from my father in the 1950s.

The Corners can be traced at least to the 15th century and I recall my father proudly telling us children that we were related to Oliver Cromwell. There hung a picture of this serious gentleman in our dining room in Great Shelford. The Corners are of Yorkshire stock, originally from Lythe near Whitby*, traceable to the reign of Henry VII (1457–1509) and even earlier.

My father was born in London on 12 January 1906 and lived with his parents at 37 Harley Street, a house with a history.

His father, Edred Moss Corner, was born in London in 1873, the fifth son†

---

* *John Corner (a member of the family from Whitby, 1824–1890) bought one of four copies of* James Cook – a Journal of the proceedings of His Majesty's Bark Endeavour *on a voyage around the world in 1890 from one F.W. Cosens F. S. A., of Lewes, Sussex. After Corner died suddenly later that year, F. H. Dangar bought it from Corner's executors and presented Captain Cook's journal to the Australian Museum in 1895 where it is still known as the 'Corner Journal'. In 1935, the document was transferred to the Mitchell Library, Sydney, where it rests today. In the course of researching this, I came across Sylvia Corner (1890–1975), granddaughter of the said John Corner, who wrote* Reaching Australia, Cook's Voyages to the Southern Continent, *and the unverified suggestion that my family supplied timber for Captain Cook's vessel Endeavour.*

†*Among Edred's brothers were Frank and Harry who were also doctors; there were three sisters – Elgie, Ethel and Hilda.*

5

of Dr Francis Meade Corner, a general practitioner in Poplar. Grandfather Corner was consulting surgeon to St. Thomas' Hospital, the Hospital for Sick Children, Great Ormond Street, and Epsom College. He held similar positions in local hospitals and was on the honorary staff of Queen Mary's Hospital, Roehampton.

He received his education at Epsom College where he was head prefect, captain of the rugby XV and a member of the cricket 1st XI. He won a scholarship to Sidney Sussex College, Cambridge, and took a first class in the natural sciences tripos of 1894. He then went to St. Thomas' Medical School, London, for his clinical studies and carried off the highest honours. In 1898, he graduated MB, BCh, and a year later he took the FRCS, going on to the MCh in 1906. He was a member of the British Medical association for many years, serving as secretary of the Section of Diseases of Children at the Annual Meeting of 1907, and vice-president of the same section, including orthopaedics, at that of 1912. He became Erasmus Wilson Lecturer at the Royal College of Surgeons, and Arris and Gale lecturer and Harveian lecturer in 1919.

Grandfather Corner was also an accomplished mountaineer and climber: he joined the Scottish Mountaineering Club in 1897 and completed 286 Munros. He was recognised for the accuracy of his recorded heights, always carrying four aneroid barometers with him on climbs.

In the 1914–1918 war, my grandfather served in the Royal Army Medical Corp as a major and his surgical expertise made him a valued member of the staff at Roehampton and in the amputation clinic set up at St Thomas' Hospital. Arthritis cut short his career at its height; he resigned all his appointments and retired in 1921. For a while he was superintendent of a convalescent home in Great Missenden but when his sight finally failed he retired to *Stratton End*, a large house in sweeping gardens in Beaconsfield and where all his many friends were very welcome.

Edred Moss Corner died on 2 May 1950, aged 77.

In 1903, Edred Corner married Henrietta Henderson of Broughty Ferry near Dundee, Scotland. Born in 1872, she was educated in Dundee and Paris and was also in the medical profession. She did her training at St Thomas' Hospital (1897–1900) and was Assistant Matron at St Marylebone Infirmary (1900–1901) and Matron at Norwood Cottage Hospital (1901–1903). She worked for the British Red Cross Society, and the St John Ambulance in London receiving the Order of the League of Mercy in 1912, and the Royal Red Cross in 1916. She was Hon. Serving Sister of St John of Jerusalem and was elected Councillor of the Urban District of Beaconsfield in 1935. Though obviously competent, she was at times a little austere.

Edred and Henrietta Corner had three children: Edred John Henry Corner, Stephanie Frances*, and Dorothy Isobel†.

The Harley Street house in which my father was brought up, is the house, it is thought, where Lord Nelson took Lady Hamilton during the zenith of his career. In the 1980s, my father wrote a fascinating description of the house and his life there. It shows his remarkable ability to recall, and occasionally his gift for 'accurate' romancing, but of most import it shows his skill in observation and writing.

A corner house on the north side of the junction with Harley Street, 37 Harley Street has a pillared entrance in Queen Anne Street. The house dates from about 1897, one of the earliest independent commissions of the architectural maverick Arthur Beresford Pite. The door had three brass name plates showing E. M. Corner, H. (Harry) Corner and E. A. Saunders.

My father described the house eloquently:

Along Harley Street and Queen Anne Street there was an iron railing some five feet high to prevent persons falling into the narrow passage, known as the area, which surrounded the basement. A gate on the Harley Street side led by steps down into the area and served as a tradesman's access to the back door. Thus the house had six floors from the basement to the uppermost. Communication between these extremes was by an air-tube in the wall. At the top, outside the nursery door, a black ebonite mouth-piece, plugged with a whistle, led to a similar end in the basement. Removal of the plug at one end and blowing hard into the tube sounded the whistle at the other end. One spoke into the mouth-piece, not unnecessarily loudly, while the listener at the other end applied an ear to the mouth-piece. Otherwise, communication was by shouting or running up and downstairs.

He continued with a description of the dining room on the ground floor fronting Harley Street, the furniture, the meals-serving lift and the 'stout wooden chest' which held items for motoring. Here the Corner family had daily meals and the more formal Sunday lunch. There was a passage which led to Grandfather Corner's consulting rooms and woe betide anyone who left doors open to allow cooking smells to reach the patients! My

* Stephanie Frances Corner married Anthony Richard Hurd MP, later to become Lord Hurd of Newbury, Baron Hurd (1901–1966), a notable politician, writer and farmer. Their eldest son, Douglas (1930–), also entered politics serving in the governments of John Major and Margaret Thatcher. Their other sons are John Julian Hurd (1931–1951) and Stephen Hurd (1933–).

† Dorothy Isobel Corner (1907-1975), known to the family as Aunt Do, was unmarried. She had a notable career in the hotel industry, first at the Mayfair Hotel before becoming head housekeeper of the Hyde Park Hotel. In 1954, she became Housekeeper at the prestigious Le Manoir Richelieu in La Malbaie, Canada.

father wrote: 'Strictness prevailed'.

My grandfather's room, both his study and consulting room, was always warm and the children were often welcomed to enjoy it before supper and before they were packed off upstairs to bed. It had one large set of windows and 'the massive roll-top desk stood by the window set obliquely so that the shadow of his right hand did not fall directly on his writing…' This desk is the one I remember dominating my father's study at Great Shelford, and under which Pandora was found, always full of papers and in some order.

Continuing his description of the study, my father recalled the bookcase which stood 'on the inner side of the fireplace and ushered, as it were, the way to the curtain which concealed the couch on which the patient would lie: beside it was a glass cabinet for instruments and disinfectants. Secretly we children used to explore this room and enjoy the anatomical pictures in the books: indeed, I began to study Gray's Anatomy almost as soon as I could read'.

Dr Saunders' study was on the first landing. This was out-of-bounds to the children; the door always being locked when unoccupied. My father described Uncle Harry's room as 'bare and uninteresting with just a plain desk, a chair or two and a gas-fire'.

The drawing room, however, was spacious and elegant, and benefited from Grandmother Corner's keen interest in flowers and floral decoration.

On entering the room, a grandfather clock stood on the left, then a short bookcase filled with what my father described as 'dull literature and novels', and armchairs on either side of the fire. Opposite was a sofa, a small table, a cabinet, and a massive upright Blüthner piano from the last century. My grandmother played the piano and composed music, painted watercolours, and wrote poetry – and brought up a large family.

My father recalled that she held afternoon and evening parties, events which he was never comfortable with.

> On some afternoons my mother had tea-parties when she liked to show off her children in their best clothes – another hateful occasion for me. But, after the ordeal, I would sneak back downstairs to sit hidden by one balustrade and wait for the party to break up: then boldly entering the drawing room … I set to on the remainder of the sandwiches.

The spare bedroom was on the second floor and it was here, my father wrote, 'that my mother slept with me, aged 5, when I was suffering awful pains from incipient appendicitis, in order that my cries would not disturb my father in his and my mother's bedroom on the floor above… Oh the agony.' On the third floor were the children's bedrooms with the main bathroom. Father rather ruefully recalls a frightful occasion in his parents' room:

when I was 2–3 years old, I got stuck on the head-railing [of his parent's double bed] when clambering over the bed. I cried out. My father, who was dressing, was so angry that he picked me off, laid me on my tummy in one hand and slapped with the other, only to add to my cries. He laughed at the recollection and so I remember the occasion, even though I was so young.

Dr Saunders' bedtime stories fascinated my father and his sisters. He came from an entomological family and his brother Charles featured in many of his tales. He had been Solicitor-General in Singapore and collected beetles. My father wrote of him:

My two sisters and I joined him on a cycle ride to Dorking where Charles, his brother, lived. They both were bachelors. Charles showed us his collection of beetles that all were small – he would not collect any larger than about a centimetre. He was rather a scruffy appearing man yet had a good humour and was friendly. I was captured not only by the collection but that such a public figure could be interested in such small things.

This led my father to a life-time's interest in coleoptery and I remember him teaching me, also at an early age, how to catch and mount butterflies, moths and all shapes and sizes of beetle, the Stag being my pride and joy. I remember having no fear of them! This continued in Brazil in 1947.

My fathers' interest in music began in that Harley Street house. Not only did grandmother Corner play the piano, but others too. Grateful patients, unable to pay the surgeon's fees,

played the piano as their token and, among these was the famous pianist Lamond*, who would give recitals of Beethoven's sonatas. But my father [EMC], who could not play, had attached to it the memorable adjunct called the angelus which, worked from pedals, unwound a roll of strong paper on which were parallel longitudinal rows of slots of varying lengths. The air came through the slots and in doing so depressed the keys for varying lengths of time so as to play the tune. The effect

* The pianist Lamond was well known in those days and I think helped considerably to inspire my father into both the piano and classical music. Frederic Archibald Lamond (1868–1948) was a Scottish classical pianist and composer, and the penultimate pupil of Franz Liszt. In 1886, Lamond met Johannes Brahms who coached him in his own works. In addition to becoming one of the early champions of Brahms' piano works, Lamond was also considered a primary authority on Beethoven's piano music.

was realistic… The angelus had a high stool and, on lifting its lid, there were packed in long rectangular boxes the rolls of music – with other boxes stacked by the wall. I learned to enjoy the angelus, in the vigour of its pedalling (when my legs were long enough), the variation by hand-levers from fortissimo to pianissimo, and the lovely melodies and prosodies that issued. I used to get up early to play the angelus for half-an-hour before breakfast, and in the summer, with the veranda-window open, Chopin, Schubert, Beethoven and Brahms resounded along Queen Anne Street – no one objected.

Other grateful patients presented gifts, among which were the three grandfather clocks standing respectively in the parlour, dining room and drawing room. One of these clocks subsequently went to Aunt Do and was eventually passed to me. I gave it to my son Andy, so that it remains a Corner clock.

Although my father enjoyed playing the piano, he hated the singing lessons which he used to have along with other children of the neighbourhood. They were conducted on Saturday mornings by a grey-haired Miss Mills. Then, there were piano lessons of an hour a week.

I remember a pretty young Miss Blake who taught me scales, arpeggios, chords and sight-reading, but I never became proficient in any way, and the lessons for my sisters and myself were given up, mainly because we showed little interest or aptitude but the Blüthner is my delight in my old age.

I have strong memories of that Blüthner and his playing. He said he played 'whatever comes into my head'. I did not like all, but his rendering of Brahms' Lullaby improved in its rendition over time and I remember that with some pleasure. He usually played in the evening when I had gone to bed.

My father's description of his Harley Street bedroom undoubtedly shows his inventiveness from an early age:

Four things stick in my mind: I had a large, rather lurid poster of the sinking of the Lusitania with a forearm of a drowning person projecting from the water… The light-switch was far from the bed. I liked to read in bed and disliked having to get out of bed in the cold to turn it off. I made an apparatus to hold up a string from the switch to the bedside so as to put the switch up and off. To fix it I knocked nails into the plaster along the top of the wall and learnt that nails split plaster.

His mother was naturally not happy about this, and said she would have admired his ingenuity if he had used picture hangers; he then did. Once, my father dropped a sixpence out of his bedroom window and it fell onto the narrow concrete parapet. He lay in bed wondering how to retrieve it and decided to climb out early the next morning before anyone was up.

I clambered out in my pyjamas, holding on to the window-sill, the parapet being without a ledge and up on this high floor, and I got back safely with my sixpence. But, Lady Patrick Manson, the wife of Sir Patrick Manson, the senior medical consultant for the Colonial Office, in the apartment over the way at the opposite side of Queen Anne Street had been awake and seen me. She told my mother and I was sent over to see her. I was full of trepidation but she received me kindly. She said she had watched with fear as I climbed on to that unprotected ledge, and she had dared not to shout to stop me lest I should unbalance with surprise. She feared I meant to walk along the ledge and great was her relief to see me climb back. She told me never to do it again, and gave me a shilling – and I did not.

My aunts Stephanie and Dorothy slept in the same room with my father and he often crept into Stephanie's bed while they played guessing games. Dr Saunders used to come upstairs to say goodnight and they persuaded him to tell them hospital stories '…the juicier the better'.

A regular visitor to 37 Harley Street was Bishop Ferguson Davy of Sarawak and Singapore. The Rt Rev Charles James Ferguson-Davy (1872–1963) was the first Anglican Bishop of Singapore, appointed 1910. I think he was an early inspiration to my father for the colonial Far East, as was Patrick Manson, an expert in tropical medicine, whose drawing room was alive with Chinese art from his time in Hong Kong.

*

My father's stammer was first noticed in 1911 when he was five. It grew worse despite lessons in elocution from an eminent Wimpole Street specialist, Cortland McMahon. He believed the stammer was the result of regular scoldings from his parents who he found so very distant and cold that he once considered running away. There is no doubt he came from an upbringing which favoured learning and discipline ahead of happiness and contentment, and he could never overcome that and allow his true feelings to show. This must not be misunderstood, for there is equally no doubt that his parents loved him, but it was the parenting styles of those times, so different from today. Unfortunately, how he was raised became the model in which he raised his own children.

That same year he had appendicitis. In order to help him convalesce, grandfather rented a house in Frinton-on-Sea on the sea-cliff in Essex called *Whiteleaf*. It became their holiday rendezvous for several years. My father remembered *Whileleaf* and Frinton with enjoyment but welcomed returning home to Harley Street and his top-floor bedroom.

Always, when I lay down to sleep in that little room on the first night of our return from Frinton, it was not the bed, the room or the house which I noticed but the horns of the London taxis: they seemed to sound home, and I can hear them still. There was an alluring eeriness from those hoots after the silent nights at Frinton which has haunted me – always sharp-eared and a light sleeper.

He remembered the cistern-room – which was out-of-bounds – up a few stairs from the landing where his bedroom was situated. Sometimes he slipped into the cistern-room unobserved to sail boats in the tank. Here I find his interest in sailing toy boats which I was to learn from him much later.

That room, however, led to a greater distraction which, very fortunately for us, no one discovered. There was a window which opened into a rectangular shaft from the basement to the roof of the house… We could get out of the window on to the fire-escape and, thus on the roof, whence from its bare edges we could peer down into Harley Street and Queen Anne Street. There were small loose pieces of mortar scattered about. I had a catapult and would shoot the bits down at the taxis as they drove along – luckily without effect. Then we could climb over roofs for about 3 houses along Harley Street before reaching a high wall as a barrier. A steep drop prevented progress along Queen Anne Street. More bits of mortar attracted the catapult along Harley Street until, one day the three of us peered down a skylight and saw a maid changing her clothes. Fascinated we watched in silence. She moved to the dressing table with its mirror tilted upwards. She saw her face in the midst of the faces of three children and, as she turned to look at us with a sublime smile, we realised our error and withdrew.

On the edge of this 'dangerous roof', the children stood over Harley Street to watch 'the marches of the Salvation Army – bugles, trombones, trumpets and hymn – while Salvation Army women picked up the coins thrown from the windows of the houses'.

This story – and more to come – came to me in a large folder from Dr Janet West in 2007. My father was one of Janet's supervisors when she was an undergraduate at Cambridge. A friendship developed which continued and strengthened throughout their lifetimes and especially in my father's later years.

How honestly my father wrote, with observation and feeling: I so wish he had been the same man in my formative years – and things might have turned out differently. Overall, he was unhappy at home. My father wrote of thinking of running away; he also commented 'strictness prevailed' but his writing does tell a happy story rather than gloomy.

*

My father went to Arnold House School in St John's Wood, London, from 1912 to 1915. This was a day school and was where he started Latin followed by Greek; he went on to Highfield School in Liphook, Hampshire, 1916 to 1919, a boarding school, and he wrote that he was 'homesick at first'. He continued with the classics and also maths and was 'school champion winning all the school sports'. I never knew of this sporting prowess, except that later he did become a good rugby player.

In the Janet West folder there was a mass of material from which I learned of more of my father's escapades of those days. Edred John Henry was, by all accounts, a normal boy and he recorded that he 'Fell off sea-wall (15') at Frinton–on-sea, when watching a hockey match on the beach… inclined to watch the game not watching step: landed plump in soft dry sand beside a baby: [my] mother very angry and scolded me who was horribly shaken. I dare not say anything.' He continued that 'Stephanie, Do and I used to run along the wide concrete breakwater at Walton end of [Frinton] beach to see how far we could get before our feet were wetted by the waves that broke and washed over and along it: shallow on the Walton side, deep on the Frinton side. Sometimes big waves nearly swept us off; I slipped once on green slime and clung to a beach ball which was passed to me.' We 'played at shooting with my new air gun… told Do I would shoot over her head but shot grazed top of her head; she screamed; parents heard: persuaded her to say she was only pretending.' At prep school (circa 1916), he 'got out of dormitory late at night: cycle rides by moonlight. One night, with another boy at Liphook Park School, got into chapel, took out two organ pipes, blew loud noises twice and just got out of back door as master came in.'

In 1919, his parents moved from London to the house *Woodlands Park*, in Great Missenden, Buckinghamshire. Great Missenden was about 65 miles from Rugby and was close to woods and good countryside. It was quoted in the *Doomsday Book* in 1086 as woodland and is now a designated Planted Ancient Woodland Site. My father explored those woods for fungi. 'A paradise for a young botanist', he wrote. From there he went on to Rugby School and went into St Hill House (now Mitchell House) where he acquired his passion for botany and mycology.

His short-sightedness was noticed at Rugby around 1920 when he could not read the blackboard. His time at the school greatly moulded his future: he continued with the classics but became bored and switched to the sciences. He was overcoming his unhappiness at home, and his stammer with treatment. He contracted very mild polio 'which stopped me as an athlete', but 'I went on botanical excursions to much disgust of senior masters'; this disgust, he said, determined his resolve! Something of a rebel perhaps – but definitely with a cause – for his passion for botany had arrived.

It was at Rugby School that my father's undoubted skill at rugby football blossomed; he became a quality player, his position being full-back. In the book *A Modern Tom Brown's Schooldays* by Michael Scott, the chapter 'Cock House Match' refers to my father; he was considered (when at Cambridge) to have been the best full-back Rugby School had produced for ten years. It was also at Rugby School where he gave up the Officers Training Corps 'as detestable' and that 'caused thereby much trouble.' However, he became a school prefect.

In 1922, aged 16, he wrote to his good friend E. Bartholomew (Barton) Worthington from Rugby:

> Lent term 1922, from Rugby: only two more days of this bloody term. I have only gone in for jumps and weight-putting in the sports, the latter I have cut. Everyone is fearfully sick, but I don't care. Raven gave the house a jaw about esprit de corps and he gave me the option of going into "dicks" or not, if I liked because he was going to make a few rather pointed remarks. He told me that if I did not form a community with the rest of the house it was time I left. Splendid isn't it? Imagine me playing ping-pong with people in hall. I have come to a conclusion nothing matters. We only live once and when we die we are gone for ever, so why worry about how unusual or selfish one is. *"Nicht wahr"* (I am learning German).

'I have come to a conclusion nothing matters', he wrote, 'and we only live once and when we die we are gone for ever, so why worry about how unusual or selfish one is'. This comment tells me much, and foreshadows his attitude throughout his life; the birth of his single-mindedness, relentlessness and the 'loner'.

In his first term, my father collected toadstools and wrote of his excitement that during his holidays on Dartmoor he found *Russula*, red, yellow and what he calls the emetic one. After finding a *Boletus* – a genus which he spent so much time showing and explaining to me as a boy – he exclaimed that biology began before a lesson. He began the study of botany seriously at Rugby and wrote that he began climbing trees 'in earnest', around 1922. He realised that he needed a microscope to follow his new-found passion and an uncle lent him one.

I remember him taking me to the Fens of Cambridgeshire in the late 1940s and 1950s and showing me the mushrooms and toadstools. He would collect the edible ones, some of a grotesque shape and colour, and in the evening we would have quite a feed. I was never ill. Looking back, how I wish I had attended more closely and learned – but then I was already in awe of him and frankly sometimes a little frightened.

Grandfather Corner was also interested in mycology. He joined the British Mycological Society and he took his son, aged 16, to one of the Society's forays in Keswick in 1922. Here my father met the barrister-mycologist Carleton Rea and Professor A. H. R. Butler, FRS. Others on that foray were Sir Frank Engelow, who became Professor of Agriculture at Cambridge, and Sir Samuel Wadham who became Director of Agriculture in Australia.

Of his Rugby School friend Edgar Barton Worthington, my father wrote that they became firm friends which lasted for life '…he into Zoology and I into Botany.'

My father had gone against his parents and school masters in his determination to study botany and there had been difficult moments, indeed harsh times, which were to affect him throughout his life. His determination to drive himself constantly shows through time and time again, and without that steely resolve, I think some of his future would never have happened. He was indeed single-minded.

In his book *The Marquis*, my father said that whilst at school he found in science 'the call for truth and understanding'. This helped him overcome what he described as 'prejudice, convention and animosity… the mission was succoured at the University of Cambridge by international tradition, great libraries and tolerance'. This was soon after the First World War.

In his last year at Rugby School my father had been inspired by Arthur H. Church's book *Thalassiophyta*.

So I began to struggle with that strange work and, as I overcame, I followed. Stiff sentences bristled with points the source of which I had to hunt… Thus I ploughed and re-ploughed until I knew much by heart.

He was introduced to Church and he began visiting him at Oxford, and a disciple-mentor relationship developed. When he went up to Cambridge he found that much of the botany taught there was uninteresting – 'dreary', as he described it. He missed lectures, read avidly, and in 1928 presented a paper on that book by Church to the Botany Club which he thought 'might have earned a PhD'.

I am discovering a young man already single-minded and *very* determined – driven almost. He was not afraid of being a loner and selfish – and science was leading his way.

UNIVERSITY AND
THE SINGAPORE OPPORTUNITY

My father went up to Cambridge in 1923. From late that year to 1927, he was a scholar at Sidney Sussex College.

He recalled two enlightening experiences in his story, *The Two Vagaries,* found in the Janet West folder, from the time he went to the college to sit for the entrance examinations. As with other memories which he considered worthy of recording, my father wrote this in later life, dating them 1993 when he was 87. The events must have taken place in 1922.

The main papers of the scholarship examinations were in chemistry, botany and zoology; the exam finished with a general knowledge paper. After taking the first three my father 'mistook the day for the last'. He had taken himself off to Madingley wood looking for fungus and was pleased to have found *Psalliota elvensis* (= *Agaricus arvensis*). On his return to college it dawned on him that he had missed the final exam. 'I was rattled', he wrote. Returning home, he 'confessed the error' in response to his father's question about how he had done. His father was angry because he had repeatedly told his son that if he was to go to Cambridge it must be by scholarship, and it seems that he had now missed his chance. He was instructed immediately to write to the College Tutor to explain the situation. Mr Knox-Shaw was understanding, and about a week later the news came that my father had won a top scholarship worth £100. 'Whereas my chemistry paper had been average, those in botany and zoology had been outstanding; as for the mistake about the general knowledge, it did not matter,' he recalled. His father forgave him; his mother had always been on his side. He thus renewed his quest for fungi.

A 'mishap' in the practical chemistry exam rattled my father. He had to make up a standard solution of potassium permanganate for titration; he 'carefully weighed out the crystals, tipped them into a flask and was filling it with the exact volume of water when, suddenly, the bottom of the flask fell out and my solution went down the drain'. The flask had 'a circular crack round the bottom, as if it had been stood too roughly on a table before it had been served to me'. Time was short; he tried to repeat the process but 'surely, made some mistakes'.

My father's zoology examiners had been James Grey (later Professor of Zoology) and Mr Saunders (later Secretary-General of the Faculties and not to be confused with Dr E. A. Saunders). They set a test question asking him 'to explain the contents of a jar which contained a dissected sea-urchin – not on the quoted list of animals for study'. My father 'knew it all and explained in detail to their surprise'. He had, out of his own curiosity and desire to learn, 'ordered from a dealer preserved specimens of various invertebrate phyla not on the lists for the scholarship papers and, among them had been a sea-urchin and a star-fish'.

In the botany examination, one examiner had been Samuel Wadham whom my father had met in autumn 1922 at the Keswick foray of the British Mycological Society. From this encounter, Wadham 'knew that I was already a mycologist and a botanist'.

My father recorded that 'these two lots of luck outweighed the two misfortunes. Anyhow, I had 2 years with a scholarship of £100 p. annum to be followed by a renewal for another 2 years while I was preparing for Part II of the Tripos. It saved my father a lot of money. I think it cost me, altogether, about £200 a year to live in College. Certainly to draw a cheque for £5 from the bank was, in those days, an extravagance'.

I remember my father one day showing me the large and distinguished white £5 note of those days, which he always kept at the back of his wallet, 'for emergencies' he had said. I never forgot that; this was around 1950. Today, I carry a note at the back of my wallet but the denomination of which I will leave to the imagination of the reader.

The second vagary was similar but not so devastating; it happened during his final examination for Part II of the Natural Sciences Tripos in botany. My father thought the start time was 9.30 am but at the time he noticed that the college was almost deserted! It dawned on him that the exam started at 9 am; he snatched hood and gown and rushed to the examination hall. He entered as the doors closed. 'I sat down in perturbation and tried to compose the essay. George Briggs (plant physiologist and the late Professor of Botany) was an invigilator. He came to my desk, and asked why I had been so late and on my telling him of my mistake, tried to calm me'. My father came out top, becoming the Frank Smart Student of the next academic year.

These two stories, from my father's early life, serve well to show how absent-minded he could be. I think that he was so dedicated to his subject that he quite forgot other things, and some that we might have thought equally important. This trait will show through in his life, and would let him down on occasion.

In Cambridge, my father lodged first in College (K1, Kew Court) and then 10 Malcolm Street. He finished his time at 27 Bateman Street. He became quite an expert on 'things Cambridge'; yet, when I was sent to The Leys School in 1954, he told me nothing of his days in that elegant university city where he lodged close to the school.

In his early days at Cambridge, my father refused a freshmen's trial at rugby football and caused much consternation. He was, however, a member of the swimming club from 1923 to 1925. Already his dedication to his subjects and learning was shining strongly, and his scholastic record at Cambridge is worthy of recall. In 1922, he was awarded a Scholarship for Natural Sciences and admitted in October 1923 to Sidney Sussex College. He took the Natural Sciences Prelims in 1924 and won the Inter-Collegiate Examination Prize for Natural Sciences. Natural Sciences Part I saw him achieve the Tripos Prize in 1925 and he was elected to a BA Scholarship in 1926. He was elected to a Research Scholarship in 1927 and awarded the Frank Smart Prize for Botany.

Much of this I never knew except that he had gone to Sidney Sussex College and I look back with sadness that he never thought it important to talk to me about his early life, especially when my successes on the sports field were becoming evident; yet this was the norm of the time… and academically I was slow.

In 1924, my father travelled to Vienna to learn German and, in 1925, he wrote that he went to Switzerland 'for botany'. In 1926, he went to Gibraltar, southern Spain and Tangiers.

His travels-to-learn whilst at Cambridge certainly show the determined man he was; and hungry for knowledge, in all of which his parents were encouraging and clearly supportive. My father wrote of his period as a Frank Smart Prize research student as 'really 18 months of pure research, during which I taught myself to draw; practically all illustrations and photographs in my publications are drawn and taken by myself'. Under F. T. Brooks, he studied the 'dreary subject on parasitism of mildews', but he did more of his own research into Discomycetes (discos), which led to five papers being published – 'enough for any PhD which I never got'.

I think that my father did not pursue a PhD because he knew he was good and decided that such a qualification would have no bearing on his future. He had no time for it; it would be in the way of learning, and he already had published papers! In 1928, his discovery of *Neotiella crozalsiana* and neoteny in the fungus fruit body from the algal soma was his first of many new findings.

Yet, of Cambridge in 1927, he wrote later in his Royal Society Personal Records of his 'being appalled at his ignorance of so much science'. He confessed that 'I dwelt on suicide but decided it would bring so much sorrow to my parents' and from then on he devoted his life 'to furthering what knowledge I could, and help others. Since then I have driven myself relentlessly'.

This relentless drive for knowledge stayed with him through his life – had a great effect on others. He was too single-minded to make a success of any relationship, unless the other person was of equally high intelligence.

In his Royal Society records, I found that my father believed that his stammer would preclude him from lecturing when his student days were over. So, fired by his interest in the tropics in his research, he thought of ways to get there, for he believed that the origin of plants was tropical. Indeed, he had got himself vaccinated against typhus in 1926. It was also the realisation of a boyhood dream – 'as a boy at school, I turned biologist. I read the lives of the great Victorian naturalists and determined to travel, as they had done, in the cause of biology'.*

His conversations with Dr A. H. Church (my father drove once or twice a week to Church's house) were a great inspiration and stimulus, the elderly botanist 'ever polite, friendly, witty, and overflowing with ready explanation'; he read all that Church had published.† My father acknowledged: 'On many a detail which I cannot recall now I taxed him, and the answers never failed; they have become a part of my botanical philosophy.'

Then in 1927, Singapore beckoned:

I was introduced to R. E. Holttum who was looking for a mycologist for the Botanic Gardens in Singapore. He encouraged me to apply and my letter to the Colonial Office was sent on to the Governor of the Straits Settlements [Sir Hugh Clifford]. I was successful and looked forward to Singapore at the handsome salary of £400/annum.

His appointment was Assistant Director of the Gardens.

On hearing that my father was about to set out for Singapore, Church gave him the utmost encouragement and hardy advice, 'Note everything, draw everything, and photograph everything' – wise counsel which my father followed throughout his career.

* *Years later, my father was flattered when an eminent scientist remarked to him: "Corner, I think you are an old Victorian naturalist."*
† *My father's copy of Thalassiophyta would accompany him around the world as the years unfolded, and on re-reading it, he said, 'I have never failed to gain new insight.'*

III

A CORNER OF SINGAPORE

My father's meeting with Dr R. E. Holttum, the Director of the Straits Settlements Botanic Gardens, in England in 1928 was seminal. The upshot was one of the most important decisions in his life both for his scientific progress and the results which later came to fall upon his family. He contacted the Colonial Office, as was suggested, went for the interview and accepted the position of Assistant Director of the Straits Settlements Botanic Gardens, to work as assistant to Dr Holttum – or so he thought.

The Gardens at Tanglin, a suburb of Singapore, was founded in 1859 by an Agri-Horticultural Society which planned it as a leisure garden and ornamental park. It was after 1874, when the society tranferred the Gardens' management to the government, that its scientific mission evolved with the arrival of trained botanists and horticulturalist from Kew. The Gardens' first Director was Henry Nicholas Ridley. From his arrival in 1888 to his retirement 23 years later, Ridley shaped the Gardens while promoting the commercial cultivation of rubber trees, an intiative that would contribute significantly to the economic well-being of Malaya and Singapore.

Holttum had been Director of the Gardens for four years when my father sailed for Singapore in early 1929. Going to the tropics as a colonial officer was a position of substance, a challenge and a leap into a world of which he must have been somewhat ignorant. I shall rarely, if ever again, use that word – ignorant – in terms of my father. He must have been excited; the prospect unbounded; the almost limitless opportunities to research and discover; yet had he fully realised and understood the very new life into which he was to be pitched? No doubt the Colonial Office would have advised, but the man I am beginning to discover was absolutely locked into science with a single-minded focus.

As I researched for this chapter, I was surprised to discover that my father was not just a 'mushroom-man' but was a most competent scientist with a broad base of knowledge. Indeed, he was a biologist, zoologist and conservationist, later consigning mycology to a lesser role; yet he continued to produce important mycological results throughout his long career. (See Appendix E for the full list of his publications and papers).

In the notes written for his Royal Society Personal Records, he stated that '1929–1941... explored extensively in Malaya Peninsula...' and that 'about 1931 turned mycology into a hobby in order to study and record Malayan forest as it was being felled... hence *Wayside Trees of Malaya* – my most successful book (three editions)'. In these records he wrote succinctly under the heading 'Malaya'; '... the unparalleled opportunity to explore primeval forest at every step'.

The scene is set for what follows and which is illustrated so well by my father's many letters to E. Bartholomew (Barton) Worthington (1905–2001)* and Robert (Robin) Hill, FRS (1899–1991)†, both to reach the heights of their scientific professions as did my father. The contents of these letters are fascinating and illustrate so well my father's work and time in pre-war Malaya. The letters help to paint a picture of his life in Singapore, how he botanised, his discoveries, his opinions and his connections with Hill and Worthington. They also reveal the thoughts and feelings of an artist with words, a highly observant man and a somewhat complicated person.

Many extracts from the letters to Barton Worthington were in the bulging file that came from Janet West. I also came upon letters at the Cambridge University Library rather by chance when I went in June 2009 specifically to look at all the photographs, including many on glass plates, lodged there. The 'easiest' (and least costly) way was by micro-film but I hadn't given thought as to how later to view them! The micro-film duly arrived and a local business copied all onto paper but they were most difficult to read, indeed in some cases almost impossible. Yet, the snippets from some indicated that I had to decipher them because the content was clearly fascinating,

---

* *Edgar Bartholomew (Barton) Worthington, CBE, was a pioneer explorer of African Lakes and their fisheries, and conducted scientific surveys for developments in Africa and the Middle East. He was also Director of the Freshwater Biological Association, Scientific Secretary of the Colonial Research Council, Deputy Director-General (Scientific) for the Nature Conservancy, and Scientific Director of the International Biological Programme. In retirement, he continued to work with international bodies concerned with water research, UNESCO, and was an active member of the Commonwealth Human Ecology Council. His book* The Ecological Century: a Personal Appraisal *(1983) well describes his rich life.*

† *Dr Robin Hill, FRS, joined the Department of Biochemistry at Cambridge in 1922 where he researched haemoglobin. In 1932, he began work on plant biochemistry, focusing on photosynthesis and the oxygen evolution of chloroplasts, leading to the discovery of the 'Hill reaction'. He was an expert on natural dyes and painted watercolours using pigments he had extracted himself. No doubt my father met him in Cambridge from where the relationship blossomed.*

indeed intriguing. At first I put the file, measuring half inch thick, to one side as too difficult but took up the challenge again in 2010, considerably helped by the kindness of Cambridge University Library Imaging Services who re-scanned all the letters with an improved system.

This enabled me to read almost everything – important not only because I had correspondence from my father from Singapore which revealed his early experiences, but also information about his photographic successes and difficulties, and how he seemed to be not so bad a socialite as I had imagined.

Still, there were words and scientific expressions which defeated me. However, with the patient help of my wife, Professor Roy Watling, Dr David Mabberley, Dr Peter Ashton, Dato Henry Barlow, Robin Campbell and others, now there are perhaps only a handful of words, not vital to any meaning, which have not been deciphered.

Hill and Worthington were my father's long-standing and trusted friends. I remember the families Worthington and Hill from the 1950s and visiting their homes and meeting the children. Robin Hill married one of Barton Worthington's sisters, Priscilla. Shelagh Wakeley (née Worthington), his elder daughter, wrote to me saying, 'Barton managed to get all his sisters except one, Betty, to marry his scientific friends who all became eminent in their specialities. He dreamt of Betty, his elder sister who had a degree from Oxford, marrying EJH; however Betty and EJH had other ideas!'

My father was clearly excited to be going to Singapore and he wrote a fascinating account of the journey later in his life. He journeyed out on the Blue Funnel liner, SS *Antenor* early in 1929, aged 23, in his earliest of days as a working scientist. On the non-stop sector from Port Suez to Penang, he recorded:

There were ten days of heaving seas, flying foam, monsoon skies and deck-games, which annoyed me. All around was novel and I, the young explorer! Times of sunrise and sunset, the rate at which the sun sank into the ocean, the skimming schools of flying fish, spouts and flukes of inquisitive whales, phosphorescence, and all the rattles and groans and sighs from the bowels of the ship as up went the stern with plunging bow intrigued me, but not the other passengers.

Places at the dining table were pre-determined and he found himself sitting next to Mrs Penelope Landon who was returning from leave in England to join her planter-husband in Malaya. She clearly loved Malaya and a friendship formed; she called him Galahad and he called her Elaine, following the practise of the naming-of-a-friend that was typical of the time.

My father remarked that deck games annoyed him; I wonder if his stammer was playing its part as it is suggested that someone with a stammer does tend to shun social events and occasions. He continued his story:

As we passed the south coast of Ceylon the fragrance of cinnamon and clove was wafted aboard. I spied my first coconut palms and wondered what other plants and fungi grew beneath them. Impatience increased as the days to the land of Raffles and Wallace grew fewer.

One morning, he noticed 'three specks on the horizon' in his field-glasses, 'as if black rocks rising sharply from the sea'; they changed into Chinese junks with dark brown sails off the northern tip of Sumatra. The following morning, he heard the chimes of the clock tower on Georgetown harbour and where he disembarked to be met by Mr G. A. Best, the curator of the Waterfall Gardens. As they drove to the gardens, my father admired the 'shady avenues of lofty trees, all unfamiliar, behind which gleamed the sea-green and sky-blue Chinese mansions.'

The gardens rested on the forested hillside and they took the 'toothed rail' to the heights of Penang Hill. (In the late 1970s, I took the same mountain railway up to the summit and saw the crowns of the coconut palms, 'waving as if giant cabbages' which my father had gazed upon.) He was inspired by the 'ropes of figs, dangling from the trunks of small trees that overhung the cuttings – the common *Ficus hispida* as I came to know so well'. He was astonished by the epiphytic ferns and orchids in the tropical forest. 'Here's a *Boletus*', he announced. It became his first tropical fungus collected (the North American *Boletus ballouii*). I can feel the excitement reflected in his words.

Indeed, 124 years previously, the founder of modern Singapore, Stamford Raffles, must also have felt the same excitement at his first sight of tropical vegetation also in Penang. In the old cemetery there, my father collected specimens of *Mahogany melia* (= *Azadirachta excelsa)* from trees he thought were probably the very ones from which William Jack, employed by Raffles in both medical and scientific capacity, had collected the 'type' more than a century earlier.

The next afternoon, the ship sailed east from the Malacca Straits passing between the tree-clad islands that led to the western approach to Singapore; berthing at Keppel Harbour at 3.30 pm. My father was met by Holttum who took charge of him.

My father wrote about his shock on observing that the hedges, lawns, and many trees were yellow green. At that hour he learned that the afternoon light has a yellowing effect, but the vegetation 'was chlorotic'. As they entered the Botanic Gardens the effect was the same. Not until he looked from the veranda of the Director's house across the Palm Valley to the Gardens' jungle was the dark green of the tropical forest apparent; he had not noticed this in shady Penang. There he saw many of the palms as yellow green like the grass.

Strong sunlight, as I had been taught, destroyed chlorophyll and the poor soil might add to the effect. Both factors seemed to account for the chlorotic appearance of the introduced plants of cultivation though neither impeded the vigour of the wild.

So E. J. H. Corner arrived in Singapore in February 1929 to take post officially on 1 March; his arrival was the beginning of a great journey in life and he came to love Malaya.

The botanical beat of the Gardens Department of the Straits Settlements, centred in Singapore at the Botanic Gardens, ranged from Perlis and Kelantan in the far north, to Singapore island in the south, and all of the intervening Malay Peninsula, to investigate the whole flora. Besides my father as Assistant Director, serving under Holttum were M. R. Henderson, Curator of the Herbarium, G. A. Best at the Penang Waterfall Gardens, and C. X. Furtado, Assistant Botanist in charge of the library.

My father's particular duty initially concerned the fungus flora of the peninsula. As an ardent young mycologist from Cambridge, 'where I learned a great deal that I had to unlearn', my father wrote that his predecessor in Singapore, T. F. Chipp, Assistant Director up to December 1920, had published a list of the fungi so far as they had been recorded.

During my father's first year at the Botanic Gardens, he discovered that the larger fungi, such as toadstools, polypores and puffballs, were strictly seasonal in their fructifications. From roughly March to May and August to October, these fungi would appear in such abundance that he never succeeded in studying them all. In the intervals he gave attention to the general flora of the tropical forests which were completely unfamiliar to him.

They were 'immensely complex', he wrote. Instead of relatively few kinds of trees, as in Britain, there were hundreds and most were out of reach for the student on the ground; the tallest reaching some 200 feet (61 metres). He picked up fallen fruits, thinking they would be easily identified by reference to the massive *Flora of the Malay Peninsula* compiled by Ridley. To my father's great surprise, identification was not readily forthcoming.

My father wrote of Malaya as an unparalleled opportunity to explore primeval forest and to learn at every stage. The herbarium of the Gardens was a 'storehouse of knowledge', but imperfectly published as regards the whole peninsula, its mountains, forests, and rivers. Not only were there hundreds of thousands of specimens scientifically arranged and more or less correctly identified by two generations of botanists, together with their invaluable field notes, but also a large number of unpublished drawings and paintings of plants, records of expeditions as far afield as New Guinea, field books, manuscripts, and all such information and details as botanists intensely interested in their work must ever accumulate. Between Calcutta, Bogor and Manila it was a unique centre of botany.

The earliest letter I have from my father from Singapore – addressed to Worthington – is dated 5 May 1929, barely two months after my father's arrival. In it, he reports that he had contracted 'Whooping Cough, caught from the little son of Dr and Mrs Willans-Green of Johore Bahru – a cough developed in the Red Sea'. It worsened in Singapore, and a few days after arriving, about five in the morning, he reported waking with a start in Holttum's house 'to find I could scarcely breathe, or inspire, whoop, whoop, whoop! For five minutes; mighty efforts for a whiff of air and it was all over for a while'. He went to hospital where his two or three fits of whooping continued every night for a fortnight, and then it lessened and until he was 'whoop-less' for over a month.

> But it is a beastly thing. It comes in the night… and you wake with coughing immediately. A cough that never seems to stop till it has drawn all the air and then almost refuses to let you draw any in again. And every time you expire, it is to the accompaniment of the cough. In a minute you are suffused with that awful irritation which comes with slight asphyxiation. You draw your legs up, straighten your back, stiffen your arms, sit up taut, straighten your legs again, and so on, till the fit passes off and leaves a splitting headache. A sort of hellish terror seizes you. You daren't go to sleep again and yet you drop off with weariness, only to repeat the same thing in an hour's time.

My father told of having three fits in an hour at one stage and 'thought I saw Hades in the last one…', but during the day he felt fine.

So he learned Malay in hospital, reading about phyllotaxis [the arrangement of leaves on a plant stem] in the only book then on the subject which is by A. H. Church – the author having given him a copy a few days before he left England. He also learned mathematics and asked Worthington to tell Hill that he has 'profited immensely from *Calculus Made Easy*; it made the hospital quite enjoyable'.

My father reported that three things may induce the cough:

> (i), strong drinks (so I have an excuse to refuse them), (ii), smoke going the wrong way but I cannot deny myself pipe and cigar, whatever else, and (iii), (you'll never guess) bananas! Eat a banana first thing in the morning and it tickles the throat so that I break into a sweat for fear of coughing and in the effort to suppress a spumatic expiration.

He added that he would miss a banana with his 'fruit and cup of tea about 6 am' – he preferred rising early so as not to waste the daylight hours.

My father wrote that he had been given a house. Clearly he did not relish the thought of sharing a 'bachelor's mess' with those who he described as 'the essence of all I dislike – jovial, sottish company, drinks, bridge, games, theatre – no intelligence – that's the Government Civil Servant – a poor class university man'.

Across the road from the gardens, his bungalow received the sounds of the tropics:

> But, shh; it is the Nocturne in D... The music of his [Chopin's] life was without discord, perfect in its beauty? Could I meet such a one; this is a charmless city and in six months I have heard only Kubelik in his decline... taken from Granta's fields, now lonely in the outskirts of Commerce. Discomfort ran like a brook... And I oft found myself sitting by sounds on a trombone. 'Perfection' is nearby... The sounding brass; harsh interruption; the band in Tanglin Barracks has begun. Damn regiments...

Here, my father's musical (and other) views are expressed with a fine tune of words.

Being the dry-season, April to June, my father reported that he is inundated with fungi.

> I shall be getting to know them better when the next rush comes. I work on the principle that all higher Basidiomycetes and Discomycetes have been imperfectly described and so I may as well make a decent description of everything I find. It is slower work but it pays in the long run.

In spite of two very wet days with 'almost incessant storms', he drove, one Sunday morning in his own free time, to the jungle at Bukit Timah, the highest point on the island at 164 m. It was dank and dripping and in spite of becoming soaked he wrote that he was quite happy. Here he met his first snake 'when stepping off a large trunk which had fallen over the path when, only two feet in front, a large 4-5' black snake, some 2 inches thick, uncurled and slithered into the jungle'. He knew it was a cobra and seeing it came as quite a shock and gave the salutary reminder,

> a fraction of a second later and I might have stepped on it. Then returning home I turned over a log and found a six inch scorpion cracking its tail at me. With great dexterity and unerring aim I hinged like a matador with my stick and caught it between the eyes, absolutely pulverising what cerebral ganglion it might have had.

Early in 1929, he first met William Birtwistle, Director of Fisheries Straits Settlements and Federated Malay States, who he described as a 'very jolly fellow… one of the nicest persons I have met' who liked to collect fish and visit coral reefs. My father had already visited a reef with him collecting seaweeds and 'treading among stony, flashy, fibrous and squishy coral and sponges. Glorious, heavenly spot'. He then reported that Birtwistle had arranged for a dinghy 'to be fitted with glass plates on the bottom so that we can lie on our tummies and gaze into the liquid depths'.

My father wrote that he first spoke with Alice – Birtwistle's wife who 'brought happiness and comfort into his [Birtwistle's] spartan life' – on the telephone soon after his arrival in Singapore. When he was in the General Hospital suffering from the Whooping Cough, it was the 'cheery, kindly and humorous voice' of Alice Birtwistle that became his companion. She was a nurse at the General Hospital.

Mr Birt, as he was affectionately known to his friends, had been in Singapore for some time before my father. He got to know the Japanese fishermen operating in the local waters well, and had learned the Japanese way. Indeed, he had visited Japan and this special knowledge was to prove important.

The 1929 meeting was the beginning of a strong friendship. My father clearly had great respect for Mr Birt. He once said that William Birtwistle was the most honest and sincere person that one could hope to meet – 'No humbug, subterfuge or ostentation invested him'. He acquired a deep mistrust of officialdom which was certainly something that my father supported wholeheartedly – here indeed was an affinity.

The letters to Hill began with a postcard dated 30 May 1929. My father described the morning scene in a small street of Chinese shophouses, his first sight of such things, as 'An early morning airing of bedclothes, mats & so on. I've never seen anything like these Chinese'. He tells of them being 'packed like sardines in their houses'. However, they are always clean, well presented and hard working. Already my father had learned that 'they never take a Sunday or a Bank Holiday off, save their New Year day'. In his short time in Singapore, he had found the Chinese most capable but thought they 'think in an odd way: they can "subtract" but they cannot "add"'.

His postscript turned to botany; there are 'hordes of mosses' and he promised to send some to Hill, saying that at that moment he was involved in fungi and seaweeds, adding 'I have found some common English toadstools here'.

That year, my father became a founder member of the Malayan Branch of the Royal Asiatic Society (MBRAS), and in November the idea of 'a little hand in the canopy' came to him, inspiring the idea of botanical monkeys.

Malaya was already becoming a paradise for my father with so much unexplored tropical jungle and a lifestyle which appears to have been quite free of restrictions and of which he came quickly to love. He travelled across increasing miles of both Singapore island and Malaya spending time initially in Johore, and on the two Sedili Rivers* along and around which he studied in considerable detail. On 27 September 1929, he wrote to Worthington about his first trip to Gunung Panti. On the August Bank Holiday, he left his house at 5.30 am by car with Ali, a Malay gardener at Botanic Gardens, and his Malay driver.

The stars were still visible in the west and the first greyness of dawn showed in the east; my father sat in the back of the open tourer and drank in the tropical morning as they drove swiftly (40 miles per hour!) along the road. Full day light had arrived as they passed over the Causeway to the mainland. He watched the Chinese getting up and as they drove through Johore Bahru and one or two villages, he observed that

> they all clean their teeth with a frayed piece of bamboo, squatting on their haunches and spitting into deep gutters; some were just getting off their couches in their open rooms; others taking the scaffolding down from their shops and others having their morning spit which is the unusual Chinese habit... they cough from their big toes upwards and spew any old way so that at the end of the day the sides of the road where pedestrians chiefly go is quite slippery. And at the best of times 'phials' of spit are a horrid sight; and hawkers with their dirty billycans of food were already selling breakfast to the early birds.

They passed two miles of jungle halfway to Kota Tinggi, then travelled through rubber and pineapple plantations. 'No crops could be more dreary', he complained.

They began the ascent of Gunung Panti about 7.30 am when the morning mists were still rising. Walking with Ali through a young rubber plantation to the edge of the jungle and after a search for the path, which they found, they continued for about three miles to the top, never once seeing the sky. Somewhere a tree had fallen down.

> [A]nd where a tree falls there a chaos: some order may be discovered in the creepers, epiphytes, and parasites, ferns, mosses, lichens, fungi which grow on the living tree but in the tangle of stems, roots, trunks, leaves, rhizomes, bark, twigs, and snapped branches which are tumbled round the decaying trunk, orientation has collapsed and I say it is a microcosm of chaos.

* In September 2012, Tony O'Dempsey told me of his accidental discovery of the jetty from which my father started his Sedili trips, standing as it was with Corner's fig tree (Ficus microcarpa, a weeping fig) still alive and opposite it. It was here that my father recorded in 'The Freshwater Swamp Forests of Singapore and Johore' of seeing 'a family of river-otters squealing and chirping happily together, foraging for prawn and fish trapped in pools and undergrowth.'

My father continued, writing that 'the trees are mighty; the botanist is puny as he stumbles among their roots and gropes for fallen fruits and flowers'. Yet, the path was good, and the jungle here was remarkably penetrable; there was little undergrowth of palms so that walking was fairly easy and probably also because the sides of the mountains were well drained. At the top and in the stream-gullies it is very different, being choked with undergrowth.

Half-way up two gigantic figs, which have evidently started as epiphytes, sent roots to the ground, formed massive trunks and simply strangled their host-plant out of existence.

My father wrote of being astonished at the variety of fruits: he noted that he could have brought back

near a hundred large fruits, and countless small ones; some like tennis-balls, some like apples, some like shuttle-cocks (the dipterocarps), and many with vaned wings. (I am sending some home so the next time you go to Beaconsfield [his parent's home], ask to see the fruits!).

They lost their way at one point and when they reached the rocks at the top he and Ali 'had rather a scramble over precipitous ground' which rather exhausted the Malay gardener. Returning to where they lost the path, they noticed the rope they had placed there, but Ali told him he was an old man, over 50, and he was weary and would wait there while my father went on to the top. So off he went alone, watchful, for he knew that there were many tigers in Johore; and they will not attack two or more men but if you meet an old tiger alone your number is up. There was a splendid view from the top and my father

gazed for the first time over jungle-clad hills to the north, east, and west, as far as the eye could see: one sea of crowns, of billowing domes, light green, dark green, pink, red, purple, brown with new leaves or lit with yellow or white flowers, and with that scintillating light reflected from the shiny leaves.

There were the birds flying about, several hundred feet below and 'all the while the valley echoed with the long-drawn cry of the eagles and howling gibbon. I trembled'.

He looked south and noticed that the burgeoning clouds were almost on him; quickly he was 'enveloped in a dank mist which turned to drizzle and drizzle to heavy rain… so off and on the rest of the day. But I set off along the ridge running south for four miles to the southern end of the mountain.'

Here he added a footnote, written in the late 1970s: 'this is wrong. The mountain runs WSW–ENE, and I was at the west end.'

The path down was fairly easy going for about three-quarters of a mile before it spread into a tangle of palms and pandans forming very wet undergrowth.

He struggled for some while but the fearful barbed thongs of the rotan palms and the long spines of nibong palms, the saw-edged leaves of Pandanus and *Freycinetia*, and the thickets of creepers which trip and fling aside were too much. He became badly scratched and his trousers were torn. The rain had turned into a storm.

The wind howled and moaned in the trees, shaking down the heavy drips, and thunder crashed around with spasmodic glimmers of lightening. So I sat on a fallen trunk under the pandans on that dull grey dripping dismal day and I ate my lunch to the rumbling thunder and the 'plonk' of dropping fruits. I confess I was afraid, for no reason… there is something appalling in the jungle: those lofty friendless trees, those unkind thorns, those melancholy trees moaning in the fitful wind. Ah me!

My father was relieved to see Ali again for he had lost his way on the return trip and had to rely on his compass; in the rain he realised that he had passed 'a red-fronded epiphyte which I had seen on my first walk along the path on my right, and there it was again on my right'. He turned around and soon was back on track.

On his second trip to Gunung Panti, he wrote:

I had a splendid scramble up the rocks with Ahmat. Now Ahmat is also over 50, and has collected plants with three Directors of the Botanical Gardens. But surprisingly youthful and he knows most of the ordinary jungle trees, leaves, fruits, flowers.

Ahmat and he went round that same precipitous north side and 'up we went hanging by roots and stem of small trees 20 – 30' high which stuck out from the rocks. When Ahmat went first, he would say "*tak-boleh*" (cannot) and I would say I'd show him, so up we went again and, if I went first, I would say "*tak-boleh*", and Ahmat would take the lead'.

Clearly my father had acquired the skills of climbing from his father – important, for he will be doing much more in the years to come, of trees and mountains.

In my father's missive of 14 October 1929 to Hill, he wrote that most of Singapore's jungle was gone even in late 1929, much earlier than I had realised. It lead naturally to the letter of 26 February 1930 to Worthington.

The content is revealing of my father's character, his way with words, his observance and opinion.

He commented to Worthington that

> Singapore must be well nigh the ugliest island in the world: because it is leased to the Chinese who, with their diligence, hue down the jungle & plant rubber, coconut, pineapple or their evil-manured vegetable gardens to scrape a living in utter disregard of beauty… they cannot know Beauty, for she is the companion of leisure. Still I like them. But I do not like the Europeans who come with the same intent. You never saw such a lot of ill-proportioned beings who seem gradually to forget all their education and have scarcely an interesting word to say.

He described professors at the Raffles College of Science 'who care more for the flavour of whisky & the easy swing of the game than the exercise of intellect'. He was full of foreboding at what the coming years might bring.

> Yet I think not, nature is too charming. A thousand times it is worth coming to the East: firstly to see the jungle and secondly to meet the yellow-man*…. He cannot know the might of vegetation who has not been in the jungle. To be in the jungle is a biological consummation. To stumble among the riot of enormous trees and to cut a path through the tangle of creepers which knit the life of the rain forest into one gigantic web, is like a dream. So long as there is sunshine the dream is pleasant & rings eerily with the cry of eagles and the howling of gibbon, but presently the pattering rain swells to a roar, lightning flashes, the heavens groan in thunder claps, the tall trees sigh, and a desolate loneliness descends, a terror like in a nightmare.

My father was most surprised that many of the fungi of the jungle are identical with the common European *Russula, Amanita* and *Boletus*.

> Truly some fungi have no earthly bounds. What is certain is that mycology looked at from a temperate angle is all askew; fungi of extra-tropical lands are derivative of the tropical types just like any other group of plants (with the possible exception of seaweeds): indeed all botany is askew!!

* In a postscript in a letter dated 4 March 1930 to Worthington, my father, in describing Chinese habits of the day, showed a side of himself that I did not know. 'I don't believe a Chinaman can cock his "john" more than horizontal: at least that is the highest I have furtively observed! & Chinese women feed their infants at the breast in the openest of places: both sexes squat down where they will to do a shit, I am becoming an anthropologist!'

He promised to write a strong letter to Prof Godwin in Cambridge to tell him that the physiology of *Helianthus* and apples and potatoes is a poor seraf of the science of plants. He said:

[O]ne must see a tree over 150 feet high with enormous canopy shed its leaves within a week, flower simultaneously with flowers opening within a few minutes of each other at a fixed time of the day and the rain of petals as they fall off, to be followed in a few days by the simultaneous sprouting of buds over the whole crown to realise the coordination which such a diffuse and apparently inanimate body can perform, and know that such has been its habit for more than a century from when it grew as a seedling in the jungle gloom, before you can appreciate the power of plants… and within a few months to observe monkeys, squirrels, birds and the fruit-bats which come to eat its fruits.

My father continued by describing an expedition to the northern state of Perlis and the challenges in taking and processing photographs in the tropics. 'My photos will show the kind of country' he wrote, feeling they were not good because 'I have printed them myself and I used Kodak and Agfa film packs whereas panchromatic plates with yellow filter are essential for good landscape photography in this country with its mistiness and low actuari value of the light'.

He mentioned that because of the high humidity and harsh midday light he overexposed most pictures compensating for underexposing the previous ones and that the high water-temperature 'makes gas-light printing difficult, and I am now taking to daylight papers, and I think I prefer the browns.' Here he referred to enclosing the formula for a hardening and fixing solution for films and plates in the tropics: he confirmed that it worked well as long as the water temperature was below 80 F: 'without it photography would be almost impossible on expeditions as once an exposure is made it very soon deteriorates, within a week'. His early experience suggested that the same solution can be used for about 36-48 quarter plates. 'But my hat, Perlis is hot. Every day the sky was deep blue and cloudless up to 1 or 2 pm and then white cumulus would gather in the North West [to] soften the ardour of the evening sun'. If it were not for the strong North West wind, he wrote, he would have 'shrivelled up and died. One perspired all night and day; still a change of action makes all the difference to the sameness of Singapore'.

My father told Worthington that while while he was away in Perlis, a Government cadet named W. C. Taylor had returned from leave and, as quarters were short, was sent to share my father's house. My father's colourful remarks showed that he had no patience nor respect for those he considered fools.

I returned to find a pink, blotchy, butcher-complexioned, fair, puerile looking person of ca. 28 years with a receding chin and boorish Lancashire speech in charge of the house, and though he could not help it, he at least is responsible for his manners which I soon discovered were completely lacking.

My father described him to be like Godwin (from Cambridge) in appearance with similar yet coarser speech and 'a puerile expression and behaviour and none of the compensatory intelligence'. My father tried to reprimand him when he found his sweaty feet on his cushions on the sofa and at times on the dining and work table where my father wrote and they took tea. My father said that Taylor would often stomp off to his room when he played a record.

I cannot relate his ignominious and discourteous, ungracious, ungentlemanly ways and acts but suffice to say I have never had to live with anyone I have at once so hated and despised.

With relief, he told Worthington that Taylor left that weekend having found 'another like himself, another singly ugly chubby cadet called Cobden Ramsay, who was at Sidney with me though I never spoke to him'. Ramsay was my father's junior at Cambridge; yet, in Singapore, Ramsay treated my father 'most patronisingly, having been here a year already before myself'. Ramsay was a magistrate and my father mused that 'these cadets may be able to pass exams in Law, but their minds are the size of thimbles'.

There is an important reference to Holttum in the next letter dated 4 March 1930 to Worthington. My father draws his friend's attention to a letter by Holttum published in *Nature* magazine about leaf-fall in the tropics.

It is largely bunkum about trees being evergreen in the rain-forest: most seem to have definite times of leaf-fall or leaf-renewal and merely as these differ in species and rarely coincide in individuals so the forest as a whole is evergreen.

He continued by describing a large fig tree in the Gardens 'which gets a new crop of leaves every four months'. During the last month the leaves began to drop off and 'then 24 hours after the last ones have gone a bright green shimmer of the opening buds soften the crown'.

He was somewhat scathing of Holttum's article. Was this when the seeds of 'a differing of opinion' with Holttum were first sown? My father had been in Singapore just 13 months.

*

In 1929, the Pacific Science Congress was held in Java. The Government of the Netherlands East Indies made elaborate preparations to ensure that delegates had information about work in progress at scientific institutions of all kinds in what is now Indonesia, and arranged a series of excursions before and after the meetings of the congress. There was a large Japanese delegation which included Marquis Yoshichika Tokugawa, a relative of Emperor Hirohito. His seniority and background is important to the unfolding story.

Marquis Tokugawa graduated from Tokyo Imperial University in 1911 where he produced a thesis on the management of the Japanese cedar (*Cryptomeria*) forest in the Kiso valley from the old records of the Owari family. He continued that study, submitting another thesis on *The Administration of Forestry at Kiso* in 1915. His works were pioneer efforts in tree and human ecology and from all of this sprang, in 1924, the laboratory for the History of Forests which he established in his house in Tokyo. Here came that great interest in trees and conservation that so allied him later to my father and the Malay Peninsula.

Others in the contingent included Professor Hidezo Tanakadate (vulcanology) from the University of Tohoku and Professor Kwan Koriba (botany) from the University of Kyoto. Professor Holttum was one of the Singapore delegates who met these Japanese delegates. Who else from Singapore was there? I don't think my father was. If his boss had gone, I suspect that, as the official Assistant, he would have stayed behind to hold the fort. Perhaps Birtwistle went and met the Japanese, Japanese who would be prominent later in this story.

*

In Pandora, I found a photograph of my father in the Malayan jungle, by a river, with a European lady standing beside a dug-out canoe. She was clearly elegant and of small stature. I put the date at pre-war, likely the early 1930s. I sent a scan of the picture to many who were helping me with my research but none recognised her. I moved on, but couldn't get that picture out of my mind. Why was it in Pandora; who was she and why unnamed?

As my research progressed, I discovered Mrs Wendy How, my father's housekeeper of his later years. She told me she had a number of documents which she had saved with my father's approval.

She sent many to me and amongst these was a letter to my father by Mrs Thyra Godber in November 1995, just ten months before he died. She told him that she had just finished reading *The Marquis: a Tale of Syonan-to*, my father's book of his war-time experience in Singapore. Thyra wrote:

I am the elder daughter of Penelope and Jim Landon. You and your wife gave them refuge in your house in Singapore after they had had to leave

Cluny Estate, Slim River. I believe my mother had helped you in a small way with your book *Wayside Trees of Malaya*. In one of the illustrations she is seen standing beside a jungle giant [tree].

It struck me that the lady by the river just might be Penelope Landon, so I wrote to Mrs Godber who conferred with her sister. They confirmed that the lady by the canoe was Penelope Landon.

Mrs Landon was the fellow traveller on the SS *Antenor* who my father wrote about in *The Blue of Elaine*, his story about his sea journey to Singapore which I found in Pandora. He later visited the Landons at Sungei Bil rubber estate, lower Perak, in March 1930.

Penelope Landon was an amateur artist. To show the distance of forested mountains, she added in European style a tint of blue which puzzled my father because he could never detect it in reality. 'In sunshine or after showers, that forest was sombre green, merging to olive or brownish, and the distance merely faded it'. He explained that it was tinted golden in the early morning light and in the evening it often was 'rosette'. However, he did suggest that there were 'a few plants conspicuous from their bluish cast'. Here my father named some such as the *Shorea curtisii* (seraya-trees), 'whose bluish grey crowns could be seen in the forest-canopy from surrounding ridges and hill-tops'. There was the Blue Mahang, *Macaranga heynei* (the common tree of open places) known by the blue tint of its leaves and there was the introduced Bermuda grass, *Cynodon*, 'which in fresh dew gave a blue cast to lawns and putting greens'. The harsh yellow green of the Lalang grass, *Imperata*, which invades waste ground, was a contrast. 'A splash of red soil, however, in the foreground of the picture relieves its poverty. Whenever I see a tropical jungle, there gleams the blue of Elaine'.

*

Pandora revealed another fascinating story, giving a description of a long-gone sound from that jungle. In May 1930, my father and Dr Geoffrey Herklots were enjoying the countryside of Kuala Pilah in Negri Sembilan. They first met at the Botany School, Cambridge, where my father was starting his research in 1928 and Herklots, from Leeds University, was finishing his PhD, later becoming a lecturer, then reader in Biology at the University of Hong Kong.

My father and Herklots were botanising along a stream that wound through the paddies.

Strange sounds came to us that we could not interpret…. Oomph – splash – oomph, in methodical repetition. Following the direction we rounded a thicket and came upon a giant water wheel of beauty that we never imagined.

They admired its simplicity of construction noticing also that a bucket 'was askew' causing the splashing sound of spilled water and the water wheel to groan as it turned.

My father reported that there were a number of such wheels operating along the river and of meeting an old Malay who used to construct them for irrigation. Pandora contained two photographs of a water wheel, taken surely at that time.

In the photos it can be seen that the water wheel is set near the bank and intercepts a slot in a bamboo barrage across the river. Thus it is driven by the current acting on the vanes which are five to six pieces of split bamboo fixed to the spikes of the wheel near its periphery.

In continuing his description, my father explained that as the bamboo tube submerges it fills and then ascends on the downstream side and as it goes over the top it tips the water into a trough 'the length, and position of which is such that it catches the water where it begins to spill and ends where the tube has emptied'.

This trough then drained into a lower one which was at right-angles and which directed the water along the channel to the padis. Some of those tubes had become loose or were not positioned correctly and they spilled too soon or too late. The noise came from the turning spindle and the splash 'by one bucket set to empty on the spindle at its side away from the trough, as the water-lubricant. The whole is constructed from local produce without nails'.

My father then gave a detailed explanation of all the parts of the 'wheel' which I have found is called the Kinchir, (my father spells it Kinchil), literally meaning 'water wheel'. Peculiar to the Kuala Pilah district and a district in Krian, they have been used for hundreds of years and were originally introduced into the Malay Peninsula by the Meningkabau Malays of Sumatra. In the late 1930s, a dam was built in one part of the Kuala Pilah district which effectively did away with the need for such methods of irrigation.

The Straits Times Annual 1939, which my mother gave me long ago, records of the Kinchil: '[O]ne cannot but regret the passing of so picturesque a relic of that leisured age before steam and electricity had made our watchword "speed"!'

My father concluded, 'by 1977, on my last visit, the scene had sadly altered'. The old wheel was almost derelict but still workable enough to irrigate the few rice paddies remaining amongst those in disuse. The sound of the wheels was gone except the groans and squeaking of the one remaining.

My father lamented that this was an aspect of suburban landscape – 'the agricultural achievements of centuries' – which modernisation was breaking up. He compared it to the forests lost from logging and rural children going to the towns and cities for work and entertainment leaving no generation to care for the villages and fields. 'The best of Malay landscape was fading: to the west of the main range of mountains it had already been engulfed in one vast passionless monotony of oil palms… Mammon claps!' As always, my father summed it up so well.

He came to love the freedom of life amongst the tropical rain forests in Malaya, as is clearly shown in his letters. As much as he was impatient with colonial society and its associated lifestyles, he quickly recognised the need to learn about the jungle trees which were being felled before his eyes, never to achieve replacement. The book *A View from the Summit, the Story of Bukit Timah Nature Reserve*, edited by Dr Shawn Lum and Ilsa Sharp, has a telling story.

In 1931, the government (of Singapore) proposed to revoke all forest reserves since they could hardly be considered commercially viable sources of timber any more – many of them had been turned over to crops of fruit trees and it was too difficult, as well as too expensive, to patrol them sufficiently to prevent theft. However, the final decision was delayed until 1936… while the *Collector* [magazine] reported: 'It has been decided to preserve the small forest on Bukit Timah for scientific and other amenities'.

Due to the determined intervention of Eric Holttum and my father, Bukit Timah reserve was preserved 'as the best remaining example of primary forest on the island'. Other reserves were allowed by the government to be extensively felled prior to abandonment.

In 1930, my father had become acutely aware that 'illegal-woodcutters had taken their toll on the Hill'. He recalled how close he got to physical violence while striving to protect Bukit Timah. His tactic was to distract the illegal wood-cutters by tossing their hats into the undergrowth while his Malay assistant snatched their axes and threw them away too.

The Chinese Chamber of Commerce complained about my father but he was vindicated and the cutting of forest product in Bukit Timah was officially banned. The *Singapore Free Press* in an article dated 4 October 1934 under the heading 'Theft of Wood – Chinese Convicted and Fined' recorded 'that wood valued at $15 [£1/15-] was stolen; Mr E. J. H. Corner… explained to the court that thefts by Chinese considerably retarded his work. In the circumstances he would press for severe punishment. The culprit was fined $30 [£3/10-]'.

My father, in his determination to record the trees of Singapore and Malaya before too late, was turning mycology into a hobby so as to pursue conservation and trees with vigour.

IV

THE TALE OF THE FROCK

In 1930, Betty Worthington, Barton Worthington's elder sister, visited my father in Singapore on her way to Australia. He recorded the visit late in his life; around 1994/5. Whilst it shows remarkable powers of recall, it also illustrates his ability to tell a story and to romance where memory fails and the story needs embellishment. Betty's visit coincided with his local leave, no doubt pre-planned. He titled his account *The Tale of the Frock*.

When visiting the London house of his daughter and son-in-law in April 1994, my father heard my sister Lindsay talking to a friend about a cream-coloured lace dress, torn in many places, 'which had been given to the friend to mend for a wedding'. When East Grinstead was mentioned my father pricked up his ears and 'my thoughts drifted slowly back some seventy years when I had stayed in the great house, as the guest of my old school friend Barton Worthington'.

The house was named *Standen* situated near East Grinstead, now owned by the National Trust. My father remembered that Worthington's elder sister, Betty, had lived in the gate-house. She had visited him in Singapore for a few days in 1930, and he had striven to entertain her. He gradually remembered 'a great exploit' and the dress 'in its pristine glamour and in its disfigurement'.

He interrupted the conversation between Lindsay and her friend and asked if the dress had been 'given to the young lady by an elderly lady who used to live in the gate-house?' It had. "Then," he said to their astonishment, "I will tell you the tale of that dress."

He began by telling how he had entertained Betty to dinner in the Grand Hotel de l'Europe where she lodged in Singapore but, as a pretty unsociable young man in those days, he was at his wit's end to know how to proceed. 'I was always trying to escape the social round by crossing over to Johore and exploring its great forests'. Betty was known for being unorthodox so my father suggested something which he knew he was good at and asked if she would like to have a day in the wild and high primeval forest which would include 'a stiff climb'. On affirmation, he advised using 'old clothes and old shoes!', and said that he will pick her up at 5 am the next morning. Betty was thrilled at the prospect.

My father collected Betty Worthington in his open, two-seater Rugby car. They breakfasted quickly and set off with sandwiches and a thermos of tea prepared by 'my Chinese house-boy… used to my early departures'. They drove north to the Causeway as dawn was breaking and east from Johore Bahru for 30 miles to Kota Tinggi where they stopped to buy bananas and a large pomelo which would supply a thirst-quenching juice in the forest. There were ten more miles before a side-road tapered into a lane and they were 'at the end of civilisation where the forest began'.

The gibbons were calling with their exhilarating whoops. Pigeons were spluttering wild nutmegs. Leaves were dripping with the night's dew. Betty was transported by the novelty, wildness and gaiety of the scene as the sun rose.

They set off for the forest having put up the hood on the car as midday brought a deluge. Father carried the soft carbolic soap for that was the antidote for ticks and leeches.

I smeared the dark brown treacly stuff, to her dismay, over her shoes and on her bare legs to the knees: then did so for myself. "You had better tuck your frock into your pants," I remarked, for women wore capacious bloomers in those days.

After tying the bananas to his belt and with the pomelo secured he slung his haversack with lunch inside over a shoulder and made sure his parang was safely sheathed before setting off – 'smelling like a hospital ward' – to the gap through the forest trail up to the western end of the long ridge of Gunmafasti.

'The sky was cloudless but I knew the quick changes in its mood and was not to be deceived'. Parting twigs and slashing with parang to clear thickets, for 'probably, no one but I had used this path in the last two or three years', they made progress but 'Sweat, sweat, sweat! It dripped from us in the saturated undergrowth of the still dripping forest'. Although soaked through, they continued with short stops to check for leeches which, thankfully had been kept at bay by the carbolic smell. 'Gibbons crashed away through the branches as they heard our approach' and eventually they reached the huge fig tree with its trunk-like descended roots; this indicated the top of the path where a vertical rock-wall led some hundred feet higher to their destination. They rested for a while, gathering energy for the climb.

My father had not mentioned tigers, leopards or snakes although they must have been there. Using the cracks in the rocks, the crevices and the sprouting vegetation they climbed, with my father sometimes pushing Betty 'who was game for anything' until they reached a small clearing surrounding the old trig station. There they sat and rested 'looking northward at the ocean of trees stretching to the distant mountains… Clouds were on them. Huge cumulus clouds had begun to burgeon. It was about 11 am. That storm was engendering'.

From that vantage point they could see the route which they had climbed. The view was staggering with trees of all kinds, palms and the 'feathery whips of the rattans and the pink, orange and red sprays of the great *Bauhinia* climbers sprawling over the tree-tops and enticing swarms of brilliant butterflies'. Gibbons were swinging through the branches and 'every so often, a noisy whirring announced a flight of large hornbills' which frequently stopped their flapping to disappear into the foliage.

This scene, primeval indeed, was just a two-hour drive from Singapore and in which my father revelled. To Betty, the carpet of Malaya spread below her was unbelievable.

They ate their lunch, discarding the refuse into the forest below; everything would be eaten or given to decay. Father knew that the midday storm would be upon them as they set out on their return journey.

[D]own the rocks we hastened, regardless of snags and hooks which caught our clothing… the wind began to sough and there was a flash of lightening with the instantaneous peal of thunder as the storm broke overhead. Then came the roar of the express-train as the heavy rain struck the canopy.

They waited, 'gathering the rents in our apparel', and the noise gradually subsided in about twenty minutes. The path down was slippery and they gathered more rents from the thorny rattans and rocks; their legs and clothing were covered with scratches and yellow muddy smears.

We emerged, grubby and lacerated, yet elated at our success, and without ticks or leeches. "Betty," I said as I deposited her at her hotel "I have ruined your lovely frock." "I shall keep it," was her reply, "in memory of this wonderful day."

Washed and folded, yet unrepaired, it had lain for sixty years in her trousseau.

Some story. Some recollection. I constantly wonder why my father left these writings so late in his life. Perhaps he was trying to recapture those glorious and happy days of pre-war Malaya; that something 'so touchingly personal'.

Barton Worthington's eldest daughter, Shelagh, sent me in 2008 copies of a number of letters from my father to hers, and there amongst them – what a huge coincidence – was one from Betty to her parents relating her jungle trek with my father.

Betty's letter, written on 7 April 1930 aboard the SS *Kashgar* on the China Sea, is passionate in the broader sense. The thrust of both stories is the same, as are the love for adventure and the great outdoors.

Well, the old *Marella* arrived at Singapore on Saturday 29th [March 1930] about 5 pm… Corner met me on the wharf, in his smart two-seater and drove me to the Europe [Hotel], then round the town a bit and out to the Botanical Gardens and his house, about three miles out. He was extremely cheerful and full of energy, though he looks thin. He took me round to the director's house [Holttum's], where we were asked in for drinks – a beautiful house with lovely Chinese and Japanese things in it, as well as really good English pictures… Corner has a very nice house too, which he did share with a man, but now has to himself – with some lovely Chinese prints etc. He gave me dinner there and most delicious all cooked and served excellently by his boy. These Chinese servants are wonderful, would you like me to bring you home a selection?

After dinner Corner suggested the magnificent scheme of taking me out to the jungle next day, it being Sunday and his day off, and we laid complicated plans before he took me back to the Europe. Next morning accordingly I got up at 5 am., and was ready in my oldest frock and thickest shoes when he called for me to breakfast at his house, and drive across Singapore Island and over the causeway to Johore, the mainland.

It was a glorious drive, two hours or so in the early morning light – 15 miles to Johore through rubber plantations, coconut groves, pineapple fields, mangrove swamps and native villages, and then on through more rubber and quaint Malay towns and odd bits of jungle to the end of the road, the nearest point to the mountain Gunung Panti, that we had planned to climb. We left the car about 9 a.m., and walked through the corner of a rubber plantation out into the real proper jungle, and then up and down for a while till we began the ascent proper – about 1800 feet.

It was thrilling really to be in the real forest – huge trees with odd waxen magnolia like flowers and buttressed trunks, palms and pandans of every size and shape, weird bamboos and grasses, and everything draped and woven together with creepers, climbing bamboos and climbing palms. The forest seems to grow in three layers: bushes, palms, grasses etc., on the ground, huge trees and palms up to a couple of hundred feet, and between the two the creepers that start half way up the trees and send their roots down in festoons to the ground and their top parts round about anywhere in the neighbourhood.

The only disappointing part was that we saw no animals. It was just as well really, for I don't know what we should have done if a tiger confronted us, as we were only armed with what Corner calls the "general chopper for jungle use", - but though we only saw one tortoise, and heard lots of weird birds, and monkeys crashing about two tiers overhead, it was thrilling to feel that there were tigers and elephants and other exciting beasts all round. I didn't quite like the idea of snakes, though, but could only walk heavily and hope they'd be more frightened of me than I of them. The only sort of snake that will really attack a man, the king cobra, abounds in Singapore!

It was pretty hot climbing that Sunday morning, and we were soon wet through from within. Still, that was nothing to the wetting we were to receive from without. This is the beginning of the rainy season in Singapore, and though on the island they haven't had much rain yet, we certainly got our share that day – about three inches in a couple of hours. It started when we were within about 300 feet of the top, at the foot of the steep rocky precipice up which we were to scramble with the help of the trees and roots draping it. Hoping it would stop we sheltered under a rock and ate our lunch. However it was soon like sitting in a river, for the water poured down the mountainside in cascades, which soon soaked us through, though provided a very welcome drink.

After a while it got less, and we proceeded on our complicated and precarious way to the top, only to find the clouds thick over the country below us and no view, and the rain falling in torrents again. It was bare and exposed and soaked to the skin we began to get chilly (the first time I'd been cold for months), so we trickled and skidded and slid and jumped and lowered ourselves by trees and roots down to the decently sloping ground once more. Of course as soon as we were down the rain stopped and the sun came out, so nothing daunted we climbed once more, to be rewarded by glimpses between the rain clouds of a magnificent view – up the peninsula with jungle covered hill after hill, looking like a dense green sea, and down over the rubber plantations to the plain of Singapore Island – it was well worth any amount of scrambling!

Looking down the precipice at the tops of the trees far below was almost the most interesting – some of them were aflame with brilliant flowers, and great palms stuck up waving amongst them. Then we heard mysterious crashing and curious animal calls way down below us, though of course we couldn't see what sort of beasts they were. We walked some way down the ridge from the top where, in a slight basin, the most wonderful things grow: pitcher plants of all shapes and sizes, orchids, though only one or two in flower at this time, and weird palms, ferns and grasses – like a glorified glass-house at Kew.

I was in luck to go there with Corner, for he could tell me all about the trees and plants etc., and what grew where, and why etc. It took us a good while to slither down the mountain again, collecting fungi and oddments on the way, and we were a bedraggled pair when we arrived once more at the car, for the rain had not stopped long enough to let us dry up. My frock had been left behind in pieces on various rocks, trees and prickly palms, and the rest of my clothes were in ribbons – my shoes just brought me to the car, and were left behind. Luckily I had brought a coat, so had something to arrive at the Europe in! We didn't get back till nearly 7 p. m., but it was a marvellous day, and topping of Corner to take me.

My father must have been impressed with the enthusiasm of Betty Worthington, a woman game to explore the tropical rain forest. He was one who respected those who were committed to his fields of interest.

*

On 22 May 1930, my father went to Fraser's Hill. His descriptions of the jungle and jungle life in his letter to Worthington clearly shows his connection to the environment in which he worked, if 'worked' is the right word to use.

Going over the pass was like ascending a celestial stairway. The road wound up, round and in and out of the valleys through the most beautiful forest. Occasionally we had a glimpse on to the top of the forest in the valley, and all the way up magnificent trees lined the roadside. The undergrowth had been removed at hair-pin bends so that one could see across but the big trees with towering trunks had been left.

He wrote glowingly of the hill, describing it as a 'little island in the ocean of trees which covers even the higher mountains'. Although the forest abounds with game he comments that one never sees anything except the odd snake and bird.

Sometimes I disturb a flock of big black hornbills feeding on the tree-tops and they lumber away with wheezy flight uttering an eerie screaming laughter.

The valleys resounded with the 'wah – wah – wah – woop of gibbons' and some booming note he could not place, and all around was strident with cicadas 'which makes a noise like an electric buzzer'. He talked of the numerous squirrels which 'croak and chatter' and a fly with eyes on long stalks which looked like an ant.

Of his ventures into the jungle he wrote warmly of his visits to a waterfall for a bathe; laying 'in the delicious cool water' and enjoying the delightful peace of it all appreciating that bathing without the annoyance 'of leeches, ticks, horse-flies or mosquitoes is enchanting'. Emerging from the pool 'to sit with Nature on a rock' he mused that he was 'fanned by the soft wind which blows up the water-courses'. He watched 'a swift skim the water or a big butterfly flopping through the overhanging branches and the dragonflies as they dart to and fro, sometimes almost in the water and they always come and peer inquisitively at me'.

He wrote about the sounds and how the waters 'roared and tumbled' to carve a way through the jungle with no humans to listen. 'Sometimes I admit it is rather lonely when a cold wind howls and I crouch under a fallen trunk out of the rain and all is dismal'.

But can one ever doubt his loving commitment to his life work?

*

In mid-1930, Barton Worthington announced his plans to marry. This elicited some of my father's most curious letters. I learned much about him from these as they were written to a close and trusted friend. The letter to Worthington of 14 July 1930 'on occasion of his engagement' was candid.

So ho! They've cop't you, have they; cop't you at last? The inestimable Stella! I fell over backwards when I read your telegram. I got up and read it again and fell over a second time.

He had in fact cabled Worthington immediately, and if ever a coded message was sent, here it is!

'Blooms Flower So Fair Quick Lest Fade Search For Worm Slowly *Cave Oppidans Natura Sylvicola Floreat Stella Bartonis*'.

My father's command of language is always worthy of note. On 29 August, he wrote again to Worthington, tongue in cheek, fearing that his fiancée Stella may have seen the telegram and that he might be banned from the family for 'all the little Worthingtons will want to know tales of the queer bad fellow in Singapore'. In this letter, my father explained the code which is full of botanical references:

'Blooms the flower so fair' – I could not believe, and still cannot believe, that you could have come upon Perfection so early in Life – some are indeed lucky – so the incredulous tone of the botanist led to imagine the most superb emblem of natural beauty, and thus begun I must continue in the same vein – or lose ground in a telegram.

'Quick lest fade' i.e. quick lest it fade; re-emphasises my former unbelief which became a great joy now that I accepted your word, but gives a warning that you must not let slip the rare opportunity for lack of appreciation especially.

'Search for worm', i.e. which might have entered by the roots and, yet unseen, would continue its ravages and would destroy your hopes. We know that a parasite in its affection may stimulate an organism to a superlative extent and then in its prime, as it were, will eat its heart out and leave an empty shell. In untold elation much escapes the eye and I feared that you might be blind to snares and pitfalls until the truth dawned on your astonished gaze and you were trapped – for a life-time, for your only life-time too.

'*Cave oppidians natura sylvicola*' i.e. beware the towns folk, or those who dwell by preference in big and artificial places, for Nature loves the woods – biologist pleading to another lest he should forsake his calling – you cannot be a master-of-animals or plants unless you have pursued them in the wild, and nowadays that means that you and I, as Englishmen, must go to some equatorial colony of the Empire, and not only for our own reward but as one's duty.

I thought you might have fallen in with a society bird…

'*Floreat Stella Bartonis*'; you know – to end with a fervent hope that all is well, contentment… Flourish Barton's Star… the Eyebright or the Loose strife? I ate a durian for your good luck.

Later in the letter he added, 'she will have you in society, you will become Bidder, and think of Miss Bidder [Thackeray]'. He tells Worthington that his wife will have him spending summer days at tennis, boating and swimming and winter at skiing and dancing.

Those priceless leisure hours when you should be after sweet Nature; she dwells in the woods. She will not come out: you must seek her. Who can botanise from the highway?

… Fast, fast the good old world is going. The wild life of forest, jungle, prairies, veldts, and deserts will soon be portion and parcel with the unknown past. When we are old men, we shall be able to say we have seen parts of the world as it has been since the beginning of the Tertiary but our sons will know only a transfigured, miserably upholstered landscape.

Here a most telling footnote, exactly as he wrote it in a letter to van Steenis about 1971: 'I had seen Barton and myself becoming biologists – zoologist, botanist – I went on; he became important.'

The letter to Worthington continued, 'We can become, we shall become, great men because we can and shall have seen things which will soon be gone forever. Do not say therefore you have sold your liberty. Can you really still wander?'

I have included most of this for it tells something of my father's views on marriage. This is important for in time he too marries and the course of his marriage is key to how this story unfolds.

In the same letter, my father – although he loved to be alone – wrote most frankly about the pleasure of having a companion in his travels, though the reference is not to a spouse.

I will tell you a secret – I am really frightened of the jungle, not the small jungle we get in Singapore, but the vast stretches of mainland where it is like wandering in some prehistoric age without companion, only God on high… when a deathly hush falls: then some palm leaf starts to wave frantically for no apparent reason, or a twig snaps and a fruit drops plonk and you think of… an encounter with a tiger.

He told of the sighing of the wind, the creaking of the trees which grind against each other, groaning 'and all the time you cannot see more than a dozen yards around, sometimes not more than two or three'.

Malaya was 'a tropical paradise' for my father. His life, certainly working, was as close to utopia as it could be; truly a seventh heaven – except for that fear which never really left him.

In the same letter, he explained how lonely he feels as he sits on the forest floor, on the rotting debris and giant roots, and all so gloomy; no sky to be seen. Yet, in his late letter of the year to Worthington dated 29 December, he confessed: 'I don't suppose there is anyone so lonely in the land, but I hate people. They always make a noise, and I cannot stand noises'.

'Xmas is over', he wrote. 'It means nothing to me. I spent Xmas day and Boxing day drawing some little stinkhorns and Saturday, Sunday following, in the *Geastrum* from Tembeling'.

These admissions too are revealing of the man I seek and strain to find. Not only does he admit to loneliness but also his hate of people and noise. This must be taken in context. His loneliness comes from a social awkwardness: his stammer must account for some of that as must his scholarly knowledge. He simply didn't have time, the patience, for idle chatter with no clear object in mind. He didn't actually 'hate people'; rather he found most people distracting and frankly a little thin, with some notable exceptions. He did not consider the sounds of the jungle as noise. He enjoyed them as much as he did music which he discussed with Worthington: 'I have Beethoven in G major and C minor, Brahms in B flat, and Mozart in G major. Brahms is the super best. Beethoven is always enchanting and magnificent. Mozart jolly'.

My father continued his discussion of music with Worthington in a letter dated 3 January, my birth date but I was still ten years off. He wrote about an argument with himself at breakfast about whether 'Beethoven is greater than Brahms?' Clearly he was in a most meditative mood and this is a side of my father I did not know. He found that in six points Beethoven was matchless.

[W]ith a bar Beethoven can hint something magnificent, something glorious, something divine, and instantly pass on, purposely unfinished (infinite).… [A]nd lastly, for which I like him best is the pure "lusus" [is the supposed son or companion of Bacchus, the Roman god of wine and divine madness] or sheer playfulness, delightful dully and nonsense, expressing joy, in which I think also he excels over Mozart. To Brahms belongs profundity: he is at once immense, vast, refined, and incomprehensible, with fascinating grandeur: lovely withal, in all that one can hear and dream.

In a footnote again written many years later he wrote: 'copied because I see that, as I sat listening in those heavy evenings, I absorbed the design for my writings, which unconsciously tried to combine these [musical] effects'.

The words of a profoundly thinking man and he finished his letter by writing:

[L]et the beauty of the land increase with the square of the distance… for very shortly the beauty will be so great that you are knocking at heaven's gates… So you see why Beethoven never wants to get there but closes again immediately. Brahms is the 'deep-down delivery' and of all matters mundane; none so thoughtful as the ocean.

My father was becoming 'the deep down delivery'. I had always known that he loved the music of Brahms. However, I had no idea of his depth of feeling and understanding of the classical greats. I am learning that he and I had similar musical tastes and desires.

*

In his letter of 10 August 1931, my father offered Worthington a story about a Golden Bough, 'of a tree with a forbidden fruit, of the dragon that guards and the guile and the wile of the little men who strive for the envied morsel'.

He was referring to the durian. My father stated that botanists dispute 'whether durian trees are wild or not', but went on to say that they are found in the dense high forest either singly and in small groups, having grown from seeds which the jungle folk, the Sakai [Orang Asli, 'original peoples' in Malay], had discarded. He argued: 'is that not as wild an origin as any – were they anthropoids it were a good example of distribution by means of animals?' He then described the durian tree as being 'stately', often reaching 100 feet or higher.

> [T]he flowers are large, white, and smell of fresh milk. They are borne in clusters on the old branches from the bark, and so the fruits hang down from the branches near the trunk. They inform the botanist that the tree belongs with hollyhocks and mallows to the Malvaceae (or is it *Bombacaceae*?).

The large prickly fruits, he said, contain several large seeds in five compartments, which he described as being 'wrapped with a creamy-white, custardy, buttery, Devonshire-creamy, toffee-like, onion-smelling pulp'. The odour, when opened, is like that of a drain 'so most people think them and the trees execrable, to be cut down and abolished within municipal limits'. No, he insisted.

When the fruiting season which lasts perhaps two weeks arrives, the Malays go out with food and bedding and they construct 'rickety little bamboo huts 20–30 feet up the tree-trunks'. They build them on triangular platforms between the trees and close to the fruits; access is by ladder. When the durians fall the Malays rush to gather them. However, if they fall at night they are left to the beasts! As he said. 'All the big game of the neighbourhood will pass under the trees in the next few weeks, but only the elephant in daylight. All intent on the fruit.'

If one thinks they are planted by the Sakai, my father disagrees, stressing that they are wild and belong to the elephants. For once, when walking beneath some trees, after the last fruits had fallen, he saw the foot marks of elephants, and their calling cards like piles of dung, scratched bark and the like. The elephants know all about these trees and their tracks, 'old and new, lead away from them in all directions into the forest. They have the first choice, men the second, the tiger third, and what escapes the other beasts, ants and beetles eat'.

He told Worthington that the previous year an elephant caught a Malay who was climbing a durian tree and crushed him in its trunk… hurled him up and down and trampled him.

A footnote (written years later) said, 'this is the beginning of durianology for it revealed the problem of what was the durian doing in the forest'.

Clearly by 1931, my father was seriously thinking about the durian and the origin of ancient trees. He was a man who believed in himself and his ideas, even if they upset the apple cart.

In the letter of 10 August, he complained to Worthington that his research papers on disco fungi have been 'very coldly' received. He had drafted the last of the series of papers on the voyage out to Singapore in 1929, and had rewritten it several times. The first four papers of the series were completed during his last term at Cambridge. 'As I expected,' he complained, 'they will not appeal to mycologists because they are too pure mycology.'

R. G. Tomkins of Trinity College had taken up the cudgels on his behalf to argue points with Prof F. T. Brooks of the Botany School, Cambridge. My father recognised that it was well meant, but felt that it was wrong for Tomkins to do so, and had written to him to tell him that: 'I wrote not for our elders but for ourselves because our elders do not want to have instruction from babes and sucklings'.

With raw sarcasm, my father concluded that their minds were made up or he would have titled his papers 'An introduction to the study of Discomycetes, for all that people know about them'. [See Appendix D, 1929-1931]

The papers provided the first 'extraneous' evidence so far given in favour of the Oxford botanist A. H. Church's 'hypothesis of the evolution of plants'. He confirmed that Church had recently written to him saying that 'he did not think my method of schematising hyphae could be improved on'.

Church was clearly pleased with the support given by my father's research, and told him that he would leave him all his notes and drawings. This he did, and according to my father's footnote, 'all the collection of "Churcharia"' was 'transferred around 1975 to the Bodleian Library'.

As much as Church acknowledged my father's work, my father admired his scholarship. 'I think he is glad to have a young disciple. I still repeat whatever you continue to report, that he will become a name like Darwin and Huxley'.

Summing up the episode, my father wryly said, 'The shadow of the Academy is again across my path'. He much preferred to be botanising in the field.

Along the same line of thought, he bemoaned to Worthington in the same letter that he will, in a few days, take over from the Professor of Biology at the College of Medicine in Singapore. 'He goes on leave: I to his place. But not to his house'. It was intended that my father should relocate to the Professor's house; that he refused for he was intensely happy living close to the Botanic Gardens 'where was all my work and pleasure… must they drag me even from my bed? It is enough surely that I stand up and stutter on their behalf'.

My father completed the letter by telling of his visits to the Sedili River on August Bank Holiday 1931, spending two nights and two days with Malays, paddling up the river in a canoe.

And the step from the boat is like a stride from civilisation to the lawless past. Among the speechless trees, around the roots we roam; ferns, fungus, mosses, creepers, palms, trunks, trunks, trunks, in pretty fearful places. Unaccompanied, I know I should go mad.

He told of his enjoyment of the 'rustic humour and the boyishness of the Malays' but not so much as the 'still mysteriousness of the forests'. He delighted that the friendship of these 'jolly laughing people' can cheer him so in these awful places.

No, my dears, I am not to be found in a white overall in a laboratory at Cambridge... And that is why I loathe the daily round, the professional perfunctoriness now thrust upon me. Birtwistle says whenever I meet him now. Don't go and marry, Corner, a wife's an awful nuisance.

Birtwistle's remark was no throw-away line. No, it was most serious and intended. He was my father's senior by 16 years and had been happily married for some years. He was a plain speaker and I believe he intended the comment as wise advice, knowing well Mr Edred John Henry Corner and his relentless determination! And my father admitted to the loathing of the daily round of those stuck in offices or herbaria; the thought of a white coat was beyond his comprehension. He loved the freedom to roam and was not to be shackled. What then marriage?

The 1931 *Annual Report of the Director of the Gardens* gives an idea of some of my father's varied work.

Mr E. J. H. Corner, Asst Director, was in Singapore throughout the year; from August 27th he acted as Professor of Biology, King Edward VII College of Medicine... Mr Corner made a short expedition to the Sedili River, Johore, in February, exploring some of the neighbouring swampy forest and collecting fungi.

He also spent two weeks in Brastagi, Sumatra, a mountain town with a cool climate and vast forests particularly on the road to Medan. This same year, my father became a Fellow of the Linnean Society and in his Royal Society Personal Records suggests that it is 1931 when he introduced 'Botanical Monkeys' and started 'hyphal systems in the study of polypore fungi'.

In 1932–33, my father was made secretary of the Malaysian Branch of the Royal Asiatic Society. In 1932, he made an important change, switching from the study of mycology to forest trees. In his Royal Society personal records he simply said, 'I became a conservationist'. By 1933, he had helped establish the Bukit Timah Forest Reserve 'as the last stand of forest on the island'; this was followed by the Gunung Panti Reserve and the Mawai Reserve in Johore.

My father wrote to Robin Hill on 8 March 1932, urging him to visit.

You must come to Singapore. I have just had a letter from Worthington to say that you feel you may be in the way. Rubbish, nonsense, rubbish,

I am waiting for you! But do not come before June or after September because I shall not be free from the College of Medicine until after May and I shall have no house to put at your disposal after September.

My father wrote that he will arrange his leave to coincide with the visit and accompany him to Sumatra, stressing that he must see something of Malaya first. Hill arrived in June but my father was unable to go with him to Sumatra and Java for the mushroom season had closed on him early. However, when Hill returned to Singapore, my father did take him on a trip 'up-country'.

Clearly, Hill much enjoyed the road to Kuala Selangor and their subsequent exchange of letters record the botanical discoveries they made on the trip. There was a cooperation between Hill in the biochemistry lab at Cambridge and my father at the Botanic Gardens in Singapore – I dare say a veritable round robin.

My father also wrote about the visit with one C. E. Carr to Ulu Tiram to climb Gunung Panti. On the top they discovered about seven orchids new to the peninsula, two of which may be altogether new and one he described as rather like a large dock 'with an inflorescence 4 ft. high, the upper 12" being a close spike of large white flowers', and a 'wonderful sight'.

He also discovered a *Lycopodium* [a genus of clubmosses] which may have been a new record.

Oh, the more I see of Panti, the more it is a dreamland… pandans, and orchids, and aroids and ginger and palms and tree ferns and didymocarps as the undergrowth…

In another letter to Hill, my father mentioned the situation of Carr – which showed that that my father was not ignorant of the ins and outs of colonial society. He said that Carr had been made redundant from Tembeling Rubber Estate and had moved to live in Singapore. Holttum had arranged accommodation in the Gardens for 'some 8 months or until Kinabalu to study orchids'. He then explained that Carr had become infatuated with Mrs Henderson (wife of the curator of the Singapore Herbarium) and that consequently he, Holttum and Henderson advised Carr to leave, which he did, returning to the UK.

In the last missive I have from 1932 to Hill, my father proved that he was indeed not devoid of social skills. After describing a specimen of *Morinda ridleyi* he found in the swamp forest on Jurong Road, he reveals that he had gone for a midnight row on the reservoir with Lady Clementi, the wife of Sir Cecil Clementi, Governor of the Straits Settlements, and had explained all to her about Malayan clouds.

In the same letter, my father reported that 'Tomorrow the Governor opens Rosedale's new "Nutrition Laboratory" as he calls it, and the sports ground etc, at the College of Medicine, and we have all had an invitation.'

The new Governor, who formerly governed Hong Kong, knew my father's friend Herklots, who used to take Lady Clementi on botanical rambles in Hong Kong. So, when my father was invited to a small and informal party at Government House, he found himself on a small couch with Lady Clementi. They 'discussed the Gardens and Hong Kong, and Herklots and herself and myself and her children for the most exalted twenty minutes in my life!'

My father had written on two occasions that he 'hates men', expressed his distate for the women of Singapore colonial circles, and had candidly admitted to being 'a pretty unsociable young man', being 'at my wit's end to know how to proceed'. Specifically, he admitted that he 'was always trying to escape the social round by crossing over to Johore and exploring, as a botanist, its great forests'.

Well now! A midnight row and a tête-à-tête with the Governor's wife! So it seems that my father was somewhat more sociable then than I had thought, but perhaps he made an effort when socialisation was for a definite purpose. It clearly was important for him, still a young civil servant, to get to know the new Governor and his wife.

My father's letters to Robin Hill and Barton Worthington of this time gave the impression of a busy life, but he also confessed that of lonely evenings. He wrote, when telling of his favourite authors that 'I took them [the books] up in Singapore, through Raffles' library, in the long lonely evenings'.

As lonely as he claimed he was, and even though, as he had written in *The Marquis* that 'he found life in Singapore distasteful', he did find 'a sprinkling of persons' who were congenial because they 'had grown to love the country'.

The Landons and William Lloyd were certainly people he respected and I believe considered true friends. So too was Murnane, the head of the Singapore Water Department, who encouraged him to try horse-botanising and rode the paths of the reservoir with him.

Colin Symington and his wife too were good friends and my father had a respect for his botanic ability. Michael W F Tweedie, Curator of Raffles Museum, and Frank Walker were other family men who befriended my father.

I am sure most 'Brits' knew each other in a colonial society like Malaya. Equally of no doubt is that the scientists in Singapore and Malaya knew each other via their work or the Club, probably both. William Birtwistle was amongst the closest of my father's colleagues from very soon after their first meeting. As for Eric Holttum, there never appeared to be anything but a professional relationship.

My father was a difficult man to get to know privately. He did his best to avoid unnecessary distraction and was often misunderstood for this, and was considered aloof.

John Gullick, a Malayan Civil Service retiree told me that in pre-war Malaya, 'it was undoubtedly a problem for individual Europeans who did not completely share the interests and attitudes of the majority, who nonetheless expected everyone to conform and showed mild resentment at those who held aloof'.

This does help explain my father's attitudes of the time, and attitudes towards him; certainly he was thought to be 'aloof and proud' but he was never 'ordinary'.

It is important, when striving to understand E. J. H. Corner, to appreciate that such attitudes caused not a hoot of concern to him – the impassioned, exceptional, and relentless botanist.

- V -

HOME VISIT

My father's thoughts in early 1933 were on his forthcoming visit home, so much so that he wished he had planned an earlier boat. Sailing on the Blue Funnel Line vessel SS *Sarpedon* from Singapore on 17 May, arriving Marseilles on 9 June, 'then overland helter-skelter', he realised that that would make him far too late for the christening of Worthington's daughter, Shelagh. He had written to Robin Hill:

> Home! I am really coming home and with 20 lbs of dried vitex-bark in 2 kerosene tins… Oh for the green, white cliffs of Albion! Do you long for the wayward pandans and that softly sighing, slowly winding, secret stealthy river, the Sedili?

My father missed the sights of Marseilles for it was dark when he arrived. However, he awoke as usual at dawn, the train hurtling along as he looked out of the window and was astonished to see that the fields, hedges and orchards, indeed, the countryside was a pale blue; barely any suggestion of green! The strength of colour increased as the sun came up and my father wrote 'from Dover to London, the landscape was blue'. On arrival at his parent's house *Stratton End* in Beaconsfield, he kept muttering that the trees were blue, confirmed by a long look at an oak he had planted. After a few days' rest, he visited the Worthingtons at Madingley near Cambridge. In his first morning there, he rose early and strolled in the countryside to notice immediately that the flowers, grass and hedges were green – 'By that freak encounter, contrast had been restored. The blue landscape had vanished, save from the mind's eye'.

He had noticed the unexpected contrast between temperate and tropical vegetation which, on reflection, he said 'should be obvious, yet, others had not remarked on it'. He muses that it might require the 'simplicity of the novice after a long stay in the tropics'.

*

My father was in England from 11 June 1933 for six months and plunged into the activities of the mycology and botany circles.

On a visit to Scotland, he found the sweet-smelling and tasting *Galium boreale* by Loch Earn and Loch Rannoch, reporting that on neither occasion were there any inflorescences. He also found several 'fung' including some polypores and what looked like a new *Boletus*, 'at least to England', he said, although he was in Scotland! The Mycological Meeting at Newcastle, he reported, was poor owing to the drought, although they "found a few nice things".

At Cambridge, he gave a lecture on figs at the Botany School to the Botanical Section of the Cambridge University Natural History Society. He also made time to visit Sir Jeremiah Coleman, a well-known orchid breeder famous for his mustard.

He made time to visit A. H. Church whom he corresponded with from Singapore, and found his mentor aged. 'He was seated stiffly in the upright armchair of the front room.... Expression had gone but his eyes twinkled and, on my enquiry of his health, he made the puckish reply: Pretty dickey'.

Although they were in the same country, my father continued to write to Robin Hill, and this series of letters revealed another part of my father's character. Referring to the sycamore-dendrons which Hill had told him about, he wrote that he had caught the snatches of a polyhorgen's dirge, 'wafted from the Muse on the mountain', and found himself singing:

Sick beneath a sycamore
I lay upon my pinafore
I never was so sick before
As underneath that sycamore!

He continued with an amusing poem which includes the stanza:

On the road to Amulree
Paused the Polyhog to pee.
And a' the burns o' Almond's glen
That frolic'd frae' the mountain then
Ran yellow wi' the santonin
An' threadin' thro' the heath & whim
Spun a tartan from his jim!

This illustrates the impish and humorous side of my father, and I can remember a little of that; his 'lavatory humour' as has been described by his goddaughter Shelagh, but really not in the modern idiom of that humour! I have racked my brains to try to recall some early moments in my life but I had done a good job of consigning them to the farthest depths of my memory. I do, however, remember the laughter in the car when, for the first time for me, we passed the sign for the village of Six Mile Bottom, in Cambridgeshire, and the conjuring-up, encouraged by my father, of such a large posterior!! This was in the 1950s.

"Rumblebottom". That was how he signed off one of his letters from this period, departing from the standard EJHC. His letters were then more personal, ending 'John', or another *nom de plume*. My father signed himself, in an undated note in 1933, as 'Bumblebee' and in a later letter to Hill as 'your humble servant, John Bumblebee'. There was also 'Bumblebottom'! In 1935 this changed to 'John Grumblebottom', and then to 'John Pandan'. In 1936 it became 'Jjohn Ppandan', a reflection of his stammer.

The time had arrived for his return to Singapore. He left on 8 February 1934 for Marseilles, joining the P & O liner SS *Ranchi* to arrive in Singapore on 2 March. My father was glad that he would be back in Singapore in time for the first season of toadstools and told Hill of the dream that he had arrived in the middle of it 'and was so vexed'.

But foremost in his plans was another visit during the forthcoming Easter to Kuala Sedili and Ulu Tiram, remarking that 'Four years should just suffice for that corner of Johore [for research for his book on wayside trees].' This says something of the time it was taking to gather information for his book and this mainly from just a part of Malaya. He sounded excited by the prospect of his return as he did with the prospect of his first home leave.

As a farewell gift, Robin Hill offered my father a book for the long journey. He welcomed it, saying that 'It will indeed help speed the time, for a boat is a dismal place – for the unedified!' Undoubtedly, he did not expect to find the same kind of distraction which he did enroute on his first trip to Singapore.

How wrong he was. His letter of 14 March 1934 to Worthington revealed the remarkable turn of events. My father sets the scene with a kind of heading: This is 'the oryx hunt' or 'the captivating Miss Brown'.

He had enjoyed the sector from Bombay to Singapore, although he found Bombay 'a beastly spot'. He had hired a car and visited the native bazaar saying that 'they are not clever in handicraft'. He found the countryside rather dull even though he 'went a fair stretch along the road to Poona'.

Colombo was a different matter. Calculating that he had about eight hours to spare, he rushed ashore, assigned himself a fast car and drove some 70 miles inland to the Royal Botanical Gardens, Peradeniya, near Kandy. He had barely an hour there, but said it was worth it, stating that 'They are much better than our Gardens because they are so much larger and with advantages in age and soil and situation'.

He then had to hurry back to catch the departing ship, but not before stealing '3 "cannon-ball" fruits from the Gardens. They are as big as one's head and quite as hard'.

The letter then takes a turn and my father's writing becomes beguiling, full of hidden meaning and metaphor.

> And whilst at sea, between whites, I pursued on fairy hills with winged feet and haunting gaze that will o' the wisp. Stealthily creeping, bounding and leaping, with fresh brown dust in my eyes, but never could I catch it…. It would pause on an eminence, fair and comely and graceful, as lithe and powerful, but oh so timorous.

My father worried that the 'thoughts of the hunter', his thoughts, would startle it.

> Never could I stay my watching 'oryx'. It was all delirious until one day it happened at tea, and the other joined my dream. My gaze wandered in that direction and instinctively the eyes of my dreams were raised to mine. I tell you, in that fell instant, the dielectric broke down and such a spark lept across I was utterly discharged; only I heard a whisper – me thinks, a hand stole into mine; a sigh and a curse I heard. In those deep eyes a new light shone; and now, my 'oryx' looked and, oh! Heavens, it turned; it turned upon the hunter fugitive. It waited to be caught. Sometimes I was tempted and strung my bow but no finger would move to lose the shaft.

For the following day he saw that 'it' had been weeping. Indeed, it had wept through the night as others danced on deck. He tried to approach it, catch it, but it passed by.

> Tears of joy, tears of spite, tears of sorrow, but not tears of anguish, can I stand. "Sister," I said, "thou may'st not withhold me when weeping is abroad; let me relieve this pitiable state? I went without noose or arrow, but with the balm of gilead. It watched me and it strayed; but I passed by." "Fool, fool", as I bit my lip, "has't no courage…?" I tried and tried, and I failed – faint heart. Even a phantom stopped me; two hands staid in mine. "Sister", I said "thou may'st not." You do not know how hopeless I am.

My father, the rather faint-hearted cavalier, sought with his conscience, his inner thoughts, indeed, his desires and resolved in decisive indecision.

> My 'oryx' strove as a dumb beast only can when it is forbidden the service of a tongue. I went and came through many a toilsome hour before I was resolved, and then I heard, I think, "thou shalt and thou shalt not". I did, and went and sat beside my 'oryx'!

They talked together for two days but it was difficult for the hunter who confessed about still being shy. The hunter had progressed but not his character; his deep inhibitions were still ruling his heart. Was he playing with fire? It was a dangerous moment, saved by their arrival in Penang, for 'I might have been dragged like Mazeppa [a Tchaikovsky opera]; it is a tarbar [tribe] of Ukraine breed visible in its congeners rather than itself'.

The father of the 'oryx' was blue eyed but mother not, 'Looking like a Portuguese issue'. Continuing, the hunter wrote:

> I cannot help smiling at the thought of its sister as brown as a berry. It wasn't really, of course, but that is part of the dream: it is but a little dusky, such a colour as our women would effect for ever, if the exigencies of the weather did not intervene.

> My father was pleased that on berthing in Penang he was collected quickly by Mr Best. My father then continued to Singapore; the 'oryx' not.

> So I had no further opportunity and, ha ha, we have not parked yet. She dwells on the hill, under those ferns that hang from the bough.... Really, will you not suffer woman and her tenderness to sit by him in his darkness? You will admit it is a joke, and what is more it is all my own joke. I know that no one else has hunted on those hills or seen through those vents of shyness that wondrous beast within.

He considered writing to the 'oryx' and concluded that he must. The letter and the hunter's story comes to an end with more of my father's deeply thought-out writing.

> Sits Sancho Panza as merrily on his ass; Ass myself, he has long since fallen down and been forgotten. You will find him under the seat-cushion on the sofa (where he had left it with the book-mark at the chapter 'The Curious Impertinent' in Barton's house – the Lodge at Madingley). I feel I am Roderick at Random. I have just started it. But, my good Bartholomew, you forget that, as it is most certainly a right-angled triangle.

At the end of this long letter, my father added a separate page, written very many years later, which stated that the 'oryx' was the elder daughter of Mr Brown, head of an old Eurasian family in Penang and owner of the newspaper *Penang Gazette*.

Mr Brown was probably David Alexander Murray Brown, educated in Harrow and Cambridge, qualified as an accountant and general manager of the newspaper. Recreation: Horse racing.

My father described Miss Brown as fairly tall, indeed taller than Worthington's wife Stella whom she looked like: 'round face, dark hair and deep eyes… and those eyes held me'. He told of her sister noticing his 'admiring gaze' and she 'admonished me for making advances during the voyage Colombo to Penang and chided me for not dancing with her sister'.

Well, my father hated dancing and organised sports although he noted that his 'oryx' enjoyed both with good technique! He then confessed that he was beset by convention: 'My father warned me repeatedly not to marry an Oriental. Europeans in Singapore despised Eurasians'. So he was troubled for 'I loved her for herself – and lacked the courage, then, to demolish convention'. Indeed what a conundrum, what a most difficult problem – and he wrote of wondering how things would have turned out if he had married her: 'No Helga, no Lindsay; a life in their house at Gelugor in the south part of Georgetown in Penang?'

When my father reached Singapore he wrote letters to Miss Brown, to which she replied. But after a while the correspondence slowed… 'then, silence. I wandered away and away with Nature… I think she would have come. What was her name? I thought of Miss Brown. I know but cannot recall'.

He proved right with Miss Brown, and wrote that this post script:

fills me with long lost love – my first affection. I was too bashful. I thought a mere botanist could not win and maintain the elder daughter of a wealthy family, whether Eurasian or not.

Much of this letter of reminiscence was written in April 1984. What a beautiful love story, and what an imaginative way to write it. I could never imagine the father I knew writing such a touching story, but he did, many years ago. Feelings of amazement, surprise, delight and then anger crept over me. Here is my father opening his heart, in April 1984, and after he had published *The Marquis*, in which not a mention of me; and he writes: 'No Helga [his second wife]… no Lindsay'.

I write 'no me, no Christine and no Sheila Corner'. Leaving out my mother and me in 1984 I can just understand, but Christine, who already was unwell – what was he thinking? Extraordinary, and oh so very sad for us all, including him.

How much I still have to learn about my father, but I am finding out and every now and then I have a tinge of sadness that it has taken his passing for all of this to emerge. For whom did he intend these extracts and why did he never fully use them in his writing? Was he hoping Pandora would fire me to action? Yes, and it did – and what revelations for me to reveal. Perhaps this is his way of apologising and completing his story.

OUT IN THE FIELD

One of the things that my father brought back to Singapore was a new camera – a Rolleiflex. The introduction of the Rolleiflex Twin Lens Reflex in 1929 was without any doubt a sensation: applying as ingenious as simple a principle that quickly made the Rolleiflex the must have professional camera all over the world. It was expensive but then he was still a bachelor, devoted to his botanical task of which photography was important. In fact, he mastered all things necessary for a botanist, including sketching and accurate drawing: this was vital for his work on the trees of Malaya. He also became a most competent painter. All this he did, following the advice of A. H. Church before his first posting in 1929.

Something must have changed at work after his return from home leave, for the insipient difficulties he had with Holttum and Henderson at the Gardens began to surface.

'No! I am not Lord God Almighty in the Gardens. I never press my point', he wrote to Worthington, followed by a footnote complaining about the incompetence of Holttum and Henderson

> which I could drive home with ease… I do not wish to be fettered to one office-stool as a Director; so I am still the independent assistant. Minutes and government service is calcifying… I have, however, taken over all the outside-work in the Gardens and have sat on the stool while Henderson has been away. He is as lazy and selfish as ever and his very inefficiency as an *Acting* [emphasis mine] Director almost grabs me to take the reins.

After more damning comments about Henderson, he continued, 'Aye aye! The gibbons howled when I returned and there was a general jubilation on the Sedili. I have been there several times, twice already to the mouth on the East Coast… Jason Bay'.

Obviously he would much rather be in the field botanising than saddled with administrative duties.

The area of swamp forest of the two Sedili rivers – Besar (big) and Kecil (small) – which my father so loved and studied in considerable detail are at each end of Jason Bay on the East Coast of Johore with sandbars forming across the river mouths.

To him, 'all natural places are beautiful but for verdure and grand forest I do not suppose the… Sedili area can be beaten in this part of the world'. To him, 'it is a heavenly spot with magnificent forest in places going right on to the sea shore'. This coast was rugged with 'the wild beauty of the unbroken forest'.

My father once took a stroll along the beach where the jungle reached the sea, at what he describes as 'that awful hour when beasts begin to stir at sunset'. As he wandered into the forest he was startled by the sight of fresh paw marks of a tiger; 'the leaves just scratched up and sand-grains slithering down.' He was extremely careful and watchful for he had made it a rule never to walk alone in the forest 'before 8 in the morning and after 4 in the afternoon'.

On another occasion, he and his companions rowed upstream and when they had left the mangroves around the river mouth and the last little village, the forest closed in. The pandans were thickly converging; they straightened to let them pass. Chopping with axe and parang they made a 'tunnel' through which their boat could manoeuvre but it was so narrow that they could touch the trees on either side. Some trees were actually standing in the water, some on stilts and others were deep in the flood tide. When they could go no further, they arrived at the last settlement of three attap thatched houses in a small clearing, with rubber and vegetables on the only hillocks and dry land for several miles around.

The only house inhabited was by a Chinese who made the small party most welcome with coffee and cigarettes. The coffee was prepared and served by a pretty Chinese girl who the Malays called Bunga – flower. My father, clearly entranced by her beauty, offered her a cigarette much to the amusement of all. Later, when the party returned to Sedili Besar my father's helpers 'spread such a tale through Kuala Sedili of a marvellous flower we had met away in the forest but that the Tuan wouldn't take'.

Talking to Aaron, his Malay guide, about a revisit, my father was given a big wink. My father benefited a great deal from Aaron's knowledge of plants and folklore.

[T]he reason why the fruit of a wild chestnut which I had picked up was called 'sarentals tangga' – which rather means 'you're had on the stairs'… for, said he, if you eat it, when you get back to your house and sit down in the evening you suddenly feel sick at, well, both ends and ere you may reach the bottom of the stairs, you are indeed sick in that disastrous manner.

Perhaps the most important plant around Sedili, commented my father, is what the Malays called the Goat's Testicles Creeper! Aaron explained: 'It grows by rivers and slings over the water like a great spud; its light grey fruit of the requisite size and consistency'. Not catching the whole of his explanation, my father asked,

'Whose? What?' and one of the others said, 'Aaron's', which he so indignantly denied that, if I had not shouted 'Order, order' I believe we would have upset [the boat]. And nobody understood, unless it were the nipa palms who were laughing and waving their fronds at us in great glee from the river-bank, saying it was a long while since they had seen such a merry boat-load. It was a jolly week-end.

My father went on to tell Worthington that his two trips to Jason Bay proved important botanically, for

I have added several plants to the flora, re-discovered some others which had been lost, evolved a particular theory of the formation and development of the East Coast of Malaya and its forest, and discovered a delightful spot for lengthy expeditions. Yet, all this is not a wit of what I intend to write of.

He had his mind already set on documenting Malayan trees.

In the *Annual Report of the Director of the Botanic Gardens* for 1934 Eric Holttum wrote that my father returned from leave on 1 March and that whilst in England he had examined specimens at the herbaria at Kew, and did some work at the Botany School in Cambridge. The annual report also records that

Mr Corner continued his study of the swampy forest of Johore. From June 9th to 24th he made an expedition to the east coast to study the coastal flora at Jason Bay and the swampy forest on the Sedili Kechil River. The locality was particularly suitable for the investigation of the succession of forest on the sandbanks which develop across the river mouths. Many interesting or little-known species were discovered, including *Inocarpus edulis* (the so-called Otaheite chestnut, not previously known as indigenous to the Peninsula), a species of *Phaleria* (a genus not hitherto found in the Peninsula), *Chisocheton pentandrus* (a Philippine species), and several other species which will need further study. Mr Corner unfortunately contracted Japanese river fever on this expedition; he managed to return to Singapore in time for treatment, and recovered after a very serious illness... Mr Corner also made several short trips to the vicinity of Mawai, Johore, and grateful thanks are expressed to Mr H. G. Grieve of Tebrau Estate for his assistance and hospitality on these occasions.

My father wrote to Worthington giving details of the ill-fated trip. He related that he began to feel unwell around 20 June and was admitted to hospital on 26 June 'on a rising temperature'. He collapsed over the next few days 'and resolved into tears'.

The Archdeacon of Singapore visited and said prayers

so tenderly at my bedside that I wept at the beauty of the English though he thought I was thinking of my sins, and I gathered I was put on the special list to be prayed for in the Cathedral. They even telephoned round to the devoutest congregationalist to pray for me nightly and in their morning supplications – so they do things nowadays.

My father's temperature rose steadily to 40.5°C and more where it stayed for three days 'during which time I can remember nothing, for I was delirious'. He rambled about many things and thought he was travelling around the world in a car:

and I would not stop at the hospital and strove to get out of bed. I kept on asking them if they knew a person called E. J. H. Corner at Singapore and did they know if he was well and at his work.

Suddenly his temperature dropped, soon becoming normal; he gradually recuperated over a week or more and got back to semi-solid food.

You cannot imagine how delicious bread and butter tastes. I believe they are going to allow me into a chair today, but if I tried to stand up I should fall flat. At last they identified Tropical Typhus.

Tropical typhus, scrub typhus or Japanese river-fever, is conveyed by a mite, which my father explained is 'very tiny, indeed microscopic, and only sucks blood once in its life-history, that is after it is newly born'. It climbs up grass in jungle clearings (it never occurs in forest) and waits. My father was bitten on the knee shortly after he started on his trip. He had a strange and large sore on his knee cap which had been very painful but was healing; he was wearing shorts being so much cooler than long trousers and puttees, 'and so I exposed myself'.

What a way to learn a lesson, for had he been wearing long trousers, he may well have been saved. In those days, with none of the antidotes of to-day, the only treatment was in nursing, very good nursing yet the mortality rate was estimated at 50 percent.

Pandora had a story about this almost fatal expedition to Jason Bay penned in the early 1990s. In contrast to his letter to Worthington, its content is similar yet very different in the manner that only my father could write.

There were records of many fatalities in the Sedili district, leaving the villages almost deserted and resulting in much becoming overgrown with the invasive *lallang* grass. The fields 'became an even better medium for the spread of scrub-typhus' and my father tells of the eye-lids of his botanical monkeys 'collecting the mites which spread the typhus'. They were not affected but two of his Malay assistants, collectors, also contracted the disease and he never discovered their ultimate fate; one was 'the delightful character Harun bin Awang Kechil of Kampong Ladang on the Sedili Kechil'. The Japanese fever was already affecting them as my father was studying the coast just south of Tanjong Gemoh. They were feeling 'hot, dry, sick, and oppressed by headache'.

> Our leader Harun (sometimes called Awang) normally so voluble and witty, was silent and not well. He sat listlessly on a rock, dry and feverish. Fresh tiger prints on the sand gave no excitement... I managed to secure a few photographs, but a headache had been coming on me for three days, which neither aspirin nor quinine could alleviate. I had scarcely eaten.

They camped overnight and my father attempted some baked beans, a favourite, but 'after a few mouthfuls I went outside the stockade, torch in hand and regardless of beast, to vomit in solitude'. That evening, the first time ever, my father failed to write up his notes although he did develop his photographic plates. They returned the next day although he and Harun were suffering considerably.

> We were in the grip of something for which we had no explanation. I decided to close the expedition. Fortunately, Ngadiman* and the two other Malays were not affected.

They reached the *prahu* around 3 pm. 'The afternoon swell had risen and there were hosts of white-horses'. Although his companions advised they all stay at a local village near the estuary, my father had reached the point of finding it difficult to stand and he was longing for the security of Singapore. He insisted that the crossing be made in spite of the danger. By skilful use of the oars, Harun and his companions kept the *prahu* head-on

---

* *Ngadiman bin Haji Ismail was my father's assistant at the Gardens and they worked together 'as brothers'. He helped enormously with the botanical monkeys from which both he and my father often received painful bites.*

to the swell; Ngadiman and the others bailed and watched the motor which offered a soothing note. My father was reconciled only to

laying full-length in the swash, almost careless of what might happen. We plunged down troughs, then head-on up the next swell, and so we zig-zagged on our oblique route. As we sank into one trough, a long fish, the *ikan parang* [the wolf-herring], leapt from the sea over the awning and disappeared on the other side.

Only by exceptional seamanship and a share of luck did they reach the mouth of the main Sedili River around dusk. Leaving Harun and his friend, the boat was refuelled and they made their way up the river taking some four hours to reach Mawai – the fitted headlight was invaluable yet the trip remained perilous. They unloaded the baggage and collections, putting all into my father's car and he set off on the drive home,

but I have no more recollection of that journey or whether I had paid anyone for their services. The last hours had been blank; something awful had got hold of me.

The following morning, my father went by taxi to the General Hospital. Feeling so cold and shivery he 'wore a thick sweater, thick flannel trousers, a heavy overcoat, scarf and felt hat. The receptionist had never seen such a sight'.

He was, of course, asked to give his name, address and details but he could not remember most. He was distraught until a passing sister intervened and swept him off to bed.

Then came darkness, interrupted by vivid and fearful dreams. I lay in the bowels of a ship voyaging endlessly round the world; when it arrived in Singapore, I was stuck motionless and forgotten and was carried on never to escape.

On awakening, he would rise from his bed, only to be quickly returned to it and 'back into that dream'. On one occasion he actually fought and managed to throw an assistant to the ground. He toppled chairs, even a table and a wardrobe. A stern voice said, "Mr Corner, I am very angry with you. Get back into bed at once." He complied meekly and sobbed, "Sister, I am so sorry. I did not know what I was doing."

Then the nightmares left him but the darkness returned. Later, he became aware of someone 'cooling my brow, moistening my lips, and smoothing the pillow'.

Henderson had cabled Grannie Corner who had wanted to come immediately to visit; the colonial office managed to dissuade her, the journey being too long.

[P]rayers had been said for me in the Cathedral* and the devout had been asked to remember me in their supplications. I owed my recovery to the care of others.

He was very weak and his vision poor. However, he noticed, through the mist, a small slim figure which he thought he recognised – 'The ministering angel of my nightmares held thin fingers of bread and butter to my lips; nothing had tasted so delicious.' She gave him sips of milk and in a day or two he had progressed to a lightly boiled egg. It was more than a week before my father could stand and indeed be given his first bath – 'I saw skinny shanks with knuckles'. He was beginning to sense the joy of life yet he still could barely manage the most simple of operations. He was taught again by that nurse

how to wash my face, comb my hair, brush my teeth, and, when the barber had finished, how to shave. I had to think out afresh every action… and not least, the penning of that shaky letter home, but pure memory without movement had not failed.

Physically he was improving more rapidly and 'was starting an incredible new life as muscles filled out'. Then she was gone. Where was she? A new nurse had taken on the duties.

My father enquired, for on leaving hospital he wanted to thank her with a gift but no one would give him her name. As time went on he never could get his mind away from that nurse.

For his early rehabilitation my father stayed with his friend Gordon Harrower, the Professor of Anatomy, but he was 'still wobbly'. After improvement and gaining some strength, he planned a holiday at the newly developed mountain resort of Cameron Highlands. He went there by train, then hired car, arriving in a 'sort of hobbling condition' at a small tavern. The next day, the manager asked if my father would 'make a foursome at tennis' and was put out at the refusal. His strength was still not sufficient to wield a racket. He wrote, 'I was used to being the social failure'.

Yet, he walked daily, gradually going further until 'I felt my old self and returned to my pursuit of mycology'. He wrote that those staying at the hotel showed great interest in his descriptions of the trees, flowers, fungi and mosses in the wonderful forest and soon he was accepted again – and as a courtesy he did offer himself for the occasional game.

*St Andrew's Cathedral, where I was to be christened in 1941.

66

Back in Singapore, his Irish friend Murnane, Head of the Water Department, encouraged him to buy a horse for his botanising to avoid a repetition of recent events. He bought a horse called Cheering and joined Murnane in rides along the bridle paths. Thus began his botanising on horseback and on most evenings he was able to travel to more distant places and to reach higher into the trees. He worked on horseback for some years but the extra height was still not sufficient. Interestingly, a photograph of Cheering appears in his book *Botanical Monkeys*.

My father never returned to Jason Bay until long after the war. He learned that Hassan had died and no one knew anything of Harun and his friend at Sedili Kechil. My father feared that, with no hospital, they perished while he was being restored. Much later, in the 1960s, when my father led expeditions to North Borneo and the Solomons,

Knowing well the cause and symptoms of tropical typhus, I always carried in my haversack a sufficiently large bottle of the modern antidote, which I kept a secret so as not to cause alarm. Fortunately there was no need.

The next letter to Worthington (whom my father now calls by his nickname, Barton, short for Bartholomew) is fascinating, not so much as a commentary of Worthington's study of Africa, but as my father's approach to and mastery of writing.*

Your essay is to hand, Barton. It is a great work, a magnum opus, an interregnum, a veritable…, an adumbration of a whole continent – said to be a dark one at that, though I have never been there – a treatise of tracts, a spokesman with a spoke-shave in all the wheels of Government, so may it roll on with that success you wish it to have.

He asked that he might keep the manuscript for a couple of weeks or so for a little editing,

for I notice some present participles might properly be past and singular which concentration prevented from becoming plural; some ambiguities and some circuitous passages. Do not think me too critical – for you say I am to spare no remark – but let me say this: do not publish it as it is. This is why. You have – I can read it in the lines – worked mighty

* *My father's note written later in life on a letter to Worthington in 1935 shows my father's interest in literature and writing: 'In Singapore I studied good books, from Raffles Library, which, happily, I had not read at school, as we were supposed to have done; I did not neglect them, and I learnt to admire the short story'.*

hard on a huge report of a huge subject in a limited time and no man can possibly digest it all at once. It needs pruning and trimming, perhaps a little further planning, but store all shearing of the superfluous bricks.

When I read this I paused to think of my present manuscript and reflected. My father continued:

I hate – hate, hate, hate, hate, hell how I hate – slovenly, verbose, redundant, loose, slangy, sloppy statements. Now I do not say that your report contains many such, and every preliminary draft is redundant, but there are many loose bits you must remove if you would that it flies straight to the one mark: as you say… Some expressions are not sharp enough… a trifle muddled [such] that you do not quite see the wood from the trees.

Then in an arcing Corner 'one-liner', 'the art of writing is to let the reader imagine as he reads and not ponderously weighed down [by] all the flight of thought with a full burden of scientifically correct words.'

My father goes on to detail a list of the main faults of the draft 'which are as precise and direct as the reader may well now expect'. He concluded that 'Plain language tells most'. Continuing, he told Worthington that he will understand all this for himself, 'as soon as the exhaustion [of writing] wears off' and reminded him that

all great things come of labour. Darwin re-wrote the whole '*Origin*' four or five times in manuscript and the first chapter at least ten times… Thackeray re-wrote the first chapter of '*Vanity Fair*', which seems so fucate, nearly twenty times. And Church, I tell you, wrote his *Oxford Botanical Memoirs* before the war (1914–'18) and re-wrote each several times before they were published between 1920 and 1928.

With another sage one-liner he concluded: 'Brevity is the soul of it, and short concise essays are the best reading'.

*

The year 1935 dawned and my father wrote to Hill on 3 January (my birth date yet 6 years early). He opened with a long diatribe of congratulation on Hill's engagement to Priscilla Worthington, finishing the opening by writing:

but you naughty fellow you unkind fellow polyhog, how dare you do all this while I am in exile so that I cannot be even an usher, a blusher or a proud congregationer.

He continued in typical Corner style, asking, 'for how has thou climbed so high to scoff upon a poor botanist?' It seemed that my father was becoming aware of his bachelor status.

Enclosing a sketch of himself juggling sheets of paper, he directed his next missive to Hill which began by telling of how busy he was – 'at the moment casting, up and down and to and fro, a series of pamphlets as illustrated guides to Malayan plant life'.* These were for the evening classes he was taking for local schoolteachers because there are no relevant books on Malayan botany to which he could refer them. Altogether he set out seven pamphlets, the first about seeds of all common local beans, fruits and palms for which he grew and drew the seeds. The second, for stems, leaves and roots, and the third tubers and rhizomes etc. Number four covered trees, trunks and buttresses and five was about climbers. The subjects for number six were flowers and fruits and the last was on the study of families.

"Do you think I can do it?" he asked Hill mischievously, adding that '104 will be *Boletus*, 210 *Boletopsis*, & 200, 200, 222, 222, 222 will be the ecology of Elysian Fields'.

He continued by telling of how wonderful had been his recent ten-day trip to Mawai where he stayed at Kota Tinggi, in the country house of a Mr Ah Lek, a rich Chinese of Borneo Motors. It was very jolly, he said, except that the house had to be shut at night on account of tigers.

The dry spell from mid-December to mid-January caused 'a terrific flowering of trees' so he decided to look at the swampy forest on the new road from Mawai to Mersing, part of the main trunk road on the east coast of Malaya.

My father concentrated on the areas where he had previously visited and he found '200 species of tree in flower or fruit in ten days, over and above all the others I had found there before. That is almost record collecting!… Among these were some marvellous stilted trees together with many which we cannot name, and I got 23 out of 24 excellent photos'.

An exciting find was a small tree of the 'Euphorbiaceae, with crimson petals, green sepals.' After a more detailed botanical description of the flower, he sketched the terminal for Hill, adding 'we do not know even a genus to fit the plant which was collected (and never named) once before from Kedah with a single sheet, with only a half-developed fruit'.

He told Hill that Henderson had apparently taken this sheet to Kew

---

* *None of these pamphlets were in Pandora and even the Botanic Gardens in Singapore has no copy. My father had willed them to the Royal Geographical Society but they are not there. I would be overjoyed to find them.*

some three years earlier and was 'unable to find anything like it in the Kew herbarium. Euphorbiaceae with petals is odd enough but being dimorphous too… well!'

He also found a new fig, 'of the massive epiphytic kind' and a new acquaintance – 'a glabrous, fleshy, thick, succulent and snapping sort of tree which they call *Spondias mombin*, "Kedondong" or "hog plum"'. The plums of this tree, he reported, are very sour, unless overripe, 'when they appear to be rotten, and all are rapidly expissated!' It amused him to learn that in three languages it might be termed 'carpel-syllabic'. His short poem in a letter to Hill said all…

Under a spreading *Spondias*
Stood Polymombin glued
And round about its bottom
Many plums he spued

Each evening of that fruitful expedition, undoubted with equal enthusiam, my father made scientific notes of the jungle trees which he had seen and photographed. In the quiet moments of those nights, his thoughts appeared to have imagined the wedded bliss of Worthington and Hill. In an oblique reference to the luxury of marriage, he wrote to Hill:

How can I address you in the singular, knowing that this is being read to you as you wallow and rise and puff and blow from a plate of porridge?

The letter ended warmly, rare for my father, 'Best love, and may none but the happiest moments brighten your presence, J'.

Another letter to Hill opened with congratulations for the new arrival 'the little stipule' and his success in matrimony. Much more explicit, he wrote telling Stella Worthington of an extraordinary dream that he had married a palm tree.

[O]ne moment I was kissed and caressed by its elegant fronds and next moment I was sitting with a most lovely dryad beneath the palm and they both got so inextricably mixed that I woke up all hot and bothered.

*

In 1935, my father visited Tioman Island which he described as 'a novelist's dream' with a few stands of coconut in the small sandy bays. The trip was with Birtwistle, using the Fisheries launch. My father wrote with some satisfaction that he had, at last, worked out the flora of several of those small granite islands in the archipelago and he had become sufficiently satisfied with his knowledge of the sand dunes 'so that I might almost write them up as my first Malayan-forest papers'.

He reported that the greatest and most exciting thing of this expedition was the diving helmet which Birtwistle had received from England about a week before they sailed. Over some four days they dived, mainly from the more sheltered west side and the water was clear with almost white sand.

Writing in *The Marquis*, my father said Birtwistle would not risk him on the first dive and had gone ahead to test the equipment. When Birtwistle emerged and the helmet was removed, 'he rolled his head with blue eyes bulging more than their wont, and said that he had never seen anything like it.' He had been lowered onto flat-topped coral and when asked why he had not wandered and explored he said that my father should go and see. He did, and did, to find an abyss all around!

My father was fascinated being down amongst the fish, the weaving anemones and 'coral as far as the underwater eye could see…. In a moment you forgot the apprehension of masks, save when a coil of the air-pipe touched the back, and caused shudders'.

He estimated their diving depth as about nine feet and when squatting there would be around six feet of water above them; when standing, it was difficult to control the legs as they were not weighted down. They wore kid gloves which protected from coral scratches but they tended to float off their hands. Frequent swallowing was required to keep their ears clear.

*

In *The Marquis*, my father told of an incident that happened on this trip. Below a tree on the central hill of a small island north of Pulau Tioman, they found a bottle – with a message in Japanese in it. My father immediately said that it should be taken to Singapore for translation but Birtwistle convinced him that it was from one Japanese fishing boat to another and that it should be left there.

Now I ask, why was my father so quickly insistent that it be taken to Singapore for translation and Birtwistle so insistent it be left? And why did my father not mention this in the letter to Hill, written at the time of the dive?

The Japanese had been active in Malaya during the 1930s buying rubber plantations, retail businesses and much more, and my father must have been aware of this, even though he makes not a mention in his letters and books. Their propaganda was increasing as evidenced by the following extract from the chapter on propaganda from Eric Robinson's *The Japanese File*.

More calculating were the numerous official and semi-official rapprochements, generally sponsored by the [Japanese] Consulate-General or by organisations such as the South Seas Association. The earliest conspicuous attempt to enlist the sympathies of influential Malays occurred in 1934 when, on 27 February, the Crown Prince of Johore was taken by a notorious Singapore Japanese agent named Kokubo to visit the Japanese cruiser *Kuma*, which had called at Singapore in the course of a world cruise. The Crown Prince was entertained to lunch.

This visit gave an excellent opportunity for Commander Yuji Senada to give 'an inflammatory speech' from which the following extract gives an idea of the type of propaganda the Japanese pursued:

There is no difference whatever between the Japanese and other Asiatics. We are all equal in every way. Let the Asiatics govern Asia and not allow themselves to be oppressed by the white races... We have taught the Chinese to be ready for any action and as a result of our recent war with them they are now strong enough to join us, the Japanese people, to drive the white people from our land. If you people, the Malays, would take us as your mother, we will always be prepared to help you when you are in trouble. The European power is now past twelve o'clock, but our Asiatic power is just nine o'clock. They are going down, while we are going up to take their place.

Kokubo proved to be a particularly dangerous Japanese agent and he or she was instrumental in arranging visits to the cruiser, through the Johore Japanese Society, of 'large parties of Malay adults and school children.' All in all this was 'a well-organised attempt to have taken advantage of the cruiser's visit to impress influential Malays and the younger generation'; it was well publicised in the press.

That same year, when the Sultan of Johore visited Japan, he was so impressed by the great efforts made to ensure the success of his visit that on the occasion of his sixty-second birthday he decorated three of the Japanese connected with the arrangements: Koichiro Ishihara, Tetsui-chiro Koizumi, and Marquis Yoshichika Tokugawa.

My father didn't mention the message in the bottle in his 1935 letter because he surely knew it contained a message. He didn't want, in 1935, to be implicated in any way. However, by the time he wrote *The Marquis*, he was free to tell of it. He must have been aware of all the Japanese activities in the 1930s, as was Birtwistle of the increasing numbers of Japanese fishing vessels in the Malayan waters.

*

My father spent some time in Trengganu in November 1935. This was his first holiday for more than a year and his due leave had reached more than four weeks. 'As I do not want to go anywhere special, I am botanising in Trengganu where I came in 1932'. He explained that he would again have gone to Johore but for Mr E. P. Swann who owned Kajang Kemaman tin mine pressing him to visit the mine again.

There was no other way then to Kemaman than by small coastal steamers, and the journey from the jetty to the mine being another 40 miles. This was achieved by river, and 'trolley-rail' through the forest. The mine, in a clearing, measured about three-quarters of a mile long by half mile wide and virgin forest was within ten minutes in any direction.

> Oceans of distant trees, concealing every rugged feature of the land, stretched as far as eye could see. As the sun sank and gilded their tops… I knew that this was perhaps the richest botanical place in the world.

He told of collecting some 500 species of flowering plant, mostly trees, 'from the forest within 20 mins walk' and he estimated this to be only half. After a night's rest and being awoken by the calling of hornbills, he travelled up a small river to camp for a few days. There, he found a Rubiaceae, described it as falling between *Morinda* and *Renellia*. Although he could not name it, he thought it may be *Cephaelis albiflora* Ridley [Family Rubiaceae]. The plant, Father remarked, 'has a tap root to Kingdom come', but managed to yank it up. He gave a description saying that the xylem of its roots is bright yellow-orange; the bark of the rootlets is bright orange-red, the colour very intense in the fresh wood.

> [W]hen I washed and scrubbed the bits of wood the drops of water flowing off the surface were yellow and my left hand has the epidermis all stained yellow as though it were jaundiced.

He reckoned that if the wood was broken up and soaked in warm water a dye would be extracted. The wood, he noted, was so heavy it sank like a stone in water. His opinion was that growing on the stanniferous soil around the mine,

> it has tinned itself and weighted its wood with some obscure stanno-anthracene… with seven hundred and ninety two pyridine rings at right angles to nine hundred and twenty benzen rings, such is its crystal-lattice. In other words here is vitamin M for Morinda.

While in Trengganu, my father wrote a very long letter to Worthington. It has a magnificent and majestic description of the Malayan sunset which never ceases to move me.

Before that, he tells that Swann had authorised 'a small felling', indeed encouraged it. My father acceded and likened himself to 'a body-picker on a battle field, I crawl among prostrate trunks: hateful, yet it must be done'.

He wrote of taking to collecting wild bananas; he had found in Ridley's *Flora* that even those common and characteristic plants were misunderstood. It was here that he discovered *Dysoxylon corneri* [Family Meliaceae] and *Paraboea floribunda*. He also found a new *Blumeodendron*, a new *Clerodendrum*, a new *Habenaria*, a new *Phacelophyrium*, a new *Plagiostachys*, and perhaps a new banana, 'not to mention several others and one for which I cannot find the genus'.

Clearly, my father was in his seventh heaven; doing exactly what he loved and at which he excelled – 'I can collect, cut about, inspect and study at my leisure, on the spot, all these tropical riches. That's what we want, and that's what I enjoy'.

He worked with two Malays who came with him, remembering one must never be alone in the jungle, and they gathered big gingers, carrying them 'on our shoulders, rejoicing, to the bungalow'. Later, and usually in the afternoons when it rained, they measured them and smelled them before committing the flowers to spirit and then cutting them up before the drying process – 'Oh, it's wonderful to lay palms in a press with all their points compressed in a notebook, to cut up rattans and to cut barks of trees'.

'And what, you say, of mycology Barton?' wrote my father before describing a tree in the valley which stood proud above the rest. He recorded that when he first arrived, it was all but bare of foliage yet, after just a week, it was 'covered with new foliage' and he could see some new inflorescences. 'How can I pause for a piece of rotting tissue, when such vigour strains before me? And what of those pamphlets, you say, on Malayan Botany?'

That day, they had cut down a white-blossomed tree which smelled so much like hawthorn that he became a little homesick... the smell was beguiling and he understood how animals of most persuasions 'rule themselves by smell'. He paused, overcome by his thoughts and flights of fancy and wrote that he saw something even more beautiful, 'indeed it could not be exceeded'. He looked out over that forest valley where there were about two miles of forest 'between him and the hills' and he saw mist-wreathed trees with the sky the blue of Cambridge; 'pearly clouds and gossamer... an old monarch with gnarled boughs and drooping leaves, it might have been miles away yet I saw it so clear'.

The white-blossomed tree was a *Meliosma*, which means 'honey scented', and it belongs to a family called the Samydaceae, a family of tropical and subtropical woody plants. He found one in Johore which had a floral formula ('those beastly things') of K4, C3, A2, and G1: 'if you remember such. 4 sepals, 3 petals, 2 stamens & one carpel with one ovule, is almost too good to be true!'

My father liked *Meliosma*; there were about ten species in Malaya. As he prepared for bed he sighed that 'this view is silvered in moonlight and I should walk forth into the forest if there were no mosquitoes, tigers or leeches'.

After more personal matters, and clearly answering a question, he launched into politics, something of which he always denied discussing!

You are right. Someone should shoot Mussolini. He's a big bully, and will go down in history with the Kaiser as the men who killed their countrymen because they could not keep their peace.… If as much money was spent by nations in the propagation of the Gospel as they do in the service of war the League of Nations would be inherent in every soul. But look at the Pope; he is afraid of his bank book.

He stressed his hate of the military which they had been seeing in Singapore. The library and herbarium at the Gardens had been ear-marked to be a munitions dump in emergency. However, Rosedale had offered one of his labs in the cellar at the College to store the displaced books and specimens 'if such vandalism must be'.

My father continued the letter on 9 November and clearly that view over the misted-valley had made a mark. Who was this man who wrote so observantly, so passionately, so softly? I don't believe I ever knew him.

I must tell you about tonight, Barton. It is most wonderful. At first, as the sun set there was a pillar of cloud to the north; its crest was ghostly white, its west was a soft emerald azure, like a dream of night, its east was faintly gilded.

At first, as the sun set, the full moon rose and both at once cast their light on this cloud, and what material in all the universe can draw and reflect light like a cloud?

Then when the moon was up, silvered burgeons loomed round, with distant rolls of thunder yet all the valleys were swathed in mist and the mist mounted up in fantastic heights so that it seemed to touch the clouds, and all glowed in silver beams. Then there came a gentle breath… and the mist moved and while it lay in the valleys, the hill-tops and the tops of trees became visible.

What are those like giant steps mounting up?

Whose hand is that, thrust out?

I think they are the boughs of trees that cloud the slopes.

What is that brow so frowning?

Whose are these silver locks?

Hush, they are the winds of clouds, and the raiment's of mist. Do you think tonight the deer will sleep?

Do the moonbeams reach through the forest?

Does the full moon stir the beasts as it stirs the soul of man?

Drip… drip… drip… everything that is living is weeping tonight.

How I wish I had known the author, and have to pause to wonder at the softness of the language, the fragrance of the description and the very observance of so much; was this the same man I left so many years later? How could it be? What changed him? Was it the war which brought about the harshness? Was it lost love?

After such passion, my father turned to something quite different, but not before he congratulated Worthington on his *magnum opus* on Africa, and commended him for his mastery of such a wide variety of subjects involved with the vast continent, and slipping in the announcement that his next home leave would be in 1938, arriving sometime between May and July. He hoped that the Worthingtons would not have sailed for Africa before then, for he would like to stay with them in Madingley; indeed, if they were to be away he probably wouldn't go to Cambridge at all. 'Let them come and see me instead, who would, for I care not a fig for the powers that be'.

The subject that my father turned to after waxing lyrical about clouds at night was ticks. He gave an account of how he was botanising as usual one day when his Malay colleagues were felling a tree and he found an unknown stemless palm with leaves that appeared to come from the ground. He began to disassemble it thinking how fine it was to be able to chop and pull and smell and break such plants instead of staring at them in a conservatory. Then he noticed a tingling on his right arm and looked only to see his shirt and arm covered with tiny ticks: his other arm and trousers were the same. He was alarmed because it wasn't a case of a few – but thousands.

His Malay friends told him that the only way to get rid of them was 'to smoke my clothes', so they made a fire and he undressed as modestly as being deep in the wild jungle allowed, and they helped him smoke every garment. Whilst my father picked ticks from every part of his anatomy he scrubbed with ammonia of the same name, being thankful of always carrying a small bottle whilst in the jungle and fortified himself with '88' – I guess a whisky – which Rosedale had given him. 'Though I smelt like a kipper', he managed to rid himself of most when he returned to the house, remarking that he had been prepared to return through the forest naked.

The Malays told my father that the ticks made nests which were hidden until one stepped on them – in this case, the nest was in the fibrous mass of leaf-bases of the palm. It was new and interesting enough for my father to have thought of writing to *Nature* on the phenomenon.

This long letter to Worthington also contained a description of a geocarpic ginger having tufted aerial leafy stems about ten feet high which my father called 'one of those incredible plants of whose existence one never dreams'. He had noticed runners coming from the base which crossed the stream and into the bank on the other side, some ten feet away. The flowers, which appeared just above the surface of the water, developed from these runners with a long tube which carried the petals, stamen and style just above the surface of the ground, while the ovary and the fruit developed underground. He thought it was

> *Elatostemma longirostre* of Ridley, known only from a few mountain streams in Malaya, not from any neighbouring country; yet in his (Ridley's) description there is nothing to indicate the astonishing habit of the plant… I shall write a little paper on it. Its flowers are upside down compared with other gingers.

What a letter, full of botanic matters, fascinating observations, and political opinions of the time!

- VII -

WAYSIDE TREES
& BOTANICAL MONKEYS

I confess that I consigned to the bin my father's first edition copy of *Wayside Trees of Malaya* given to me by my mother. Frankly, it meant nothing to me then except the name on the spine. The name was my father's but I was angry that he chose not to respond to the many overtures of reconciliation by me, my wife, and his family. All had been scorned mostly by a deafening silence.

A first edition is of considerable value, but it's not the monetary value that mattered. What I threw away was a real piece of Professor E. J. H. Corner, simply Mr Corner when it was first published, and that, with the wonderful benefit of hindsight, I very much regret. So, I must make amends and write about it for most non-scientists, non-botanists certainly, would not have heard of it, being first published pre-war just before the Japanese Occupation of Singapore. The book has certainly a worthy story and, clearly, a timeless future.

The 1939 Botanic Gardens annual report announced the impending publication of *Wayside Trees of Malaya*, my father's first major publication:

> Mr E.J.H. Corner completed the manuscript of his book on "*The Wayside Trees of Malaya*", and printing was begun during the year. This work deals with about 950 different trees, native and introduced, and still does not touch the majority of trees of primitive forest, which must number some 1500 more species. Mr Corner's book is based almost entirely on his own observations during the past ten years, and is the first considerable work on tropical plants which is based on field observations rather than on the description of dried specimens. It should be a most valuable aid and stimulus to the study of local plants. It will be very fully illustrated.

The first edition was printed in Singapore in July 1940 by the Government Printing Office. It was published in two volumes, the first being

78

the descriptions and the second containing all the black and white photographs taken by my father. These two volumes were to help considerably in the Japanese understanding of him during the occupation of Singapore and was, indeed is, the right testimonial and memorial to a visionary scientist. He wrote many books and papers but none, I believe, required quite so much virgin work and enormous effort.

The idea of a book on the trees of Malaya was born in 1929, the catalyst being the logging and destruction of the forests. In that way, *Wayside Trees of Malaya* was born of the chain-saw. This new-fangled and noisy thing, developed by Joseph Buford Cox and Andreas Stihl, preceded the stirrings of the book by just a short time and was the direct cause for it. As the trees fell in the tropical jungles of Singapore and Malaya, witness to the destructive power of this new tool, my father in 1929, allowed a falling seed to germinate in his mind – he realised that something had to be done to prevent the loss forever, not only of the timeless trees, but the eco-systems which they harboured. The noise of the saws indeed was deafening, and his effort to preserve and record matched the screams of this destructive technology.

Not long after his arrival in Singapore, my father realised that the unique tropical jungles of Singapore and Malaya were being reduced by commercial and un-commercial logging by individuals seeking money or basic sustenance, the latter being so hard to complain of. What seemed not to be realised, or not admitted, was that once a rainforest had gone, no amount of replanting would bring back the original unique ecology.

The preface to all three editions of *Wayside Trees of Malaya* sets the scene for the project.

To write a book about Malaya for all who find beauty and inspiration in the life of the country has been my object. We sorely need books about natural history, whether they be for schools or for grown-ups because, in our exploitation and destruction of natural resources, we must not forget that one mark of civilisation is the regard men bestow on wild things. It has always seemed to us the duty of biologists to prepare from time to time books on natural history which will serve as guides and companions above all to amateurs, in whom the flame of knowledge burns brightest, that each generation may play its part in preserving the natural history and the wild life of the country. We have chosen trees as our subject because all the native richness of Malaya depends on the integrity of its forests. If a delight in trees and a respect for their majesty can be created, even among a small body of persons, our country will never suffer the tragic domestication which many lands have tamely undergone. Botanists know too well that when forest is destroyed the ancient verdure of the earth is lost forever; trees depart in flames and no mantle descends to clothe our ignorance.

In a letter to Stella Worthington, my father gave insight to the style and approach of his book.

> The book will cover six to eight hundred kinds of tree, all of which I shall have seen and studied myself alive, not merely in the herbarium. It is difficult to reduce so much to simple speech, yet without simple speech we do not know what we are talking about; I grow to hate and learn to despise technical jargon.

A wonderful example of his simple use of language is the description of the tropical jungle that my father wrote in *The Life of Plants* published in 1964. I, a non-scientist, can understand it and, through it, have become intrigued to learn more. It begins:

> On its canopy birds and butterflies sip nectar. On its branches orchids, aroids and parasitic mistletoes offer flowers to other birds and insects. Among them ferns creep, lichen encrust, and centipedes and scorpions lurk. In the rubble that falls among the epiphytic roots and stems, ants build nests and even earthworms and snails find homes.

In a 1960 paper written from the Botany School, Cambridge, he opened: 'The forest, which until recently covered Malaya, must be divided into three constituents, the lowland, the mountain and the limestone'. They all have their own special problems, however they clearly indicate that Malaya is the point-of-meeting for northern and southern vegetation. This might have been anticipated simply from Malaya's geographical position, however, and at that time, 'Malaya has neither figured so prominently in plant-geography nor has it been the scene of great exploration'. Most chose the larger and more remote islands of Malaya neglecting 'the promontory of the mainland'.

My father then made strongly the point that Malayan botanists still had much to discover 'and to contribute to Asiatic phyto-geography' and after reading van Bemmelen's account of the geology of Indonesia he was ever more convinced 'of the importance of Malaya in the evolution of one of the world's chief floras'. That forest, unrecorded, was being lost forever and fellings on a larger scale were happening on mainland Malaya.

My father wrote of being troubled; he felt it incumbent on him to study as best he could what was disappearing from the face of the earth. This forest seldom repeats itself and harboured many rarities which, 'for aught anyone knew, might be exterminated'.

He turned gradually to the study of trees which, by force of circumstance, he had to do as they were felled. He visited the forest clearings between the mycological seasons and soon he became a conservationist.

During his rambles, he discovered a stretch of swamp-forest being felled by Chinese woodcutters along the western part of the Mandai Road in the north of Singapore and where he could study the felled trees for, in many cases, their height prevented him from reaching their extremities. Such specimens that he collected were mostly sterile yet some of them could be identified and had not been recorded for the island.

Yet, he realised that it was impossible and impractical to record the forest trees of Malaya and thus a book on wayside trees was taking shape in his mind. He made his intention clear in its introduction.

In the scope of this work come the trees of gardens, roadsides, orchards, rice-fields, waste-ground, seashores, riverbanks and the secondary jungle both of the lowlands and the mountains – the trees, that is, of waysides. Forest trees have been omitted on principle because they are so numerous and they cannot be classified without recourse to their detailed botanical structure. Nevertheless we have mentioned by their vernacular and botanical names most, if not all, of the timber trees so that their affinities with the more familiar ones of garden and orchard may be understood, and we have incorporated briefly in the descriptive section the mangrove trees so as to complete the list of woody plants of the seashores. By this means it is hoped that from the earlier works of Foxworthy and Watson, which are out of print, our less technical account will lead on to the more botanical records of Malayan tree-families by Symington, Henderson, Sinclair, and contributors to the *Tree Flora of Malaya* (volumes 1-3). Certain forest-trees, moreover, like the Tualang and Kempas (*Koompassia*), Seraya (*Shorea*), Kapur (*Dryobalanops*), Pelong (*Pentaspadon*), Pauh Kijang (*Irvingia*), Kembang Samangkok (*Scaphium*), Ipoh (*Antiaris*), Oaks (*Lithocarpus*), and Jungle Holly (*Streblus*), have been included either for their unmistakeable appearance or for their abundance in opened country or for their remarkable and fascinating flowers, fruits or leaves...

This was still a huge challenge but that was something my father relished. As he wrote in his letter to Stella Worthington from the Land of the Dendrons, 'I have found my project a great deal more difficult and complicated than I ever expected'. The reality of studying trees in those days, many of great height, is not realised until I tell you what my father wrote to Worthington only 17 months after his arrival in Singapore in August 1930: 'I am achieving my desire to climb a tall jungle tree and make an observation post on the top'.

There was one, on the Mandai Road in Singapore, the top of which he almost reached at his second attempt. With the Gardens' woodsman Sinnathamby and his collector Ahmat they tackled the tree. Sinnathamby and

Ahmat made the top by means of creepers, but my father struggled half-way as the men said that the creepers would not bring him any higher. He reported that he was glad for this as 'it looked an awful drop, some 60 ft'.

So they resorted to tackle: 70 feet (21 m) of Manila rope plus a block, about 80 six-inch (15 cm) and eight-inch (20 cm) nails, and some half-inch (1¼ cm) wire cables with hooks. Ahmat and Sinnathainby drove in the nails and fixed one block aloft with a small rope dangling down to pull up such things as a camera.

My father climbed creepers for the first 60–70 feet finding it hard on the fingers, pulling so hard. For the next 20 feet or so they used rope and nails in the trunk, and the final 20 feet, which 'I have not achieved yet' was thought to require more nails. The additional challenge was to negotiate bends in the trunk and my father wrote that 'it still requires a pinch of courage… at a height of 70 or 80 feet by nails projecting only 3–4 inches'. He also commented rather ruefully that 'you cannot brachiate here or you will have a hive of bees singing around, or a snake, or some ferocious ants; it is all slow and wary in the jungle!' When he finally reached some 100 feet or more into the rainforest, he found himself 'in the centre of a leafy dome', a view beyond imagination, with other tall trees, some quite nearby, and creepers everywhere.

This certainly described a challenge of botanising in the 1930s, a challenge which my father overcame by a simple, ingenious solution – botanical monkeys.

The idea had come to him in 1929 when he saw trained berok monkeys at work plucking coconuts in Perlis. The berok was the best of the macaques for such activities because 'it rejoices in that form of destruction which makes objects crash down'. What more could he want? He envisioned a school for botanical monkeys which would allow him to 'transect the forest in an ecological survey'.

'I would breed my own superior race and it would be free of the parasites which beset the village berok', he proclaimed.

My father reported that 'everyone laughed at him', but the doubters would be proved very wrong.

*

My father's letter to Hill in April 1933 gives some insight into the detail of his study, the care to which he went. He found there were, on average, 110 trees per acre representing some 50 species of which he could identify all but 60 (out of a total of 550, or so) from their bark characters. He decided to photograph the trees in three stages; the whole tree, the bole and finally the bark at about 18 inches (46 cm) high.

'You may think bark photos dull, but they are really very jolly, because barks, as you know, have such varied characters, and open up quite a new field of study to me', my father wrote, and he felt sure that no one by then 'has made such a survey of all kinds of big tree in a tropical forest', adding that it was great fun. Here was happiness at work, a joy which predominates in E. J. H. Corner's botanical writing.

In February 1935, my father was in Malacca on a trip up-country 'studying and photographing wayside and kampong trees, and I go slowly along the roads looking and frequently stopping'. One thing he had to do in preparation for the trip was to load photographic plates. The monsoon winds were changing direction, resulting in terrific humidity and my father 'had to perform the operations stark naked because every movement caused fresh streams of perspiration and I was afraid the sweat would drip off my wrists on to the plates'.

He had been particularly keen on studying the mango trees in the kampongs because they were 'fine old trees like gigantic dendroid-oaks'. Of the binjai (*Mangifera caesia*), he was assured by his Malay friends that when this tree fruits, and that is rare, they gather the fruits when they are nearly ripe 'and eat them at supper because the fruits ripen only in the night'. They are sour in the day, indeed preceeding days, and then in the early evening, 5 to 6 pm, they ripen.

On this trip, my father was surprised at finding an Artocarp 'new to the flora' in the kampongs. Unfortunately, the evening was overcast not allowing photography, which annoyed him. However, he did find 'a rather nice species' of Bignoniaceae – not generally his favourite tree having a poplar habit – in the Malaccan cemeteries which he did photograph. The very photograph of *Stereospermum fimbriatum*, the Snake Tree, appears on Plate 33 in Volume 2 of *Wayside Trees of Malaya*.

In his letter to Hill of February 1936, my father reported that 'the Government have provisionally entered the sum of $3000 [Straits Settlements dollars] for next year to publish a book on the wayside trees of Malaya with about 200 plates'. The Director's annual report of the Gardens of the same year recorded that my father 'spent the greater part of the year working in the general herbarium, preparing for the publication of a book on the common trees of Malaya'. In fact, the records for this work were built-up over some ten years from 1929 to at least 1939, and he was delayed considerably in his preparation of the book by having to cover Henderson's duties in the herbarium and also Henderson's mistakes in plant identification there.

At one point, my father had thought of using a sketch of Penelope Landon under a jungle tree in the book. Writing from the Malayan jungle to her son in Belgium in July 1936, Penelope explained the circumstances:

We left about 8.30 as he [Corner] wanted to photograph a tree along the road, and the best time is between 8 and 9. We waited a bit for the sun to clear and then [he] took it with me beneath to give an idea of height. Then he said if I could make a good sketch he would use it as a frontispiece for the book.

For unknown reasons, the sketch, if drawn, was not used.

*

On Christmas Day 1936, my father wrote to Stella Worthington. He explained that 'I have written, written, written and rewritten since April. It is all about the book [*Wayside Trees of Malaya*] as you may guess'. He told of finding the challenge of the book much more difficult and complicated than he originally imagined, due in part to the 'rotten lot of botanists in this country ever since it became inhabitable' and that botanical knowledge 'is little more than school certificate standard in the eastern tropics'. Then, in lovely contrast, he wrote:

[D]id I tell you my latest distortion? If one was to walk north and south, and east and west, over hill and mountain and valley in this country, one could learn a new kind of tree every day for seven years and still have more to learn.

He told Stella that he had been to a reception at the Hongkong and Shanghai Bank and that from noon to 2 pm he had consumed seven glasses of champagne. He had slept all afternoon for he was to attend a dinner party given by the Holttums that night. Immediately he adds, 'I have given poor Holttum some "shakings-up" this year because he is so soft and lets everything slip and go backward'.

He then explained that they have had a series of troubles, around the 'same time as the shameful abdication of Edward VIII'. The Tamil coolies at the Gardens had been on strike for more money 'which I hope they will not get' so he had to reorganise the labour.

Then the futile Mr Best, our Assistant Curator, is at last to be sent home unfit for work; he was almost blind, as he was a year past but I cannot launch into all our difficulties; suffice it to say that I no longer submit to anyone or thing where I think something must be done.

Before signing off, he fires this broadside at Henderson who was visiting Kew and had met Worthington:

If ever there was an ass, a sloth, an elephant and a hippopotamus in one it was him – a real doge… I am sorry to be so uninteresting, but I am muddled and confused with the hundreds of problems that I have solved in the last few months.

My father openly admitted that he no longer submits to anyone. That attitude also certainly pervades *The Marquis* where he gives the impression of being the boss at the Singapore Gardens. I believe this attitude came to rule his life. I'm also interested in his remark that Holttum was 'soft'. Ironically, this very description of being soft was suggested by Gordon deWolf in an email to me as one of my father's 'weaknesses' during the Occupation and after.

Although my father had spent the greater part of 1936 working in the general herbarium covering Henderson's duties while Henderson was in Kew, my father managed two study tours for *Wayside Trees of Malaya*. The Gardens' annual report of 1936 states that:

At the end of February he spent a fortnight travelling through Malacca, Negri Sembilan, Pahang and Selangor, to photograph specimen trees and to discover their local names. In July he spent a month in Kedah, Perlis, Penang and Upper Perak, which have many trees not found in the south; he visited especially the neighbourhood of Alor Star, Arau, Baling, Penang Hill, Grik, Kuala Kangsar and Pangkor, studying trees at the rate of twelve different kinds a day for the whole month. He paid particular attention to local names in Kedah and Upper Perak. Many interesting discoveries, such as the following, resulted from this tour.

The fruits of a rare *Elaeocarpus* were being sold in the market at Baling; several kinds of trees, supposed to occur only on the east coast of Malaya, were found to abound in the forest-coves of Pangkor [an island off the western coast]; several species of *Ficus* new to the Peninsula flora were found to flourish on the padang at Grik; the Tembusu was found to be almost unknown in Perak; a tree described by Jack [William Jack, the Scottish botanist] more than a century ago and subsequently not collected nor recognised by local botanists was found to be a well-known village tree with the name of Sentang. The wealth of trees in this country is in fact so great that even the common ones are still imperfectly known. It is much to be hoped that Mr. Corner's book when completed will form a basis on which not only the specialist but all who take an interest in plants may build.

The intention that not only the specialist will understand his book was to serve him well in the future, and the report continued that

Mr. Corner took about 60 photographs of trees on these expeditions. Mr. Corner also undertook a short expedition in April [1936] to the neighbourhood of Mawai, continuing his study of the freshwater swamp forest. He also made numerous one-day excursions to the same district.

All through my research, I have been aware of the growing tension between my father and Eric Holttum. Indeed, Deborah, Holttum's younger daughter, confirmed it. However, with plenty of hearsay, implication and opinion, I have not been able to pin down absolutely the specific event which might have precipitated it.

Eric Holttum did not appoint Henderson as his Assistant when he became Director of the Singapore Botanic Gardens in 1925. Then in 1928, Holttum told my father that a vacancy existed in Singapore for Assistant Director. My interpretation is that Holttum didn't believe in 1925 that any of his serving scientists were either sufficiently qualified or able to take on such a responsible post. He was waiting for the right man to show up; he must have heard about my father, from Arthur H. Church perhaps, and sought my father out during his home leave in 1928.

In my father's letter to Hill dated 4 March 1930, just over a year after his arrival in Singapore, he commented on Holttum's article in *Nature* as 'bunkum'. Yet, he informed Hill in September 1932 that he was 'installed in Dr Holttum's house and very well we are getting on also'. On Christmas Day 1936, he had written to Stella Worthington saying that 'I have given poor Holttum some "shakings-up" because he is so soft and lets everything slip and go backward'.

My father's outspoken letter to Hill on 3 March 1937 offers a good pointer to the root cause of the troubles. He said that as a matter of principle, he would not leave Singapore, the Gardens, until Holttum came back from his leave. Explaining this, he said that he had

some words with him, because I am afraid I consider him a poor feeble little man quite incapable of directing a department and he has been playing most unfairly with me because he is a funk.

My father apologised for saying that but affirmed its truth – 'I have had to do all the difficult jobs in the gardens of amending others' mistakes... In my studying of tree-specimens in the Herbarium I found a terrible confusion and ignorance. It is the work of Henderson who has no botanical knowledge or education'.

Henderson had wrongly identified and distributed some 5,000 to 6,0000 specimens of plants in 12 years! The only reliable identifications they had in the herbarium were those by King & Gamble from 1880-1913*... 'So when

* *Sir George King and J.S. Gamble published a series of papers in the Journal of the Asiatic Society of Bengal entitled* Materials for a Flora of the Malayan Peninsula. *This was a hangover from when Malaya was part of British India. The papers were brought together and published by West, Newman & Co. 54, Hatton Gardens, London, over parts LXXIV & LXXV. Sir George was the Head of the Royal Botanic Garden in Calcutta.*

I want to identify a plant and learn what one is I look up the oldest and dirtiest specimens'. My father then noticed that

> Henderson had put 5 genera, including 2 different families, under the Rambutan genus *Nephelium*! But I will not enumerate any of his incredible blunders: they would fill pages. I have therefore been putting the herbarium in order so far as the common trees are concerned.

This, he said, delayed his work on the book on wayside trees by many months: he expected to find everything in order but he had to identify everything from first principles.

My father then explained that he is the Assistant Director of Gardens and Henderson is Curator of the Herbarium. Yet, whenever Holttum was away he left Henderson in charge, as was the case when Holttum visited Penang in January 1937, Henderson having returned from leave on 20 December 1936.

> [T]he first I knew of it was that I found Henderson on the Director's chair on Monday morning, Holttum having carefully arranged to send me that week to do an interdepartmental survey of opium stocks! By God and the Devil I was angry.

My father wrote Holttum a letter demanding a written reply to his enquiries as to 'who, what and why the Assistant Director's job might be'. This apparently shook him and my father wrote that he will go on shaking him if he doesn't improve, adding that 'I have always been polite and obliging and self-sacrificing; he thinks I will do anything'.

Apparently, Holttum really was shocked by this; my father felt strongly that the department was going to pieces.

> [A]nd to find myself subjected to a man without manners, knowledge or qualification such as Henderson, makes me kick like the wildest untameablest horse. I now acknowledge no senior or superior with the result that Holttum goes sneaking about afraid to say anything to me. What are you to do with a worm?

Again he remarked that 'I now acknowledge no senior or superior'. My father's title was Assistant Director, so why did Henderson seem to take preference? Probably because Holttum knew that Henderson was not up to the job of Assistant Director but, being the senior man by years at the Gardens, Holttum gave some deference to him. If that is so, and it is my surmise, then my father's comment of Holttum's poor management was correct.

Yet, in the *Malayan Establishment Staff List* as of 1 July 1939, under the heading Botanic Gardens, it shows Dr Holttum as Director (wef 25/5/1925). The next in the list is Assistant Director and on the right of it, it indicates Curator of the Herbarium, suggesting Henderson at that time!

Below this, on the left and under the title Assistant Director, is M. R. Henderson and on the right, Curator of the Herbarium. His appointment was on 18/9/1924, over four years before my father arrived.

Below his entry and on the left is E. J. H. Corner and to the right Assistant Director, Singapore; his appointment being with effect from 2/2/1929.

This makes me think: Who did Holttum consider to be Assistant Director? This was my father's question too. His criticism of Holttum was an example of his trying to improve things at the Gardens; to bring leadership to management thus effecting a better organisation and more efficient structure for the future. He did have something of a business mind as well as a sharp scientific one but his style rankled and this made enemies; the impetuosity of youth. His tact was often – too often – tactless!

*

In April 1937, my father's younger sister, Dorothy, visited him from England and joined him on a 'tree-journey' to Kelantan and Trengganu in north Malaya. In the village of Kampong Berok close to the Thai border, my father chatted with the locals about their names for trees. They were soon joined by an elder who had in tow a berok monkey on a chain. In conversation, the elder expressed his sadness that his monkey was becoming too old and savage to be kept much longer. But he was unwilling to sell it because of its ability to climb and collect coconuts. It wasn't long before another villager joined them and, sensing my father's interest, told him that he had a much younger monkey that was more clever and would do anything that was asked of him.

My father decided then and there to buy this younger monkey for, after a haggle, the equivalent of 28 Straits Dollars, about £3.5. He called the monkey Merah meaning 'red' in Malay because 'when he is old his JT [slang for penis] is scarlet!'

I have checked the dates my father gave when recounting his monkey stories and they don't add up. He had the idea on that visit to Perlis in November 1929 and clearly he was using botanical monkeys in 1934 when he contracted swamp fever. Yet, he wrote of his sister Do's visit in 1937 as if it was then that he 'discovered' monkeys for the purpose. Also, in an article for *Zoo Life*, my father reported: 'the first which I had, in 1937, far exceeded my expectations, but after six months it died of an obscure illness. During that time it had collected botanical specimens from more than 350 species of trees, on one day collecting specimens from twenty-four trees exceeding 100' in height, which could not have been obtained by any other means short of cutting down the trees.' One should allow some licence in story telling, but how much, particularly on matters of import?

However, it is clear that by 1937, my father was using his monkeys in his official fieldwork. The annual report of the Director for that year recorded that 'In August Mr. Corner took two plant collectors to Fraser's Hill during his local leave. With the aid of these and his botanical monkey it was soon discovered that there was still a great deal of botanising to be done'. In the same report, Holttum wrote that collections in the Bukit Timah Forest Reserve 'were made by the botanical monkeys, Jambul and Puteh'. My father found them indispensible, and was convinced from his experience 'that the pig-tailed monkey is the best companion for the Malayan botanist; indeed, I think, for the Malayan naturalist'.

My father learned that both meat and fish were definitely not for the menu of captive beroks. Whilst wild in the trees they fed on insects, lizards, small spiders and if lucky, bird's eggs. The staple domestic diet was cooked rice and plenty of raw vegetables and fruit. Raw eggs were permitted only once a week; any more frequent and the berok became upset. It also enjoyed a bath but of equal importance was the training and the words of command which must be in Kelantan Malay.

Further, my father was warned that no berok would obey him until it had been reduced to tears by thrashing. In *Botanical Monkeys,* he recorded that 'I wrote down the words of command and gave no thought to chastisement'. However, he learned that chastisement was necessary and was administered with stick and whip. My father added, 'a choking collar is definitely required for the domination which Master must achieve so as to control the beast with words of command'.

After two months of training, my father reported that Merah could 'collect what I indicate by shouts of Malay words and judicious jerks on his neck'. He listed 17 words of command known by Merah and stated that he 'has all the possibilities of a human being, and even to trying to talk'. My father worked Merah as high as 130 feet in the forests of Johore and Merah collected some 50 specimens. If a specimen became hung up he climbed down and freed it, following his string line 'like Theseaus in the Minotaur's maze'.

My father explained that although they could be trained to do so, plucking coconut is unnatural for the berok as coconuts are generally too large and heavy for 'unguided handling and without offer of food'. He said that his botanical monkeys 'pursued their natural lives among the wild trees, and our task was to make use of this untrammelled enthusiasm'. He drew attention to 'an aspect of evolution which is apt to be overlooked... how animals came not merely to exist but to enjoy their existence'. He also observed that there were two periods when it was unsafe to handle the monkeys.

There is the universal time of dusk, when they become bundles of uncontrollable nerves and will start and bite in fear, even if offered food.

We put them into wooden huts for the night, before dusk, and they sleep heavily and peacefully, though with the first dawn they rattle and shake their cages to get out. The other time is when the monkey is becoming adult and has begun to sharpen his growing canines by grinding the lower ones behind the upper. He sits with hands on the ground, stroking his incipient ruff with his feet, and grinding with a mouth full of saliva. Pay no attention! Wait till it is over! A deep monkey-bite is very serious, for the slightest break of the skin caused by their teeth becomes septic.

He also discovered that the berok is completely immune to the irritation caused by rengas sap. Therefore, the monkeys were able to collect specimens from 'those poisonous trees of the Mango family so abundant in the forest and yet, through avoidance so little known'.

The botanical monkeys caught the attention of the press. A photograph of Merah appeared in *The Straits Times* in 1937 and the *Singapore Free Press* in 1938. In 1938, in the inaugural issue of *The Straits Times Annual*, my father wrote that by the end of 1938, Jambul and Puteh had done considerable work in Bukit Timah Forest Reserve with the one or the other being sent to work every day. He concluded with one of his memorable one-liners: 'it seems that these two must be congratulated, moreover, on being the first apes to enter Colonial service!'

My father's fame with his botanical monkeys spread well beyond the shores of Malaya. In August 1938, on his way for leave in England, he visited the Puget Sound Oceanographical Station in Vancouver to see, as he wrote, 'the great seaweeds of the Pacific'.

He arrived on the last day of the autumn session for the botanical students of the University of Washington and when they realised he was from Singapore he was bombarded with questions about the botanist who had employed monkeys as his collectors. (By chance, an article about this had appeared in the local newspaper that very morning.) After introducing himself, to their great surprise, he was asked to give a short discourse on the monkeys, at the conclusion of which there were many volunteers 'not only to be my monkeys along the coast of Friday Harbour but, indeed, in Singapore'.

*

There are no more letters for 1937, 1938 or 1939 to tell of my father's duties and activities of those years. There is only the Director's annual report for 1939 which states:

[A]fter his return from leave, Mr. Corner resumed his visits to south-eastern Johore, and a week's collecting was carried out in July near the Sedili River. Some interesting plants were found on the hill known as Tinjau Laut, east of the river. Mr Henderson twice visited the neighbourhood of Pontian in south-western Johore... One visit was to the island of Pulau Kemudi, in the Pulau Pisang Group, the other visit was to peat forest, of which there is a considerable area remaining near Pontian. The flora was found to be similar to that of the forest formerly existing near the Jurong Road, Singapore, felled 1932-'33 and studied by Mr Corner. The peat forest of Pontian is also similar in many respects to the fresh-water swamp forest of SE Johore, but differs notably in the scarcity of the genus *Eugenia*... The three Botanical Reserves in Singapore mentioned in the Annual Report of 1938 were finally gazetted as Forest Reserves during the year. This designation is for purposes of administrative convenience; the Reserves are primarily for the preservation of typical areas of natural vegetation, and control is entirely in the hands of the Gardens Department. For the purpose, the Director of the Gardens is gazetted as Conservator of Forests. Regular patrols at Bukit Timah have reduced cutting of timber to very small proportions. Two arrests were made for timber cutting during the year. New growth in areas formerly devastated continued satisfactorily. Six arrests were made in the Kranji Reserve, where men were regularly employed in making a boundary path during a considerable part of the year. At Bukit Timah, collection of specimens and naming and labelling of trees continued. The numbered trees were increased to 440, but not all these have yet been identified. Nearly two miles of paths were made in the Reserve during the year.

Holttum made no reference to my father returning from home leave with a bride.

- VIII -

SHEILA BAILEY

As I look back, I am surprised that I never thought to ask my mother what brought her to England and how she met my father.

Pandora led me also to research her background and I found out how she came to meet E. J. H. Corner is a story of chance, being in the right place at the right time – karma.

My father married at age 33 a girl of 19 – an American, coming from a different country and culture. Surely my father was by then something of a confirmed bachelor, fully involved in his work which presented, almost daily, new challenges both botanical and administrative. I can imagine him being set in his lifestyle.

My mother was born on 8 May 1920, the elder daughter of Dana Clark Bailey (1880–1929), a teacher in New York, and Dorothy Kavanagh (1892–1976). My mother's parents were married in Torquay in the west country of England during the First World War. Dana Clark Bailey was in Europe serving in France with the American YMCA for almost a year from 1918 to 1919, so they married in England rather than the USA: this was convenient because their parents, initially at least, were not entirely supportive of the marriage given the difference in age between them.

When my mother was born, her father was 40 and her mother 28. By then, they already had a son, Dana Kavanagh, born 22 November 1916. On Christmas Day 1921, another daughter was born: Mary (Molly) Dorothy, who would feature large in the future of my immediate family.

My maternal grandfather was a history teacher of some reputation; he was a leader in his field having graduated from Tufts University, Massachusetts. He wrote a textbook on American social history, *A New Approach to American History* (1927). On the strength of this, in 1929, he was sought out for the post of Head of the History Department in the ethical cultural school Fieldston in New York. However, he had barely taken up this post, the family having moved to New York with him, when he contracted pneumonia in the epidemic of 1929 and died shortly afterwards in hospital, principally because there were not enough oxygen tents to go round. His

92

death was particularly devastating for my mother who, of all the family, had been closest to him and seemed to have been the apple of his eye. She never really recovered from his loss but it instilled in her a strong sense of independence and duty. This independence and strength of character was to show its hand particularly during our evacuation from Singapore, 13 years hence. And how important is 1929? Mother lost her father, and her husband to be was arriving in Singapore.

There was no pension or social security to support the family and consequently Mrs Bailey had to take over her husband's classes as best she could, often, she said, 'only a few pages ahead of the class she was teaching.'

My maternal grandmother, Dorothy Kavanagh, was born on 26 March 1892 in La Grange, Hinsdale, Illinois and she continued her husband's history courses for a number of years and also did other work at Fieldston. In 1942, she left the school and took a machine-tool course in Yonkers, New York; this enabled her to help build bombers at the United Aircraft Co. in Tarrytown, NY, until the end of the war when she moved to the Washington area near to Richmond, to live at the house called *The Mouse Hole*. Dorothy Bailey was a musician, writer, avid gardener, and great supporter of all wildlife and a member of the Pohick Episcopal Church in the Pohick area of Fairfax County. She died in 1976.

My mother was the great-granddaughter of John Kavanagh, a captain in the Union Army during the American Civil War who died at the decisive battle of Antietam on 17 September 1862. He had gone to New York as an émigré from Dublin in 1849. In Ireland he had been active with those who rebelled against the British – the faction which eventually became known as the IRA! For this reason, he was 'forced' to emigrate.

Through him I can trace my forebears to the Pilgrim Fathers – they may even have been on the *Mayflower*. The family goes back to the early settlements in Massachusetts and prior to that to Kidderminster in Worcestershire in 1570; such a coincidence because some four hundred years and many generations later, my daughter Katie was in that same Kidderminster – going to school. We lived in Areley Kings, near to Stourport-on-Severn for almost 30 years till 2004, just four miles south of Kidderminster.

John Kavanagh was a true Celt and the essay 'From Lower Annagh to Ballingarry, the Life of the young Irelander, John Kavanagh (1826–1862)' by Edward Culleton paints a vivid picture of a man who supported the early rebellious movement of Ireland.

He was a most energetic and fearless officer. He fell at the head of his company in the heat of action in the great battle of Antietam on the 17, September [1862]. Captain Kavanagh had won for himself the enthusiastic devotion of numerous circles of friends. He was comparatively a young man; less than thirty seven years of age; of medium height, slender but sinewy frame; fair complexion and of prompt decisive mental habits. Had he lived he would have carved out a bright career as a soldier for few were so brave or thoroughly devoted to his profession and few possessed nobler or more generous qualities. He left after him, to mourn his loss, his devoted wife and seven children.

Captain John Kavanagh of the 63rd Infantry is listed amongst the New York Officers on the New York State Monument commemorating Antietam.

I knew the Kavanagh part of the Bailey family name was from Ireland but I had no idea of the long and proud history of that name, controversial or not. It is a worthy name, be it Christian or sur, and now I know why I was christened John Kavanagh.

My Uncle Dana K Bailey (1916–1999) graduated from the University of Arizona with distinction as an astronomer in 1937 and went on to be selected Rhodes Scholar (1939) at Queen's College Oxford, subsequently obtaining a DSc. He also did post-graduate work at Harvard.

Uncle Dana became a noted radiophysicist, astronomer and botanist, and was a life-long explorer and traveller, serving as part of an astronomical expedition to Peru for Hayden Planetarium and as a physicist on US and British expeditions to Antarctica and the Falkland Islands. In the 1940s, '50s and '60s he was a physicist at the Rand Corporation and the National Bureau of Standards in Washington and Boulder. Later in the 1960s and '70s, he took a position as a radiophysicist and research botanist for the National Oceanic and Atmospheric Administration (NOAA), and a physicist at Rhodes University, Grahamstown, Republic of South Africa. His work was widely published in important professional journals.

Those who knew him well share a great respect for Uncle Dana as a unique and perceptive scientist who contributed richly to the knowledge of atmospheric physics, solar physics, and radio wave propagation and its applications. There was the botanist, the mountaineer, explorer, and lover of geography, art and music. As an Oxford graduate he had participated in Byrd's third Polar Expedition in 1939.

So, Uncle Dana was as innovative, inspiring and given to a variety of expertise as my father, and both could be very difficult. There is indeed a strong parallel.

In mid-year 1941, Uncle Dana was a supervisor at the Bartol Research Laboratory of the Franklin Institute in Philadelphia. His work was particularly on the study of cosmic rays. He joined the US army and went to England, as a Captain and attached to the Royal Air Force where he worked initially in Radio Propagation at the Ionospheric Laboratory at the Slough Radio Research Laboratories. Uncle Dana pioneered broadcasts being transmitted around the curvature of the earth, and radar too thus giving greater warning of approaching aircraft and missiles.

Before he returned to Washington early in 1944, Uncle Dana worked for a time at the Interservice Ionosphere Bureau at the Marconi Company laboratories at Great Baddow in Essex. It was during this time that he met Dr Tom Eckersley. Through this connection, Tom and Eva Eckersley became close friends of my mother – this later proving to be a most important friendship.

Early in August 1945, Uncle Dana accompanied Colonel Earl Holliman to the Philippines before going to Tokyo in September of that year to learn about and record Japanese progress in ionospheric research. This work provided friendly contact with Japanese scientists who came to admire Dana Bailey. Later in his life he became a research botanist with a passion for the subject. He identified and named the then oldest tree in the world, the *Pinus longevea* Dana K Bailey, one of two species of bristlecone pine, and was honoured for this and his extensive contributions to the study of the bristle cone pine. He died on 27 August 1999, having lived a scientifically successful life with private life failures that compare with those of my father's.

Mary (Molly) Bailey was born in Clarendon Hills, Illinois where she attended Hinsdale School. In 1928, she transferred to Fieldston School where her father taught. After a year, she dropped out of college and joined *The Washington Post* in 1942, and subsequently Fairchild Publications as a journalist, retiring in the early 1980s. She moved to England in 1987 and passed away in 2012. Molly was married to Lt Cdr Max Michael, an American Navy officer. I remember the wonderful pictures of naval aeroplanes he sent me at Twyford School in the 1950s. I also remember the early transistor radio Molly gave me which I hid from my father.

When Grandfather Bailey died, to ease the pressure on the family, mother was shipped off to stay with her maternal grandmother in San Diego although she was back in New York a few years later to finish her secondary education. Inevitably, her education suffered, but even so she won prizes for English, was a voracious reader and wrote clearly and concisely.

The money for education in the main focussed on the other two children. If grandfather Bailey had lived things might have been very different for my mother; indeed this story might not have been.

Despite and perhaps because of these setbacks, Mother developed a very pioneering, determined, and creative spirit from an early age. She set up her own nursery in New York and made such an impression with her ability with young children that she was persuaded by a Cambridge professor, Max Newman*, and his wife, Lyn, who were on sabbatical at Princeton with their child, to travel to England to set up a similar nursery in Cam-

---

Max Newman joined the Government Code and Cipher School at Bletchley Park on 31 August 1942. There he contributed to the important development of the Colossus computer.

bridge – just at the time when E. J. H. Corner was returning to England for his second home leave.

At that time, September 1938, for a teenage girl to set off on her own across the Atlantic to a new life was certainly a bold and exceptional step.

This was the catalyst for the future of E. J. H. Corner and Sheila K. Bailey.

Top: My grandfather, Edred Moss Corner, around 1903.

Below: My father, his elder sister Stephanie, Dr Saunders and my father's younger sister Dorothy (Do), around 1924.

Left, top and bottom: My father with his botanical monkeys, around 1939.

Top left: My father photographing a tree in Senai for Wayside Trees of Malaya.

Top right: My father with Hassan Harun Awang (third from left) and others seated among buttress roots.

Bottom left: My father on bottom rung, learning to climb the tall trees.

Bottom right: My father's open, two-seater Rugby car on the road to Genting Sempah, 1932.

Top: My father with Frank Kingdon Ward on the Sedili, late 1930s.
Bottom: My father with Pen Landon, mid-1930s.

Top: Dr R. E. Holttum, 1930s. [Reproduced with the kind permission of the Director and the Board of Trustees, Royal Botanic Gardens, Kew.]
Bottom: My father on the bench with friends in front of his house, 1930s.

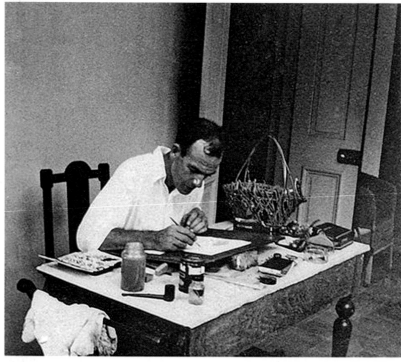

Left, top: 30 Cluny Road, mid-1930s.
Left, bottom: My father at his desk in 30 Cluny Road, mid-1930s.
Top and bottom: The lounge of 30 Cluny Road, 1930s.

Top: My mother, early 1930s.
Bottom (from left): Dana, Gramma Bailey, Molly and my mother, around 1937.

Gramma Bailey with Molly in New York during my parents' honeymoon visit.
[Courtesy of Tim Mahony.]

*Top: My parents in the back garden of Stratton End
on Christmas Day 1939, after their engagement.*

*Right: My parents on their wedding day in front of
St Peter's Church, Barton, Cambridgeshire.*
[*Both courtesy of Tim Mahony.*]

Top (from left): Priscilla Hill, Stella Worthington and my mother in late 1939.
Bottom left (from left): Jane Williams, Bill Williams and Kate Williams.
Bottom right (from left): Peter Williams and Tim Williams.
[Both courtesy of Peter Williams.]

Top: My father on the front lawn of 30 Cluny Road.
Bottom: My parents with their MG in Singapore.

Top: My mother with me at my christening at St Andrew's Cathedral, 9 June 1941.
Right: My father with me, mid-1941.

My parents with me in the garden of 30 Cluny Road, early 1941.

- IX -

COURTSHIP & MARRIAGE

Just as I never asked my parents about the circumstances of their meeting, I also never asked them about their courtship, wedding, and the early days of their marriage. By the time I was of an age where I might have shown such interest I was beginning to suffer the consequences of their marital difficulties.

It was on my father's home leave in 1938 when he met Sheila Kavanagh Bailey. This was the silver lining to having his leave delayed by Henderson's failures in Singapore; if he had gone on leave without delay, my parents would not have met.

In the middle of 1938, my father had spent time with his parents in Beaconsfield and also the Worthingtons close to Cambridge. Sheila Bailey came to England in September 1938 and stayed with the Newmans at their farm near to Comberton, just outside Cambridge, which was not far from the Worthingtons in Madingley.

She was introduced by the Newmans to E. J. H. Corner at a party given possibly by the Hills, and a few months later they were married.

Not surprisingly, as an attractive, intelligent and high-spirited American, my mother made an immediate impression on all those she met in England which was then still a rather dull and conservative society. I feel sure her prospective English in-laws were impressed too. I can't help thinking that she was much influenced by the early loss of her father and whilst she was never a person to take hasty decisions she must have been impressed by the tropical scientist from Singapore, the prospect of a life in the colonial tropics, and the introduction by the Newmans whom she greatly trusted, as did her mother.

Did either of them think about the cultural differences and family background or discuss them? I think not. I don't believe such matters were *hors de combat* then. My father had his head in his work clouds and had experienced a young life where his father ruled the roost and that Dickensian way was normal to him. Broadly speaking, he expected to be obeyed and I am sure my mother respected him but 'to obey' was never in her mind. She had engendered her own freedom in America, by necessity. So, two strong-minded people of very different cultures were brought together. But I have no doubt that at that time they found love. I think both were subconsciously looking for it.

I have no information on the short courtship and I can't help wondering if my father had been advised in Singapore that it was time for him to be married, to have a wife who would smooth his way on the colonial social round of which he was uninterested, uncomfortable and hated – he had described himself in *The Marquis* as 'a crank in that pleasure-seeking society'. It could too have improved his chances of promotion.

Clearly, his great friend Worthington had been pushing him towards it for some time – even towards his sister Betty. Hill was happily married but Birtwistle had sounded a clear warning.

My parents wrote a charming letter together to Stella Worthington on 26 December 1938 from my paternal grandparents' house in Beaconsfield. It gave news of the engagement – a Boxing Day lunch – and showed their happiness of the moment and gave their immediate plans.

> Sheila sends her love to Barton – I knew I was getting mixed up – and she says I am to send mine to you – I do! You see, we are both writing this letter.

My mother was resting after much Christmas fare so my father actually penned the letter. 'Listen to what she would write herself, had she not an admirer'. He described the engagement ring as

> colossal (that is Sheila's conclusion); in fact it's meaning to us is so big that we know not how to describe it. (Sheila is passing out of a coma; John is cooking by the gas fire).

He had put it on her finger himself. 'Gold and Emerald, for Malaya and Hibernia [Ireland]'. He continued by making brief reference to their intended visit to Hawkshead (the Worthingtons' Lake District home) before leaving for America in February.

They thanked the Worthingtons for the splendid gifts, a bowl and some Bach records which they have already been playing, as well as spinning tops. He joked that he will have 'a special topping-pocket made in our hand bag' so that they can spin tops whenever.

> We are dual! Sheila also says if I (not we) do not take our, my bath this minute, we, I shall be late for dinner. (What the devil does she, we, he, anything mean?)… Please forgive this awful pickle of idiotic remarks but remember we, he, she, it, they – i.e. the Kavanagh Corners, are always yours to command, John and Sheila, (she has woken up).

I remember tops, spinning tops, and was encouraged to the skill by my father. We played frequently in my childhood – and he made them too.

My father wrote to Barton Worthington on 11 January 1939 from Vatches Farm, Cambridgeshire, the Hill's home. He began by wishing Barton many happy returns of the day calling it the unlucky day (13th) when he was born, then he announced the news

> of what you have so long tried to engineer and what I have so long stubbornly resisted – February first is to be our wedding day, 2.30 pm. at Barton Church. I do hope you and Stella can come.

He then confirmed that they sail for New York on 11 February, return to England on 10 March and sail for Singapore on 1 April, adding, 'the more I know Sheila, the happier appears our future'.

So they went to church to be wed from Robin Hill's house, travelling to Barton village about 4 miles south-west of Cambridge. The wedding announcement of E. J. H. Corner and Sheila Kavanagh Bailey appeared in *The Straits Times* of Singapore a fortnight later on 14 February 1939.

After the wedding, they drove to Devon for a few days at Hartland Point before travelling to Ireland where the rest of the British honeymoon was spent in and around Giants Causeway, County Antrim. When I read about the Hartland Point stay in Pandora, it immediately caught my attention because, when I was young, sometime in the late 1950s, my father took his family to Hartland Point for a holiday staying at a hotel right at the Point, by the Lighthouse, which I can remember much enjoying. This was after his divorce from Mother, and this time, he took his second wife. He never mentioned to me that he had been there before.

Marj Goodhue, my mother's second cousin and her closest and lifelong friends, told me that my father and mother arrived in New York on 17 February. They visited Dorothy Bailey, his new mother-in-law, and Mother's siblings Molly and Dana. My father and Dana got on very well. From photographs which I have from the Cambridge University Library Archives, it is clear that they fitted in a lot on that visit, including *Prides Corner* in Maine, and spent time with family and friends as one would have expected.

As planned, my parents left England for Singapore on 1 April aboard the SS *Agamemnon*. On the way, they stopped in Penang, as announced in *The Straits Times* of 14 April, clearly as part of their honeymoon.

But the honeymoon was short. There were clear undercurrents appearing in the marriage even in those earliest of days. A new life had started for them both and it was to be full of delights, yet fraught with difficulties and daunting challenges.

*

Back in Singapore, my father continued his pre-marriage lifestyle – by this I mean he continued his almost total focus on his work. He certainly must have been happy when his new wife took so easily and naturally to the botanical monkeys and helped with his botanising. However, he did not seem to realise how very different and challenging this new life was for his wife – an American – in British colonial society. The transition from America to England and then Malaya, in just a year or so, for my mother, aged 19, must have been extremely difficult and taxed even her. My father appeared to have made no real attempt to introduce her 'around' and didn't appear to notice my mother's discomfort.

Mother made mistakes like putting the wrong people together at dinner parties without realising they were socially incompatible. I think my father didn't tell her because I don't think he thought of such things himself, being socially naïve. However, he became cross, often angry, when these 'errors' occurred. I feel sure that, quite unwittingly, the seeds of their marriage failure were sown early in their life together.

Henry Barlow's book *Swettenham* tells of the difficulty Frank Swettenham had when he returned from leave in the UK with a wife, and the analogy with my parents is compelling. Swettenham in 1877 was Assistant Colonial Secretary. My father in 1939 was Assistant Director of the Botanic Gardens. Swettenham had, Barlow wrote, 'undoubtedly made a good start learning Malay, distinguishing himself before and during the Perak War. At the same time he had made enemies'. My father had quickly become fluent in Malay, learning it in hospital in 1929 and was clearly a most able (if not yet distinguished) scientist. He was competent too at making enemies!

Swettenham left for leave in England in March 1877. As Barlow observed:

> [A]t the age of 27, Swettenham must have recognised that for his career, if for no other reason, it was now appropriate that he should marry. A charming young wife would work wonders for his image in Singapore. Single ladies of the appropriate age and background were always in short supply there, so leave in the UK was just the opportunity Swettenham needed to find a bride.

My father was 32 when he went on home leave in 1938. He had made 'enemies' not through war but by being unsociable, a little aloof and very single-minded, indeed not fitting well into colonial society. More and more it seemed clear that finding a wife was on his mind as he returned to Britain that year.

For Sheila Bailey, like Sydney Swettenham, 'the prospect of an exciting life with a dashing husband in a far-flung outpost of empire must have had its attractions'.

According to Barlow, Sydney Swettenham

was almost certainly homesick, and even then perhaps subject to irrational outbursts, which no doubt caused embarrassment and sometimes offence to her social acquaintances. Swettenham's job, as Assistant Colonial Secretary, took him away from Singapore… for long periods. This no doubt made Sydney even more miserable, left as she was on her own in a strange tropical city. Additionally, she would have had to cope with a backlog of jealousy which Swettenham's ability… had engendered. Where a more mature woman could have shrugged off or disregarded vindictive jibes from the wives of her husband's colleagues, this would have been difficult for Sydney, and it is likely that she withdrew to a large extent from Singapore social life as a result.

The comparison continues. My father had a significant job requiring much travel away from Singapore and I think it likely that 'the colonial wives' did jibe at the charming young American girl who knew nothing of colonial life. I bet Mother held her ground and that might not have helped.

Years later, Mother confided to her friend, Marj Goodhue, that when she stepped into my father's life in Singapore she found it very difficult for it was something entirely new to her.

This was confirmed by Paul Tanner, Mother's son by her second marriage. Mother told him that in her letters from Singapore to friends and family she was always positive and sounded happy: but in reality she wasn't. She struggled with the colonial practices which were totally alien to her.

This was 1939, and there was the beginning of an idea that war was looming, though the idea that Singapore could fall was then beyond comprehension. In the midst of this all, I was born on 3 January 1941. I constantly wonder where we all would have been if that war hadn't intervened. Would my parents have remained together? Would my early upbringing have been happier and schooling easier? I will never know and though I am finding my father, there is still a long way to go.

- X -

MARRIAGE DISRUPTED

Amongst the revelations of Pandora was an article written for the Michael-mas edition of *The Kings Messenger*, 1941, the magazine of Kings School, Singapore, the only jointly-written article by my parents. It was all about the botanical monkeys; indeed I might say their botanical monkeys.

It was published in September that year which turned out to be the school's last, due to war. I have read it many times and I see the strong influence of my mother in the writing although the substance of the information would have come from my father. It is titled 'Monkeys', and I am sure she wrote most of it. It is relevant because, through this, her gentle and perceptive character can be discerned. She was good with children and was a teacher at the school.

Rattle, rattle, bump! It is scarcely dawn but Merah is eager to begin the adventures of the day...' As he shakes his box his neighbour, little Fatima, 'hoots a cheerful greeting.' The third cage holds the babies Teh and Bauh who also welcome the new day with a tussle and it won't be long before they are taken to the nearby trees 'where they can jump and play and pull faces at each other until nightfall comes again...' They are known as pig-tailed monkeys by reason of their 'funny short tails which curl over their backs, like a pig's.' They are quite different from the Kra-monkeys in the Botanic Gardens. 'The homes of our four monkeys were in the northern part of Malaya, and southern Thailand, up among the jungle tree-tops, where they ate such queer things as long gray stick-insects, caterpillars, flower-buds, wild fruits and nuts, especially those fruits which are very sour...!' They also enjoy butterflies and even the occasional mushroom for which they have to foray on the jungle floor. The large jungle ant is a particular delicacy and 'their sharp little eyes dart this way and that, never missing anything which might taste good, and they are very clever at knowing which mushrooms or caterpillars are poisonous'.

The article continues with a description of the monkey's early life; how as a baby it 'clings to the fur on their mother's sides and rides upside down under her tummy'; when a few days old it is taught to walk by setting it down, the mother walking a short distance away and encouraging it to follow and every day increasing the distance, returning to it when it cries. This is repeated until 'the baby lifts its heavy head and takes its first step! When this happens the mother is so pleased, she chatters and chatters, and makes funny smiling faces, and almost before you can say Jack Robinson the baby has learned to play little games of Tag and Hide and Go Seek!' This is clearly my mother's writing for my father would have written 'hide and seek'.

At this point serious teaching of the baby monkey begins… short walks and encouragement to climb small trees learning how to hang from the low branches and jump from tree to tree. The first teeth appear at 5/6 weeks and the mother then watches carefully to be sure it doesn't eat anything poisonous. 'She is very funny sometimes, snatching a fuzzy caterpillar from her child's hand, sniffing it, and then throwing it furiously away!' The babies usually learn quickly and soon are playing with 'its other monkey friends and becoming less dependant on its mother's help and guidance, until it finally becomes another grown-up member of the monkey-band.

The story continues by telling that in Kelantan and Perlis the Malays have learned to use these monkeys for their ability to be taught to climb coconut palms and throw down the fruit. The commands first taught are the words '*naik*', (Malay for 'go up'); once they can reach the top of the tree they learn '*turun*', come down, '*ambil itu*, fetch that, *belah itu*', over that side, and '*ambil lagi*', fetch more.

Merah and Fatima, however, are even more clever and useful, and are employed by the Government for work in the Botanical Gardens… for they have learned how to collect leaves, flowers and fruits from the tallest of trees which they will break-off and throw down… according to command which is always in Malay.

The monkeys were described as generally diligent workers but could also be very mischievous and fun loving, requiring their master to be patient and understanding. Sometimes, when he should be working, Merah would just sit down and refuse to budge, or perhaps he would go up a tree and leap from branch to branch, in pursuit of a butterfly, ignoring every order from below! The two 'babies' Teh and Bauh, were being trained for work in the Botanic Gardens, and though they admired big Merah and pulled faces at him from a safe distance, they became very frightened when he came too near. However, they all lived contentedly in their master's garden.

The garden was designed to allow them good freedom and the accompanying photograph showed them wearing a collar with a light chain attached. This was connected to a long and fairly loose stretch of wire between two tall trees thus allowing them to 'climb and run about in all directions, and there is a framework of bamboos between the trees for leaping and swinging on'. Close by was their bath! A big tin tub where they could swim during the hot days. However 'Merah is not so fond of his bath as Teh and the little ones, who swim round and round under the water.'

When the gardener appeared crossing the lawn late in the day there would be great excitement for the monkeys. They knew he was fetching their meal

> of rice before they go to bed. Papaya and banana, or mango or some other fruit in the early morning then rice again in the evening. How they do stuff their pouches, and pull faces and croon away to each other, till it is getting dusk and they are led into their boxes – for, you know, like you and me, they are just a little afraid of the dark.

In finishing the article my mother, for I'm sure it is she, wrote:

> [W]hat a fine thing it is to be a monkey, climbing trees, swinging upside down, no clothes to keep clean or faces to be washed, no teeth to brush or shoes to put on! Just a bit of shouting and yelling and bristling of fur when a dog comes into the garden or an eagle flies overhead.

It is jointly signed, S. K. and E. J. H. Corner.

*

When I was born at the General Hospital in Singapore on 3 January 1941, the monkeys soon were no more. Professor Ho Coy Choke wrote to me:

> your father cared for you. When we were on Kinabalu he told me he disposed of his botanical monkeys to protect you from harm from jealous Macaques.

My father may have said so but he was inaccurate; he kept at least two monkeys right up to the last days before the Japanese Occupation – and by that time Mother and I had already left for Australia. His book *The Marquis* states that he kept the macaques as does *Botanical Monkeys*. Coy Choke could not possibly have known that, not having read the books. However, it's interesting to know that my father had talked about me on Kinabalu in 1964, because I had by then left home.

*

In August 1939, a meeting took place between the Governor of Singapore, Sir Shenton Thomas, and my father which was to prove important. This was a time of defence planning and whilst embroiled in that, Shenton Thomas, and I quote from Brian Montgomery's book *Shenton of Singapore Governor and Prisoner of War*,

> was thinking seriously of the need for up-to-date scientific advice in order to preserve the fauna and flora of Malaya, particularly the creation of game reserves. He applied officially to the Government of Kenya for the temporary services of Captain Archibald Ritchie, Chief Game Warden of Kenya, whom he hoped would come to Singapore and advise the Government.

After Ritchie arrived it was not long before, and again I quote from the Montgomery book:

> The Governor, with Ritchie and Mr E. J. H. Corner, a British officer of the MCS Settlements, made an extensive tour of the Malay Peninsula. It was a difficult and prolonged expedition during which they climbed to the summit of the highest mountain peak on the mainland [Gunung Tahan in Pahang at 7,200 ft]. Afterwards Ritchie's advice provided the basis of a report from which the Game Laws of Malaya were first drafted. This tour was interesting also for Shenton, as it was his first meeting with Mr Corner.

Here I find discrepancy. Montgomery's book suggests the tour including Gunung Tahan was in 1939. Yet, the report of the Director of the Botanic Gardens clearly dates it as 1937. I believe the Gardens' report to be correct. Since arriving in Singapore, my father, as a fully qualified botanist, advised the previous Governor, and following him Sir Shenton Thomas, on the upkeep and maintenance of the Government House gardens: because of this, I believe Shenton Thomas was more than just acquainted with my father; they knew each other really quite well and in my view rather earlier than the Ritchie expedition.

*

At the outbreak of World War II, the armed forces of Malaya comprised a small garrison of British troops, two Malay Regiment battalions, a few companies of Volunteer Forces and the Johore Military Forces. There had never been in existence any policy of arming the people of Malaya and training them for military service. All manpower was dedicated to economic activity, specifically the production of rubber and tin. Although the Naval Base had been completed in the north of Singapore in 1939, the island was not the fortress that it was made out to be. The British were counting on the French to defend Indo-China, thus securing Malaya from the north. This strategy was sound until the fall of France in 1940 changed the whole outlook. Malaya became entirely vulnerable from the north, and with it Singapore, linked to Peninsular Malaya by a causeway.

As 1939 progressed, it was becoming clear that trouble was close by – that the Japanese surely would come. Yet, far too many people continued their social rounds, played tennis, and drank their whisky sodas. To them Singapore was impregnable. Churchill had said so. The fighter planes will arrive and the navy will protect us. Ignorant trusting bliss prevailed.

Even then, every household was given a copy of the ARP (air raid precautions) handbook and lectures on ARP had been given in most offices; hundreds of air raid wardens were appointed. These were the first indications of the future that the public noticed. Soon came the problem of planning food supplies in an emergency and then a variety of matters ranging from wartime censorship and propaganda to transport organisation and allocation of the country's manpower.

It had been decided at the highest level that if war came there would be no attempt to evacuate the densely crowded and built-up central district of Singapore. It was decreed that in the event of air raid all must stay put; even the digging of trenches for shelter was discouraged as impracticable due to the high water table.

Governor Shenton Thomas, when citing the opinions of the military and air force chiefs argued that as

> Singapore is fortunately situated, out of range of any likely enemy bases, the only aircraft which would attack the fortress are those launched from aircraft carriers and therefore neither very numerous or very capacious, nor of very long range.

By the end of 1939, almost every European in the Colony had been registered and a manpower bureau opened. This enabled a decision to be reached regarding men in 'key' positions who could not be spared from their regular jobs in an emergency, leaving all other 'non-essentials' free to volunteer for wartime duties. Sir Shenton, in a speech late in 1939 said, 'Malaya's state of defence preparedness is not unsatisfactory'. (I think the use of the double negative was intentional; did he realise that because of language most Chinese and Japanese would be unlikely to understand it fully?) Yet, the fighters didn't arrive and the navy had only two capital ships, the battleship HMS *Prince of Wales* and battle cruiser HMS *Repulse*.

In 1941, as a practical precaution against Japanese aggression, British officials, who had been engaged hitherto in essential services, were conscripted into the Singapore Volunteer Service. My father was one, being appointed Food Production Officer. Thus, he joined others who were granted leave and went into camp for training on weekends, usually for a couple of days.

On 21 November 1941, my father received a letter from Professor J. B. Cleland from the Botanic Gardens in Adelaide of which the opening paragraph says: 'We shall be very glad to see you [in Adelaide] between April and August next year'. This illustrates how little, even 10 or 12 weeks before the fall of Singapore, people realised the seriousness, indeed likelihood, of impending invasion and capitulation.

*

About this time, my father was in the garden at Cluny Road with two of the monkeys, Che Minah and Su, when he heard a rush behind him. It was Puteh charging, as my father wrote in *The Marquis*, 'with open jaws and slobbering fangs'.

My father was not wearing his normal protective gloves but he put up his right arm as a shield in an attempt to ward off the attacker. Instead of burying his long teeth into my father's neck, Puteh plunged his teeth into his arm and wouldn't let go. My father considered squeezing his jaws but realised that that would have risked another bite, so he tore his forearm from the monkey and rolled clear. A long slab of forearm dangled from the bone.

In the General Hospital, the chief surgeon, Mr Munro, operated and, after several hours of local anaesthetic, joined up the pieces. The arm swelled to the shoulder and my father became more feverish. He kept thinking of all who had told him not to have dealings with monkeys lest he met the same fate as King George of Greece who had died from a septic bite from his pet monkey. After a week in hospital he was discharged, arm in sling, and told not to use it for four months. He was invalided out of the Volunteers and recorded that because of the onslaught of Puteh he never became a prisoner-of-war.

Puteh remained savage and showed his anger whenever my father approached. His fangs were sawn off but other than causing gum infection and boils it really didn't work. While the monkey was still under the anaesthetic my father put him into a cage from which he never emerged. He simply could not bear to part with one who had been such an inspiration and, he wrote, 'erstwhile companion'. When the invasion was clearly imminent, and two days before the surrender of Singapore, he returned to the house and liberated Merah before shooting Puteh.

*

On 8 December 1941, when the Japanese army landed on the undefended beaches of north-eastern Malaya, my mother was teaching at Kings School. I was barely a year old.

The many photographs I now have of us, a family, in Singapore just before the war, show cheerfulness with not a sign of the impending disaster, not even in the brief photo captions. For example, my mother wrote of some, 'the last snaps taken at 30 Cluny Road' and the date is 20 December 1941, just 57 days before the capitulation of Singapore when the Japanese were already remorselessly driving south.

My father, like others with perception, could see the writing on the wall in spite of the assurances of Churchill, the Governor and the myriad of military commanders. The end was indeed nigh. As the Japanese swept down the peninsula, Europeans, particularly women and children, left their homes in great haste, even panic, to make their way southward, eventually to Singapore. Word had got to some by the authorities in Singapore to make quickly to the city where evacuation was probable.

A number of my parents' friends found their way to our Cluny Road house. They included Jim and Penelope Landon, Mike Ash, Dr John (Jack) Reid, Susie Napper, Colin, and Ellen Symington and their twins, Morag and Ian. Throughout December, Singapore was being increasingly shelled and bombed and to any thinking person it must have been clear that the island was doomed.

There suddenly was hope with the arrival of the *Prince of Wales* and *Repulse*, tasked to intercept the invasion fleet. However, all turned to gloom when, sailing without air support, the battleships were sunk off the east coast of Malaya on 10 December. The carrier that was to have accompanied them had run aground in the West Indies and never reached Singapore.

Judy Bryning sent me this poignant poem which gives a view of those tragic sinkings:

I saw two ships come sailing by,
Ere Christmas Day, ere the mourning.
Following a star prophesying war,
The two ships leaving Singapore.

People watched from the Seaview Hotel,
Feeling the portent they feared to foretell.
Of lives cut short and deaths in hell,
Not the predicted short affray.

No Christmas reds, just wartime grey
On the two ships sailing by.
The red was bled and washed out at sea,
Come Christmas Day and the mourning.

There was an opportunity for Pen Landon to escape on a small ship, the SS *Kuala*. She didn't want to take her jewellery in case it became lost, and left it with her husband. Jim, decided to stay, thinking, as did many, that if Singapore should fall it would not be long before the British retook it. It was agreed that her jewellery would be put in a glass jar and hidden under a flag-stone in the bomb shelter that my father had dug in the garden of the Cluny Road house. The *Kuala* was sunk off Pompong Island on 14 February. After swimming to shore and helping treat the wounded (she was with the Malayan Medical Auxiliary Service) Pen joined the SS *Tanjong Pinang*. That ship was in turn sunk around 17 February in the Banka Strait. Pen Landon was never found.

*

My mother talked very little of when she and I escaped from Singapore, but my father must somehow have had influence to find us berths on the SS *Orion*, one of the earlier refugee ships to leave. On 31 December 1941, it departed for Australia with over 1,000 people on board: naval, military and RAF personnel – including wounded troops – British, Australian and Indian nurses, civilians, mainly women and children. Its captain was Arthur Lewis Owens.

The *Orion* was a single-funnelled P&O liner with air-conditioned public rooms and bakelite and chromium fittings – amenities which set a new standard in ocean travel when she was launched in 1935. As World War II broke out, she was acquired by the British government and converted into a troop ship, carrying troops to Europe from Egypt and New Zealand.

Peter Tanner, my stepfather, told me that Mother did remember the ship being blacked out most of the time and the situation being very tense. She remembered that all were in particular fear of imminent attack by Japanese midget submarines which were known to be operating in the area. These were highly dangerous waters and it would be a miracle if one 'made it'. I passed my first birthday in these conditions, three days out from Singapore.

To find out more about our escape on the *Orion*, I posted messages on Internet forums of Children of Far East Prisoners of War (COFEPOW) and Malayan Volunteers Group (MVG) and took out advertisements in *SAGA* and *This England* magazines. The responses from *Orion* refugees or from their families and friends were detailed and moving. From these sources, I was able to piece together a picture of our dramatic flight.

*

The complacency felt in Singapore by the civilian population remained until it was seen that evacuation wasn't so much a choice but a necessity.

Nigel Killeen, then aged nine, remembered his parents listening to the radio when the Japanese invasion began and seeing bombing and flames from Singapore city. The next thing he recalled was his father driving him and his mother to the docks. 'Mother (was) crying because she didn't want to go but he insisted'. Joan Lardy recalled, 'she just grabbed us and a silver bowl on the hall table and left with us four children (with Ted the baby under her arm) and Elizabeth Yeo (a 16-year-old young Chinese girl she had adopted)'.

Jane Jennings got a telephone call to say that they should be at the docks in half an hour to go to Australia. 'There was no time to think about it.' Yvonne Spranklen's experience was similar.

We had one hour to pack one suitcase and get to the docks; our fathers evidently saw us off but I was too busy crying because I could not take my pram (X'mas present) but was allowed my doll (still have it).

June Dunnett's mother was luckier; she was allowed to take two cabin trunks on board. Refugees from Malaya were told to bring only the bare necessities. Morag Walmsley's family duly complied.

But when we arrived in Singapore to board ship some people were allowed to bring all sorts of items, not considered necessities. Mother was very upset about this and said had she known; she too, would have brought more.

I wonder what my mother packed? Necessities surely, but also my Christening silver: a mug, egg cup and pusher spoon which we still have, rather battered.

Bridget Hayward was a refugee from Kuala Lipis, where her father was the District Officer and a member of the Pahang Volunteers.

I can remember him arriving dressed like an Australian soldier and saying 'Hello Tricia can you be off in two hours?' His brigadier had given him four hours leave in order to tell my mother that she must go to Singapore – not by KL as she would be stopped – and to make sure she understood that we must leave the country as they were 'not going to hold this'. We spent a fortnight in Singapore waiting for a passage. My brother has the original telegram which mother sent to her father in England on Dec 28th 1941 saying 'Going Australia with children'.

For Eileen Carey, whose father was a rubber planter in Selangor, there was never any prospect he would travel with the family to Singapore to see them safely off. 'I gave him my teddy to keep him company'.

While passage on the evacuation ships were arranged for some, other families had to fend for themselves. Susan Herbert's father was working for The English Electric Company and at the time Henry Waugh was the company's agent in the Far East. Susan found a most informative letter dated 15 January 1942 from Killara, Australia, which was written by her mother, Mrs A. M. Herbert, to her Tasmanian mother-in-law:

> The following morning I went to Henry Waugh's office to see about a boat, etc. and all I could get from them was that they would cover the passage but to make my own arrangements…. Each day I went along to the P&O office and eventually was told at 5.00 pm that I would be leaving the following morning, 7.00 am on board. I managed, luckily, to buy Sue a warm coat (it was the last of her size left in Singapore) and get some travellers' cheques from the Bank.

June Dunnett wrote: 'I do remember that the night before my mother and I embarked on the *Orion* we spent the night sitting under palm trees. I think it was outside the Raffles Hotel [which then faced the sea]'.

Even for those fleeing directly from Singapore, the situation was no less uncertain. Sandy Lincoln's family was torn when his grandmother could not get a berth on the departing ship, but that was a problem that had to be dealt with after a truly close shave. Sandy related:

> The front of [our house] was surrounded by sandbags. Mother had gathered everyone into the hall. The Japs bombed the petrol dump near the Japanese golf course which was at the end of Kay Siang Road. It made the most terrible noise. Mother, on an impulse, grabbed Norman from a cot to hug him and at that moment a lump of shrapnel flew in, whistled past Gran's neck – she said she could feel the breeze as it passed – and landed right where Norman's head had been. Mother had been urged to get out with Norman as soon as she could, but she was reluctant to leave my grandmother who was unable to get a passage out. However, she decided that she and Norman must go when they could. Gran also urged them to go even though it meant that she would be left behind.
>
> At this point fate took a hand. The morning they were due to go, my father was working but got permission to take them to the boat. Of course they were allowed to take very little luggage, just one case which was filled mostly with nappies for my brother, and baby food. Gran at the last minute threw a few extra things in a small bag, 'just in case', and they all got into a car.
>
> Literally, just as they were leaving, an army car drew up in their drive, stopped their car, and said they had come to requisition their house. Daddy said that his mother-in-law was still going to be living there as she could not get a passage out – and they were told to take her

too. Sure enough, when they went to the office to collect Mother's ticket they were handed two, which is how, by sheer chance, Gran also managed to get out with Mother and Norman on the same boat.

Sometime in December 1941, Allan Proctor's father, an electrical engineer in Muar and a member of the local volunteer force drove his family to Singapore to seek evacuation. The party included Allan, age 7, his mother, his sister Hilary age 8 months, their dear amah Ah Foon and Nola Barron, age 7, whose parents were on leave in Australia. Allan's mother, Freda Mitchell, wrote regularly for *The Straits Times* before the war and her account of the evacuation is exactly what my story needs about the *Orion* experiences. It is descriptive, sensitive and paints so well the picture of those extraordinary times and the people caught up in it. Poignantly, I realise that Mother and I were on the docks that New Year's Eve day, at about the same time.

We sadly said goodbye to all our servants, but Amah begged to come with us to help look after us until we could get a boat. We arrived eventually in Singapore… There was no room at any of the hotels or at our friends' homes; we finally found ourselves at a school which had been turned into an emergency hospital.… I left Amah with the children and told her that if any bombs came she was to stay where she was until I came to her. I then went down to the canteen to get some food for myself.… I made my way to the counter and was waiting my turn for food when I heard what sounded like thunder in the distance. I turned to a small woman at my side and said, "Was that thunder?"

"Thunder!" she replied with a strong Australian accent, "Thunder! Them's blooming bombs!"

Then the lights went out. We scrambled madly for the door. There were no shelters we knew, but our babies…! With some difficulty I found my way to our dormitory and there found Amah sitting quietly on the bed with baby strapped on her back, Allan with his dressing gown on and a blanket rolled up on his knees, was at her side. Nola, the other little girl, had panicked and rushed screaming from the room. I told Amah to stay there whilst I ran to look for Nola. By this time the sirens were wailing and the noise of the bombs closer. I found Nola screaming wildly at the top of the stairs, and I slapped her hand, partly because I was frightened myself, and partly because, instinctively, I knew it was the only thing to do. We hurried back to Amah and groped our way downstairs. By this time the confusion was terrific – children were crying and mothers blindly searching for their children. We all crowded together in a passageway and waited for the "All Clear". As we lay under the bed we could see through the archways the gleam of the night sky. One of the bombs hit an oil dump nearby and the flames shot up into the sky. It was actually about half a mile away, but it seemed closer to us, lying there in the dark. Then, for the first time, Allan began to cry.

"Mummy, we shall all be burned", he said, "and if we die Daddy will be left all alone."

At this I felt myself crumble inside, but I comforted him and said to Amah in Malay, "Oh, Amah isn't it terrible." For the first time I felt real fear.

Amah put her arms round my shoulders and said, "*Tida-apa*, Mem – Never mind, Mem – the big *Tuan* up on high will take care of you. He knows Mem has a *hati besar* – a brave heart. Look baby is well, she is sleeping. Nola is quiet, Allan is brave. Why worry, Mem, the *Tuan Besar* is there, and he knows what is in your heart."

I felt the tears sting my eyes, but with Amah's arm around me and her small body close to mine I was no longer afraid, but calm again.

At the time of embarkation, fires were burning out of control at the docks. The harbour had been heavily bombed the night before and the streams of arriving passengers were anxious and confused, bordering on panic. Bridget Hayward recalled:

> We had to be on the quay at 7.30 am with all our luggage which we had to carry on board – obviously no spare labour – a woman without children helped my mother. It must have been hell keeping three children quiet for four and a half hours in that heat.

The picture unfolding of those moments prior to departure, and the awful moment when *Orion* sailed, is very poignant.

Minutes before the ship's single gangplank was raised, a friend of Graem Castell's mother, Bess Pickthall, forced her way back onto the wharf in a last-minute attempt to speak with her husband. She was left behind. Mrs Castell took charge of the Pickthall children, 14-year-old Elizabeth and younger brother, Richard, left on board, for the rest of the war.

Freda Mitchell's final farewell to her beloved amah is told here:

> After I had carried our luggage past the barriers, I turned to say goodbye to Amah. She held Allan and Nola close and snuffled on Hilary's neck. Her eyes were full of tears. "*Selamat Jalan*, Mem – Go in safety." We could find no words then. I turned blindly from the barrier. Then I heard loud cries, "Mem! Mem!" I turned round to see Amah struggling to get past the soldiers on guard, tears streaming from her eyes. With the butt of their rifles they were roughly pushing her back. In her hands

she held baby's basket which held her bottle and flask and baby food. In our grief we had forgotten them and without them I would have been in a terrible predicament. I turned on the soldiers in such anger then that they stood back with a hangdog air. Amah gave me the basket. Her hair was dishevelled, and her spotless jacket was crumpled. But the soldiers, recovering from my blast, took her by the shoulders and pushed her roughly away. Meekly her head went down and she turned quietly away. I never saw her again.

Many years later, Judy Bryning recalled those extraordinarily hectic moments of impossible decision before departing for the *Orion*. She reflected on that moment in her poem, *New Year's Day 1942*, Singapore.

No time to choose
Which part of your life
To put in the suitcase,
No time to lose.
A race against time,
A time against race.
Which part to part with?
Which place to replace?

Break with the present
Becomes break with the past.
Like an unhealed sore,
What went before?
Breaks with the past
To become the present.

Presents from Christmas
Abandoned at New Year.
Forced, not fickle
The parting was
From teddy bear
And red tricycle.
Who got away?
Who ended up where?
Mrs Self was seen floating,
Her head in a chair.

No time to choose
Between hope and fear
To put in the suitcase,
To face the New Year.

Graem Castell's father was in the crowd swarming the dockside as the ship pulled away. Sailing time was scheduled for about 7 pm. However, when the air-raid sirens sounded, the Captain ordered that all passengers be taken well below deck for safety and decided to sail earlier. Like the many fathers in that crowd, Castell did not know if he would ever see his family again. He reflected: 'The same was true for the wives and children waving bravely from behind the ship's railings as their husbands and fathers stoically raised their hats in response'.

I wonder if my father was one of them. He had to have been.

In *The Marquis*, my father wrote that there was an air raid the afternoon that the *Orion* set sail, and bombs were falling on the quay. Some felt sure that the ship left early because of attacks on the docks leaving some evacuees stranded. My father carried the invalid son of the Symingtons up the gangway. He wrote of their evacuation as being in January 1942, but I know they also were on the *Orion* with mother and me. We all appeared on the passenger list. I am surprised that he had forgotten the date we all departed. New Year's Eve 1941 – the year of my birth.

I can't help wondering at my father's description of taking the invalid son of a friend up the gangway whilst bombs were falling. It's not so much the description but that nowhere does he describe the evacuation and sailing of his own wife and son, that very same day, on the same vessel. Who saw us off? Perhaps he made two trips to the docks, but there was no mention of his family. Could all that subsequent bitterness have influenced his writing? Sadly I think it did. What an awful thing is hate. *The Marquis* was written in 1980/81, long after the evacuation, and he allowed his feelings over subsequent events to influence what he wrote.

I have also thought hard about why my father did not come with us, escape as so many others had? Holttum was in charge of the Gardens. Perhaps the marriage was rocky even then. But was there another reason?

*

Kit Cox, who together with her late husband, Bob, became our good friends as they lived close to us in Melbourne, recalled '*Auld Lang Syne* being sung soon after departure'. Yvonne Heritage wrote:

[W]hen we had sailed for a while after leaving Singapore, there were big explosions behind us at the docks, ships being blown up… but we still had Japanese subs following us firing torpedoes. The Captain set a zig-zagging course to avoid them; I remember our food sliding up and down our tables.

Sometime during the night, the *Orion* was joined by its escorts, two Royal Navy destroyers. At first light of New Year's Day, the *Orion* was found by the Japanese air force and attacked. Fortunately, the destroyers put up a great barrage and prevented the aircraft from hitting their mark. The late Tom Irlam, speaking from his army speciality as an Air Defender, said: 'I am not surprised; as the aim of air-defence is to prevent the enemy interfering from the air with the conduct of operations on the ground, the navy did their stuff'.

The *Orion*'s intended route was to Sydney and Melbourne and then Perth (Fremantle). However, as enemy submarine activity made passage through the Lombok Straits dangerous, the Captain then charted a course through the Sunda Straits into the Indian Ocean to make Perth (Fremantle) the first port of call. Yvonne Heritage and Barbara Tulley both recalled how they frequently disappeared below decks when the warning siren of submarine attack sounded, locked in by the automatic doors, oblivious to what was really happening although they heard the sound of torpedoes skimming by.

Fortunately, the refugees reached the safety of Australia on 6 January 1942 – six days after they had escaped Singapore. This was considerable speed achieved by extraordinary means. As Sandy Lincoln said,

> After a while it was noticed that the *Orion* was going much faster, and this was because the Captain had decided to let out the ballast, something virtually unheard of, just in order to get out of those dangerous waters as fast as possible.

Still, the *Orion* hit a mine as it neared Australia, but it did not go off.

*

On disembarkation at Fremantle, a doctor stood at the top of the gangplank and examined everyone's wrists. Some refugees were temporarily housed in the Toc H or the Home for the Deaf and Dumb.

The Castells, now seven including the Pickthall children, were to spend the next two years in Australia. 'It would be many months before my mother and Aunt Joan received word of their husbands,' said Graem Castell.

Allan Proctor's family left the ship at Sydney and sought passage to New Zealand where they had relatives. In 1944, they returned to the UK on MV *Port Alma* via Panama, New York and convoy to Bristol. Only after the war did he learn that his father was killed in January 1942.

My way home to England with Mother was also along that general route, but via Melbourne.

*

When I began my research in 2006, a lot of information came to me but, at the time, I hadn't appreciated its significance. My initial challenge was to write the story for my family, not as a book for general publication. Some of this information was superfluous to the original intent. Fortunately I stored most. Whilst trawling through it again I found a copy of a memorandum from the Department of the Interior, (Victoria, Australia). It is couched in the usual formal language and titled 'Evacuees from Singapore Landed at Melbourne on 11th January, 1942, Ex *Orion*', and I quote:

> The Purser advised me that the people on board were voluntary evacuees and that each had paid his own fare… (National Archives of Australia)

On arrival at Melbourne, those disembarking had to register at the Town Hall where lodgings were arranged.

My wife and I had visited the magnificent Melbourne Town Hall for a concert. As we sat listening to the music of Beethoven and Dvorak I felt a chill. I turned my head and, despite the elegant surrounds, could not stop myself trying to imagine that day in January 1942. We had evaded disaster and there was a life ahead of us, but that evening I remembered the unhappiness of some of that life… The Dvorak was his *New World Symphony*, my mother's favourite, and mine too.

The memo about evacuees from Singapore continues:

> The passengers disembarked at about 3.30 pm and by 6.30 pm they had all proceeded to their accommodation. The hotels used were the Victoria Palace, the Federal Hotel, the Batman Hotel, Carlyon's Hotel and Hotel Windsor. These hotels were regarded as preliminary accommodation only: the evacuees will be found other accommodation as soon as possible at prices within their means. Accommodation is not easy to get in Melbourne and it would have been quite impracticable to have found at such short notice what might be termed final accommodation. I arranged for the hotel bills to be submitted to the Commonwealth Sub-Treasury at Melbourne for payment.

Our first and temporary billet was at 2 Grange Road, Toorak, where we lodged for probably no more than a week while something more permanent – 'Dandenong' – was being found by my mother.

I believe the Tweedie and Walker families must already have been at that Dandenong house waiting for us. In the records at the National Archives of Australia our Toorak address is given in full but the Dandenong one only said 'Dandenong'. On enquiry, the Archives told me that if one was going to a known address, friends or some such, the complete address was not entered in the records. Because of this it took me more than two years to trace the address and the story to that is worthy of mention.

Tim Walker, born after the war, thought he remembered the name of the accommodation as *Paradise Farm*, Dandenong. I made many efforts to find where the farm is or was but to no avail. We scoured possible localities for Paradise Valley, visited the Historical Societies, left notice-board messages, called at the pubs, looked at maps – but nothing.

Then, in March 2008, when Belinda was looking through drawers of old family photographs and cuttings not related to Pandora, she found an airmail envelope with most of the Dandenong address on it. It was postmarked 4 April 1942 sent by my mother to Gramma Bailey in New York. It contained a lock of my hair but not the letter. What a stroke of good luck. Mother must have given the envelope to Belinda many years earlier. But how did mother get it? Probably when she cleared her mother's house in 1976.

Some of the address of the sender is legible although the full name of the road is covered by the censors seal! We misread the address initially but after Belinda had slit the envelope and held it to the light, all was clear: *Rossmoyne Park*, Stud Road, Dandenong, Victoria, Australia.

We visited the house and discovered that whilst *Rossmoyne* has a large garden, it is not the five acres of the original bush property; it is now suburbia. Dandenong is some 25 kilometres south of east from Melbourne City, and Paradise Valley is in the Dandenong Ranges, not far from where I live. I have now found both houses and they remain, from the exterior, much as they were in January 1942.

In February 2011, Belinda and I dug out our old photograph albums, long consigned to the back of a cupboard hiding in another old suitcase. What should be amongst them but three albums compiled by my mother which she had passed on to us a great many years ago. Peter Tanner told me they are the albums my mother originally made for her mother, and 'rescued' them when clearing her house in Virginia in 1976. Altogether, there are 762 photographs of pre-war Singapore, Australia, America and other places, all from 1941 to 1947. As we went through them, we found photographs of people, many, but not all, named, and dates which confirmed or changed my previously held beliefs about this story.

The first surprise was to find photographs of Morag Symington with us at *Rossmoyne*. This means that her mother Ellen and twin brother Ian were with us. And there it was: a photograph of me with Ellen and Bobby Walker and another with Morag.

There are also photographs of Charles and Anne Tweedie with Vera, their mother, and others showing the Walkers and their baby, Susan, who was christened at the time, my mother being Susan's godmother.

Tim Walker confirmed that his father was already in Melbourne when Singapore fell and I think my father would have known that and even where he was staying. Consequently, I believe my father knew the *Orion* was making for Australia and that my mother knew to go to *Rossmoyne*.

Mother and I left by sea for America in May 1942 on the SS *Matsonia*. From the captions to the pictures in the album Mother prepared for her mother, it is clear that we arrived in San Francisco in early June. Mother wrote 'Farewell California' in the album dating it late June 1942. We went on to Maine to stay at *Prides Corner*.

In August 1942 we went to Ocean Park, Maine, and arrived in New York in early October 1942. There is a photo dated 10 October showing me with Mother, Gramma, Molly and 'Bum', the dog – a very happy family photograph indeed.

I have little record of the New York stay except a few old photographs of me on the roof of an apartment, and birthday ones of 3 January 1943. We must have left America soon after that, for the photos of us in England start on 1 March 1943. Peter Tanner thought we sailed on the *Queen Mary*, a recollection from something Mother said to him years ago.

*

I have wondered why my mother did not remain in America, but chose instead to take us on the journey to England under the blitz during the time when the U-boats were attacking ships in the Atlantic.

I believe my father told Mother that he would send her money to England so we must make haste there. When we left Singapore, my mother would have had some money, but it would have been sufficient only to get us to England and my father, if he knew our route, would hope Gramma Bailey might help and his parents too when we arrived in England. I am sure all did in their own way.

That my father had sent my mother money was substantiated by his will. It caught my attention when I first read it, although I didn't appreciate its full significance then. Item 5 of my father's will dated 25 July 1994 states that he sent his wife money in January 1942, being her compensation 'which amply reimbursed her for any loss she may have suffered'. He must have sent it before the fall of Singapore on February 15 (how could he have sent it afterwards?) and between our evacuation on 31 December 1941 and that February date. How, before the actual fall, did he know what was lost and what therefore he owed her?

The significance of the clause in my father's will is not just the evidence that money was sent, but how the clause was framed:

and I further declare and confirm that she can make no claim on me for War Damage Compensation from Malaya (1942 – 1945) as I sent her £350… which amply reimbursed her.

The clause answers a question raised in the story of E. J. H. Corner, but also raises questions about the character of the father I hoped to find.

*

While we were safely landed in Australia, my father remained in Singapore, a civilian government servant who was invalided out of the Singapore Volunteer Corp. With the capitulation of Singapore, he must have awaited the future with great uncertainty and concern.

I learned from the Singapore Oral History interview with George Alphonso, who was Horticultural Assistant in the Gardens before the war, that shortly before the fall my father was put in charge of the Gardens staff. All the seeds were taken for safe storage to the White House Hotel in Rochor Road, the intention being then to plant them in the 'vacant areas' as a source of fresh food. Alphonso commented:

> but we never had the chance. The Japs… At 9 in the morning [every day], the Jap planes were all over, bombing the areas, so we had to take shelter. We did very little planting actually.

George Alphonso vividly remembered one incident which shows my father's frame of mind at the time. The Japanese were almost in central Singapore, and the tension was high.

> This was at our White House Hotel… The ground floor was a bar and these Australian troops, they came in and they were boozing away. They were drinking. Corner came down, happened to come down and he was furious. He caught one of these chaps and banged him, pushed him against the door. He said, "You should be outside fighting!" He says, "What are you drinking here for?" He pushed them all out. And this shows that Corner… He's a very hot-tempered man.

And I comment: a man of deep conviction. My father wrote in his Royal Society personal records that

> I overcame my stammer in Feb 1942 when at last I felt in charge of myself. In the Botanical Gardens Singapore, I felt both repressed and deceived by R. E. Holttum (Director) and M. R. Henderson (Curator), they being my seniors. I did write to the Colonial Secretary – 'why should we be expected to grope after lights that have failed?' but the reply was discouraging – more reproof.

With the impending fall of Singapore, he must have felt that at last he was his own boss. Indeed, this is one of only a few references I can find of any admission that he had 'seniors'; and it might suggest that he knew what was to come for him. The truth is that he never completely overcame that stammer and comments in later years suggest the same. He stammered in 1960. I know that.

As doom approached for Singapore, my father was 36 and by this time his duties were wide and varied, not based only at the Gardens.

These last days of Singapore, when the Japanese pressed home their attacks, are written in countless books and reports but my father wrote graphically in *The Marquis* that

> in February 1942, after days and nights of incessant din, as artillery approached, bombings and sirens increased, and the town came under the ding-dong of mortar fire – "ding" as the mortar fired and "dong" as soon as it could be said the shell exploded.

Firing stopped at 3 pm on 15 February. Then quiet; an eerie peace descended over the death and destruction. The official surrender was completed by 5 pm.

My father had been itinerant, moving to and staying where his duties took him. He finally 'came to rest' at the Fullerton Building where the Governor and other officials had moved. This building stood at the mouth of the Singapore River and the Governor took office on the first floor; as Food Production Officer, my father found himself in the Agricultural office on the fourth.

The quiet of that Sunday afternoon was deceptive. Some dismantled cars, throwing parts into the sea off Jardine steps. The military of both sides were searching for deserters and prisoners of war and looting was rampant.

My father settled down for the night with his mind in turmoil; what was to happen to Singapore. What of all his work and was it already looted, even destroyed? He searched his mind as to how 'treasure houses of knowledge, which had no military significance, might be saved from what seemed surely to be a temporary occupation'.

If they were looted it was impossible to see how funds might ever be found to enable a fresh start – and news of looting during the past two months had been frequent; everything was smashed and destroyed, even before the Japanese had arrived.

He was particularly concerned about the Botanic Gardens, Raffles Museum, the libraries of Raffles College and the College of Medicine, Government offices and Government House, writing that 'the whole progress of science in the Malay peninsula seemed doomed'. The British in Singapore were now powerless with the allies hundreds, even thousands, of miles away, so my father decided, at that private and desperately lonely moment, to throw in his lot with the Japanese.

- XI -

THE NOTE

I knew of the rumour that my father had possibly been a collaborator of the Japanese during the war. My mother had mentioned it to me some 50 years ago, and beyond a brief moment of surprise, I gave it little thought.

Before I read the copy of *The Marquis* that he had put in Pandora, I knew absolutely nothing of my father's wartime experiences and little of his work in Singapore. His book led me to in-depth enquiries which revealed fascinating insights into his character, and some information which I almost wish I had not discovered about my parents' marriage.

I set about finding out once and for all whether my father had been a collaborator. I had to set the record straight, for better or worse, not least for my family and me.

On 16 February, the day after the surrender of Singapore, my father had tried to return to his house from Fullerton Building to collect all his manuscripts and drawings but was turned back by Japanese sentries 'with surprising courtesy'.

Information was coming through that British civilians were to be interned the next day and that they were to parade at 11 am on the cricket ground, the Padang, which was in front of the sea. They were to bring what baggage they could carry.

My father spoke to several foresters and agriculturalists in Fullerton Building about the vital need to ask the Japanese to help secure and save the collections and records in the Botanic Gardens, but he met a strong resolve that the British must stand together 'in custody and humility… in a fraternity that wealthy times had scorned'.

That night, in the Agricultural office, my father ate what he called his 'last supper' after which he went to bed, 'thinking… thinking… thinking… and fell asleep thinking'.

He woke 'with the first grey of dawn and was laughing and saying what a fool I am; of course… of course'. He had dreamed of seeing himself go to the Japanese authorities to explain the situation and being received with open arms. I think that to say he dreamed could have been thought a convenient way to explain the forthcoming events. It certainly was romantic writing but it also foreshadowed what essentially happened.

So, on 17 February, my father dressed and around 6.30 am hurried to see the Governor. At the door of the Governor's office, he met the Governor's aide-de-camp who, following orders, was on his way to order my father to see the Governor immediately.

In his office, Sir Shenton Thomas gave my father a pencilled note in which the Governor asked the Japanese authorities to preserve the scientific collections, libraries and matters of historic importance, particularly the Raffles Library and Museum and Botanic Gardens.

My father wrote: 'he handed me the note and, with a twinkle in his eye, charged me to deliver it'. Why did he write that the Governor had a 'twinkle in his eye' when handing over the note?

Brian Montgomery, when writing *Shenton of Singapore, Governor and Prisoner of War*, wrote to my father enquiring about the note. My father replied:

> I cannot recall the exact words of Sir Shenton's note; it was in my hands for only half a day. It was not addressed to me but to the Japanese Authority and was signed simply 'T. Shenton Thomas'.

My father told Montgomery that he didn't realise at the time to what this would lead. However, he remarked that the 'twinkle' was implying 'Do what you can'. I gave this a lot more thought and feel that it could also mean 'the plan is working'.

The reply to Montgomery was three years after *The Marquis* was published, and it is extraordinary that my father never gave details of the note in his own book.

He returned from Sir Shenton's office to show the note to his companions and to ask if any would go with him to the Japanese. This was in vain: all determined to stick together 'which I would not', my father wrote, 'and I saw that at heart they were not scientists'.

Thomas Kitching's entry for 17 February in his war and internment diary, published as *Life and Death in Changi*, states:

> EJH Corner is in charge of the storage of valuable records etc. to be put in the Raffles Library where they should be safe: he had heard of my 30 years diaries, photographs etc., and came to ask about them. So, on his instructions I labelled the suitcase SCIENTIFIC RECORDS OF T. KITCHING. CHIEF SURVEYOR. SINGAPORE. And deposited it in his room.

This adds credibility to the idea that there was a prepared plan of action in which my father had a role – or at least the contents of the note was being spread in Fullerton Building. If either is true, it is then sad that my father would be very soon branded as a collaborator.

In 1959, my father confided in Dr Peter Ashton, one of his research students. Peter wrote to me of my father's great concerns in February 1942.

How the senior members of the British community holed up in a building on the Collyer Quay [the Fullerton Building is on Collyer Quay] yet, as it became apparent that the city was lost, remained unwilling to approach the Japanese command.

When the British civilians left Fullerton Building for that parade on the Padang, my father locked himself in his fourth floor room in case the building was searched by the Japanese. He was determined to hide and stay. He could see the parade through a small window and around 1 pm observed that 'a long straggling column walked eastwards'. He didn't know their destination but the rumour was Changi Gaol. Of that trudge, he wrote: '[It]… must have been the saddest sight for the Singaporeans, the saddest in Singapore's history. I waited in uncanny loneliness after the commotion of weeks – as if Armageddon with all the devils of hell were at hand – until that slavish scene was concluded'.

As he 'rested' in the quiet of the heights of Fullerton Building, the enormity of the disaster began to strike home. My father realised that Singapore was lost and there was no hope of the British returning soon, if ever. The looting and senseless destruction had to be stopped and the places of knowledge made safe.

What wise words, what foresight. He was also far-seeing enough to realise that if or when the British returned, there would, as with all such occasions, be that window of opportunity when the looters would strike again and all that they might have achieved would be lost at the 12th hour. I believe he was aware of this possibility all through the Occupation, and his prompt actions when the British did return bear this out.

The British in Singapore were now powerless and this was when my father made his decision 'to throw his lot' with the Japanese. He wrote in *The Marquis* that he 'couldn't think of another choice'. He had not lived in Singapore to 'enjoy salary and pension, for there were better elsewhere'. He had gone to Singapore 'not for the social round which held no appeal' but to satisfy his driving urge 'to understand the complexity of the Malayan forest, to probe for myself what I have always regarded as the hypothesis of evolution'. A very brave decision, for the consequences might have been dire. He never expressed any doubt; he never wrote of uncertainty. His loyalty was to science.

Two Japanese particularly influenced my father during the years of the Occupation; Professor Hidezo Tanakadate (1884–1951), and Marquis

Yoshichika Tokugawa (1886–1976), the latter being the last lord of that most eminent clan which ruled Japan for so long. It was through their efforts, with help from just a few Europeans, and 'unnamed locals', that the invaluable records of and in Singapore were conserved. There were other Japanese who gave invaluable help, amongst them were Professor Kwan Koriba, Dr Yata Haneda and Lt. Tadamichi Koga. There could also have been a 'direct line' to the Emperor who could be considered the master-mind of it all.

Later that afternoon, my father took the Governor's note to the Japanese. To reach City Hall from Fullerton Building, he had to cross the Singapore River – the Stink River, as it was then commonly known. Its foetid smell was caused by the discharge of waste from the jumble of lighters moored in it and the rows of godowns that lined its shores. Here, Straits produce – the tropical products, mainly botanical, that were collected from jungles and plantations in the Malayan archipelago – was traded, bringing wealth and prosperity to Singapore which now lay in tatters. The main bridges – Elgin, Cavenagh, and Anderson – were guarded. Following a tip-off that a footbridge (long gone now) was left unguarded, he crossed the river in a journey that would take about eight to ten minutes on foot today. At City Hall, he ran into the Japanese Military Police, the *kempeitai*.

The Japanese soldiers could not understand why my father was there but one of them told him to sit down and offered him a cigarette. After an hour or so, my father recognised some Englishmen who were coming and going from the Municipality Office. He persuaded the soldiers to allow him to go to that office where he found the former president of the Municipality, Mr Rayman, who was arranging for various British people to remain out of internment in order to repair and maintain essential services at least until Japanese replacements arrived.

My father told Rayman why he was there, showed him the note, and asked for an urgent interview with the Japanese officials. Rayman immediately realised the importance of that slip of paper and, possibly forewarned by Sir Shenton, gave priority to my father to meet Kaoru Toyoda, formerly the Japanese consul in Singapore, then Director of the General Affairs Section of the Syonan Municipal Office.

Toyoda, whom my father described as a 'cultured and clever man', took the note and read it carefully. He then informed my father that a professor was arriving from Saigon to take charge of scientific affairs and that he should return at 10 am the next day. My father was then given an official pass and armband. He felt huge relief; he was 'safe' and there was progress although he had become prisoner 2307.

That a person appointed to take charge of scientific affairs would arrive immediately after the surrender of Singapore lends weight to my theory that the conservation of scientific and cultural material in Singapore was also pre-planned by the Japanese.

En route to Fullerton Building, my father realised that he was close to Hylam Street where, some days previously, he had taken his Chinese houseboy, Lee Moh Kwee, and family. Behind Lee's house was a dripping tap under which my father managed a sort of shower. All the reservoirs had been captured by the Japanese days before the surrender and what little water which reached Fullerton Building was needed for the hospital that had been set up there. Father gave Moh Kwee three of the four hundred dollars he had.

Upon his return to Fullerton Building, a sentry stopped my father. The soldier looked at his armband, spelled out 'Kona *san*' and waved him on. Looting had already started in the building. There were broken doors, strewn papers, and even photos of children crumpled into pages of a Bible. Father reflected that the looters were taking revenge on their colonial masters. The Agricultural Office had also been looted and his suitcase had been ransacked. As he gathered his things together and salvaged what he could, particularly pencils, paper and clothes – realising that they would have to last him for how long he knew not – he heard footsteps.

It was Mackintosh, a staff member of the Post Office that had occupied the ground floor of the Fullerton Building for many years. Mackintosh had been ordered to stay and await the Japanese arrival, and he invited my father to his flat at the top of the building. After depositing his repacked suitcases in the flat, my father returned downstairs where he unexpectedly met William Birtwistle. It appeared that Shenton Thomas had ordered Birtwistle to stay at his post because of his knowledge of the Japanese and fishermen.

My father told him his plans and why he too was in the building. Birtwistle was enthusiastic and explained that when he visited Japan before the war, he found the Japanese to have the highest regard for science.

Hidezo Tanakadate, the professor whom Toyoda said was coming from Saigon, arrived at City Hall minutes after my father left. Tanakadate wrote of his first meeting with Toyoda in Singapore in his memoir, *Achievements and Reminiscences*:

> I gave my name card to Mr Toyoda first. As soon as he saw my face, he said 'Mr Corner was just sent to you with this letter from the Governor-General'. Mr Toyoda handed me the letter and looked for Mr Corner in the crowd but he was not there anymore. "He will definitely be here by 10.00 am tomorrow morning. I would like you to seize and protect the Botanical Garden and the Museum with him", Mr Toyoda said... I replied to them, "I came here in order to conserve culture. The requisitioning of the Museum is my first objective". Everybody there, including ex-mayor of Singapore, Englishmen, and Japanese people, glanced at one another and looked pleased with my answer. Then they

came to shake my hand with strange face. It must be a surprise for the enemy that a scientist came from the university to conserve culture.*

Professor Tanakadate was appointed Director of the Raffles Museum and Botanic Gardens immediately after the professor received the note from Shenton Thomas. In *The Marquis*, my father wrote, 'this note, so precious to me, was taken by Professor Tanakadate to Tokyo in 1943 where, with all his own property, it was consumed in a fire that raged after an air raid'.

In 2000, I learned from Dr David Mabberley of an article in *Asahi Shimbun* about the note. He had written about it in his essay, 'A Tropical Botanist Finally Vindicated' published in the *Singapore Gardens Bulletin*.

I am grateful to Professor Tadashi Kajita, Chiba University, Tokyo, who led me to the newspaper article published in Japan on 9 April 1942.

The literal translation I received from Professor Kajita reads:

I truly hope that you would conserve the museum and the botanic garden at least. For that work, I hope you use Corner who was the ex-vice director of the Botanic Garden.

Tanakadate, to become known affectionately as The Professor in *The Marquis*, was described by my father as a 'quaint old gentleman with a long nose, large glasses, nodding head, thick untidy hair, and ugly face, who stooped in rumpled clothes, clutching a crumpled felt hat'.

A vulcanologist and geologist from Tohoku Imperial University of Sendai, he took an early opportunity to explain to my father why he had been sent to Singapore, and some of his background. His English was moderate but he claimed to know many British places and had lived in Italy. He said he had travelled extensively as an official Japanese delegate and had attended the Pacific Science Congresses in Vancouver and Batavia (Jakarta), the latter in 1929. He had come to occupied Singapore and Malaya to investigate the conditions in the Raffles Museum and other scientific institutions on behalf of the Emperor of Japan who, as a biologist, was deeply concerned about the safety of scientific material.

My father quickly realised that Tanakadate had taken a liking – 'a paternal liking' – to him, and he soon drew my father into the open with regard to what he wanted and hoped to achieve. In showing his full understanding, Tanakadate exclaimed with a sweep of his arm, that 'we must conserve'. Toyoda, who had been watching and listening to all of this then returned the Governor's note to Tanakadate which, my father wrote, 'sealed my destiny'.

* *I have reproduced this exactly in the Japanese style of translation that came to me courtesy of Deborah Holttum and Prof Mikiko Ishii.*

At that moment, Eric Holttum was brought into the room, having cycled from the Botanic Gardens. He was introduced to Toyoda and the Professor and was issued with an official pass and armband and instructed to return to the Gardens. Holttum was clearly unaware of the internment order. He had stayed at the Director's house, and that proved to be very important because he prevented much early looting.

Tanakadate wrote that on 18 February my father came and helped him. Thus, Tanakadate 'took over the museum and Botanic Gardens and began their conservation'.

So began a chapter in my father's life which has caused great controversy, very mixed views, hate, and from some, much praise. This was the end of those bewildering first days, those astonishing first days, and of which my father wrote that the Governor's note appeared to have had the desired effect. But there was one more important event to record. The Professor decided to call on General Yamashita for they had been students together at university and had remained friends.

The General had moved into a large and dominating house, *Rosemount*, in Grange Road. When the car stopped, my father was requested to stay in it while the Professor went to the door of the house. There was a sentry who paused occasionally to look into the car. As my father sat and reflected, he could not help 'weighing the acts of the Professor against the grim reports of the General'.

Some two hours later the Professor appeared and got into the car. With his characteristic sweep of the arm he said 'it is good'. The General had not only agreed with the Professor's action but he had sought to promote his plans.

I believe the General was already aware of those plans. My father wrote in *The Marquis*: 'we had moved not only from strength to strength but from bottom to top'.

Some time later, the Professor admitted to an order from General Tojo who had said that when the fall of Singapore was imminent, and it was clear that the might of Nippon would overrun and occupy Southeast Asia to Timor and New Guinea, all high commands were to hold the contents of museums and libraries and all scientific collections and these were to be maintained in the countries where they belonged for the benefit of the people.

This is another indication that the preservation of materials in Singapore by Marquis Tokugawa, Professor Tanakadate, and the ex-British colonial officers was pre-planned.

In 2009, Professor Yoji Akashi, who has access to diaries of Marquis Yoshichika Tokugawa, wrote to me:

There are several references in Tanakadate's book '*Nampo Bunka Shiset-su No Sesshu*' (Saving Cultural Assets in Singapore) about your father and Birtwistle. Some references overlap with your father's account in *The Marquis*. On 19th February, Corner visited Tanakadate following Toyota's introduction at Municipality Bldg. On 18th February, Maj. General Manaki Tadanobu, Director General of the Military Government, ordered Tanakadate to take over the administration of the Botanic Gardens and the museum. Tanakadate appointed Corner as his secretary and interpreter, the effective date being February 20th.

In this same book Tanakadate wrote 'Corner was given the task of increasing food production, Birtwistle recovering the fishing industry'. So, I conclude, Birtwistle was in the plan.

As a first step to conservation, my father suggested to the Professor that notices, similar to those put up by the Japanese Military Authority on requisitioned buildings, should quickly be put on the doors of the Raffles Museum and Library, the herbarium and the Botanic Gardens, as well as various offices in Fullerton Building where there were also large quantities of unpublished records. Toyoda immediately helped by offering a small Municipal car to the Professor for the purpose. In the Agricultural office in Fullerton Building, the Professor wrote the notices forbidding entry using the back of the many papers scattered on the floor. My father posted them on the doors of the relevant offices.

They met Birtwistle in the Fisheries Office and the Professor listened to him intently with the occasional nod of his head. They went on to Mackintosh's flat where the three had a simple lunch. 'It all seemed so easy and yet so incredible', my father observed. On 21 February, Tanakadate requested that William Birtwistle join them at the museum.

My father was surprised that the unassuming Tanakadate could carry such weight among the 'smart uniforms' of the senior Japanese military. It would seem that he was given full authority for his assigned tasks.

During one of their early visits to the museum, Tanakadate and my father met the chief clerk of the museum, Quan Ah Gun, whom my father greatly respected. My father had known him since 1929 and initially thought his name was 'Argon'. Tanakadate was wary of all Chinese but quickly summed up Ah Gun and, liking him, appointed him as chief clerk of his new establishment – the museum, library, and Botanic Gardens.

In his diary entry of 12 June 1942, Ah Gun wrote that two Japanese officers came to the library which was next door to the museum. He quietly refused them entry saying that the library was closed to strangers on Professor Tanakadate's instructions. The officers went away without complaint. Ah Gun continued 'at that time I didn't recognise the Marquis and his secretary Ishii'.

In 2011, Osman Latiff who had worked before the war in the Gardens and knew something of my father told me that the Japanese military took no notice of my father. The Japanese scientists had full command of the British three – Holttum, Birtwistle, and my father – and the military were so informed.

Perhaps that it was with this knowledge that my father and Birtwistle

began to sequester material that might attract unwanted attention such as letters of Stamford Raffles, which were hidden in the rafters [of the museum] and retrieved in 1945, and the golden Kris of Malacca which was placed in a safe. Eventually the marble statue of Queen Victoria from Government House and portraits (mostly of English notables) from Government House, the Colonial Secretary's Office and Victoria Memorial Hall were placed in the museum for safe-keeping. They also realised that the many and substantial private libraries were in acute danger so they drew up a list of valuable libraries and systematically collected and deposited the books in the museum building. By the end of March 1942 an estimated 40,000 books had been saved and by the end of the year the figure was doubled.

*

The Burmese campaign was still under way when Singapore fell. In December 1941, Frank Kingdon-Ward, a good friend of my father who had stayed several times with us in our Cluny Road home, was in Singapore on some mission details of which he would not divulge. As a captain in the British military, he had earlier made a number of visits of exploration to the eastern Himalayas – including Burma – and I have to wonder if he was mapping key areas of Burma for the British who were foreseeing the surely imminent battles, knowing the Japanese would make a big push for India.

During that December 1941 visit to Cluny Road, Kingdon-Ward was writing up his account of the flora of the Burmese frontiers when, very suddenly, he was called back to England. He left in great haste, without even saying farewell to my father, or my mother, or myself, and he even left behind his diaries and maps which my father found on his desk!

During the early days of the Occupation my father recovered the Kingdon-Ward material. However, he was worried that should the records fall into the hands of the Japanese Military, they would both implicate Kingdon-Ward and almost certainly himself. My father confessed all to Tanakadate who, after listening carefully, told him to say nothing. This was a relief and that at least told him something of the Professor's thoughts of the military. Tanakadate's reply also said something of the importance of my father, and indeed the other ex-colonial officers, to the Japanese scientists and their mission in Singapore.

While Tanakadate occupied the Director's house, Holttum, my father and various Japanese officers, officials and translators were assigned the Assistant Director's house – our old house. My father used to get up before dawn to read the reports of British and Australian officers which had been left on the tables where they were being translated into Japanese. Often he would be asked to explain words and passages by the translators; he had somehow already established a trust.

Holttum had told my father that our house – a distance away and across the road from the Director's house, each out of sight of the other – had been looted by the Gardens' labourers. Yet, my father had wondered why Holttum had not prevented that and had not made efforts to rescue the numerous irreplaceable papers and paraphernalia.

Things lay everywhere in the house and garden and, as my father and Tanakadate arrived, some labourers were still there removing things. My father gathered together what he could, particularly things of scientific value, all under the watchful eye of Tanakadate.

Among the material saved were those that A. H. Church's daughter had given my father during his home leave of 1938 – unpublished notes, some paintings, the original drafts of lectures, and an unpublished manuscript on British marine algae. The packages containing Church's papers and my father's own scientific notes seemed to have been the last items to have attracted the looters' attention.

They were strewn on the floor, under the porch, down the drive, and around the garden, as if the looters had been taken by surprise; many bore the marks of military boots, not the gym-shoes of the Japanese soldiery.

My father gathered up everything and took them in Tanakadate's car to the Gardens' office. There, they were packed again and sealed with Tanakadate's chop.*

Clearly, Tanakadate was happy to see my father save some of his work papers, and this made the Professor ever more determined to conserve. Conversely, General Percival and those directing the defence of Singapore were clear that if the city fell, a scorched earth policy was to be followed so that nothing of value, either military or civilian, would be left for the conquerors. As with so many of the plans to defend Singapore, this also failed.

I note that my father said that scientific papers were strewn about as if the looters had been surprised. I wonder might Holttum had, after all, discouraged them?

* These papers were returned to my father after the war. They were, by David Mabberley, deposited at the Bodleian Library in 1975.

In *The Marquis*, my father made an interesting remark when describing this episode. He said that he left many other more personal items like cutlery, towels and the like so that 'the finger of jealousy' could not be directed at him. I pondered this comment. Who did he think might be jealous, and why? Some of those items were undoubtedly my mother's. Did he not care about that? After all, he had taken care to hide the Kingdon-Ward records and the Landon's jewellery.

About ten days after the surrender, a Japanese Professor of Hydrobiology from Shanghai University came to the museum with three officers. My father was asked to take them to the Sailors Institute, the suggestion being that wireless sets were being collected by the Military Police and stored there. At the Institute, my father was requested to show them the Chart Room. Following a conspicuous sign in English, they came to a large room filled with maps and charts! The Japanese Naval intelligence had been informed of this room, and the officers started gathering papers, all the while chatting and laughing. My father realised that all those maps and charts of the Pacific and Indian Oceans were vital to the Japanese in the next stage of their military advance.

No effort had been made by the British to destroy this nautical library; the shambles in this Chart Room was due to the scramble by British and Australian fugitives who looked for any map that would help them to escape by sea from Singapore.

- XII -

AT WORK IN SYONAN-TO

As March 1942 progressed, a return to some kind of normality was beginning to happen. Professor Tanakadate had managed to affiliate his 'institute', the Gardens and museum, with the Military Administration and particularly the Food Control Office of Malaya. Birtwistle and my father were introduced to the Food Controller, a Korean called Hironaga, who my father described as being short and formidable with sharp features and high, flushed cheeks. Birtwistle was to be his fisheries adviser and my father was given the responsibility for fruit and vegetables, under the supervision of a Japanese official. The Professor wrote:

> Secretary Corner, who was a Commissioner for Food Production before the war, became an assistant to the Director of Food and got involved in increasing food production. The former Fisheries Director and currently curator of the museum, Mr Birtwistle, also became an assistant to the Food Department and worked half a day for the city authorities. Mr Corner made researches on suitable locations for growing vegetables, the size of plots, and other facilities. He also opened the warehouse belonging to the British which contained agricultural tools and fertilizers, distributed them to the Food Department, the Botanic Gardens and the former Governor's Residence.
>
> Together with me, he also formulated policies on the protection of model vegetable gardens which were started in various parts of Singapore before the war began. We continued to cultivate a model vegetable garden which we had made on the south side of the west gate in the Botanic Gardens, and we made new ones on the north side as well. We improved the vegetable garden on the north side of the palm fields. The tennis court in front of the Director's residence was turned into a tapioca plantation. This was our vegetable production plan which we reported to the city authorities.
>
> On the fishery side, I ordered Birtwistle to supply fish to the market, following a request by the City's Director of Food and the Director of

Commerce at the end of February. At that time, fish was caught on the eastern coast, but most of them were purchased by the military, so very little appeared on the market. Birtwistle, accompanied by two Chinese fishery supervisors who were his former subordinates, met the fishermen. He heard that the catch decreased by 20 percent since nocturnal lighting was banned at sea. Fortunately, ice-makers were still in business, so it was possible for fish to come to the market in the morning.

We gave out ID cards to fishermen, and that number exceeded 2,000. Fishing ground was expanded to the city's western coast as well. By the beginning of March, two tons of fish arrived at the market every day, so the administration of this was transferred back to the city authorities. At the same time, Corner and Birtwistle were formally appointed by the city authorities as officers. These issues are not directly related to the work of the Botanic Gardens, but I am reporting them because under British rule the Gardens was involved in wartime food and production plans.

My father and Birtwistle prepared reports and advised on local customs; they took Hironaga to see the markets, market gardens and fishing stakes. For this work, which normally was mornings only, my father and Birtwistle were paid $50 per month (about £6) by the Food Control Office; this was really not a salary or wage but in lieu of rations. The jobs lasted around three months when the funding ran out.

The Municipality took over and wages were again paid but my father and Birtwistle were transferred into a new department which became attached to the Department of Education. This restored Birtwistle to his beloved fisheries and my father, although describing his duties as tedious, acquired through the work important contacts in businesses and associations which were to help as the days and months of Occupation went by. He visited many organisations and thus vitally learned about all the smaller streets and alleys of Singapore – the back-doubles in today's language.

My father had a role in rice rations. In the event of a siege, which was thought would last only six months, Singapore had agreed to supply rice to the Rhio Archipelago south of Singapore! 'With a map from the Dutch Consulate,' wrote my father in *The Marquis*, 'I plotted the requirements, island by island, as I estimated the populations in the mysterious region'. With clerical assistants 'whose enthusiasm waxed at our novel investigations, we sampled imports in the pythoned crypts of the Stink River, shuddered at the bloody stalls of the Muslim abattoirs, woke the sleeping dough-boys on their tables where they sprinkled currants deftly along the twists of dough – a currant per loaf – and so defied with fancy bread the Food Controller's baking orders, and discovered why the guts of Changi pigs, fed military swill, obtained a better price than those of vegetarians from Johore'.

*

Hironaga had a passion for pineapples. He wanted to visit an estate and asked my father to arrange for one. The one selected was in Johore not only because it was larger than those estates in Singapore but also particularly because the journey there would take them over the Causeway where my father could see something of what had happened in what he called 'the mysterious assault on Singapore'. The eastern part of the peninsula towards Kota Tinggi was ruled out because of the presence of Chinese guerrillas, so it was decided to go to the district between Gunung Pulai and Pontian. In early March 1942, the party made up of Hironaga, his young assistant Lieutenant Kondo, a Malay driver and my father, set off in the Professor's car.

Only a short section of the Causeway had been blown up, at the Johore end, and had easily been repaired with planks of wood from the nearby sawmills around Johore Bahru. The town was deserted and showed signs of the effects of war and looting. The highway to the north was also deserted and they turned off the road to Gunung Pulai reservoir which was out of bounds because British or Australian troops were thought to be still circling the forest! The stench of decay soon became very apparent; my father discovered later that it came from the heaps of Chinese corpses – bodies of the massacred workers in the rubber and pineapple estates of Ulu Tiram – which had been thrown into the thickets by the road. The village of Gelang Patah, which was where the Japanese broke the lines, was devastated. My father knew this village well being on his route to visit his friend W. G. Lloyd at the Pendas Estate. Houses were looted and the rubble of war lay everywhere; there were piles of tins, bottles and discarded military equipment and even rifles and machine guns. This had been Yamashita's camp.

Just beyond the devastation there stretched to the horizon a field of pineapples. The Japanese were astonished and when the car stopped on the verge, Hironaga and Kondo jumped out, drew their swords and slashed off the heads of pineapples, slicing them and after laying down their swords began feasting on the fruit. At this moment, my father had a violent thought: he would grab their swords, cut off their heads and leg it into the jungle which he knew very well; the bodies could be hidden easily where the smell of death was emanating and the car driven into the Pendas River. Then he realised he would have to kill the driver whom he had known for years.

In that moment, he also realised that if he so acted he risked his friends in Singapore, not least the trust of the Governor, and the good work only just begun would be for naught. He hesitated and the moment was gone. The Japanese had eaten their fill and were loading the car. They returned without incident except that later, when my father mentioned the fleeting idea to Birtwistle, he was flabbergasted that E. J. H. Corner could have thought of such a thing.

*

Professor Tanakadate had arrived in Singapore just two days after the fall, seemingly in some hurry, direct from Saigon. The Marquis Yoshichika Tokugawa, on the other hand, journeyed at his leisure down the Malay Peninsula visiting the Sultans on his way, to be sure he knew where their loyalties lay, and to establish himself with them before arriving in Syonan-to as Supreme Consulting Adviser to the Japanese Military Administration and as Civil Governor of Malaya.

Sultan Ibrahim of Johore had became a personal friend of the Marquis during the 1920s when they met during the Sultan's visit to Japan. Tokugawa had in fact visited Malaya on two occasions long before the war, and had formed friendships with the Sultans, and had come to understand their histories and problems. In his autobiography, *The Last Lord*, he remarked that he was critical of the British who, unlike the Japanese, showed no attempt to study the people and culture of those they conquered. He paid particular attention to the Sultan of Johore on both the visits.

One of these visits was in May 1921. As recorded in an edition of the *Asahi Shimbun* newspaper, the Marquis was, on arrival, unexpectedly met by the Sultan of Johore who invited him on a tiger hunt. When the Marquis returned to Japan in July, he brought with him maps and 'materials of the jungle' he collected. When the Japanese invaded Malaya, he accompanied General Yamashita's troops and was warmly received by Sultan Ibrahim when they reached Johore Bahru at the end of January 1942. General Yamashita and his officers then stationed themselves at the Sultan's residence, Istana Bukit Serene, and the state secretariat building, Sultan Ibrahim Building, to plan for the invasion of Singapore.

My father wrote that the Marquis 'was not an agent of the military or in any way ruled by politics; however, he had, over time, grown to know and become interested in Malaya'. I have now to question this comment.

When Japan entered the war in December 1941, the Marquis proposed to the War Department in Tokyo that he should be sent to Southeast Asia to make sure the Sultans were safe from any military rape and interference. He argued that his experience and awareness of court Malay made him the ideal man to assure them. General Tojo, not being familiar with the customs and nuances of Malaya, duly appointed the Marquis, giving him the rank of General. The Marquis arrived in Singapore soon after the fall, and the Professor reported to him daily, usually in the evening, to discuss actions and plans.

One evening, my father was invited to meet the Marquis. "Should I bow?" he asked the Professor who had already instructed him in that etiquette. "Follow me," was the reply. Dressed only in shorts, shirt, stockings and shoes, my father found himself bowing to a most distinguished general dressed immaculately, in high boots and carrying a long sword. As the bow was returned, my father noticed a short, middle-aged man with thinning hair, a pale complexion, strong nose and 'kind reassuring eyes'. The short exchange was in Malay and my father was impressed by the welcome.

This record of my father's first meeting with the Marquis, published in 1981 in my father's book, is at variance with what he confided to Dr Peter Ashton in Brunei in 1959 as they prepared for the Mount Kinabalu Expedition. Peter was one of a very few to have that special trust from my father, and during an informal evening chat, my father had reminisced about his war experiences. Peter wrote to me about what he was told of the first meeting with the Marquis:

> In due course, he [Corner] was led to meet Marquis Tokugawa, Japanese comptroller of all learned institutions within the captured nations, and emissary of the Emperor, whom Corner consequently had to approach on all fours.

On all fours! This is quite different from my fathers' description in his book. I do think that his recollections are tinged with licence – when it suited him.

*

Professor Tanakadate, in his book *Nampo bunka shisetsu no sesshu* recorded the arrival in Singapore from Saigon of Tadamichi (Chuga) Koga of the Japanese army's veterinary department. Koga was well known in Japan as being the Director of the Ueno Zoological Garden (Tokyo Zoo). Given the rank of lieutenant though he disliked soldiering, he had been sent to Singapore to inspect the zoological collections in the museum. He was soon co-opted by the Professor to be one of his advisers because of his international experience, knowledge of biology, command of English, and most important, his friendliness.

Koga's diary records that he went to the museum on 14 March and met Professor Tanakadate for the first time. He also stated that he met my father on that same day. My father, however, writing in *The Marquis*, said that he and Birtwistle were introduced to Koga towards the end of February 1942. More inaccuracy in *The Marquis*, though of little importance.

Koga's diary entry for 17 March stated that 'Dr Corner drove me to Sea View Hotel where we met the Marquis'. On 21 March, 'I went with Corner to the house of an English zoologist who had lived in Singapore, and brought out the books'. This was the house of M. J. F. Tweedie.

Tweedie's *Poisonous Animals of Malaya* was in the process of being printed at the Malayan Publishing House in Singapore when Singapore fell. Dr Koga and my father retrieved many copies from the looted premises at the end of March 1942; others were found in Kuala Lumpur which Koga had bound at his own cost. He sent five hundred copies to the Museum later that year.

Another book that was saved was Colin Fraser Symington's *Foresters Manual of Dipterocarps* about the main timber trees of Malaya. Symington had worked in Malaya from 1927 to 1942, and my father had known him since 1929. This scientifically important book was issued from the Museum by the Japanese towards the end of 1943.

*

 Koga's official residence was the Assistant Director's house in the Gardens which he shared with Holttum and my father. (My father had in fact lived in that house, a house near the museum or in Lermit Road as 'a sort of commercial traveller'.) Koga described Holttum as being 'very silent' and my father as 'still young and spoke a lot in a stuttering manner'. So my father's stammer had not fully left him in 1942.

Living under the same roof gave my father and Holttum a chance to get to know and understand Koga. Evening conversations were animated and far ranging, including once, after dinner, of 'singing the songs and cries of birds of Britain and Malaya'. Koga responded in good voice and the evening air was momentarily filled with the calls of the night-jar, the cuckoo and others. Koga also recorded that 'Mr Corner and I sometimes played the piano at the residence with a single finger' – a duet of single-fingers perhaps!

There was clearly a friendly relationship, so it is strange that my father wrote in *The Marquis* that he used to polish Koga's boots. If he had been so ordered, that might be different, but my father doesn't say that; he writes as if it's the most normal thing in the world.

On 10 March 1942, when General Yamashita visited the Botanic Gardens, my father's quick thinking saved Koga from embarrassment or more. As the preparations were almost complete it was noticed that there was no flag-pole. My father had a massive bamboo cut and positioned in time for the Japanese flag to be hoisted.

*

During this active month of March 1942, when the systems and routines were being set up by the Japanese scientists in Singapore, my father joined the Marquis on a motor launch tour of Keppel Harbour. On request, my father pointed out places of interest whilst trying to hide his astonishment at the number of Japanese freighters in port. He counted some 120 freighters which were over 5,000 tons, all being loaded with the spoils of war.

This was the harbour from which mother and I had left just nine weeks or so earlier, yet my father makes no reference to that evacuation at a point in his writing where such reference, even oblique, might be logical.

The grounds of Government House, once the official residence of the Governor of Singapore, were managed by the Botanic Gardens and continued to be throughout the Japanese Occupation, though it was used as an official guesthouse, presumably for very important people. Although the Gardens were under the supervision of my father, Professor Tanakadate sought a supervisor for the grounds of Government House. He was recommended the wife of the Swiss Consul to Singapore, Mrs Gritli Arbenz, by Mamoru Shinozaki of the Foreign Ministry. Mrs Arbenz, a renowned socialite in Singapore, was a graduate of the botanical college in Switzerland and had been living on the island for 25 years. The Professor did employ her to supervise the maintenance of the former Governor's residence and also to look after the Museum.

In May to June of 1942, the Professor went to Sumatra, leaving his duties to Mrs Arbenz. He reported:

> Ms Albenz suffered from nervous breakdown during my absence. She was upset by the dramatic changes in the past year. She had no news from her three daughters in Australia, their house being destroyed by the Australian Army and natives. She could just about communicate with the Japanese, but she could not bear the new life. Nevertheless, she came to the residence every morning at half past nine and looked after the flowers.

The Swiss Consul Arbenz was strongly anti-British and was included on the Far East Combined Bureau's security list as a risk. He was also on the Singapore Police's Special Branch risk list. I wonder if Tanakadate knew of this and was the appointment made for the knowledge she had of the British?

In *The Marquis*, my father told of a plot involving Mrs Arbenz to arrest and turn him over to the military police. My father was with Harold Northunt, former Registrar-General of Statistics, and William Birtwistle in the Museum, awaiting the return of Tanakadate, when a large car, Japanese registered, drove up and parked outside. 'With a bound of a tiger', my father wrote, 'a Japanese leaped out followed by Mrs Arbenz and her malicious grin!'

The Japanese was Mamoru Shinozaki, the pre-war Press Attaché at the Japanese Consulate. Shinozaki had been arrested by the British on 21 September 1940. He had been under surveillance by the Singapore Special Branch for some time and was found guilty of two charges of acting in a way prejudicial to the interests of the British Empire. He was fined S$1,000 and given three years of rigorous imprisonment. He was released when the Japanese took Singapore.

Shinozaki seized Birtwistle, the closest to him. Mrs Arbenz shook her head; he then seized Northunt, who was a big man, but Mrs Arbenz 'simpered' something and smiled. Shinozaki was about to seize my father when in came Tanakadate who both Shinozaki and Arbenz had presumed was not there. He realised what was happening, spoke animatedly to Shinozaki and bundled him and Mrs Arbenz into the car which drove off. It transpired that Professor Tanakadate had realised there was a plot, had secreted himself in the Museum and laid in wait behind the door.

Professor Mikiko Ishii, when she was translating *The Marquis* – rather was writing her version – sought Shinozaki's explanation for his relations with Mrs Arbenz. Shinozaki replied:

Immediately after the fall of Singapore I visited Mr Arbenz, Consul General of Switzerland who represented interests of the Japanese Government following the outbreak of the Pacific War, for receiving items and the Imperial Crest of Chrysanthemum kept at the Consulate General. After the occupation, I gave him assurance to protect his residence and personal safety as well as provide the Arbenzs with convenience and assistance… One day Mrs Arbenz came to my office complaining that an Englishman had insulted her. She took me forcefully to the Museum. That was the first time I met Corner-san. There was an air of tension because neither of us knew what was going on. I had no power to arrest enemy personnel nor to intern them. In short, it was Mrs Arbenz's demonstration to show off her air of importance through borrowed authority. It was a poor theatrical act by which we were fooled by the hysterical lady.

My father never spoke badly of, nor had ill feelings for, Shinozaki until after that unpleasant incident. In his book *Syonanto Monogatori*, Professor Togawa wrote about meeting Shinozaki and asking why he and my father didn't get along when they shared a common responsibility to save people and culture from the war. Shinozaki replied: 'I regret for my haughty manner at that time. Corner-san also had some misunderstanding. He thought I was a military police officer as I was wearing a military-like uniform. I don't think I spoke to him with an abusive language nor did I strike him'.

On 20 June 1942, Mrs Arbenz was involved in a car accident. The Professor and my father rushed to the hospital to find that she did not survive. My father had written disparagingly of Mrs Arbenz in *The Marquis*, describing her as 'Sweet as honey, then venomous and malevolent, she turned on helpers to accuse them of her own shortcomings; vituperation she had, not green fingers… She slapped faces and called the Muslim gardeners pigs until nearly all our trusted helpers were threatening to resign… Because I tried to soften these attacks I became the *bete noir*'. Some thought my father was the culprit behind the accident. I think not. He was never stupid.

*

Professor Tanakadate's book contains a short note about my father's involvement in the development of the Shonan Shrine on a hillock behind the Ford Factory where Percival surrendered Singapore to Yamashita. The shrine commemorated the Japanese soldiers who perished during the Battle for Singapore. The colonel responsible for the building of the shrine ordered the planting of trees in the area for he had plans of a forestry park in the future.

He called on Mr Norn [Nuen], manager of the Penang Botanical Gardens, from the prisoner-of-war camp, and he asked him and my father to design the new park [called *Syonan Jinja*]. They advised that trees should be brought from the Botanic Gardens. Water lilies were also to be moved to the pond in front of Shonan Shrine. The POWs tried to replant some trees, but because they were not familiar with tropical forestation, the plants did not grow very well. The landscaping of the shrine was completed in December 1942.

The Professor also wrote about how Marquis Tokugawa became the Director of the Botanic Gardens and Museum, thus sealing the relationship between my father and the Marquis.

On August 28th [1942] Marquis Tokugawa, advisor to the Malay Military Authorities, volunteered to take up the posts of director of the Botanic Garden and the Museum. Enough groundwork had already been carried out, so I had no hesitation about leaving the job to Marquis Tokugawa who is a botanist by training, especially with Mr Akira Satoh as his assistant.

These writings of Professor Tanakadate were amongst the many things that came to me via Robin Miller. All had originally been supplied to Robin by Professor Mikiko Ishii who worked on a Japanese version of *The Marquis*. It is interesting to have the point of view of Professor Hidezo Tanakadate. They show a true scientist and his sympathy for his employees; such a contrast to the Japanese General and the military. I conclude that he, like my father, was a romantic and my father respected him and the Marquis because they were dedicated scientists – the Japanese men of science as he wrote of them in that introduction to Symington's book. My father, on the other hand, hated the Japanese military and said so frequently.

The Japanese military police, the *kempeitai*, seemed 'unconcerned' about the 'free' civilian British scientists because Marquis Tokugawa, in the early days of occupied Singapore, 'took a stand against the opposing views of employing the British scholars'. According to Professor Yoji Akashi (who has access to diaries of the Marquis), the military police, fearful of subversive activities, had complained to Tokugawa about allowing them to continue their research. Tokugawa dismissively replied 'Isn't the Japanese Army strong enough to counter their subversive activities?'

Still, according to Akashi, Professor Tanakadate was glad to see Lt Koga arrive. He had sent Koga, now a military lieutenant in uniform, to live with Holttum, Birtwiste and my father so that it would appear to the military, the *kempeitai* in particular, that the British were kept under surveillance.

*

As the Emperor of Japan was an avid biologist, Koga was keen to send a collection of bird skins, molluscs and marine animals to him. The bird skins were selected by Koga who took my father's advice in not picking type-specimens and rarities. Father chose the molluscs and the marine animals which he and Koga had collected from Pulau Blakang Mati (now Sentosa Island). These were important collections, for the Emperor was a specialist in marine biology and they had to be carefully recorded as to when and where they were found. The visit to the island was made with caution because there were land mines and the areas to search were limited. According to my father's record in *The Marquis*, the state of the sea was appalling. For three or four miles south of Singapore it was full of human ordure; 'dead rats, cats, dogs and human bodies flowed from the rivers. The high-water level on the beaches was a strip of filth'.

The challenge of sorting, labelling, packing and being sure all was clean kept Koga, my father, and Holttum busy for quite a time. They packed, unpacked and repacked. Professor Akashi tells me of an episode recorded by Koga in his diaries relevant to that process of packing.

My father, Holttum and Koga were bottling samples of sea shells and sponges in alcohol when Koga asked them to bring pieces of cloth for packing. Koga checked the pile of cloth that was brought and found amongst them old socks.

"Throw them away; not to be used for packing," Koga said.

Holttum replied, "The socks have been disinfected and will be clean."

My father said, "They are thoroughly disinfected with alcohol and should be no harm."

Koga responded, "The used socks, even if they are clean, cannot be used because the samples are to be presented to the Emperor."

My father and Holttum, remaining incomprehensible with the explanation, asked, "Doesn't the Emperor put on stockings?"

This episode struck Koga. It showed him that there was 'a difference in the national characters between Japan and Britain'. Here is an example of culture or logic difference. I am surprised that my father and Holttum didn't know that; after all Birtwistle was acquainted with the Japanese way.

At last all was correct and Koga's commanding officer gave it clearance; the collection travelled with Koga to Saigon and hearing no more it was assumed all reached the Emperor safely.*

Of this collection and dispatch to Emperor Hirohito, my father wrote in his Royal Society papers that 'it filled me with hope in those anxious times that, with imperial supervision, we could conserve the scientific records of the colony'. The Royal Society papers also records an earlier collection for the Emperor – in 1929, soon after my father started work in Singapore – that would cast light on my father's cooperation with the Japanese during the war: '[A] Japanese botanist (Dr Yoshikadzu Emoto) arrived in Singapore to collect them [slime-moulds] for His Majesty and it fell to me to lead him to suitable locations on the island'. This is evidence that the Emperor was aware of the British scientists and my father at the Singapore Botanic Gardens way before the Japanese Occupation of Singapore.

Lt Koga's next assignment for Tokyo was to recapture as many animals as he could find from those that had escaped from Rangoon Zoo and send them to Japan. The giraffe was caught some distance from the zoo and was returned by train; every time the train came to a bridge it stopped, the giraffe's head and neck lowered and it passed safely. 'How different', my father wrote, 'from the other news of fighting coming from Burma'.

Koga introduced my father and Birtwistle to two senior colleagues who were recognised by the white gloves which they wore even in the heat of Singapore. Colonel Hamada was a regular visitor to the Museum and he studied the collection of snakes. General Takahashi, who spoke English extremely well, was Commanding Officer of the Veterinary Service and whenever he met my father and Birtwistle he asked after their families.

In the middle of 1943, General Takahashi came to the Gardens to look for my father. He was walking up the road to the band stand when a military car drew up and out stepped the General, wearing white gloves as usual. Also as usual, he asked after the family. He gave my father a tin of '555' cigarettes that had become very difficult to find and took a photograph of him so that my father could send it to his family.

My father wrote in *The Marquis*:

And the years have not dimmed this memory. Where my family was I knew not. Brief letters told of voyages, newspapers of sinkings; whether they had arrived I had to banish from my thoughts.

How those words say so much. Yet he wrote 'where my family was I knew not', not where my wife and child (son) was! Where are those brief

---

* After the Japanese surrender in 1945, all the specimens were returned and ticked off the duplicate list that had been left at the museum. Birtwistle remarked that the whole affair had been proof that, as long as scientists ran the museum, it would never be looted.

letters and where were we supposed to have arrived? Did he know our intended destination? I am sure he knew where we hoped to go. Nowhere can I find his mentioning that the £350 he sent was collected. The photograph taken of my father by Takahashi came; it was kept because of the uncertainties of the POW mail and Mr Birt took it to England in October 1945, over two years later.

This is the only reference that I have found where my father mentions his family, even by implication. After a lot of thought, I believe I can appreciate that under those circumstances one simply has to 'banish thoughts' and press on with whatever life is offering; yet, reading so many books of the war in Malaya like Thomas Kitching's *Life and Death in Changi* and Adrian Wood's *If This Should be Farewell*, I find that most in that situation think of their families and write about them if only to hope all is well and help to keep up their spirits; indeed they try to find out about them. My father never referred to letters home; did he write any from occupied Singapore? There was none in Pandora.

Professor Akashi told me of an entry dated 2 April 1943 in the Marquis' diary which says that my father received a letter from 'Mrs Corner of her safe arrival home in England'. No mention of me but at least he did know, by 2 April 1943, that we were safe. Mother wrote quite promptly for we had arrived in England late February/early March that year. I wonder how she addressed the envelope, how she knew where he was?

*

A certain Japanese soldier whom my father soon came to call 'the little soldier' became a regular visitor to the Gardens. In *The Marquis* there is a picture of him, with my father, in the front of the house at Hinton Way. It is wrongly captioned, 'in the Singapore Botanic Gardens'.

The 'little soldier' was Pte Shuichi Asakura. He was a small man, always in a hurry and, I think, remained a Private throughout the war. Over that time, he amassed a large collection of dried plants which Birtwistle kept for him at the Museum. He was a keen botanist and wanted both the Malay and English names. On one visit, he showed them a thorny specimen which he wanted to identify, and which he was told was *Bougainvillea*. After a pause, he muttered Bougainville many times and couldn't understand how they knew of the fighting on Bougainville Island!

My father wrote: 'his attitude to us was as pupil to teacher, even son to father'. A lasting friendship ensued, well into peace time.

This is the second reference my father makes to relationship. Of Tanakadate, he suggested it is as of father to son (my father) and here, of Shuichi Asakura it is 'even son [Asakura] to father'. I find this curious as it was written in 1981, so long after his real son was long gone. What am I to think? I try to be impersonal and unbiased but it can sometimes be tough.

*

I learned from my correspondence with the Tokyo Zoological Society that my father was invited to join the courtesy visit to the Japanese Governor of Johore on 29 March 1942. Another purpose of the visit was to inspect, or 'honour' as my father wrote, the Istana Bahru, the palace of the Sultan. The party comprised three professors –Honda, Ohtsuka and Esaki – with the Marquis, his secretary Ishii, Koga and my father.

First of all, Koga visited the Sultan's zoo because he hoped to transport some of the animals to Tokyo, especially the orang-utan. He was shocked to find that the orang-utan and most of the animals had been killed, or had died from starvation, during that fatal month of February 1942. The visiting party then went on to the house of the former British Adviser to Johore which had become the residence of the Japanese Governor. Koga, the professors and the Marquis were ushered in to meet the Governor. My father was left at the entrance, though given tea and cigarettes. Soon a relative of the Sultan, who my father knew, came in, looked at him with astonishment and suspicion and was clearly too frightened to utter more than a brief, formal greeting.

Lunch was being prepared; the elderly Japanese lady who was setting a large round table in the hall asked my father how he liked the Japanese, to which he replied 'in an accommodating fashion'. After some time, the whole party came to the hall accompanied by a rather elderly man clutching a straw hat and carrying his jacket over his arm. His clothes were ill-fitting, yet this was the Japanese Governor of Johore. The governor smiled at my father but did not bow. Through Koga as interpreter he asked my father to make himself at home and be at ease!

There was a vacant seat between the Governor and the Marquis as the party was seated for lunch. Dr Koga rose and asked my father to join them unless he preferred to have lunch on his own – something of a command I think. The Governor stood and motioned my father to the vacant seat where he was given knife, fork and spoon and the Governor, with chopsticks, plied his plate with a variety of the 'choicest of dishes'.

Clearly my father was an 'honoured' guest, seated as he was between the Governor and the Marquis. This was just over a month since the occupation of Singapore. My father wrote:

I came always to associate the most dignified yet natural courtesy with the company of the Marquis and he too would introduce me as the author of *Wayside Trees of Malaya.*

Professor Tanakadate, too, recognised my father's contribution to science through the book. Tanakadate had retrieved from the Government

Printing Office most of the remaining stock of *Wayside Trees of Malaya* – 'because it was in demand' – and presented copies to important visitors. In uncharacteristic humility, my father, with reference to these books, once said, "Little did I think that the little achieved would come to my aid."

So began the relationship between the scientists in war who were quite separate from their military. This must have been very difficult for British internees even to begin to understand, particularly when it became known that my father not only appeared to have much freedom, but had also lunched with the Governor and the Marquis in his general's uniform.

After lunch, the party went on to the Istana Bahru where the Sultanah greeted them, for the Sultan was ill. Professor Esaki told my father that the Istana had become the focus of senior Japanese officers because it was from its tower that General Yamashita had directed and observed the attack on Singapore. My father hid his interest but Japanese cameras were out and clicking away, those of Professor Esaki and Dr Koga certainly. In fact Koga's camera jammed, and he hid in a cupboard and made a repair.

Everyone climbed the steps to the tower and Esaki told my father that General Yamashita had established his secret headquarters there. It was known that the British would not voluntarily have shelled the Sultan's domain.

The window of the tower was shuttered but there were two small holes, 'as if whittled by bayonet', my father recorded, through which Yamashita had trained his field-glasses on the Japanese assault. The square parapet had a view right over Singapore Island where the main hills were easy to identify. On the inside of the parapet there was a crude map of this view over the island with the hills of Bukit Panjang, Bukit Mandai and Bukit Timah marked in Japanese characters. My father said it was 'painted in black, in broad lines of charcoal'. This was the route followed by Yamashita's onslaught down the arterial Mandai Road of Singapore. Could this charcoal map still be on the wall, painted or plastered over in the ensuing years?

On the west wall of the tower there was another map, about three feet by two, hung as a picture, on which was shown the plan of attack: the direct assault across the Straits of Johore, the capture of Tengah Airport, the drive down Bukit Timah Road, the feints that would be set up, if required, on the beaches to the east and west of Singapore town, and, as my father described in *The Marquis*, 'that little onslaught on Pulau Ubin, near the Naval Base, which fooled General Percival'. It was with the greatest difficulty that my father kept his composure that afternoon in the tower, 'that ugly tower', as he wrote.

The visitors showed all their excitement except the Marquis. My father sensed that that trickery of using the tower shocked the Marquis as he reflected on the awful happenings of only a few weeks earlier – the artillery barrage which preceded the assault 'as if it had been an earthquake that crumbled the British Empire', the terrible slaughter, and how a Japanese lieutenant had trodden for fifty yards over dead bodies while crossing the blown-up Causeway before setting foot on firm land.

In one of the very few references I remember my father telling me about this war, around the early 1950s, was how the brave Argylls were mown down by machine gun fire leaving many yards of dead bodies.

He remembered how Lloyd of the Johore Volunteers had said that he heard the hammerings and shouts of the Japanese to the west of Johore Bahru as the assault craft were being built and assembled. This was where, just a year before, my father and Lloyd had landed to the surprise and indignation of the small British garrison placed there. 'So here', my father wrote, 'at the very last natural obstacle (the Straits and Causeway) which the British had to its advantage, it had been caught unprepared'.

My father recorded the Istana visit in detail because it was imprinted on his mind. However, mention of the Istana Bahru visit is missing from Marquis Tokugawa's autobiography and diaries. In late 2009, Professor Yoji Akashi wrote to bring my attention to this enigma.

Because, for reasons unknown, pages in the diaries [of Tokugawa] for the period between 11 February and 29 May 1942 are missing, there is no way to ascertain your father's visit to the Istana… It remains a riddle why the pages are missing. Yoshichika left Tokyo on 11 February and arrived at Singapore on 5 March. Then, he left for Tokyo on a month-long official business to consult with military leaders about Sultan affairs, and he returned to Singapore on 2 July (1942). It is presumed that he had with him the diaries during the business trip. Did he rip off the papers to conceal something that might incriminate him in some affairs? I do not know. The Governor of Johore was Itami Masakichi, Maj General retired, whom Yoshichika visited often. Yoshitomo [not mentioned in *The Marquis*], Yoshichika's son, was an interpreter serving in the Governor's office in [Johore]. He returned to Japan because of illness on 11 November 1942.

Could it be that the Marquis was not impressed by the trickery of using the Istana and he preferred it unrecorded? I think there is another reason. The Marquis had travelled with Yamashita's army to that palace and seen it set up as a headquarters in end January 1941. It's not unusual for Japanese simply not to talk about something with which they were uncertain or not in agreement; '*muzukashii*' they would say – 'too difficult'!

It is becoming clear that the Marquis was certainly, first and foremost, a man of science and his code was probably not that of the military. His given rank was to provide him position in the military equal to Yamashita. This was perhaps to allow him to achieve the conservation of all things scientific.

In my theory, I believe General Yamashita knew of the Marquis' position and mission well in advance, and there was some quid pro quo between the Emperor, the Marquis and the military. There must have been a plan before the conquest of Malaya and Singapore to use the Marquis' contact with the Malay Sultans, in particular the Sultan of Johore, cultivated long before the war.

The Japanese plan of conserving scientific material coincided with Shenton Thomas' foresight, as evidenced by the note my father requested. This resulted in my father, Birtwistle and Holttum being kept out of internment in order to look after scientific matters for both the British and the Japanese.

ACROSS THE FENCE

Around April 1942, two Japanese artists in civilian clothes appeared at the Museum asking where they might find materials for their work. My father, being an artist himself, knew exactly where to go but hadn't been able to get authority nor the keys to the colonial government Art Store. He suggested to them that they enquire at the Custodian of Enemy Property and gave them the address. The keys for the store were obtained and my father took them, as he had offered, to the block of flats in which the Art Store was located. The building was uninhabited and seemed totally looted. Taking a back way into the building from a little-used street, it was discovered that the store was untouched. The artists quickly realised that all they wanted was there, indeed much more than they needed. Delighted, they asked my father to return with them two days later to collect the materials they had selected; they took there and then what they needed immediately and when my father asked if he might select something, they gave him a child's paint box – for which he bowed courteously, but the insult stung him into action.

Sunday in Singapore was still a day of rest and the streets were almost empty. At dawn, my father took the Garden's lorry with some Tamil labourers and removed almost all the contents of the Art Store and hid them in the herbarium of the Gardens bundled up to look like botanical specimens. This all happened within sight of the *kempeitai* offices – very risky indeed!

On the Monday, when my father took the artists back to the store, there was of course nothing remaining in the open room. My father explained about the risk of looting. However, he did send them to another small store where they found what they needed.

The art materials my father saved, supplemented by what he had earlier found in the Survey Office, found their way into the Civil Internment Camp. Thus, artists in captivity were supplied with a host of art materials including paper and even canvas. In the audio tapes which Professor Mikiko Ishii gave me of my father's after-dinner speech in Tokyo in 1983, my father referred to shows in London where some of the pictures painted by the Changi prisoners had been exhibited. He enquired of his audience where they thought the material came from to paint those pictures?

> They were the ones I stole under the eyes of the Japanese one Sunday morning and every time I look back upon that, I realise, now that's a very daring thing to have done, but I knew the situation, understood the dangers. I sized it up and I pulled it off.

He explained that no one could have known their source because he couldn't tell them.*

Not infrequently, my father reflected if he was doing the right thing. He questioned himself as for whom he was really working. Was it for the return of the British or 'openly for the Southern Empire'? Always, the middle-road came to his aid – that to save all the records for posterity. Without a doubt, the British internees accused my father of being anti-British and pro-Japanese; yet it seems that the Japanese considered Tanakadate to be pro-British. So both men acted warily; the Professor had the note, which few knew of the existence, and my father felt impelled to act on its instructions.

On 1 September 1942, it was officially announced that the Marquis was appointed President of the Museum and Botanic Gardens. These two operations had been joined into a sub-division of the Department of Education in the hierarchy of the Municipality. Policy was the responsibility of the Marquis, helped by the Professor until the end of 1942 when the latter made a trip to Japan. Thus, Professor Kwan Koriba became the Director of the Botanic Gardens in December 1942 and Dr Yata Haneda the Director of the Museum. My father, Holttum and Birtwistle were made advisers and thus they learned that nothing of importance took place which was not agreed to by the Marquis.

The Marquis' first undertaking on becoming the President of the Museum and Gardens was to rearrange the back rooms of the museum and the adjoining library with the intention of setting up a large and convenient public office in what had been the main room of the former public library. When the Professor had taken control, he had told my father to keep everything that might be useful over the next few years and consequently my

---

* *Wayside Trees of Malaya was apparently available in Changi Internment Camp. Dr John (Jack) A. Reid, according to his biographer, 'was one of a small group that took up botany, using Corner's Wayside Trees of Malaya. Thus began an interest in botany which has been a source of pleasure ever since'. In September 1945, my father gave copies of the book to M. A. Donk and Captain Gerardus J. de Joncheere, two Dutch ex-prisoners-of-war who came to work at the Gardens and recover their prowess in Botany. De Joncheere told my father that during his captivity he had learned by heart the text of that book (which he had taken with him) and then smoked its pages as cigarette paper. So a book by one who was considered a collaborator was an inspiration in extremely uninspiring circumstances.*

father, with Birtwistle, had accumulated clothing, books, stationery and the like and all was stored in those back rooms. They must have been well filled.

It was decided by both the Marquis and the Professor that British soldiers would be used to assist with the heavy work of moving things and clearing the extra space; they were to come from the POW camp at Changi. The work could have been completed in a few days but my father was told by the Marquis that there was no hurry, and that the soldiers must be given a good lunch and tea.

Thus, a Captain Foulkes and Captain Lowe appeared and for three weeks from 12 September 1942, they brought daily some twenty soldiers from camp. The soldiers were usually different each day but the officers remained the same. The reason for changing the men was to ensure as many as possible had a good lunch and tea, just as it had been decreed.

My father was in charge of shopping for the food and, wearing his official enemy-alien arm-band, went early every day to the Orchard Road Market to avoid most of the Japanese shoppers. The stallholders soon got to know him. He was served quickly, often with muttered words of news, and he was charged the minimum possible.

The Professor paid for half the cost, totalling some $500, and told my father to pay for the rest himself though how he thought my father could do this one wonders! The Marquis, however, asked to pay his share, and the balance was found for my father by the *towkay*, Chua Ho Ann.

The Professor came to the lunches and talked with the soldiers who must have been surprised not only to receive such hospitality but from such a small, seemingly ineffectual person with a quiet voice. My father was also instructed to supply the soldiers with clothes, books, pencils and the like, and all came from that store. One lunch time, the door opened gently and the Marquis looked in. My father rose to greet him and he confided that his rank prevented him from speaking with the prisoners, but clearly he was happy to see that all seemed well.

Despite the Military Police's proximity, no one ever questioned my father or Birtwistle as to where this contingent of prisoners came from. The *kempeitai* must have noticed these goings-on; it was their job so to do, but there must have been policy coordination and they knew not to intervene.

Here, we have another example of the Japanese scientists and their oh-so-different attitude to the war situation. It must have been difficult, risky and dangerous to help prisoners in this way, but help they did and it should be recorded, but not in any way as a defence of the atrocities of the military and the *kempeitai*.

By chance, in 2011, I was relayed information from Keith Andrews by Jonathan Moffatt of the Malayan Volunteers Group. While researching on his father who was with the Royal Artillery, he came across a file at the UK National Archives containing the POW Questionnaire completed by a

Capt David Neville Ffolkes (as spelt) after his return from the Far East in 1945. Ffolkes is the same man my father called Foulkes. Capt Ffolkes wrote:

In July 1942 I was in charge of a working party of 15 men at Raffles library in Singapore. While there I came in contact with two British internees also working under the Japanese. They were Mr Corner, previous to the fall of Singapore of the Botanical Gardens and Mr Bertwistle (sic) formerly of the Ministry of Singapore Fisheries. On three occasions these men rendered assistance to the Allies in the following ways:

1. When the Japanese Naval Authorities came to the library to take the charts of the North Australian waters, Corner managed to hide these charts and later destroy them.

2. When the Japanese civil authorities were collecting all optical instruments, Corner took all those in Raffles museum and library and buried them in the Botanical Gardens.

3. When the Japanese propaganda dept. began a series of anti-Australian articles in the press & radio they wished to lay hands on any books on Australiana, then in the library. Corner & Bertwistle (sic) removed & hid all these books. I was a witness (as well as an accomplice) of this last act. Other witnesses - Capt. Dennis Lowe 16th DEF: Regt (Singapore) RA.

This too was the same Capt Lowe. I was intrigued to receive this information because my father never mentions the incidents in *The Marquis*. Could he have forgotten them? Hardly, as he recalled vividly the visit to the Chart Room, Anson Road, and the burying of Pen Landon's jewellery in the Gardens. It was as if he wasn't writing *The Marquis* to defend himself but to defend the Japanese scientists.

*

Throughout the Japanese Occupation, there was a Chinese man who frequently took enormous risks to help my father for little or no reward. He was Chua Ho Ann who helped pay for the meals given to the soldiers working at the Museum. My father wrote in *The Marquis*:

He had the fortitude of a hero and was the friend to the friendless. Though coarse in appearance and speech, his bearing was confirmed when he spoke to the Professor or the Marquis.

Chua Ho Ann, a Chinese coolie, came to Singapore from China in 1922 and worked initially at the dockyard, labouring, before somehow acquiring the right to maintain prawn ponds and a charcoal kiln in the mangrove forest of the Pandan River. My father got to know him when the Gardens

Department was given charge over this forest as an official reserve. There was no budget for any maintenance people, and Ho Ann offered to take care of the reserve on the understanding that he may continue with his prawns and charcoal. It was agreed and by default, he became honorary chief warden, a post he served well and earned the name of *towkay* – chief.

My father often visited Ho Ann's traditional wooden house on stilts by the little Pandan River and got to know the whole family. When Singapore fell, Ho Ann was arrested and imprisoned for three months. His wife and family escaped by hiding in the mangrove, up to their necks in the water, and bobbing under when soldiers passed.

Early in June 1942, thinking that Ho Ann was gone forever, my father was surprised when they passed each other in the street, although with scarcely more than a blink of recognition. Ho Ann then went to the museum to find my father, and my father confessed at being very careful, 'lest he be playing false.' After much questioning, he accepted Ho Ann's explanations and introduced him to the Professor who, on my father's recommendation, reappointed him to the position of honorary warden of the Pandan Reserve. By sheer hard work, Ho Ann prospered and developed his prawn ponds and the charcoal business and supplied food to the Japanese.

Ho Ann offered to help my father if he needed money. Through him, Father raised around $30,000 (£3,500) in 1942 which he gave to the Bishop of Singapore to keep his diocese going on what my father called 'the profits of the prawns'! The Bishop was at a loss to know how he could repay, but my father replied that he should not worry for 'the heathen require no reward'.

Occasionally, when Ho Ann found my father alone, he would thrust $2,000 (£233) into my father's pocket. One day in 1944, he went to the house near the museum where my father stayed and put the same sum into his hand. The door burst open and a detective rushed in. Ho Ann turned on the man and pushed him against the wall, checked him all over for weapons and demanded in a strong voice to know what he was doing because he, Chua Ho Ann, had been ordered by the Military Police to watch those *orang puteh* [white men]. The money was in my father's pocket; the detective left, outwitted, and a very dangerous situation was averted. Ho Ann burst into sweat, and never was so foolish again.

When in need, my father recorded, he telephoned a number and whispered 'Ho Ann' and left brief messages. What Ho Ann supplied was used mostly to help the underpaid staff at the museum and Gardens so that their services could be retained. His 'open house' kept many unfortunates, and he supplied rifles to the Chinese guerrillas in Johore. When the Occupation was nearing its end, he was a leader of the Association of the Black Cross, formed by Chinese citizens to bury the dead on the streets of Syonan-to according to their religion, judged from race and clothes. As a born entrepreneur, Chua Ho Ann bought up the match sticks in Singapore just a few days before the Japanese surrender, and then traded them for the hard currency of the British Military Administration, 'to the envy of less astute rivals'.

When my father was preparing to leave for England in November 1945, Ho Ann was being arraigned for collaboration with the enemy, the witness against him being a Japanese turncoat. My father put Ho Ann's affairs in the hands of a legal firm and in time the charge was dropped. Brigadier McKerron, of the British Military Administration went to Ho Ann's house to offer him a reward or honour for his services during the Occupation; it was refused.

'As the Professor helped us', wrote my father, 'so Ho Ann helped the unseen'.

*

October 1942 brought a revision of the position of all internees, apparently caused by the failure to arrange an international exchange of civilian prisoners. The Military Administration introduced, through Mr Asahi the Custodian of Enemy Aliens, a passport accompanied by an oath to be sworn individually and containing a photograph of those still employed in the town. The internees at Maxwell Road raised a strong objection to the terms of the oath but, as my father recorded:

> [S]o far as the three of us were concerned it made no difference; it was our job to remain at the Museum and Gardens as long as possible in order to assist the Japanese scientific control and to prevent looting.

They could not escape 'and orders had to be obeyed; intrigue was folly', he wrote. The English wording of the oath was a translation of the Japanese text which was vague. Asahi and the Professor had persuaded the Military Administration to alter some clauses because, as the Professor said, 'they could never be signed by the British'. The new terms were explained not only to Holltum, Birtwistle and my father, but also to other internees working at the Museum under Mr Asahi's orders.

My father and Birtwistle were experienced enough with the military methods to know that 'in extremity' such scraps of paper would be worthless but not to sign would terminate their motive and that of the Professor. This signing was hated by the POWs and they mostly never forgave those that did. 'We must stand together as one and as British' was the call – the decision was black or white, no in between – but they mostly had no idea of the importance of what Holltum, Birtwistle and my father were doing.

The Maxwell Road internees, mostly Europeans who were allowed parole to assist the Japanese with work in Singapore, persisted in their objection and refused to sign. Their spokesman, someone my father identified only as Mr B, (for Be-done-by-as-you-did [from *The Water-Babies*])', came to the Museum on November 3rd 1942 to direct us to follow their decision and, without even asking our point of view, said with assumed superiority that the British must now stand together.

To the question why they should not act as those free from internment and supplying essential services, Mr B gave no reply. It was 12.15 pm and the Professor entered the room, punctual as always. He was infuriated by the sight of Mr B; some weeks earlier, the Professor had forbidden his entry to the museum as *persona non grata* and now he had the impudence to interfere in the museum on a matter in which the Professor had 'striven on behalf of the internees'.

Mr B was immediately ordered out never to return again. The Professor knew that if Holttum, Birtwistle and my father refused the parole and oath, and were interned, his plans would also be finished; all their plans would be for naught. On 11 November 1942, the three were taken to Mr Asahi's office where they signed the parole and took the oath on the Bible though Asahi did politely suggest that was not necessary. 'The twinkle of Sir Shenton Thomas' eye was ever in my eye', wrote my father.

In *Shenton of Singapore*, Brian Montgomery includes an account by Dr Cicely Williams, a medical doctor interned in Changi who was ordered by Asahi, the Custodian of Enemy Aliens, to participate in writing a report on the food situation in Changi Gaol. This account is relevant not only because it gives insight into my father and Birtwistle's day-to-day relationship with the Japanese, but also gives another person's perspective of cooperation with the Japanese.

I have decided to include much of what she wrote, being too important to my story to précis.

Asahi was a very decent man who had lived in England, and he now wanted six men to leave prison and go to work in his office, with one male and one female doctor to write and report on the food situation in Changi. I think it was pure decency on his part to give some of us the opportunity of a change…. We were driven to Singapore in a lorry…. I was given a flat to myself in Maxwell Road and later Katherine de Mowbray joined me there. Our office was in the Chartered Bank Building in Raffles Place, and we walked there daily from our flat. We generally had lunch in one of the little Indian or Chinese restaurants close by… So life was really very pleasant and a wonderful change from Changi Prison.

I know some men in our party, to whom we owed so much, thought it most unwise for us to be on parole at all because we went about freely and were therefore in danger. But I thought it an unparalleled opportunity of seeing Singapore under the Japanese rule and of keeping contact, though always slight and risky, with many of our friends; also by seeing something of the Japanese we had a chance of getting privileges for the internees in Changi.

Altogether we had an extraordinary, yet "strangely pleasant" four months, but I had lost all my medical notes and was very anxious to resume medical reading. All the libraries, with their invaluable cultural records (public and private), had been swept up by the Nipponese into Raffles Museum. The two Englishmen, John Corner and Birtwistle, the former Director of Fisheries, assisted by Quan Ah Gun (Chief Clerk of the Botanical Gardens) were trying to rescue from destruction, or removal to Japan, everything that they could. Birtwistle had been ordered by Sir Shenton Thomas to remain at his post in Singapore because of his unrivalled knowledge of the fishermen, who provided so much food for the city's population.

However, I found it impossible to gain access to the museum without personal permission from the Japanese Professor Tanakadate, to whom I tried to get an introduction. The only answer I got was an invitation to lunch with him, and John Corner and Birtwistle, at Tanakadate's house. We had naturally been unwilling to "fraternise" with the enemy, so we refused. Then the invitation was repeated "in a way that he hoped would be unobjectionable to us", ie Mr Corner and Mr Birtwistle were asking us to lunch, but the meal would be at the Professor's house.

After some qualms, Katherine and I accepted this invitation, first because I badly needed access to books, and secondly we did not see the wisdom of being implacably unfriendly to a man whom we knew was trying to help us. So we went to lunch. Personally, I did not like Tanakadate; he was a nasty old man, but he was prepared to do quite a lot for us. He took us for a drive in the Botanical Gardens where we all sat and drank orange pop in a kiosk. At any rate, from that lunch substantial advantages flowed; we were able to work in Raffles Museum and Library, sorting the looted books and reading on our own account; we persuaded the Professor to send a large number of books to the civilian and military camps; we urged the importance for all prisoners of walks outside prison walls, and the need for relatives to meet each other – both these facilities were granted. Finally, I was allowed to keep books for a medical library at the women's camp.

We never regretted anything we did during our "time outside" and I do not believe the way in which we behaved did any harm to our prestige in the eyes of the Asiatics.

The more I find out, the more I come to understand the time, and circumstances, and certainly I am beginning to find my father – not as a father but as a man in this most extraordinary of situations and times. He had courage and was undaunted by the many who could not perceive that and therefore understand his actions. His single-mindedness and vision was ubiquitous: to the ignorant it must have seemed selfish, but some of those ignorant were educated enough to know better.

- XIV -

SAYONARA

For the next two years or so, life for my father continued with the conservation of scientific records and botanical excursions, and getting food and money to the POWs. Indeed, he managed considerable botanising in this period and was well supported by Professor Koriba. He developed his Durian Theory (see Appendix A) with the encouragement of Koriba and achieved valuable work for botany which was to come to publication after the war, including the monograph *Clavaria and allied genera*. He certainly continued his botanical and mycological collecting as the dates on the very many specimens now stored at the RBG Edinburgh and those few duplicates at Kew indicate.

However, the *kempeitai* was then taking a closer control of things, as was the military generally, so Holttum, Birtwistle and my father, as well as the Japanese scientists, had to exercise great care.

In the latter part of 1944, my father had two bouts of flu and was bed-ridden for several days. Dr Ogkawa, a medical friend of Dr Haneda, gave him injections of camphor as the last resort for a failing heart. I was surprised to hear about camphor injections and consulted Professor Lee Seng Teik from the Singapore General Hospital and Professor David Crompton who consulted the World Health Organisation. Both said they had no knowledge of camphor injections. Professor Lee thought it was used as 'a desperate measure during the trying circumstance present at the time.'

When Professor Kwan Koriba took over the welfare of Birtwistle, Holttum and my father, he arranged new accommodation for the latter two men in the ground floor of the Director's house in the Gardens. They moved in on 13 December 1944. Upstairs lived the Aide-de-camp to the General commanding Syonan-to. 'He was a cheerful young man, almost communicative, whom we met frequently', my father wrote. And significantly, he added, 'He possessed a shortwave radio and listened to the BBC.'

One day in 1945, when news was so scarce and no one really knew what the future was, my father was tempted to listen to that wireless. The ADC had the habit of leaving for work in the morning and returning later in the

158

afternoon. My father decided at noon (news time) to tune in and see what he could learn. Holttum was left downstairs keeping watch. As my father turned the knobs, he heard the sound of a car approaching. He immediately returned the settings to where he had carefully remembered them to be and shot down the backstairs just as military police tramped up the main stairs to remove the wireless set. This was the only time in three years that he had tried to get news directly and, by the grace of God, they – for Holttum was an accomplice – escaped detection. My father subsequently described this episode in a memorable one-liner: 'There is no law of averages for exceptional circumstances'.

The more I researched, the more I think that as things progressed and generally seemed to go well for my father in those most terrible of times, he became more confident in himself and took many risks regardless of how they might affect others. Did he really consider that alternative action during the pineapple excursion? It reads well, and perhaps it's what he wanted to believe, but surely he would never have considered anything that would have put at risk his work of conservation; he had become obsessive about that.

*

When I was in Singapore in 2007, we visited the National Archives and amongst the war information, I found an oral history interview with Dr Humphrey Morrison Burkill, the son of Dr Isaac Henry Burkill who was Director of the Gardens, 1912-1925. Humphrey Burkill was Director, 1957–1969.

The interview, though short, was quite wide-ranging; it tells of the arrival of Tanakadate and that my father and Holttum were allowed to remain out of internment. He said of my father:

He was up to all sorts of funny things, some good, some bad. The nature reserves in Singapore Island which Corner had control of, this was part of his duties. There's a big mangrove area down at Jurong, Pandan. And he had a Chinaman there, Chua Ho Ann as honorary warden. Well, Ho Ann was, when we're not looking, he was allowed to take a certain amount of mangrove for making charcoal. He had a sort of back-hand remuneration. And when the Japs came, he had a big charcoal contract with the Jap navy.

The interview continued and told of the clandestine radio listening which was apparently not an isolated incident.

Holttum did tell me that whenever the Japanese Director, who lived upstairs, went off to work Corner would nip upstairs, turn the Jap's radio on and listened to the news. Well, that was a death sentence if you were caught doing that. And that obviously worried him.

Burkill also revealed that Holttum was a Quaker, 'a real man of peace… but Corner was difficult… they were always quarrelling'. The fact that Eric Holttum was teetotal and my father was not, might have contributed to their mutual 'dislike', as did the fact that my father smoked; indeed, he was rarely without his pipe, and enjoyed a glass of whisky – and Eric Holttum hated all of that!

My father thought Holttum slack in his management. He appeared to give more lead to Henderson in the early 1930s than my father, his official Assistant, and he 'allowed' Henderson to make so many mistakes in the herbarium, clearly without checking.

However, there can be no doubt that Holttum was a most eminent scientist and botanist. In 1931, he became the first man in Singapore to achieve a breakthrough with orchid hybridization, paving the way for today's orchid industry in Singapore and Malaysia. In 1936, he founded the Singapore Gardening Society to raise the standard of horticulture. In his 27 years as Director of the Singapore Botanic Gardens, he introduced a large number of flowering trees and shrubs from tropical North and South America, Africa, Asia and Australia which are extensively grown in private gardens and commercial nurseries throughout Malaysia and Singapore today.

*

On 8 January 1945, a military order was issued that my father, Holttum and Birtwistle were to be interned for six days. They were taken to the Civil Internment Camp in Sime Road, by the golf course, where they were incarcerated with others in a hut and ordered not to speak to anyone or to leave the hut without a Japanese guard. They remained there from 10 January to 15 January. The purpose was to show that they were, as enemy aliens, subject to the Custodian and Military Administration – a flexing of muscles, so to speak.

They were told that they were civil internees, which they had always thought of themselves, and that they were under the Camp Commandant, 'which we never recognised', wrote my father, 'and had nothing to do with'. They were given the same food and drink as the rest of the camp and my father wrote that he spent his time 'on calculations for my botanical work'. He had a small notebook 'so full that it could occupy me for weeks'.

When they were freed, the three were collected by Professor Koriba and Dr Haneda in their cars. My father recalled that they were taken straight to Professor Koriba's house for a bath and then to a banquet specially prepared. Their internment had grieved Koriba and Haneda.

The other camp internees must have seen this departure and wondered at what was going on. One can only guess at the feelings, coming of course from understandable ignorance, yet look at what those internees had had to endure – the very worst of awful conditions and death for too many – and here was a brief imprisonment and 'escaping'. It is no surprise therefore that there was anger.

Yet, there were some internees like Ernest Hodgkin who had a clear perspective. In his diary entry of 17 January 1945, published in *If This Should Be Farewell*, he wrote:

> Last week Holttum and several other Europeans were brought into the camp after nearly three years of "liberty" in the town. After a few days of close confinement in the guard room they were removed again taking with them seven days of rations; what has happened to them we do not know. They have very unjustly been accused of being Quislings by folk who can't think themselves into the shoes of anyone but themselves. For myself, I have never ceased to be glad that I refused to go and work with them more than two years ago; I would never have been happy in the difficult situations in which they must often have been placed.

*

Each day in the Gardens, Professor Koriba would rise to leave about 3.30 pm. My father would be alerted by the scraping of his chair and, on departure, they would bow to each other with Koriba saying, 'Kona-san, I go home now'.

In *The Marquis*, my father wrote about hearing the 'telltale shuffle of military boots down below' one day in June 1945. They came upstairs and a 'prolonged discourse' took place. There were two unfamiliar voices to which Koriba replied at intervals with a grunt. Then my father heard the clicking of a revolver. The boots departed without a word from Koriba. Soon, the scraping of his chair was heard and Koriba too departed at the usual time.

On Koriba's desk was a revolver with a box of ammunition. To my father's great annoyance, it seemed as if the officers had been telling him how to use it – to shoot my father and others at the slightest chance perhaps? When everyone had left for the day, my father called the local staff together and in explaining what had happened, he put them all on their honour not to touch or remove the revolver and its ammunition. It remained on the desk, pushed to one side and partially covered by papers, until the Japanese surrender. Professor Koriba never referred to the weapon or mentioned it.

My father wrote of Koriba: 'As the gloom of disaster deepened over Syonan-to, our confidence in him was never shaken; he could have left in safety, in view of his seniority, but a profound sense of duty to the post that he held put that aside and led him to internment'.

In June 2012, Dr Nigel Taylor, the Director of the Singapore Botanic Gardens, sent me a note telling me that a colleague, S. K. Ganesan, had in his possession a copy of *The Marquis* annotated by my father. The annotation is very interesting. It is in my father's hand and probably dated January 1995, the year before his passing. It says:

> Note to p. 144 – the revolver. My account is not strictly true. Kwan Koriba told Prof U[y]eno a few months before he [Koriba] died [1994] what he had never told anyone. When the military officer had shown Koriba how to use the revolver, he pointed it at the back of my [my father's] head and said in Japanese 'This is where you shoot him when the time comes'. I had my back to them and never knew. This was the cause of Koriba's anger and loud oath. It is the only evidence I have that the Japanese intended to shoot all British prisoners and internees if there was a battle to recapture Singapore.

Then came some momentous news. A Swiss lady, known to my father and Birtwistle, came secretly to see Birtwistle. She told him 'in hurried whispers' of a most confidential matter that had come to her from a reliable source. It was news that Japan would surrender before the end of August and that there would be no bombing or fighting in Singapore. This must have been after the atom bomb attacks on Hiroshima on 6 August and Nagasaki on 9 August.

She was very careful not to be seen talking to an enemy alien and requested that Birtwistle tell only Holttum and my father; if either was to be interned then to tell her fiancé who was in the Sime Road Camp. The three had to believe her not only because of the tremendous risk she had taken in coming to tell them but also because it had apparently been leaked 'by Washington'.

The Marquis had already been recalled to Japan in the middle of 1944. Why was he recalled? Was it realised that the war was lost and a relative of the Emperor was to return to his homeland? The Marquis, as noted in his obituary, was one of a very few select people to whom that closely guarded secret of the impending surrender was given in Japan. It was conveyed to him personally by the Emperor's brother, Prince Takamatsunomiya.

*

The morning of 15 August 1945 dawned. Birtwistle gave instructions to the local staff at the museum to lock the doors and to wedge them on the inside. At 2.30 pm that same day, Japanese guards came by lorry from the Civil Internment Camp to collect him, and then Holttum and my father. Birtwistle stood in the back of that lorry and was driven along Stamford Road and Orchard Road to the Gardens, with sullen Japanese guards. He was cheered wildly by the crowds 'as if in Roman triumph'. After Holttum and my father were collected from the Gardens, they were all transported to the Sime Road Camp again. They had been warned by Professor Koriba that this was done for their safety in case of lawlessness. I think it was a condition of the Surrender that all British civilians should be detained on orders of the British Commander while his troops occupied their houses, no doubt checking on what was there and what had been happening, looking for collaborators and some lead as to what had been going on.

Ernest Hodgkin referred to this last incarceration in his diary entry of 25 August 1945, actually written after the surrender, but those in Camp had not yet officially been told.

> The same day Holttum, Corner and Birtwistle were sent in; they had been working in the town all this time, Holttum in the gardens and the other two in the Raffles Museum. Naturally they are somewhat unpopular, they are regarded as Quislings. I cannot believe this to be true of Holttum but there seems to be good reason for believing that the other two have gone out of their way to help and praise the Nips.

I wonder why this change of thought with regard to my father and Birtwistle between January and August 1945? It was clear to all that they had worked with the Japanese in the Gardens and Museum whereas Holttum remained mostly at the Gardens and was not seen to be working with the enemy. It does show the thinking of the time and of those in camp – strong and understandable feelings. Indeed, such feelings were polarising simply to those in camp and those out of camp and these were to remain strong and powerful for many years after the war, even to today.

*

On August 19, all the Japanese records and also many of Dr Haneda's scientific records and papers were bunt by the Japanese. On 21 August, all Japanese posters, maps and notices were taken down in the Museum and also burnt. That evening, Quan Ah Gun and the assistant Le Doux, who had been a loyal comrade of Birtwistle, sealed and nailed up all doors to the museum and library and had the foresight to arrange for local staff to be on guard, particularly overnight. The destroying and burning of Japanese papers and records continued to the end of August.

On 2 September, news of the surrender had filtered into the camp. The internees awaited for some official proclamation from the British Command but no news was given as the internees were thought to be physically and mentally incapable, after so long an ordeal.

Chua Ho Ann made contact with my father and took his message to Professor Yata Haneda. The message was that the guards should be strengthened at both the Museum and the Library, lest Japanese control broke down. The reply was that the guard had been doubled for day and night. Notes were sent also to Quan Ah Gun and Dr Furtado at the Gardens, via a member of the Swiss Red Cross, asking them not to relax their vigilance.

*

On 5 September 1945, the Japanese flag over the Cathay Building was lowered around 3.30 pm Tokyo time. Ah Gun had already raised the Union Jack at the Museum at 3.00 pm that same day.

Singapore returned to Singapore time and the Gardens, Museum and Library came under their new Director, Dr Gilbert Archey, the Officer-in-Charge of Monuments, Fine Arts, and Archives for the British Military Administration. Previously the Director of the Auckland Museum in New Zealand, he was given the 'courtesy' military rank of Lieutenant Colonel, and he remained in charge through to March 1946.

My father had attuned himself to a new and different life under the Japanese and, whilst there was always danger lurking, he had overcome most difficulties and learned well the new ways. In September 1945, he must have expected freedom for weeks; yet, when it arrived, after the moments of joy, what did it mean? The life of three and a half years was gone. Did he still have a job and what of his joyous previous life collecting and researching in the wonderful Land of the Dendrons? Was he in danger from his own side? What of his home, his possessions, his friends – and his family?

All of these thoughts and reactions must have scampered through his mind. I find it almost impossible to understand his feelings at that moment, but I am glad to have faced the challenge of attempting to get my mind around it.

For my father and undoubtedly all concerned, life was to change absolutely. The British were returning, and as the Japanese withdrew, looters found that new window of opportunity which Holltum, Birtwistle and my father had so feared from the beginning. Their hard work, misunderstood and despised by so many, must not be lost at this last hour.

Quan Ah Gun and Dr Furtado, Assistant Botanist at the Gardens, were called to the Municipal Office at 9 am on 6 September and were interviewed by the British Officer in charge. They were asked to keep their departments running as before and to await further instructions. The officer then ordered two armed police to the museum where they took up their duty at 1 pm that day.

Birtwistle left the internment camp that afternoon and went straight to the museum to check that all was well. He then went to help with the arrangements for fish supplies to be delivered to the camp. In the evening, Dr Furtado brought the Gardens lorry, that faithful lorry, to collect my father from the camp. The ruling was that civilians were to be left in camp until they could be returned to England, but this didn't suit my father. He was acutely aware of what can happen with military takeovers and, after all that had been achieved, he was not about to be 'locked away' and then 'shipped away' risking the loss of all to the new arrivals and their ignorance.

As my father saw the lorry coming to the camp, he jumped the wire and ran to it. On arrival at the Gardens he went immediately to the labourers' quarters to greet the men, women and children and then to Professor Koriba's house to greet him, Dr Haneda, Oshima and Sugewara.

It was this day, 6 September 1945, that the Municipality changed hands from the Japanese to the British.

This meant a considerable time gap between the surrender on 15 August and the official changing-of-hands, and this was why my father was so concerned about looting. 'There were running through my mind', he wrote, 'the thoughts which had troubled me in February 1942 and had brought us all together'. He was concerned that in his uncertainty of the new administration there might be nothing he could do for them.

Before he left, Professor Koriba gave my father his manuscript on Malayan trees, his scientific notes and some personal things for safekeeping at the Botanic Gardens. My father asked Professor Koriba if he trusted him to which the reply was immediate and affirmative.

On 7 September, my father went with Ah Gun to the museum where they set up the royal portraits as the Professor had done in the British Room. 'Our purpose', wrote my father,

> was to display to the new administration what Japanese scientists had done under the directions of the Professor and the presidency of the Marquis. We had lived through the occupation in the panoply of aspiration; now we faced the pragmatic.

This same day, Chua Ho Ann gave my father his brother Soo Ann's car for his personal use and, that evening, whilst walking in the Gardens, he 'thanked in my heart' all who had helped to sustain it. This car, according to a letter from my father to Holttum deposited at Kew, was 'commandeered' by Archey, and was 'gradually appropriated' and came to Henderson who refused to return it.

What impressed my father was not so much the consideration and generosity of the Japanese scientists in victory 'as their perpetuation of these qualities in defeat'.

On 8 September, Colonel Gilbert Archey went to the museum to meet my father. He immediately took charge of the museum and Gardens and my father became his ADC.

Koriba, Haneda and the other Japanese scientists were interned by the

British on 11 September 1945. When my father heard this, he tried to arrange the release of Koriba and Haneda to work in the day time, if not to stay at the Gardens at night, but he was told that they preferred to remain with their own people. My father never knew if that was the truth, but guessed that they expected that he and Birtwistle would quickly leave for England thus leaving them in the hands of unsympathetic foreigners. My father did manage to return to them some of their personal luggage that had been stored at the Gardens and herbarium, but he was not allowed to see them.

Early in October, my father submitted, via Colonel Archey, personal reports on both Koriba and Haneda which he, with important help from Birtwistle, had written. These were destined for the British Military Administration. According to Mrs Yukie Kanie, Dr Haneda's daughter, these reports certainly saved her father from being tried as a war criminal.

*

On 8 September 1945, my father again visited the Istana Bahru, the Bukit Serene Palace of the Sultan of Johore, this time with Archey.

I also wonder if this visit was connected with that of Brigadier Willan and Colonel Hay to interview the Sultan. Certainly, when my father and Archey arrived at the Istana, they found Brigadiers, in British uniform, discussing horses over drinks with the Sultan's retinue. Could Willan have been one of these Brigadiers? Yet my father wrote as if his visit with Archey was separate from that of Willan and Hay's.

My father wrote that 'something began knocking in my head'. He left the group and with the help of an elderly servant and a nephew of the Sultan, it was confirmed that there still was a map on the wall of the tower. My father told Archey all about the March 1942 visit and they both took the stairs to the tower (the lift still being out of order). There they found the charcoal sketch and the map hanging exactly as it did in 1942. For some reason the Japanese appeared to have forgotten this evidence which implicated the Sultan in working for the Japanese!

Colonel Archey photographed the map, the charcoal sketch and the view from the tower. They wanted to remove the map immediately but were wary of so doing without permission. The next day, Archey obtained permission from the British Military Administration and with two young British officers, clearly from Intelligence as their shoulder flashes suggested, my father revisited the Istana where Tunku Mahkota duly gave permission to take the map, indeed to remove it there and then.

My father had asked the intelligence officers – and Colonel Archey had made them promise – that this historic map should be returned to Raffles Museum as part of the archives of Singapore. The intelligence officers took it to the Military headquarters which had been re-established at Fort

Canning, and the map has, apparently, been lost. Not even a photograph of it went to the museum. After the war, the bunkers of the military headquarters were sealed and forgotten. When they were reopened in 1988, the rooms were found to be flooded. As no one knew of the history of the map, it was not searched for; in any case, the map was not found amongst the materials recovered.

After his return to England in 1946, my father wrote several letters to the War Office in London to ask about the map, and he called in person as well, only to be given the impression that they thought his story was manufactured. This view changed only when he gave some detail that had to be beyond dispute.

My father later learned that a photograph of the map had been printed in a secret military document or periodical of the War Office but it could not be found. It seems extraordinary that no one at the War Office realised that my father was the only one on the British side, besides Colonel Archey and his attendants, who could confirm the authenticity of that map.

My father remarked that had he not been so honest, he 'would have rolled up the map and taken it to sell at some future time for a lot of money, but this is how the scientist is diddled by the non-scientist!'

In 2009, my father's associate, Roy Watling, former President of the British Mycological Society, wrote in reply to my questions about father and the map, 'he [Corner] was very miffed that after giving the British commander and the War museum details he was not thanked or recognised'.

My enquiries in 2007 revealed that there is no record of this map in London, at the Imperial War Museum or in Singapore at the National Museum, the National Library or the National Archives and Record Centre. The present day Director of the Auckland Institute and Museum was unable to find the photographs taken by Colonel Archey. When I was in Auckland in 2008, I visited the museum and could find nothing relevant in Sir Gilbert's records, and subsequent exchanges with the museum produced a blank.

Professor Ishii also enquired about the map for her Japanese version of my father's book. I gather she found nothing and made very little mention of it in her story.

'I think it possible', my father much later commented in *The Marquis*, 'that some Japanese, who visited the Istana Bahru sometime in 1942/'43, may have photographed it and who knows, it might appear yet!' Had he forgotten the photographs of Esaki, and Koga's camera jamming?

I did make an effort to find a photo of the map in Koga's records. Hiroshi Ohira of the Tokyo Zoological Society went to great lengths to find Koga's old rolls of film and sent me all the relevant photos, but alas none of the map was found.

My search for the Yamashita map continued into 2013. The latest I have is from the Head of the Department of Collections Access at the Imperial

War Museum. He had found correspondence in 1979 and 1981 from my father enquiring after this map.

On 21 April 1981, my father wrote to the Director of the Imperial War Museum about the map. He said that he had 'pursued all possible sources except one [the Sultan of Johore]'. He reported that he had checked, without success, with the authorities in Singapore, with the Auckland Museum in New Zealand where the photographs of the late Col G. Archey are kept, and the records of five Japanese officers in Japan who also took photographs of this map in 1942. He went on to the point of his letter: 'it has occurred to me for a long time that the map may have come into the possession of Earl Mountbatten. I read today in the newspaper about the opening of his home [Broadlands], collections and war-mementoes, to the public on 1 April. In the interest of history I would like to probe this possibility'. In the postscript, he explained that he had not written about this possibility before, 'because of the tragic demise of Earl Mountbatten and I have waited for the misery to subside'.

It was confirmed about a month later that the map does not reside at Broadlands, the Senior Guide there stating that neither he nor his archivist could trace any reference to it.

I learned that the Chief Librarian at the Ministry of Defence Library had been involved, and his reply to my father was that 'there is no evidence from what you relate that the map ever found its way back to the War Office. It was probably used as "raw" intelligence material for SEAC's [South East Asia Command's] intelligence digest, and then alas finally destroyed'. The Public Records Office was also contacted, where it was noted that these events predated the Public Record Act of 1959 – 'For most foreign commands overseas the documents would be left or destroyed'.

As was typical of my determined father he wrote back: 'Yet the truth will out, and I am led to believe that this 'annihilation' of the map was political'. He was, in fact, considering asking for an official enquiry into the fate of the map.

Although this map clearly shows the incompetence of the British and Allied commanders – and it was politic for the British 'to lose it' – I am sure it still exists as I am certain that somewhere in Japan, some of the photographs taken by the Japanese remain.

In 2009, during my exchange of correspondence with John Gullick who was with the Malayan Civil Service, he told me:

The only person I can think of who might be able to help you is Datin Patricia Lim Pui Huen, who was until recently a vice-president of MBRAS [Malayan Branch of the Royal Asiatic Society]. Her family home is in Johore Bahru and I believe that she still lives there.

I wrote to Patricia Lim, and she replied that 'General Yamashita's battle plans drawn on the parapet should still be there under the white wash and could still be un-covered… recovered'.

I realise that the Sultan of Johore is the only person to whom the question about the map has not been put. Through a contact, a retired admiral from the Malaysian navy, I have, via a letter from him in March 2013, approached the Sultan. Contact with the ADC of the Sultan was established but there has been no progress as this book goes to press.

XV

BACKLASH

I am surprised that my father made no effort to exonerate himself from the nasty back-chat and claims of collaboration which lasted for so many years after the war. I am told he was a proud man and considered that he had nothing to defend, but the talk must have weighed heavily on him.

I know he was very disappointed not to have been invited to attend the ceremony when Raffles' statue was returned to its rightful position at Empress Place on 6 July 1946. He was still very much persona non grata; the truth of his war time in Singapore was mostly unknown and those in the Malayan Civil Service, and Government, were still very suspicious. He wrote to enquire of the occasion and was sent copies of the speeches. As he expected, there was no reference to any of the circumstances that led to that ceremony.

Seven months after Singapore became Syonan-to, the statue of Stamford Raffles was still in place in Empress Place, gazing out to sea. It became a concern lest the Japanese damage or destroy it, and it was decided to remove it to the museum. To this end, the agreement of Professor Tanakadate and Marquis Tokugawa was achieved.*

On 13 September, the operation to move it began and was undertaken by a British civil engineer who was still employed by the Municipality. It was my father who suggested that the statue be moved to the rotunda of the museum and those in charge were persuaded to agree. The statue had to be lifted off the pedestal and laid on the ground before the pedestal could be raised and moved. A gang of Tamil labourers was used for the actual removal. As the statue was being raised to the horizontal, to the singing of the labourers, a spout of water gushed from the lower part of the statue and the song turned into jubilation and shouts of joy for 'Raffles is pissing on

---

* *The translation of Tanakadate's* Achievements *records, '…the Sir Raffles bronze was moved to the Entrance Hall [of the Raffles Museum]. The statue of Sir Raffles, the founder of Singapore, was in the centre of the City in the Victoria Theatre Square, but was to be moved to the Museum. Otatsu, the Mayor, came and ordered it to be moved to the middle of the Museum. It was moved mid-September'.*

Syonan-to'. The engineer said it was a sign from heaven.

On 22 September 1942, the statue was in its new position below the dome of the museum. Its head reached to the level of the gallery which my father walked every morning and occasionally he enquired of the august gentleman if he appreciated the new arrangement; Raffles, I hear, kept his peace!

I have wondered why Sir Shenton Thomas kept his peace with regards my father's wartime record. Was he asked? Did he speak? These remain open questions.

In 2009, John Gullick wrote of my father and Shenton Thomas in our correspondence:

> Shenton Thomas had in 1942 approved what he proposed to do, and after the war so did the CO (Colonial Office) – and that sufficed… I can say that in the early years after the war, when I was in Malaya, there was extraordinary bitterness among those who had been interned or been POW against those who had escaped that ordeal.

'Shenton Thomas had approved what he [Corner] proposed to do'. This suggests what I believe, that it was my father's idea to which Shenton Thomas agreed. I checked this with Gullick, in case a slip in the wording had led me to a wrong conclusion; he confirmed what he wrote. The Oxford Dictionary of National Biography, in its record of my father, also clearly suggests the same: 'looting preceded the takeover, so the governor acceded to Corner's request that he be allowed to carry a note to the Japanese entreating them to preserve the scientific collections. A ship of Japanese technicians and officials had been sunk and they were replaced with British people: among them, Corner became a "civil internee" in the botanic gardens'.

The journalist Michael Brown wrote for the 16 August 2005 edition of the *Sunday Express Review*. In the article, 'Secret heroism of the men who grew orchids for the Japanese', there was reference to a trial that occurred during the second of my father's end-of-war internments in August 1945, Brown wrote:

> Corner then faced a humiliating 'trial', called by the POW camp commander and officiated over by a newly-arrived New Zealand colonel [Archey]. No charges were brought against Holttum and Birtwhistle [sic] but the list of accusations against Corner seemed damning. Then Corner was allowed his say. He called on the Church of England Bishop Wilson, then Bishop of Singapore, to speak out as one of the very few who were aware of his subversive extra activities for the Allied prisoners. The astonished camp commander (British) apologised and asked Corner to shake his hand. The cleared trio were eventually repatriated.

Michael Brown's telling is flawed. This 'trial' could not have been during internment since it involved the newly-arrived Col Archey after the war. My father has his own version of that trial. It is similar to, yet very different from that of Brown's – and my father doesn't call it a trial.

He wrote that rumours of his complicity spread in the Maxwell Road Internment Camp after he signed the oath of obedience offered to all internees by the Japanese. The rumours were fostered by a Mr B and 'his unlucky colleagues', and even by Bishop Wilson, who had every reason to know better. These rumours prospered, my father commented, until after the Japanese surrender when Mr B and others came to the museum and openly accused him, before Col Archey, of their arrest.

'Pent up for three years', my father wrote:

I exploded and made them apologise before the Colonel [Archey] and the Museum staff for what I called a damnable lie. They were obliged to shake hands with me, and I reflected on the old motto '*Dieu me garde de calomnie*' (French, God preserve me from calumny).

In 2011, I returned again to the files in that folder given me by Dr Janet West and those containing the letters to E. Barton Worthington. There, in the letter to Worthington of 10 August 1931, is a footnote which says:

in a few days I must take over from the Professor of Biology at the College of medicine… **Mr B of *The Marquis*** [my emphasis].

The Professor of Biology at the King Edward VII College of Medicine in 1931 was Professor B. A. R. Gater, M.A. (Cantab.), D.I.C. Professor Gater (1896-1976) was interned in Singapore during the Occupation in the Maxwell Road Camp.

I wonder how long it was after the war that the Colonial Office finally recognised and approved my father's work during the occupation of Singapore. If given, this recognition seems not to have reached many for there was much bitterness after many years – and my father was aware of such ill feelings.

In 1977, Dr David Mabberley, my father's last Cambridge research student, had invited my father to his wedding.

When he discovered that I was to marry a Changi POW's daughter, he asked not to come to the wedding, but it must be admitted that my father-in-law to be said that HE would not come to the wedding if EJHC was there.

This incident illustrates the depth of those feelings 32 years after the war.

*

When *The Marquis* was published, it was reviewed by two people with most contrasting opinions.

Donald Wise, a journalist and Australian, wrote 'Strange memoirs of a man of science' for the *Far East Economic Review*, published in the 12 February 1982 edition. It was a scathing review. Wise had been a prisoner of the Japanese.

The other was by Sir Hugh Cortazzi, the then British Ambassador to Japan, in May 1982. Published in the *Journal of the Malaysian Branch of the Royal Asiatic Society*, it gave an entirely different and more balanced perspective.

Eric Holttum, on reading my father's book, was absolutely furious. I learnt this from his daughter, Deborah, who wrote:

[H]e became very angry because it was so one-sided and failed to recognise my father's part in it all and there's no denying the acute stress the book had on father at the time.

Spurred by my father's book, Holttum made a statement which he lodged at the herbarium of the Royal Botanic Gardens at Kew. Deborah kindly sent me a copy and with her approval I quote:

In 1929 a Pacific Science Congress was held in Java. The Government of the Netherlands East Indies made elaborate preparations to ensure that delegates to the Congress had information about work in progress at scientific institutions of all kinds in what is now Indonesia, and arranged a series of excursions before and after the meetings of the congress. There was a large Japanese delegation which included the Marquis of Tokugawa, Professor Hidezo Tanakadate (vulcanology) from the University of Tohoku and Professor Kwan Koriba (botany) from the University of Kyoto. I was one of the Singapore delegates and met these Japanese delegates.

Two days after the surrender of Singapore in February 1942, I cycled into the city and went to the Government offices in the Fullerton Building. There, by chance, I met Mr E. J. H. Corner, Assistant Director at the Gardens, who had been seconded to organise food production in Singapore after the Japanese attack on the north of Malaya. He suggested that I should go to the Municipal Offices [City Hall]. I did so and by good fortune there met Professor Tanakadate. He recognised me at once and said, "I conserve cultural institutions, and I want you to remain at the Botanic Gardens to maintain them for the future of this country." I felt it to be my duty to comply with that request. Later that morning, Professor Tanakadate met me at the Gardens. We found that the Japanese military had chalked notices on the Gardens Office and Herbarium requisitioning them for military use. Professor Tanakadate rubbed off the military chalk-marks with his own hands and substituted his own notices. He also asked me to lock up some of his personal valuables in the Gardens safe. He then went to the Raffles Museum and Library, of which he also took charge, and later to Java, to see that the Botanic Gardens at Bogor and associated institutes were placed under protection.

Looking back, it appeared to me evident that Professor Tanakadate had long been assigned a role in the Japanese military plans for the invasion of SE Asia. When he went to Japan later in 1942 Professor Tanakadate made a personal report to the Emperor, as he told Corner when he returned to Singapore. I believe Tanakadate's mission in SE Asia was due to direct orders from the Emperor. The Emperor's personal assistant, in his study of Mycetozoa (an Imperial hobby), who also attended the 1929 Congress, spent a day soon afterwards in the Singapore Botanic Gardens collecting specimens.

As regards the Marquis Tokugawa, he travelled southwards in Malaya a few days after the Japanese army, calling on the Malay Sultans, to assure them of their protection. I believe that this role had been assigned to him, and that it is significant that immediately after the 1929 Congress the Marquis stayed with the Sultan of Johore, who organised for him an elephant-shooting party. I know of this because Professor Geoffrey Taylor (from Cambridge), a delegate to the 1929 Congress, went to Japan, where he had dinner with the Marquis, and on the dinner menu were steaks from the Johore elephant.

After reaching Singapore, the Marquis had some important role in connection with the Japanese military government and the civilian population. He was not concerned with scientific institutions until Tanakadate asked him to assume the title of Honorary President of the Gardens and Museum, with a view to ensuring that the military did not interfere with Tanakadate's arrangements in his absence on his visit to Tokyo. The Marquis continued in this position until he left for Japan in the middle of 1944. Mr Corner, in his book *The Marquis*, relates that he resolved to attempt to co-operate with Japanese authorities in the preservation of scientific collections, libraries etc., *and that he asked Sir Shenton Thomas (Governor of the Straits Settlements) to write a note requesting Japanese support for Corner in this activity.* [My emphasis for here is another implication, rather statement, that the idea was my father's]. He did not show me the Governor's note. But as regards the Gardens and Museum, Tanakadate took action without meeting Corner. [This is true, but my father had given Shenton Thomas' note to

Toyoda who in turn gave it to Tanakadate.] Subsequently, Corner was able to suggest other important salvage work outside the Gardens and Museum. By far the most important salvage was that of the final proofs of a book written by C. F. Symington on trees of the *Dipterocarp* family, the most important family of timber trees in Malaya. Symington had spent years of research in preparation of this book, at the Forest Research Institute, Kepong, near Kuala Lumpur. Tanakadate ensured that the printing of the book was completed, wrote an introduction and arranged for publication. In the later chapters of his book, Corner let Tanakadate fade out of the picture and implied that the Marquis was the more important person. In this, I believe, he was unfair to Tanakadate, without whom Corner could have done nothing.

This statement, like my father's book, was written long after the events and I believe both authors, even with the best of intentions, had allowed some of the finer detail of the circumstances to fade from the memory. Their stories are similar yet different; I know that my father came to hate Eric Holttum and my father allowed that, after the war, to spill over into his family. It's only in recent years that I have come to understand things better and I realise that that hate was very much misplaced. I do know that someone black-balled the vote when Holttum was put forward for election to a Fellowship of the Royal Society of London. Could that have been my father? Sadly I believe it was.

The Marquis was my father's way of explaining much of his actions during the Japanese Occupation, and Holttum's involvement was superfluous to what my father wanted to write and say. He disregarded Holttum's actions just as he did on other matters – like leaving out my mother and me from the story – except just once by implication. He, my father, and his relationship with the Japanese were the centre of his story.

Deborah Holttum wrote to me in 2008:

How much you can gather from father's statement, written, as it was, so long after the event, I'm not sure. But I'm sure that much of that stage of his life, during the Occupation, must have been indelibly imprinted in his mind. When I witnessed his distressed demeanour when talking on the phone to Robin Miller [who had hoped to make a film of all of this but it never reached fruition] about it there was no doubt in my mind how much this still affected him.

Do remember that at the time his statement was written Corner was still alive, and from time to time something would crop up to upset father concerning Corner, and his health deteriorated, noticeably; on one occasion when he was delirious, and rambling incoherently (quite a lot of Latin amongst it) Corner's name cropped up quite a lot. When father was in hospital – and profoundly deaf, as he had been for some time – I had to explain to the nursing staff that if he mentioned Corner, in any context, that it was a person to whom he was referring, and not something in a corner causing him concern.

Two very different kinds of people had differing yet similar views of what happened although the end result was much the same. Corner and Holttum, *vive la difference*.

*

In 2007, I was trying to find records of the compensation paid to prisoners of war, and I believe my father was paid a good sum, when the professional researcher that I had employed stumbled on a report. He didn't find the information about the compensation, but the report gave an official view of my father's war-time activities.

This *General Report on the state of Buildings, Museums, Monuments and Gardens in Malaya* was written on 8 November 1945 by a senior British officer of the British Military Administration:

(iii) Mr Corner and Mr Birtwistle were retained at the Museum by the Japanese. They had no executive authority, but were able to make suggestions to the Japanese directors for the better preservation of collections and books.

By their foresight and initiative many valuable books and records from outside sources were saved from destruction: chief among these are the Chief Secretary's Library, Attorney General's Library, 586 volumes of Malayan Archives of the East India Company and five law libraries. The action of these officers in remaining at their scientific posts despite the adverse view of this which inevitably arose among those who were interned, has had results of the utmost value and scientific importance, and is to be highly commended.

The 17 November 1945 edition of *The Straits Times* records that:

Behind the announcement that the Raffles Library will soon be reopened is a story of how some of the biggest law libraries in Singapore were saved from destruction when the Japanese took over the country in 1942. The man who saved these valuable books is Mr E. J. H. Corner, former Assistant Director of Gardens SS. When Singapore fell in 1942 Mr Corner obtained "carte blanche" from the Governor, Sir Shenton Thomas, to do what he could to preserve scientific books, records and so on, under the guise of handing over the Museum and Botanic Gardens to the Japanese. Mr Corner went round personally and was able to save the law library of Braddell Bros., as well as Mr Richard (sic) Braddell's personal library transferring them to the Museum. During June, July and August, 1942, the law libraries of Drew and Napier, Allen and Gledhill, Sisson and Delay, Chan and Eber and Donaldson and Burkinshaw were transferred to the Museum. Other private collections of books were also grouped and brought to the Museum for storage. By this means a very large number of books was saved. Now clerks are working overtime to sort out these libraries and send them off to their owners. Mr Corner, who stayed back to help with the clearing up, is on his way back to England for a well-earned rest.

In spite of the report and this article, published in the main newspaper of the region in November 1945, which so accurately explains what my father achieved in saving so much, my father's actions remained under suspicion for too many years.

I have no doubt that David Mabberley's title 'A tropical botanist finally vindicated' is absolutely correct. David told me he owed it to my father to write the article. Indeed, Brian Montgomery, the author of *Shenton of Singapore*, wrote in his book:

Professor Corner's book *The Marquis* reveals him, all too belatedly, as a great man, possessing courage and determination not often seen; above all, he had the moral courage to stand his ground and put up with much unfair criticism and comment. For, not surprisingly, he was often the subject of jealousy and accusation by some British prisoners of war, who saw him apparently free and untrammelled while they lived as prisoners in hardship and privation.

Shenton Thomas' note, which too many doubted existed, and some still doubt, did exist and the subsequent story surrounding it is one of selfless, even relentless devotion to a duty that the British military particularly could not accept. This I find understandable considering the times, but too much misinformation was being put around and the important issues became clouded no doubt for political reasons. People were, as always, blinkered to the view which they wanted to believe.

My father hated the Japanese military and said so frequently but he found very different Japanese in the scientists who came to Singapore. A letter from The Professor, Hidezo Tanakadate, to my father from Tokyo dated 3 March 1948 clearly shows the warmth of friendship.

It is a great miracle that we are both still alive today although in places far apart on the globe. I shall never forget your blood-and-tears toil in the midst of unprincipled enemies, to protect scientific treasures and cultural equipment against the vandalism of the people and soldiers. Whenever I recollect those fateful days in Singapore in February 1942, I seem to hear the grotesque croakings of the frogs in the night squalls at the Botanical Gardens and I am moved to tears, and I would like to express my sincere gratitude for your painstaking earnest collaboration with me which I as a member of the enemy did not deserve… Here in Japan, the ravages of war finally caught up with me one night in July 1945, when all the scientific material and documents gathered and compiled by myself during the past thirty-five years went up in flames during a raid [including Shenton Thomas' note]. Only a pencil and two dictionaries were left to me, and so I am no longer a scientist and the Tanakadate School of Vulcanology came to a premature end…. Mr Tokugawa told me that a newspaper in Singapore had stated that the Japanese Army had done only two good things while in Singapore: one was the manufacture of a vaccine solution by the military medical staff and the other, the almost perfect conservation of the Museum and the enlargement of the library. Thanks to your effort I have been able to contribute to this last.

This was written just three years before Tanakadate passed away; my father wrote the Professor's obituary which was published in *Nature*, Vol. 167, 14 April 1951.

*

In 2007, the late Roderick MacLean of the Malayan Civil Service, introduced by Audrey McCormick, wrote to me:

I first came to Singapore in 1950 and I found to my amazement that the expatriate community was divided into those who were 'in camp' and those who for various reasons were not caught by the Japanese. In such an atmosphere your father was not understood by the 'in camp' crowd and wisely decided to cut his links and pursue his career in South America.

I think your father was badly directed and not understood by lesser men. My impression from a brief contact in 1964 was of a hard man, difficult to know unless you had read *The Marquis*; I think he was a brave man who put his profession first and deserves great credit for his role in Singapore 1942–1945.

MacLean introduced me electronically to Mary Turnbull, also of the Malay Civil Service and author of *A History of Singapore*. She told me how grateful she was to 'Corner and his Japanese superiors' for protecting all the pre-1860s archives in the Raffles Museum because this enabled her to write her doctoral thesis and her book on the history of Singapore. When Turnbull arrived in Malaya in 1952, my father had long since left and the stark problems of the Communist Emergency were overshadowing memories of the Occupation. Yet, she said, 'amongst former civilian internees, Corner's name still conjured up bitterness and contempt as a collaborator, traitor, and self-seeker'.

Turnbull gave important perspective to this lingering feeling:

I hope you don't find some of my comments too distressing, but presumably you want a rounded picture and know your father's wartime career made him a controversial figure. It wasn't just that he was spared prison camp. There were a few other British internees who were employed by the Japanese to work outside in town for a time – doctors, journalists, engineers, the Bishop etc – and some spoke kindly of individual Japanese they worked for, though none spent so long in semi-freedom or lived in the same comparative comfort; but they all regarded co-operation as a necessity, not a source of personal and professional satisfaction, in the way that your father did. Actually I was surprised he was so dismissive of all his countrymen. There wasn't much intellectual stimulus in colonial society in general in the 1930s Singapore, and most expatriates' horizons didn't extend beyond golf and bridge. But there were also some very able scientists and other staff in Raffles College, the Museum and Government departments, and some of these people were still there when I arrived in Malaya in 1952. About your father's scientific career there was, of course, no controversy at all. He was universally admired by his colleagues and worshipped by his students.

She gave further insight in a letter to Michael Brown and in connection with the proposed film:

Your letter refers to Corner being 'obliged to carry on, almost as normal', but it would be truer to say 'incredibly lucky to be able to carry on, almost as normal'. Undoubtedly he had anxious moments, but far from 'enduring great hardship', he certainly had a more comfortable time than any other British and Allied prisoners or the vast majority of the Asian population.

Of *The Marquis*, Turnbull said it 'was hailed as a unique and fascinating insight into an extraordinary episode', which it certainly was. 'Indeed it is remarkable', she continued, 'in that he makes almost no attempt to soften, explain or excuse, nor to set the experiences in a wider context. This is left to the reader, and some of it makes chilling reading'.

As a conclusion to her letter to Michael Brown, Turnbull said:

Corner comes across on the evidence of this book as a man for whom Science took priority over people and who brooked no interference with his plans – as seen in his satisfaction at the internment of an irritating colleague [Mr B], his glee at the death, in a car crash, of someone he saw as an obstacle [Mrs Arbenz], his relief at the Japanese decision to keep other scientists in prison camp. Above all, his willingness to sign an oath of obedience to the Japanese, which disgusted fellow British prisoners and was in stark contrast to the resistance of others – the Gurkhas, for instance, who refused to a man to submit even when the Japanese killed their officers in front of them. On the other hand, Corner did have the courage of his convictions, and never wavered in his praise for the Japanese he knew and worked with, when such views were deeply unpopular.

After reading Michael Brown's 'Secret heroism of the men who grew orchids for the Japanese', which I sent her for she hadn't before seen the article, Turnbull responded in May 2008:

> The official reaction after the War was to admit that some co-operation with the Japanese was inevitable and only to condemn as collaboration action which aimed to damage the Allied war effort or which resulted in injury or death. There was no question of your father's work doing that, and I don't think even his most bitter critics ever asserted such an accusation. Every internee working outside the camps had to sign a pledge of obedience, but other internees were angry that your father had so readily signed the required promise of co-operation – as he shows in his book.
>
> On the other hand, the reference to his secretly helping internees sounds rather dubious. This would have been so dangerous that it would have been a risk not only to himself and his colleagues but to their work, and everything in your father's book – and as far as I can judge in his whole life – points to his giving priority to his professional work above any other relationships. Supplying food etc to prisoners involved contact with networks in touch with the camps – terribly dangerous – the sort of thing that resulted in the imprisonment, torture and death of so many civilian internees in the notorious Double Tenth incident. And there is no evidence he did this.

Turnbull is not correct in this view. The tapes that Professor Ishii sent me confirm his help for internees, assisted by the *towkay*, and I don't think my father would have made up the references he makes to this in *The Marquis*. Turnbull continued:

The only help he might have been able to offer would have been to try to persuade the Japanese to take some former colleagues out of the camp into his team – and his book makes clear that he didn't want any of them to interfere and spoil his work. 'He is completely honest in the admiration he expressed for his exceptional wartime Japanese colleagues and considered them superior to their colonial counterparts. In his book he indicates that he was rather glad to see his former associates out of the way behind bars. This wasn't collaboration in any harmful sense, but it was understandably galling to many of his countrymen whose experience at the hands of a quite different sort of Japanese had been humiliation, suffering and sometimes extreme brutality.

Reading about your own family experiences reinforces the view that I get from your father's book that, while it is right to challenge the portrayal of him as a traitor and collaborator, I think it would be wrong to go to the other extreme and paint him as a hero. But without doubt he was a very distinguished and remarkable scientist, who achieved a great deal and left a valuable legacy.

Mary Turnbull's writings, I believe, offer a balanced appreciation.

*

My father was not the only one who was accused of being a collaborator and ostracised. William Birtwistle was too. On his return to England after the war, his life became uncomfortable because too many considered him to have collaborated and so he went to Eire where he settled with his wife, Alice, in Skibbereen. Birtwistle wrote to my father frequently between 1949 and 1952.

Here are some extracts from those letters; he particularly was worried about the 'outbreak of peace' in Singapore, as was my father.

I always felt anxious about the outbreak of peace… I feel somehow that surrounded as we were by 'enemies', it was preferable than being surrounded by friends of the kind we both knew… I find it so difficult to hate nations. There are so many good ones among the sodden masses and who are worth so much… in many ways there was some strange satisfaction in having nothing [in occupied Singapore], yet having so much. There were no tax forms to fill, and few conventions. Poor coolies were our friends. We had no 'talks over the radio' on the latest films, scandal in parliament, or strikes… how often I dread the outbreak of peace.

I wish I could win a sweep and organise an expedition to some place with you and I as chiefs… I remember after the 1914–1918 war someone said in Liverpool that he thought the world was being populated by the worst instead of the best. I am beginning to believe it… Thank you for your letter and the snaps. I think it is a good thing to see one-self without any flattery. I had no idea I looked so old [6 June 1950]. It would be agreeable if there was an exclusive circle of the best people. Shadows of old Tanakadate; soon there will be Japanese in London. It would be fun if Koriba could come… I have become quite cynical.

I have thought about this letter and on reflection think it may well show the feelings of many who survived war, with all its horrors and dangers, who find themselves returning to their home country and discovering it so different from that which they left behind. We hold cherished memories of the past and, even perhaps subconsciously, we expect nothing to have changed. The reality is often a great shock; and difficult for many to come to grips with, absorb, and adapt to. What had they fought for?

How to live again with people, family and friends who never experienced what those returning had endured, and to which they have had to become hardened, and many feel unable to talk about? How can one explain and describe the circumstances of war in all their guises? Virtually impossible and I am sure that after the war, people really didn't want to relive those circumstances. I feel sure my father went through all of this. Indeed many from those days had that British stiff upper lip; it wasn't done to cry on another's shoulder. Many suffered deeply and so many were misunderstood.

In the final chapter of *Botanical Monkeys*, my father wrote:

When peace returned and I hoped that the good old days would be restored, I planned again a school of botanical monkeys. The experiment had succeeded. The tragedies had brought their sad lessons. We would improve. That dream died as it dawned. Often in Amazonia, I wished for Merah and Puteh.

My father was reminiscing in 1990, as he penned the manuscript, clearly recalling the happy times of Malaya. I can appreciate his wish to return to those days, but this, sadly, could never have been anything more than a pipe-dream.

XVI

TO THE OTHER SIDE
OF THE WORLD

My mother and I arrived in San Francisco from Australia in June 1942. We sailed from New York in February 1943, arriving in England either late that month or the beginning of March. At that time, my father's whereabouts must still have been unknown to my mother, beyond that he was incarcerated in Singapore. I don't think that even then she had any idea of what he was doing, even if he was safe. I am equally sure my father's parents knew nothing either and certainly not the circumstances of his 'capture' by the Japanese. My mother did write to him to tell him that we were safe in England.

I don't know why we went so quickly to England rather than safely see out the war in America. It must have been imperative because we crossed the Atlantic at a dangerous time. I conclude that it was for money, the money my father said would send. I feel sure that this plan was discussed before our evacuation and mother knew what to do. And we did post-haste cross two vast oceans by ship in six months during war!

On arrival in England, mother and I stayed with Grandfather and Grannie Corner in Beaconsfield, in the large house on the fringes called *Stratton End*. Mother's photo album confirms we were there on 1 March, with pictures of me, with dog, in the garden looking settled and well turned out.

I can remember the chimes of the grandfather clocks, the lovely big garden and collecting the silver foil from that garden in the mornings – the radar-reflecting foil dropped by the Germans to confuse the British radar.

We went on to Robin Hill's house, *Vatches Farm* in Grantchester, in March and in May 1943 we were at *Rainscombe Farm* with my cousins, the Hurds. There are pictures of the farm, Aunts Anne and Isabel, Douglas whom mother called Doug, Julian whom she called Jo, and Stephen. There are pictures with me and Grannie Corner. We were back at *Stratton End* in June 1943 and the album has photos of Uncle Dana in uniform. My mother wrote, 'Dana's farewell, before going to Washington and the Far East'.

The album reveals that in the Autumn of 1943, we spent time with the Worthingtons at their house, *Keen Ground*, Hawkshead, in the Lake District close to Windermere, no doubt to be away from the bombing. We were back at *Stratton End* by my birthday of 1944 and the photographs show me in party hat with Douglas, Julian, Stephen and James (the dog); the house is clearly shown in the background, the only photos I have of *Stratton End*.

By mid-January 1944, we were in Buckingham with the Newmans (Professor Max and Lynn), the pictures being of me with Edward and William, their children. In April 1944 we were at *Weatheroak*, the Eckersley's house, near Danbury, Essex.

Then, in June 1944, we visited Girton, to the north of Cambridge where Belinda and I lived so very many years later. The photos show Mother, me and Gladys in a garden. This could have been a temporary stop before moving to Great Shelford because the next ones are dated June 1944, showing Mother, Linda Wickham from next door, and me in the garden of 15 The Park, Great Shelford.

I was pleased to find the photos of us at *Rainscombe*; those were happy days and we were there again in April 1945. The farm is south of Marlborough and just north of Oare where the Aunts lived at Bennetts. Under the delightful picture in the garden, my mother had written 'the beloved Aunts "A" and "I"'.

We had moved to Great Shelford by Spring 1945. My memory of those times is woolly; I was only four and a bit. I do remember the VE (Victory Europe) celebrations on 8 May and recall sailing a grey painted metal model destroyer in the *Rainscombe* swimming pool. There are many pictures of that time, with friends and neighbours and of the VJ (Victory Japan) Day party on 15 August 1945, both in our garden and the street. It seems that Elizabeth Morley, later to go to school with my wife, Belinda, won first prize for her dress-of-the-day and I was second in my sailor suit, now with my son, Andy.

In June 1945, we visited Sandsend at Whitby in Yorkshire with Bobby Walker, from Singapore, and her children Sue, Mike and Tim; there are pictures of all. The village is located at the foot of Lythe Bank, a short drive from Whitby where many 'older' Corners are buried, going back to the 18th century. We were in Grantchester in July 1945 and among those pictures of me are ones of Peter and Gladys Le Mare. It looks like a picnic trip. They were, I believe, friends from Singapore.

Amongst the pictures are two family photos dated January 1946 showing the reunited Corner family: my father, Mother and me – good quality pictures and happy ones. Yet, at that time, my father was very busy trying to sort out the Colonial Office matters. He was out of work. I wonder if my mother knew that. The next few pages are of photos showing me with my father during our visit to *Rainscombe* for Easter 1946, and a photo dated 12 May 1946 showing me with Uncle Dana's sword, the samurai sword he sent me which I still have.

In June 1946, the three Corners went to Ireland to visit the Birtwistles. Some pictures show me with my father on the beach. Here, I learned about model sailing boats; we were sailing one. Our stay in England was coming to an end and there are a few photos of the family in Great Shelford dated August and September 1946.

The last photos of the album are of America, dated February 1947, including pictures of me at *The Mouse Hole* – my maternal grandmother's house – in the snow, and one of the house, a part view but the only one I have. I vividly recall the weeks at *The Mouse Hole* but was surprised to see how close the woods were to the house! The album brought back some of those happy memories… memories that would become sad ones.

*

My father returned from Singapore to the Great Shelford house in time for Christmas 1945. I was amost four but I can't recall a joyous reunion. I do just remember a father returning; this was the first time I was old enough to know him and I recall some things like a rather sombre man yet most of the photos show me as cheerful.

Beyond that, I do remember my new friends in the road, the Morleys, Wickhams (no relation to the Twyford Wickhams) and others and going to the Great Shelford village school, and Sunday School at the village church of St Mary's, which I didn't much like. The album photo shows me smartly turned out; my mother would not have had it different, and quite rightly.

Belinda and I visited the village in June 2007 and called, without any prior notice, at this Shelford house. The owner rushed from greeting us at the door to return with a postcard which she gave to me. It was addressed to Mrs John Corner, my mother, and was dated 4 May 1946! It was from Aunt Do, who was then Head Housekeeper at Hyde Park Hotel, wishing her happy birthday for 8 May, and saying that a parcel was on the way from Selfridges. The owner of the house told us that they had recently moved in and when they redecorated the sitting room, various cards and papers were found which had slipped behind the tiled fireplace surround. Why she kept them one will never know. She had no idea where we lived, or that we were to visit. What she put into my hands was a postcard yellowed from 61 years of warmth!

Whilst walking in the garden I noticed a man next door. I called over the fence and in conversation mentioned that we used to live here in the mid-1940s; the Billings were our next-door neighbours and I remembered them having a three-wheeled car and a motor bike. "Yes," he said "I am married to one. The Morgan is in the garage and I still have the motor bike!"

We walked up the road and visited the house opposite where the Morleys lived. The present owner bought it from them and told me stories of Shelford and the very church at which I attended Sunday school. I tracked down Richard Morley via his sister Elizabeth living in Canada who was known to a long-time friend of Belinda's. Elizabeth sent me two photographs of the VJ celebrations, similar to the ones I had found in the album. I keep in touch with Richard after a gap of more than 50 years.

In those days I was called Kay. My father was Edred John Henry but called John to avoid confusion with his father, Edred Moss. I was named John Kavanagh but called 'K', which became Kay, to avoid confusion with my father John! I grew to dislike that as a name and reverted to John in the early 1960s. Pandora revealed a nickname used by my father for my mother and enquiries today confirm that no one knows of this! On a birthday card from my father to Mother dated 8 May 1946 is the name 'Beck'.

*

When my father returned to England he must have been troubled. His writing in *The Marquis* gives the impression of a serene life, taking excursions, continuing his research and of conversations with the Professor and the Marquis. Yet it cannot have been. His life in Singapore, even though he had the support of the Japanese scientists, was one of almost daily risk because neither he nor anyone could know if and when the military police would pounce. Then, almost suddenly, the war was over. He was free and looking to return home. No doubt he felt relief but in many ways it must also have been a great let down, a huge anti-climax. He had to leave the Colonial Office when he had so much more science to give. He was married with a young son and likely little money and few possessions, all being lost in Singapore.

On 17 May 1946, my father wrote a demanding letter to Holttum in Singapore, clearly in anger, about his returning to work in the Land of the Dendrons:

> I have a horrible feeling there is going to be a hell of a row over the "Gardens Dept. S.S.". I am scheduled to return [to Singapore] in October, but I shall not return without a proper new appointment at this end & that must be pan-Malayan.

He stated clearly that he believed the Colonial Office had broken his contract, indeed all their contracts, and he made clear to Holttum that they must be offered new ones. Then my father laid down some conditions: he would consider nothing if the Singapore Gardens were to be separated from the Waterfall Gardens in Penang, or if it was to come under 'Agriculture'. In either case, he said he would 'raise as much row as I can, personally and from biologists in England'. He closed his letter by hoping that 'we do not now witness the end of Malayan botany'.

My father wrote another letter to Holltum on 27 August 1946, setting out his feelings and attitudes in bold and scathing terms. He confirmed that he would return to Singapore as soon as he could, suggesting an arrival by the end of October 1946. His purpose was

> to obtain from some Governor a statement that my appt. as Asst, D. of G, S S, has been abolished. I have tried to obtain this in England from Col. Off. & had no answer since March.

Further, he wished to discuss what position he might be offered. He said that, as someone in the Colonial Service without an appointment, he would formally meet the Governor and that, as he wasn't yet appointed to the Botanic Gardens, he could not negotiate through Holltum as Director of the Gardens. He made it clear that he would not accept the position of Assistant Director of the Gardens citing it as 'a new and junior appt. to what I have held'. However, if Holltum was to put my father's name forward to be his successor he would accept, being his duty, saying 'in the hope that improvement will come'. If this did not transpire, he planned to take legal action on the grounds that his position had been abolished without notice to him, resulting in his dismissal 'and the destruction of all my work in Malaya'.

Writing that their botanical work whilst in office in Malaya had by 1946 reached a low state, he confirmed that only by strong objection and enormous effort could it be restored. My father pointed out that the Dutch were already planning a new Botanic Garden in the Celebes and that there was a programme of enlargement in Sumatra. On the contrary, 'Penang Waterfall Gardens have gone to the limb of Agriculture'. Scornfully, he voiced his belief that 'this is a plan for more kudos' for George Allen, a member of the council of Raffles College. He argued that 'none of the major Bot. Gdns. of the world are affiliated to Universities' and Raffles College has taken and really destroyed 'the Economic Garden, therefore what guarantee in the future'. Scathingly, he suggested that all the Gardens needed was a junior lecturer in botany with a groundsman and personnel – 'I imagine he [Allen] merely hopes to use "us" as teachers of 3rd-rate botany to Asiatics'.

He stated that he had not received any official acknowledgement of the books he had sent and that he didn't expect it 'from men who interned Dr. Koriba. We have enjoyed such a cheat as is worthy of the third-rate administration of the British Colonies'.

He ended by plainly saying that assuming he would return to Singapore, he would, before he departed, contact all botanists in Great Britian 'informing them of the state into which the Gardens Dept. S.S. has fallen'.

In the top left corner of this letter my father added, 'If there is no room for me & my family in the Botanic Gardens please let me know, so that I can write to Chua Ho Ann' where accommodation was assured.

What a letter! Forthright as was typical of my father, but I doubt that it was helpful. He was hardly polite to Dr Holttum and such attitudes would only harden the resolve of the Colonial Office.

My father didn't make the trip. No post in the East seemed likely, although he had hoped for a position in Buitenzorg Gardens in Bogor, Indonesia. Reading this correspondence, not only do I see a very angry man, understandably so, but I see a tired man going about things in an antagonistic way.

In 1946, Murray Ross Henderson was appointed Acting Director of the Singapore Botanic Gardens. When Eric Holttum retired from the Botanic Gardens in 1949 and assumed the chair of Professor of Botany at the newly formed University of Malaya in Singapore, Henderson was promoted to Director of the Gardens.

I believe that Holttum appointed Henderson and left my father out to dry. My father had made his own bed from the early 1930s and his attitude to Dr Holttum was bringing its returns.

My father was medically boarded out allowing him to retire from the Colonial Service on medical grounds, with pension. The British Military Administration had exonerated him from wrong doings during the Japanese Occupation, but it was thought that retiring him was the best way for all concerned because the feelings of those interned were running very strong against those not interned, and something had to be done with him, being a difficult man! The matter of his time during the Occupation would not go away. My father's intransigence sealed his fate although I can well understand his utter exasperation.

Officially, he remained persona non grata and nowhere do I find any reference to his visiting the Colonial Office to give his side of the story. My father was not a man given to excuse and explanation; he had very high standards and these may well have rankled with the Colonial Office.

The letters between him and Holttum show that he was angry and feeling very let down by all around him, and there was little he could do.

Terry Waite spoke of these things at an address at the Remembrance Service held at the National Arboretum, England, on 17 August 2008:

> [T]hose who endured the hardships of those [war] years either as serviceman, workers at home or wives and children can take comfort in the fact that the trauma experienced then can, and frequently does, diminish as we grow older.
>
> For many this has been a long process as when former prisoners were returned to their home countries in 1945/6 the majority were told not to talk about the experience but to forget it and get on with their lives. As a result, many wives felt a deep sense of isolation as there was a significant part of their partner's life that was closed to them. Many

former prisoners who followed the injunction found that instead of speaking about the past and gradually exorcising the pain they were condemned to relive the experience in dreams and nightmares.

Of course this tension within the family, often hidden from the outside world and certainly not understood within the family rubbed off on the children. There is no blame to be attached to these experiences. In those days the authorities knew no better and families had to cope as best they might. It reflects enormous credit on the vast majority, who, despite enormous handicaps managed to survive and survive well.

My father was not strictly speaking a prisoner in Singapore but his life was not one of freedom; he was a prisoner of circumstance. I believe he may have chosen not to discuss his experiences with his wife and family. However, blame was placed for the forthcoming family problems as time went on, and somehow I felt a cause.

Did my father feel it difficult to discuss his experiences because of all the pointing fingers? Did he believe there was something to be hidden? Was there a feeling of guilt? For whatever reason, he increasingly denigrated and belittled his wife and berated me for my poor school reports such that the atmosphere in the house became so tense and strained that it eventually became impossible to live with.

Still, I can recall the happiness of my boyhood in Great Shelford, of making friends in the street and enjoying the trains which regularly passed through the local station a few minutes' walk away. Here began my interest in collecting train numbers, and of course I wanted to be a train driver. In Pandora was one of my train-number collecting books, published by Ian Allen, a well-known publisher of such things. My father knew how much I enjoyed collecting the numbers. Was this why he included the book?

I cycled up and down The Park on my tricycle, the road being a cul-de-sac and unadopted and safe from traffic; with friends I played cowboys and Indians in the undulating shrubby common-land at the top of the road and behind the station platforms. I remember Christmas celebrations and finding an orange at the toe-end of my stocking with a small packet of Sun-Pat raisins. We enjoyed making all our decorations. The Christmas tree was lit by unguarded candles, and there was never a fire! The mechanical toy train I was given for 1946 Christmas – gauge '00' with just a circular track, I recall – kept me well occupied.

My father must have been busy sorting out what to do next and where his work would lead him. I suspect he had become accustomed to warmer climes and that he sought something which included those. He was already convinced that research in tropical botany was vital to the understanding of so much and this must have had strong influence. His botanical motto was: 'you should always go and see for yourself'. And so to Brazil and the

Amazon he would go, with UNESCO.

This new job was my father's second since leaving Cambridge in 1928. I am sure he was encouraged to it by his good friend Julian Huxley who was elected the first Director-General of UNESCO in December 1946.

Late in 1946, there were three UNESCO Principal Field Scientific Officer jobs advertised, one of which was for Asia and based in Malaya to set up and organise the Field Science Cooperation Office in the Far East. My father had known that the post in Asia was to be created, and he had shown interest and applied. UNESCO went as far as to write to Worthington in Africa for a reference. However, there was a delay in that FSCO decision for Asia and my father was redirected to Brazil.

The job of the Principal Field Scientific Officer in Brazil is well described in the 1947 'Programme for the Field Scientific Co-operation Office, Latin America' (UNESCO/N/S/3/1947 Paris March 25th 1947 by Patrick Petitjean):

> To obtain first-hand knowledge of the scientific organisations, research and personnel in Latin America, with the object of assisting scientific co-operation between Latin American countries and, through the Counsellor for Field Stations at Paris, between these countries and the rest of the world. The exchange of scientific information, the calling of regional conferences, the arrangement of expeditions and the issue of publications will be considered. So far as possible, visits will be made to scientific institutions, etc., to gain personal contact and to discuss the ways and means of co-operation. The start will be made at Rio de Janeiro and San Paulo, and thence to Belem in connection with the Hylean Amazon project. Later in the year, the Principal Field Scientific Officer will visit the capitals of other Latin-American countries.

The pressure to find a position, and a salary, must have been enormous for my father at that time. He also allowed his love of the tropics to rule his mind – the thought of having time to continue his work which he had begun in Singapore and Malaya. The prospect seemed to have made him disregard that this job would be fraught with political intrigues and battles to the extent that he would have to be as much a politician as scientist. Politics was something he hated; it was not him. He was something of a loner yet here he was about to start work in a vast and new international organisation.

In my research about the UNESCO job and Brazil, a common thread came through – my father couldn't get to grips with the political side of it all. Competent scientist as he was, he was not good in the patience stakes and he had differences of opinion with the political people. Communication was not always swift and mostly over long distances by letters and telegrams. From what I learned, he usually was right in his views but often didn't express them in a tactful way. My father continued to claim to be non-political through out his life, and I believe generally he was – particularly when it suited him.

XVII

FRACTURE

In September 1946, when the decision to go to Brazil was close to being made, my mother was pregnant (as she wrote in the caption of one of the album photos) and soon we both were off to America to stay with Gramma Bailey in preparation for the birth.

Gramma Baily wrote to me on 6 December 1946, addressed c/o Grannie Corner at *Stratton End*. This letter, full of information, shows my American grandmother so well.

She began by telling me that she had just sent some parcels to England being the last day for this until the coal strike was settled. They were Christmas presents, cards and the like. She told also of having posted a parcel to *Beaconsfield*, Grannie Corner, 'for your father's birthday, though I must admit, it contains nothing very exciting'. She was clearly most disappointed not to be able to include 'some of the cigarettes & tobacco as planned, but such things seem a bit scarce at present, and the particular kinds he prefers were not available in time'.

She reflected that in a month mother and I would start our journey to America and that soon I would be looking out for post from England. She told me of some of the daily life I could expect, and with excitement wrote:

You too can watch the Juncos & Chickadees, and an occasional Titmouse come to the lovely feeding station which Uncle Dana built, not far from the front windows, where I now sit writing & watching my beloved birds. You & I will range the woods together, while your mother is resting... and bringing back more wood. We shall learn the names of the birds... and perhaps a few of the stars, if you are permitted to stay up a bit later, one night a week! Such wonderful stories there are, about the stars, and how I do look forward to reading aloud to you, or singing with you – but will do lessons together too, won't we? Whatever is to be done, exactly as your mother & father tell us – only it will be fun to do it with you Kay! I can't tell you how I look forward to it!

On my sixth birthday, Mother and I sailed to New York. Aunt Stephanie's diary records: 'Friday 3rd January (1947) SS *America* with Sheila & Kay scheduled to leave Southampton midnight on Saturday so little plan of going down Sunday to see them off is spoilt.... Another week later – SS *America* arrived New York Monday evening – worst crossing in Captain's experience 48 hours late! Kay only sick 24 hrs – Sheila spent whole voyage in bed'.

Grannie Corner sent me a postcard just before we embarked saying: 'To Kay, Just a few old friends from Beaconsfield who come to wish you & Mummie a Happy voyage & a very good New Year, Goodbye my dears, Love from Grannie'. Goodbye rather than farewell could suggest a thought of finality. I had spent happy times with her and Grandfather Corner since late in 1942, and they must have wondered when, indeed if, they would see us again. Grandfather was 74 and Grannie 75.

Pandora contained a postcard from SS *America* from me to my father wishing him a happy birthday. That he had kept this for so long, and earmarked it for Pandora, shows that for him they were also happy times, and he wanted me to know. But were they happy times?

That we had 'gone ahead' was, at first sight a thoughtful decision, to allow my mother and me time with the American family, and the birth of their second child, before another adventure into the depths of a distant country.

Mother had planned to have the baby in California and to stay with friends who had a doctor friend who would deliver Christine. However, as he had a nervous breakdown, Mother called her close friend and second cousin, Marj Goodhue, and it was agreed that she would stay with Marj in Norwich, Vermont, till the birth. I was to go to my maternal grandmother, Dorothy Kavanagh Bailey, who had by 1947 moved from New York to live in the woods near to Lorton, Virginia, in a small cottage she called *The Mouse Hole*.

The name of Gramma Bailey's house was very apt. I slept downstairs though I can't remember if there was an upstairs! In the early mornings, I lay in bed and watched the many, many mice scrambling around and on the bookcases. Sachets of poison were carefully placed on the shelves but somehow the mice that I saw didn't bother with them – nor did I. Health and safety hadn't been invented. Common sense and learning to be responsible prevailed and I was taught not to handle the poison. I live to tell the tale, as did many of the mice!

I remember the woods, the wild animals, catching a Luna moth and an Albino Sulphur butterfly, and being bitten by a raccoon! Gramma Bailey had bird tables, birdhouses and ponds for the aquatic wildlife. She was passionate about wildlife and conservation and she invited all to come to her tables and even befriended a black snake (Black Rat Snake, *Elaphe ob-*

soleta), which she called Nicodemus, to keep some control over the moles, mice and rats that abounded in the deeply wooded Virginia countryside. Pandora beautifully records the day that she caught Nicodemus about to devour a frog by the pool during a season when frogs were scarce. My mother told me this story in a letter, having witnessed it. '…a frog has re-appeared in the pool on two different days, and Gramma just rescued him, the other day, from "Nicodemus" her pet black snake who was heading for the rock where the frog was sunning himself! She gave Nicodemus a long lecture about eating up all the mice and moles but NOT the frogs! She was so funny – but it was funnier still to see the snake curl about and glide away, like a naughty boy'.

Gramma Bailey was a teacher, and Pandora reveals how much help she gave me in education and the world around me. I was very fortunate in the happy if strict environment of her care. She taught me the names of the animals, birds, moths and butterflies and we spent many hours, both day and night, watching them, the stars and the wild life, and learning the calls. I well remember the migrating wild geese and being excited at my first sight of the Cardinal and Blue Birds. Her passion for conservation and care of the wild animals has stayed with me, further encouraged by my father in the following years.

In Pandora, there are exercise books where pictures of the wildlife have been pasted with their names and the phonetic calls of the birds recorded. When I read these, after all those years, it brings back happy memories and I can so easily picture the scene – I can hear the rustle of the turtles in the undergrowth, the calls of myriad birds and the whistling and whooshing of the migrating geese in perfect 'V' formation. Other old school exercise books are pasted with greetings cards, mostly from this time in Virginia: Easter cards, Valentine cards and the record of a trip to *The Washington Post* organised by Aunt Molly.

Grannie Corner wrote to me in America on 26 February 1947 with a sketch of herself and Sandy her dog on the letterhead. She thanked me for the Valentine card I sent her – an American tradition which we followed – and told me of my father driving away from the house in his own car to be mended. She makes a point about it being his own car, and infers that it will travel to Brazil to join us.

Daddie is going in a train and a boat and a train to Paris tomorrow [UNESCO] – ask Grannie where Paris is. We have had such a lot of winter and snow – and so cold – even Sandy shivers – and the windows are all frosted in the morning – but there is no little boy to come running through my room to dress in front of my fire.

When he was visiting UNESCO, my father sent me a postcard from

Paris, dated 12 March 1947 with a picture of Hotel Mont-Fleuri on the front. He wrote, 'This is the house where I am in Paris. I hope that I shall sail soon to America. Thank you for your pictures. They are very good. Now the spring will be coming. Give my love to Gramma and Mollie, ooo xxx, Daddy'.

A friendly card from father to son. Other letters in Pandora from this period often include a sketch; one is of himself sitting by the radiator in his hotel room, with pipe of course!

Mother's letter to me from Norwich, Vermont, on 17 April 1947 said, 'That was the nicest letter I have had – done all by yourself! Thank you very much. Isn't it exciting that Daddy is coming to see you. Have a lovely time with him, and write and tell me about it. The flowers and birds sound so exciting. We had more snow yesterday but today it is gone, and the grass is going green, and a few birds are coming. I wish you and Gramma were here to tell me the right names! I am still waiting for Araminta [the name my parents used for the unborn baby], but I think she will come very soon now. Shall we call her Christine? Daddy and I think that would be a nice name for a girl'.

On 19 April 1947, the birth was announced by card:

Dear Kay,
It's me!! I'm a sister I arrived April 19th my name is Stephanie Christine. I weigh 8 lbs 15 ½ oz. My parents are Daddy & Mummy.

Christine was born at 2.45 am in the Mary Hitchcock Memorial Hospital, New Hampshire.

Aunt Stephanie's diary records: 'Saturday 19th April 1947, cable from America… grand-daughter Christine arrived… John (EJHC) was there by Sunday'. He flew from Paris on Saturday, 19th April, Transcontinental & Western Air, arriving in Washington DC the next day. My father stayed only a short time – possibly only a day – before continuing on to start his new job in Brazil.

On 21 April 1947, I wrote to my mother, clearly helped by Gramma B, thanking her for the telegram and giving her news of my activities; I then had my own garden and vegetable patch. Mother replied on 23 April from Norwich thanking me for my drawing of Christine. She tells me she thinks Christine

looks like herself, but, please tell Gramma that Daddy thinks she looks a little bit like you, and a little bit like Molly. Your garden sounds lovely… I will think of you and Molly meeting the aeroplane on Saturday you must write and tell me all about it.

This was to be the arrival of my father.

In a postcard dated 15 May 1947, my father told me we soon will be in Brasil, as he spells it. He asked after my bow and arrows and whether Molly had got her passport. Was it already planned that she should visit us in Brazil? In any case, it suggests that all was well between father and Molly in May 1947.

On 6 June 1947, Mother with baby Christine left Vermont to come to us at *The Mouse Hole* where we stayed until we left for Brazil.

*

My father's frame of mind in this period is well shown in his letter to his mother-in-law dated 1 March 1947. This is the only letter from him to her I have. He wrote, cheerfully, from the Natural Sciences Division of UNESCO House, 19 Avenue Kleber, Paris, but is critical of the Colonial Office.

He thanked her for the 'newsy' letter about me and Mother. He remarked at how happy we all looked in the photographs Gramma sent, photographs which he placed on his room mantelpiece. Then he wrote: 'I think I was very much as Kay and grew in body and vigour before I took to the art of study, so please do not worry yourself. It is, indeed, very good of you to take so much trouble'.

This indicated that my grandmother was concerned at my learning ability and I read my father's response-of-understanding with interest. I hadn't realised that I was experiencing these difficulties early in my life. No wonder Gramma B helped me so much, yet that education was all to be lost soon after we returned to England in 1948 and when I first went to Twyford School in January 1949. She must have discovered something about my ability, rather lack of ability, to learn, as she was a teacher.

Enclosed with the letter was a fatherly one to me hoping I was enjoying the outdoor life and that he and I soon would be throwing stones again – he taught me 'ducks and drakes' – and collecting seaweeds. The stone throwing and seaweed collecting began on a visit to Ireland, which I just remember; we were visiting Uncle Birtie in 1946. I like my father's letters; the scribe was warm and friendly. If only he had exuded that in person, and into later years. If only he had maintained his understanding of my slowness to learn – and helped.

My father confessed to feeling guilty at parking us on her and wished he was with us 'so that I could go on and keep Sheila happy, but fate has decreed otherwise…'. After a year of patience, he explained, 'waiting for an ultra-stupid Colonial Office to say no [to his returning to Malaya] to all hopes of scientific progress has led to this new step'. He reflected that, curiously, he stepped out on this new venture from Robin Hill's house just as they did eight years ago for their wedding.

'This Colonial Office, too,' he complained, 'kept us waiting for all our leave and gave no help for us to visit you in America [the honeymoon]. With a touch of frustration he wrote that 'important people' are becoming worried and are starting to ask questions and he added that 'it is futile for me to be sorry…!' Perhaps this could have been the beginning of the Colonial Office realising what my father had achieved during the occupation of Singapore. With some finality, he said that he had a new job and he will focus on that and 'not return to sweep up colonial messes'.

My father told Gramma B that he arrived in Paris on 27 February 1947 and that was his official first day at UNESCO. He was excited by the novelty and excitement of the challenge ahead but was frustrated that he could not recall his French. He was scornful of French breakfasts 'unless you call a cup of inferior coffee and two slivers of toast something worth eating! But these difficulties will soon subside. Even the door-handles work the other way'.

He reflected on the distance between him and his family, clearly looking forward to being together and seeing all again. With the UNESCO conference in Mexico, he expressed hope that he will be able to 'hop up' to visit Gramma B. 'I have been reading files all day and abstracting. Now I must walk, for the first time in my life, down Champs Elysee'.

He finished by asking Gramma B to send the letter on to Mother knowing how much she liked to hear all the news. The rest of the letter is missing but there is a part that says, 'now I _ her very dearly'.

I re-read the contents of Pandora again in 2010. I had listed everything and typed out all the letters. The list is a long document; Appendix B is a short summary. In this re-reading, it soon became clear to me that when I first went through Pandora in 2006, I didn't know the story. I had no idea of what I was going to do with the information, and particularly because it brought back memories I didn't want to recall, I skipped through it and missed things, both literally and metaphorically. An important new discovery was that there were additional copies of some letters in the suitcase. One of the letters was the original of the one above where the finish was missing. The original closed with 'who loves her very dearly, as you must know'.

Where would my father have obtained this original and why would he have copied it, and leave out that important ending, and then placed both in Pandora? It suggests that he was looking through the content, probably later in his life, and forgot that some key letters were already there and put in the original.

That my father found all of these letters, and kept them for so long is strange indeed. Where did he find them? With his subsequent hate for everyone connected with my mother I am surprised, all those years later, he simply didn't destroy all such things. So here is a hidden message of Pandora, revealing a side of my father I hadn't met.

*

In June 1947, Brazil called and the life-changes began. We flew to Rio de Janeiro on 23 June, from New York, Christine being just three months old, and I, six and a half years old. I remember almost nothing of that journey except the travel to the airport when I fought to stay awake, and that it was a long journey. It was a night flight, and the plane was a Constellation, possibly a Super Constellation.

In those days, crossing the line – the equator – by plane also enjoyed a ceremony, as it did by sea, and we all were later given a certificate by Pan Am recognising the crossing. The certificates were put in Pandora.

Brazil! What a glamorous destination, but I was too young to have any appreciation of that. I'm surprised, with hindsight, that I was told so little about it all – or was I and have forgotten! My father had arrived in Belem in May, having sailed from Genoa on the SS *Argentina* arriving in Rio on 2 May 1947.

In his 32-day journey from Genoa to take the post, he made stops in New York, Boston, Washington, Chicago, Miami, Porto Rico (San Juan, Mayaguez), Trinidad and then Rio. The purpose of this route – besides his flying visit to Mother, Christine and me – was to learn of the extensive United States-Latin American relations in science and of the interest that might be shown in the Hylean Amazon Project. It was realised that a great deal of support could be expected from the universities, museums, and other official scientific departments. Contact was also made with the Caribbean Commission in Trinidad. This really was a selling-job.

The Singapore Free Press announced on 19 July 1947 under the title 'Ex-Malayan Heads UNO Mission to Amazon':

Dr E. J. H. Corner, former Assistant Director of the Singapore Botanic Gardens, has just left Paris for Brazil, accompanied by Dr Basil Malamos, a Greek specialist in tropical medicine. Dr Corner is heading a team of scientists of the United Nations Scientific and Cultural Organisation in the first international attempt to solve the mysteries of the largest unknown area of land and water in the world – the 4,000,000 square-mile Amazon basin of South America. Three experts have gone to Brazil and a fourth shortly will be en route to start a research station there, probably at Belem. The main purpose is to obtain data to improve living conditions everywhere in the tropics. The fourth expert to join the group will be Dr Paolo Carneiro, a Brazilian bio-chemist and a member of the educational, scientific and cultural organisation's board.

We were billeted in an apartment in Niteroi which was across the bay from Rio. It was above the Casino Icarai, across the tram-lined road from the beach, Praia d'Icarai, where I learned to swim and spent a lot of time. I made kites out of paper and wooden sticks and flew them, often successfully, on that same beach. The 'holding' handle was a baby milk powder scoop! I was good at making bows and arrows, the arrows being small branches.

The story of our time in Niteroi could never be complete without mention of Etty (Eveline) whom I remember so fondly. She was employed to look after me and Christine; we also had a maid who cooked and cleaned. Etty was born in Brazil and was 15 at the time of coming to help us. I tracked her down to Montreal, Canada, in 2007, and we have since exchanged many memories and photographs. Etty had asked, '…what happened to the beautiful girl I loved so much?' My sister Christine was that beautiful girl, and what a lovely memory to have of her. My mother and Etty kept in touch for a long time but correspondence waned in Mother's later years so news of Christine waned also.

I went to the British School in Niteroi where I learned Portuguese and apparently could speak it quite well. Yet, my education was definitely not progressing. I was to suffer for the lack of learning! I think I 'ambled' through classes. Why do I have absolutely no recall of the schooling? My teacher noticed that I was long-sighted and I had to wear glasses for reading and even my sunglasses were prescription. I was told to wear glasses all the time and I hated them.

My father continued to encourage me to collect and dry-mount seaweed. There they were in Pandora, some of the ones I still remember collecting, dating from 1947–1948, and as crisp and bright as the day they were dried. These were collected at that glorious beach in front of the flat, and some at Saco de Sao Francisco. The expert to whom I had sent colour attachments for identification was curious that some were found at Saco as there was no previous record of them being found there.

Where were they when I left home in 1960? Might they have been in the storage box my father had made for me after we had returned to England and on which he painted the scene from the apartment of the bay, boats and scenery of the beach? With other things my father found them and stored them away, for what purpose initially I really wonder. His second wife would surely have disposed of all she could had she found them, as she did often go through my room and took things like letters from my mother. Did he think I would return, or perhaps he had already formed a plan to leave them to me?

Our view from the apartment was across the sweeping bay and over the water to the mountains of Rio with both Corcovado and Sugar Loaf visible. It was a wonderful life for a six-year-old – still no emphasis on learning and so much beach life to enjoy. I lived on that beach and my hair became sun-bleached. My mother called me back for lunch or whatever by placing a towel on the balcony or waving it. I often avoided noticing the towel!

I remember that after learning to swim, but absolutely not before, I was allowed a plastic inflatable ring which I thought was wonderful. My friends had them and I envied them floating in the waves, mostly great rollers and often good breakers. To our right was an outcrop of rocks which I frequently climbed and explored and I so well remember seeing a big sea horse one day when I was mooching underwater. Might it have been a *Hippocampus ingens* which grows to about a foot?

I used to swim out to the diving board on a concrete base a little offshore and learned to dive. On one of father's home visits we swam out together and on climbing the concrete base, which sloped a little, I slipped on the seaweed. It was low tide, and fell forward cracking open my brow. I remember blood everywhere. Fortunately, there was a passing rowing boat and the occupant took us to the shore whilst I held his shirt over the eye. We went to the doctor and I remember his putting some cloth over my nose, which smelled evil. I wanted to go to sleep but didn't know that that was the idea, so I resisted and recall the stitching – six stiches in all. I still bear the scar of that episode (the stitches, not the event!).

I also recall something that frightened me. Black 'butterflies', or the like, at times covered large patches of sand and I avoided them like the plague. What could they have been? They seemed to chase me. The memory of a six-year-old can be unusually colourful!

We had English friends who lived away from Niteroi around the headland at Saco de São Francisco, a suburb of Icaraí, and I used to play with their son Robin. For a long time I couldn't remember his surname but after much searching and Pandora letters, I found that he was Robin Valentine and that his parents, Jock and Meg, were good friends of my parents. I wonder how and when they met, for they will play a part in the story to come.

I hoped to find Robin because he frequently visited us in Niteroi and would certainly have some recollections of those days of me and my parents. This was a critical time which saw the serious deterioration in my parent's marriage. Sadly, Robin died in December 1993 in Leicestershire, England.

*

From mid-May 1947 to the end of the year, my father spent 125 days in Rio, much of which was at his Rio office but which included visits home. Soon after arriving in Brazil, Father visited Belem-do-Pará; from 1-16 June he visited Belem again, and Manaus, and Cuiabá, and from 31 July to 23 August he went to Cuiaba, Manaus, Belem, São Luis, and Recife. In August/September he was in the Guianas, Venezuela, Colombia, Ecuador, Peru and Bolivia; in November he attended the General Conference at Mexico City (when he had hoped 'to hop over' to see his in-laws but that was not to be). From 5 October to 22 December, he made a major trip taking in Paramaribo, Georgetown, Caracas, Bogotá, Barranca, Costa Rica, Mexico City, Quito, Lima, Río Perene and La Paz.

My father was designated secretary of the Conference for the establishment of the International Institute of the Hylean Amazon. In his 'small office', he did much of the work himself. His secretary could not do everything, indeed she didn't then have the knowledge.

All in all, this gave him little time to be with his family and I have no doubt that on his short visits he was tired and had much preparation to do for the next trip or conference. In time, the visits became shorter and fewer. It was a challenging position for us all.

The card he sent me from Balboa, Canal Zone, dated 5 December 1947, suggests that things were still normal. He wrote that soon he would be home and we can go swimming, commenting that I would by then 'manage a few strokes'. He continued, 'You tell Mummie that she must come flying with me next year. I am waiting for the aeroplane to go to Quito'.

I remember him telling me, in the 1950s, that he missed one of his flights; the plane crashed with the loss of all.

For many reasons, some definitely not of his making, the Brazil job became progressively more difficult and immensely political for him; he decided to give up late in 1948 and resigned soon after – but what part did the failing marriage play in this? A considerable part I now feel sure; or was the job and its demands partly to blame for the failing marriage? It was a difficult and tough amalgam and surely both contributed.

Those later days in Brazil were not full of happiness for any of us. My mother was in mental anguish and this inevitably rubbed off. June 1948 saw the troubles develop. The marriage was really in difficulties; it was foundering and there was violence, both physical and particularly mental, which affected mother and me. Marj Goodhue reminded me of an incident which I had almost forgotten. It was late 1947. My father was driving mother, myself and Christine to the Valentines around the headland from Niteroi. We were on a cliff road and he was shouting at my mother that if she didn't shut up he was going to drive the car off the road and kill us all. Christine, thank heavens, was far too young to know anything of this. Life at home grew strained, very difficult and my mother was clearly increasingly unhappy; indeed she was not well in body and mind.

Was this why my father asked Mother's sister Molly to come and stay as a companion? Perhaps he had hoped that Molly would stay at home and look after us children for the times when he wanted my mother to join him on his travels, to share a little of his career-life with her. Mother was an adventurous person and I can't imagine her not wanting to take at least some trips. I think the two sisters did not get along; they quarrelled. Molly's visit appears to have been a catalyst for the disaster to come.

One of my father's colleagues, his boss, who became a close and trusted family friend was Dona Heloisa Bertol Torres. She became Christine's godmother at her christening in Niteroi on 20 July 1947 and was to play an important part in future events.

Her letter of 1951, written in response to my father's request for specific evidence, which he listed, to support his case in the divorce proceedings, tells of the arrival of Molly Bailey.

> When Mrs EJHC arrived in Brazil I had the opportunity of meeting her and of seeing her frequently; she won both my appreciation and my esteem. As her husband, Mr E.J.H. Corner, had to travel frequently he made arrangements for [his wife's] sister, Miss Molly Bailey, to come to Brazil and keep [her] company. After the arrival of Miss Bailey [Mrs Corner's] attitude changed entirely; she decided to set out for England leaving [her husband] behind, notwithstanding all the efforts on my part and that of some other friends [Jock Valentine being one] to change her mind.

Molly told Paul Tanner (my half-brother) some years ago that when she arrived in Niteroi she found 'a very tense and strained atmosphere' although she doesn't remember specific incidents. She said that my father would 'constantly denigrate and belittle' my mother. Whilst Molly knew that my father could often be 'charming and great company', she also said that he would often inflict 'severe emotional pressure' on Mother and this was taking its toll. Molly did recall 'a strange incident in the Niteroi house'; I was playing with a toy cannon which fired matchsticks and one accidentally hit my father on the leg. He was 'furious'; he took the cannon and started firing matchsticks at me, asking me how I liked it. I was seven.

Early in 1948, we moved from the flat to a semi-detached house nearby. It had a large rear garden. Etty sent me some photographs of those days, those bitter sweet days, and one of them is of a family group, my father, Mother, Christine and me. My mother told Belinda, many, many years ago, that my father made her get out of bed for a family photograph which would have been taken early in 1948 when my mother was quite unwell with a suspected miscarriage, carrying Lindsay. The family portrait that Etty sent me was the very one.

Life continued. Molly enjoyed the social rounds and the tennis, of which she was accomplished, and I am sure my mother came to enjoy the times when her husband was away, which gave some peace from the mental and physical stresses. I became increasingly retiring.

Things came to a head in mid-June 1948 when my mother refused to let my father back into the Niteroi house and he never visited again. The catalyst for this major decision which affected everything from thereon was my mother's refusal to move to Manaus.

Immediately after his exclusion from the marital home, my father visited São Paulo, Cuiabá and Manaus, to where he had relocated; the object of this journey was to transfer the office of the PFSO, Latin America, to Manaus as the seat of the Hylean Amazon Project. This relocation was a job requirement. Why was it such a hurdle for my mother? The '*Object*' of the Hylean Amazon Project says clearly that 'the start will be made at Rio and San Paulo and thence to Belem'.

My father therefore knew, from the start, that Rio was a temporary base and that a move to Belem (later changed to Manaus) was inevitable. So, I firmly believe that Mother knew of the plan from the beginning and that the eventual refusal was entirely due to my learning difficulties and the abuse, both of which had to be attended to.

I learned more of the 'house-exclusion' from a letter to Dona Heloisa which my father wrote from England on 10 February 1949, when my parents' divorce was on the table. He told of mentioning to Heloisa that Jock Valentine 'with whom you spoke about the action of the two sisters in turning me out of the house and in refusing to come to Manaus'… 'and particularly how I behaved', and that Valentine had attempted to persuade my mother to allow my father to return to the house and to go to Manaus with him; all of us to relocate. My father explained to Heloisa that my mother felt strongly that Manaus was no place for a young lad to live, the climate and the like, and he hoped Heloisa could, with her considerable knowledge of Manaus, help persuade my mother to move. The Governor had offered accommodation for us all and it was after all for perhaps only six months 'by when my contract with UNESCO would have expired and we should have had to consider other plans'.

Dona Heloisa wrote of Manaus in 1951, in testimony of my father and Mother's divorce:

[A]s a matter of fact, the climatic and general health conditions in Manaus, for children living in good social circumstances – as was the case – are not bad; I had the opportunity of mentioning to Mrs Corner the example of children in my own family who, born and brought up in Manaus, were perfectly healthy and also of foreign children who live there and, when of school age, go to their own country, but come to Manaus for their holidays. It is well to remember that, as he was still a very young child, John Kavanagh Corner did not yet require a boarding school at that time.*

---

* It is true that I did not require a boarding school at that time. However, all this travel set me back in my education which was to show up starkly in my earlier days of school back in England in 1949. I had been on the move from age one to eight attending schools of enormous variety – the village school in Great Shelford

My father wrote of Manaus in his general newsletter of December 1948, some six months after the house-exclusion:

I like Manaus, and it is a wonderful centre for this International Institute, but it was rebuilt about 70 years ago and has not progressed
since…. The light in Manaus is so bad that you cannot read between
6.30 and 9.30 at night, nor use a radio… It is a strange and wonderful
city of [the] last century [19th] and a glimmer of modernisation.

My mother's refusal to go to Manaus and to let my father back into the
Niteroi house must have been for a very good reason for she was a rational
person not given to whims and fancies.

If the abuse was continuing then, that was reason enough for Mother
turning my father out of the house; she was pregnant and had suffered a
threatened miscarriage. I can also now begin to understand why she, indeed perhaps she and Molly, didn't want to go to Manaus, even for a short
time. Perhaps Manaus didn't include Molly, and was my mother recognising my educational difficulties and wanted these to be addressed without
more distraction from yet another move? My mother must have felt it better to keep the status quo; he working from there and visiting us from time
to time, giving us respite from his abuse. So she had banned him from the
Niteroi house – actually demanded he left – then we all sailed for England.

I believe that the potential move to Manaus was the excuse my mother
needed to get away, to seek rest from all the troubles which had become
severe. My father knew from early on in his job that Belem (later Manaus)
was to be his HQ, but to be so far from help was not what my mother wanted or needed; at least in Niteroi she had friends, was close to Rio and help
was close at hand if needed, even at short notice. If Molly was not included
in the invitation to move, and it looks as if she too was adamantly against
it, I think she was somewhat 'outraged' that her new life and leisure was
abruptly to end. She enjoyed the life and had left a job to come to Brazil.

I believe there was another reason for Mother turning my father out of
the house. It had to do with the 'ratting' my father referred to in a letter to
Julian Huxley late in 1950, saying, '…and, now, I will tell you, but please
keep it to yourself as confidential – indeed, do not trouble to answer this
– my wife 'ratted' on me the day I came back from Manaus on my way to
Paris, 21st May 1948'. I believe this to be the most likely cause yet I cannot
find out what the ratting was about; it occurred about a month before the
house exclusion.

to the British (school) in Niteroi. I hadn't settled to learning: indeed, hadn't prop-
erly learned to learn – and read – and I was seven with eight in sight. My Ameri-
can grandmother clearly noticed my learning difficulties early in 1947.

Nothing in the information I have discovered suggests that he resisted the turning out. I can only surmise that he knew he had done wrong.

Mother, with Lindsay due October 1948, took a major decision and decided to return to England, with me, Christine and Molly. But why England and not America? I think that it was a combination of things which included the fact that divorce had to be actioned in the country of marriage, and my mother did hope that her in-laws would have sympathy and look after us. My American grandmother was by then 56, on her own and not well-off, even after the war work. Perhaps Mother was also hoping for a reconciliation.

As I ponder these times, I come to think that Mother would not have, in June 1948, moved anywhere with my father; the stresses he was causing her, indeed us, had become intolerable and her mind was made up. She had to get away from that environment not only for her own sake but also for that of her unborn child, and Christine, and me, and my education.

None of these things were going to be addressed in Manaus.

XVIII

CARRYING ON WITH UNESCO

After my father was turned out of the family house in June 1948, my mother, her sister Molly, Christine and I returned to England, departing Rio de Janeiro on 6 September and arriving Southampton on 17 September. We sailed on the RMS *Andes*; my father continued in Manaus.

Pandora contained the official itinerary of the *Andes*, a brochure, and the passenger list which shows Mother, me and Christine as well as Miss M Bailey. It also included a dinner menu for a special evening. Mother must have kept them and my father found them and included them in Pandora.

My mother wrote a friendly, if slightly formal letter to Heloisa Bertol Torres who was Christine's godmother from the *Andes*. It concluded:

Heloisa, I won't write to you again except to tell you of the children, from time to time, as I think you will prefer this. John has made it very clear in several letters that both you, Jock and Meg, feel that I am showing him a great moral wrong in taking the action I am, so it will be more comfortable to both of us not to discuss it any further.

This suggests that my mother did not wish to influence any third party, but it also indicated that neither Heloisa nor the Valentine family believed my mother was right. However, they could not possibly have known of the abuse my mother had suffered.

*

About 20 October 1948, after Mother had left with us to go to England, my father wrote a long general newsletter to his friends like Robin Hill, no doubt Worthington, and others. It was most unlike him to write such a general missive and I haven't seen or heard of another. He certainly was very busy so he wrote it to save letters to each of his friends.

This letter is important because it gives in detail my father's work and the situation in which he had to operate. To say that the job was complex, stressful and a thankless task would be an understatement.

I am so terribly busy all day, from 7 till 5 or 6 that I am too tired and bored with letters to sit down and write any more in the evening. So I have decided to try to answer lots of queries all at once by means of duplication of this letter.

He was thankful that his friends wrote to him; their letters kept him in touch with matters outside Manaus and UNESCO, for he felt most isolated and, I add, his family was gone.

He was left to rearrange the office since his American female secretary had resigned, as did the cook, because, he said, of the interference of Miss Celia Neves, the head of the Bureau of Budget and Personal Administration, UNESCO. Nevertheless, my father said he liked her and Antonio Barsanto dos Santos of the Department of Public Administration, Rio. That gave my father three official members of the secretariat of the Interim Commission of the Hylean Amazon Institute, and three secretaries (one Peruvian, whom my father brought from Lima and 'who works very well and hard, through all the troubles with me'). He recorded that they go botanising on Sundays.

My father was then living partly in the Governor's palace and sometimes in the house of the manager of Manaus harbour who was away on leave in England. The Institute's one-room office and its insufficient library were in the Commercial Association of Amazonas. He had found new accommodation, with funds to support it, when a telegram arrived from UNESCO requesting he 'suspend all payments and further commitments in this fund until they have rectified some mistakes of theirs in Paris'. In frustration, he wrote a very strong letter to UNESCO, pointing out that if the funds were stopped he would lose the opportunity of new accommodation, which was difficult to find, and they would have to relocate to Rio until matters were resolved.

He fumed at the ignorance of UNESCO in their handling of overseas matters and complained of the 'terrible trouble with the governments of the Member States of the Interim Commission to honour their word and to supply funds for 1949' which he anticipated but not to the serious degree. He was getting no help from headquarters in planning, and UNESCO had 'put an ambitious and unscrupulous boy of 30-odd as the Headquarters Coordinator for the Amazon project; he not only lies to me but takes every opportunity to thwart what I advise'. Still, my father thought that he might be able to scrape through.

At this point of the letter, my father recorded that his friends (to whom he was writing) had told him that he was difficult. He countered by drawing their attention to the facts – of his achievements during three and a half years 'with enemies to save the libraries and collections of Singapore and ask yourself who is the difficult and incapable person'.

My father continued to complain about the many 'ambitious lizards' he had to deal with. An External Relations Councillor sent for the Peruvian conference had attempted to cheat everyone 'by sending on a false telegram to the head of the Peruvian delegation'. This man knew that my father knew his trick and was therefore 'telling terrible stories against me in UNESCO house, so as to discredit me and save himself'. My father had to intervene in Peru to prevent him causing untold damage. He commented on this episode in two classic one-liners full of meaning:

If a man is reviled, you can be sure it is because he is honest, in this rotten hypocritical world... and we have killed our best, in two wars, and we are thinking of killing now our second best, to save the rogues.

Even with the administrative work and handling intrigues, my father explored the forest when he could. During his time in Manaus, he established a small forest reserve nearby in Flores and vigorously continued his efforts for conservation, as he had done in Malaya. In spite of all his difficulties, he always had his eye on the ball and never wavered from his work and he rather nostalgically recalled his botanising in Malaya.

I have made quite a number of expeditions into the forest, and nearly got lost last night. There are many more insects than in Malaya, and many more birds, but the forests are not so rich or so high.

On one botanising trip, he discovered a fungus which apparently was last described in 1888 in Ecuador and had not been seen since. He was so surprised that for a moment he doubted himself! Although there were many lovely creepers in the forest of the *Bigonia* kind and wonderful palms, there was no botanic garden in Manaus where he could check names. He felt more isolated here scientifically than anywhere before, 'thanks to the total failure of the UNESCO science service that has no conception of tropical requirements'. He had to purchase scientific journals on his own account.

He not only despaired of the lack of intellectual life, but also bemoaned the lack of music and time. What little spare time he had in the evenings he used in writing up his research notes to the light of a kerosene pressure lamp.

I have to do everything from cleaning my shoes and giving the cook money to writing to Ministers of External Relations and entertaining my staff, that I get practically no time. I have also to learn Portuguese, which I speak mostly in the day time and badly.

He explained that he puts up with these difficulties only because he saw no future for tropical botany without international studies. Yet, UNESCO had selected, for the first, perhaps the most difficult set of countries to do this. 'Can you imagine anything meaner and more despicable, and they expect me to do in all directions what they have departments for'. To communicate, it took a letter and then at least three telegrams before he got any reply. He singled out Huxley, who had little enough time himself, as being helpful; the others he dismissed as 'a miserable lot of townees'.

In some desperation, he wrote of having 'heaps of friends all over the world who will support this Institute if only we can get the funds to start it. So we struggle on, with fits of depression, and then suddenly something happens to brighten up again'. Then unexpectedly, he confessed:

> Of course, I feel the absence of my family as the most terrible desolation that could have befallen me, and I have no news about Kay or Christine now for two months. I hope they are well, happy, and not too cold.

Well, that takes one's breath away! I am sure it was written from the heart and without any spin. Whilst this general newsletter is not dated (unusual for my father) it has to be after 8 October when his assistants arrived and shortly before 24 October, the Manaus centenary, which he anticipated in the letter. It was therefore written not only after his exclusion from the Niteroi house but long after we had left for England; indeed we had arrived about a month before he penned it. He was clearly upset by those most serious of personal events, and he expresses his feelings – something he rarely does.

The truth of it all was hitting home, and hard; my father was coming to face reality. It was not surprising that he had no news of us; this lack of communication sadly illustrates the seriousness of the family problems.

I wonder how my mother explained it all to my father's family in England, and what did he tell them before our arrival?

*

The controversy generated inside UNESCO by the International Institute of the Hylean Amazon (IIHA) project was matched by the turmoil caused by President Eurico Gaspar Dutra's message to the Brazilian Congress in September 1948 requesting ratification of IIHA's statute, approved in the Iquitos Convention of April 1948. This statute had to be accepted by at least five countries directly involved in the proposal.

The message generated enormous impact among Brazilian lawmakers, the public, military officers, scientists, journalists, intellectuals and many organisations of the civil society. There was a radical division between those who favoured international cooperation as a way to develop Amazonia and those for whom the IIHA project expressed imperialistic interests over the region. Several items of the statute were considered threatening to national sovereignty, both because IIHA would have excessive autonomy and because Brazil's specific importance in the institution was too limited.

In 1951, the presidential message concerning the IIHA was killed in the Brazilian Congress. UNESCO stopped financing the IIHA in 1949 due to pressure from the US, and no alternative Latin American funds were offered. The Iquitos Convention was never ratified by the Brazilian Government because of strong political nationalist opposition.

I asked many about my father's days in Brazil during this period, and few have any information because he rarely, if ever, discussed it. However, David Frodin, one of his PhD students wrote to me in 2009 saying:

I recollect your father worked well with a number of individual Brazilian scientists (who may also have not been happy with the tenor of the political regimes of the day); he did mention a name or two.

Peter Austwick, my father's student at Cambridge, said:

Looking at the Brazilian episode I learnt from him that his reason for leaving the post was because the finance from the U.S. was primarily to counter the spread of communism and only secondarily for tropical forest conservation to which he was passionately committed. After all, even then, one realised that there was far too much money to be made from the timber and maybe too there were those who thought ahead to beef and oil production.

My father wrote that in 1947-48 he was his own master in Latin America. He had made a similar comment about Singapore and this confirms that he was a man who preferred his own company and action. As the Executive Secretary of Hylean Administration, he saw that he must become an administrator for others, and realised that this really was not his ideal work environment. It severely curtailed his natural inclination and passionate desire to explore and research, unimpeded, unmolested. He was, simply, the wrong man for the job.

As I learn of these times, I can't help drawing a comparison with his time in Singapore during the Occupation and after. There, he worked well with the Japanese scientists, as he did with those in South America, and a 'radical division' grew up in Singapore between those 'in camp' and those 'out of camp' just as there became one between those who favoured international cooperation as a way to develop Amazonia, and those 'for whom the IIHA project expressed imperialistic interests in the region'.

I have no doubt he felt a sense of *déjà vu*. He must have been down-hearted at the sign of another 'failure' not of his making just about 20 months after the loss-of-post in Malaya. I wonder if this frustration was the root cause of his behaviour at home?

*

My father completed his Durian Theory in Manaus. He had re-established his own research as an aside to the post with the Hylean Project, research being where he was most comfortable and successful, and where he was in full control. He sent his paper to the Linnean Society for publication but had written to his friends that 'but for ought I know this Society is defunct', and adding a sting to sarcasm, said he didn't think it will understand what he wrote! His scathing remarks about the Linnean Society shows not only his attitude towards other scientists he judged less committed than himself but also his brittle frame of mind at the time. His marriage was failing; politics and administration hindered his freedom to research; clearly he was getting fed-up, when he wrote, 'Pride fell through the deception of UNESCO in Paris, and research was restored'.

Clearly, he felt misled by those in UNESCO who initially described the post. It reminds me of his earlier Singapore remark about the need to follow lights that have gone out.

My father resigned for the second time in his life and planned to return to Britain. His resignation letter dated 8 November 1948 cites family commitments:

I can no longer bear these responsibilities without sacrificing those which I have to my family. These responsibilities have already lead (sic) to my parting from my family, at the end of June… The position in which my family finds itself in England is such that I must return as soon as possible.

He was in Paris in mid-November 1948 from where he wrote his final report on the Hylean Project for UNESCO. He was back in Rio in December from where he wrote me a cheerful two-page letter from a hotel near the top of Corcovado on 12 December.

I am writing in the train from Corcovado because I am living in a hotel near the top.… It is in the forest and lots of fungus are growing all round.… It is Sunday and I am going to see Robin and Meg and Jock [Valentine] in Niteroi. I am going to take the dirty old Barca [paddle steamer] & I am going to take the bonde [tram] past Icarai. Do you remember this?

Here he sketched the diving board on which I slipped. On the second page is a large sketch of a pirate. 'Who is this? Now the train is off and I cannot write straight any more, jigglety, jiggle'. He then sketched the skyline of Rio with Corcovado and Sugar Loaf prominent.

> Are you coming to London to meet me? What shall we buy Christine for Christmas; an umbrella or a stick of barley sugar?

This letter clearly shows that there had been contact after Mother left with us for Britain. My father not only knew where to write to us, but knew that I had a puppy (which he briefly mentioned in the letter). Did he believe that reconciliation was not only possible but likely?

*

Research into Dona Heloisa's archive in the Rio Museum in 2010 led me to realise that my father faced serious financial troubles as a direct result of the hold on expenditure by UNESCO. Specifically, his retirement, holiday pay and other emoluments were put on hold pending the sorting out of the Rio imprest account that he operated. Not only was his good name in considerable jeopardy but he was in financial straits, needing money for the move, the new house, my school costs and living expenses. I am certain that that led not only to his visit to Paris but also to his prompt return to Rio.

My father wrote an official letter dated 2 April 1949 to his friend Julian Huxley in his capacity as Director-General of UNESCO. After stating that he had been informed by a UNESCO Staff Relations Officer that he was entitled to 'salary for 54 days accrued leave, etc, and for Provident Fund benefit', my father continued by stating that he had written twice to the Personnel Officer (UNESCO HQ) to which he received a reply that settlement was being withheld until the result of the audit of the Rio imprest account which my father controlled was known. My father was astonished that he should find out in this way and being a most serious matter he considered it would also be of the greatest concern to the Brazilian authorities and those of the other Latin American countries in which he was involved and travelled to.

> Accordingly I am sending copies of this letter to the President of the Interim Commission, IIHA, with the request that it should be brought to the notice of HE the Minister of External Relations under whose Ministry I worked in Brazil, and, if necessary, to the notice of other Member States of the Interim Commission.

My father pointed out to Huxley that official audits had been carried out by Price Waterhouse, Peat & Co. (Rio de Janeiro) on 31 December 1947, 20 March, 20 June and 20 December 1948, and that the statements would be in Huxley's possession. He affirmed that for the last three months of 1948 he had the help of the finance officer, Sr Antonio Barsante dos Santos, who was from the Ministry of Finance (Rio de Janeiro) and who was assisted by Miss Celia Neves. On 20 December, just before he left Rio, he had confirmed with Huxley that the accounts and office records had been passed to the President of the IIHA Interim Commission (Dona Heloisa Bertol Torres), and it was clearly understood that all was in order.

> If in the interval since my leaving Brazil queries have arisen I think that I should have been informed so that, as a party concerned, I could have had the opportunity to expedite matters.

He added that he had experienced very great difficulty, since he started in the job, in obtaining a financial statement from the Comptroller, UNESCO, covering his office expenditure; in fact he never received a satisfactory statement such that he could understand how the office accounts stood in Paris whilst 'there was dual operation of them from both ends'.

He then recounted numerous misunderstandings, particularly that arising from Professor Auger who suggested that my father was unwilling to visit UNESCO HQ in Paris early in January to discuss all of this.

> I have written to the authorities in Brazil to correct this misapprehension and I would repeat to you the assurances that I gave on the phone and by letter to Professor Auger that, after 22nd January, I hoped to be free for such a visit.

This date, my father explained, was critical because his wife 'was seriously ill, and my son aged eight was going to boarding school for the first time'. This, he further explained, left him without any help to take care of us children.

> Unfortunately this date did not suit the plans of Professor Auger and all I can do is to repeat my regret I repeated to him. Perhaps you could get Professor Auger to reconsider what I told him so that he too may be able to correct his impression.

As the letter comes to a close, my father said that in spite of his many efforts to follow correct financial procedure, he was unable to understand why he was being penalised in this way. He requested that Huxley bring this matter into the open by bringing it to the attention of the highest authorities to clear him and others of any 'ugly suspicion'.

> I would ask you to be so good as to inform me what is, or is thought to

be, at fault with the audit of my imprest account in Rio and why payment of personal dues to me should be withheld pending rectification of an account that I have endeavoured for many months to maintain correct.

I know, from other letters, that his contract with UNESCO did allow for the withholding of funds if there were any account irregularities, but no doubt in small print. Unfortunately, I don't know the conclusion of this matter but, from the father I knew, I feel sure he was exonerated – I remember a man always straight-down-the-line with money.

On 10 February 1949, my father wrote to Dona Heloisa Bertol Torres from *Tilbury Hall*, England. After dealing with the accusations of Augur, he tells her of his domestic situation.

> in addition to many other domestic arrangements about the house, including a very sick wife whom I feared would have to go to hospital... She went to hospital on 19th January, leaving me without any reliable help to look after 3 children, and I had to take Kay to London to catch his train to school on 21st January.

In this long and wide-ranging letter, he stressed to Heloisa that he did his best for the Hylean Project 'under circumstances that led to the disruption of my family and my office, through reasons beyond my control, and so I think it is well that I should hand on to someone else who, coming in fresh, will see more clearly than I could how to proceed'.

In assessing UNECSO's role and approach, he said: 'UNESCO makes the error of trying to force where encouragement and inconspicuous leadership are required'.

I have to break here to record my shocked reaction to part of this letter. If he had followed his own advice, in the years that followed, I would perhaps not have left him. He forced and pressured me, indeed so much that I became very muddled and depressed in so many things and particularly when trying to choose subjects in later years at school and then of career. I just couldn't talk to him, confide – yet he writes so wisely. If only he had shown that wisdom, encouragement and 'inconspicuous leadership' to me, and his wife, our lives could have been totally different.

I am also astonished by his comment that 'I tried my best under circumstances that lead to the disruption of my family and my office, through reasons beyond my control'. He blamed the workload and travel – even the move to Manaus – for the disruption of his family.

The letter continues in a rhetorical debate about who might succeed him. My father thought that Bolivar was the best but named others who might warrant consideration. His concern about Bolivar was that 'he has five children, and they must and will come first in his plans'.

Here is another important statement. If only he had put his children, indeed his wife too, first in his own plans.

My father wrote another letter to Heloisa on 11 June 1949 in which he informed her that 'Kay is at boarding school down in Winchester and as happy as schoolboys can be' and that I am playing cricket and swimming. Apparently I was saying '"shurrr-up" in true British way!' He told Heloisa that he had made me a toy box on which he painted scenes of Rio, the Bay and mountains. He closed by 'wishing I was in Manaus botanising with Luis Emygdio and Ducke, not writing official letters as I had to do'.

When I read this, I was reminded of the toy box. I remember him painting the scenes in his small but well-equipped garden shed. The box sat under the window in my bedroom at Hinton Way which overlooked the side garden where we had tea or coffee and where the swing-seat was ensconced. Some of the things in Pandora must have come from that storage box but then so much of what was mine has gone – including my stamp albums well pasted with a multitude of foreign stamps.

*

As my father was wrangling with UNESCO about financial matters after he had lost another job, he clearly had not lost sight of the irreplaceable research material, and family and personal things which he had left in Singapore, indeed was compelled to leave behind.

It was now more than three and a half years since his departure from the liberated island. He wrote to Holttum in Singapore on 18 August 1949, confirming that six packages had arrived with notes, but that there were many more things missing. In apologising for asking again, he added another excellent one-liner about 'the great swindle when the knights of the white feather took charge of Malaya'.

He told Holttum that he wanted 'his' map of the Mawai region of Johore which had important field notes on the distribution of the river flora. 'It was with my notes… they are the key to my work on the river'. Also 'the map of the Sedili Kechil Kuala Sedili Besar'. He said he could return both maps within a month.

My father then listed five scientific books before asking for 'a list of the plants collected by Nauen and myself in Langkawi and Gunung Baling in Nov. 1941'.

He wrote scathingly of Henderson noting that he 'has worked them through and removed the field-notes without reference to me. Funny way of cooperating to split a piece of work into two parts! But I suppose all loot is fair play to militarists'.

He said he had 'lost' his cameras which were in a large tin box behind his herbarium seat. 'Surely a little thought would have referred unknown contents to me before their disposal'. That reflex camera was damaged but it was given to him by Church's daughter and was cherished. 'Who stole those two cameras out of the box, so carefully labelled by me? Let him explain to the Custodian of Property'.

Holltum replied on 1 November 1949 and referred to the Bills of Lading for the cases containing fungus-material in formalin which he said my father should have received. He advised that 'a great many *Ficus* specimens' had been sorted out, 'and that they will be dispatched shortly'. He also notified my father that Henderson had posted 'to you a list of the plants collected by you and Nauen at Langkawi etc. in 1941', and would contact him about this. In confirming that one book had been found, Holltum advised that many of the other things were missing, including the precious Sedili and Mawai maps.

Holltum added, 'I understand from Henderson that the Colonial Secretary has received a letter from you about reprinting *Wayside Trees*'. He explained that the Government printer hoped to type-set in January 1950 and that they didn't want 'major corrections and additions' – small corrections and additions were fine. He advised that my father would soon receive an official letter on this.

I can understand my father's disappointment, even anger, that so much was 'lost'. What a shambles and clearly some of his belongings were 'acquired' in his absence by 'friends'.

This loss of his important research material, his resignation from the UNESCO post and the resulting arguments about financial matters, and certainly the condition of his family life contributed to my father's frame of mind in late 1948.

He was then an angry, frustrated, disconnected man but still arrogant and proud.

Top: My father and William Birtwistle wearing enemy alien badges, February 1942.

*Bottom (from left): The Marquis Yoshuchika Tokugawa,
unidentified, Hidezo Tanakadate, and my father.
Note his seating position with head lower than his Japanese 'seniors'.
[Courtesy of Yoshitaka Tokugawa.]*

Top (from left): Molly, Gramma Bailey, myself and mother, New York, around late 1942.

Bottom: Elizabeth Morley and me in fancy dress, The Park, Great Shelford, VE Day, 8 May 1945.

Right: My parents with me in our garden at 15 The Park, Great Shelford, Cambridgeshire, early 1946.

Overleaf: My father's self-portrait and letter to me from his hotel in Paris, 1 March 1947.

1ˢᵗ March 1947   PARIS
                      FRANCE
                      SATURDAY

My DEAR KAY
            Is THE SUN
SHINING AGAIN ? ARE you
LIVING OUT OF DOORS AND
RUNNING INTO THE WOOD WITH
~~TH~~ THE DOG? I HOPE WE
SHALL SOON BE THROWING STONES
AGAIN AND ~~OF~~ FINDING SEAWEEDS
WHEN THE ~~I~~ SEA RUNS OUT DO
YOU REMEMBER HOW I CARRIED
YOU ON MY BACK IN IRELAND?

        HERE IS A PICTURE OF ME

*Top left: My father botanising in Scotland in 1953 on the way to
a family holiday in Glenluce.*

Top right: Aunt Do with Aunt Stephanie's dog, Coolie, around 1965.

*Bottom: Dona Heloisa Bertol Torres and Paulo Carneiro,
Christine's godparents at her christening in Niteroi, 1948.*

Top left: Uncle Dana and me at Weatheroak, March 1944.

Top right: The Hurd family and me at Rainscombe Farm, April 1945.
(From left) Douglas, myself, Aunt Stephanie, Uncle Anthony, Julian and Stephen.

Bottom: My parents with me and Christine in our garden in Niteroi, early 1948.

Left: Etty (Eveline) with me and Christine on Praia d'Icarai beach, June 1948, just a few days before we sailed to England.

Top (from left): Christine, myself, Lindsay and Grannie Corner on the swing in the side garden of 73 Hinton Way.

Bottom: Lindsay (front) and Christine, around 1955. At the end and to the right of this path at back of Hinton Way was where I hid my letters and money.

Top (from left): Christine, Lindsay, my father, Grannie Corner and Chew Wee Lek, his research student, around 1962.

Bottom left: Barton Worthington, 1930s.
[Courtesy of Marthe Kiley-Worthington.]

Bottom right: Robin Hill, 2011.
[Courtesy of Dr David Hill.]

Top (from left): Stephen and Douglas Hurd, myself, Lindsay, Helga, Aunt Stephanie and Christine at the picnic on Twyford School's sports day, 1953.

Bottom (from left): Lindsay, myself, Christine, unidentified friends and my father on a beach, around 1957.

Top: Sports day at Twyford School, 1953. Bob and Betty Wickham presenting a prize.

Bottom: Twyford School cricket 1st XI, 1954. I am seated second from left;
Robert Tully is captain, seated centre.

(From left) Christine, Peter Tanner, Lindsay, Robert Tully and myself on a holiday trip around 1956.

Overleaf: Our wedding photo in front of Great St Mary's Church, Cambridge. (Back row from left) Roger Wagstaff, Catherine Hann, myself, Belinda, Pamela Coulson and Philippa Shaw. (Front row from left) Jeremy Rose, Elizabeth Tanner, Marney Rolfe and Anthony Rose.

My sisters Christine (left) and Lindsay at Christine's wedding, 4 September 1971.

FAMILY RUINED

Late in 1950, my father wrote to Julian Huxley giving the clue for the marriage break-up. In this letter, he told Huxley that he wished he was still in Brazil 'for I would have succeeded in the Hylean Institute but for a stab in the back'.

He continued, asking Huxley to keep it confidential, that his wife 'ratted' on him the day he began his journey from Manaus to the UNESCO HQ in Paris on 21 May 1948. 'I should have resigned then', he said, but the reason for not so doing being that he didn't want to let down those who were going on the Huallaga Expedition.

He had hoped to cope until February 1949. However, his plans had to change when, in November 1948,

> I learnt, from a friend in Cambridge, of the sayings & doings of my wife & her sister, who had returned together from Rio, & I saw that I must return to my children (3).

And so he did, arriving late December 1948. My father further informed Huxley:

> [M]y wife left me on 19th January 1949. We are now in the beginnings of litigation – and that is that. I have the children.

That was the date – 19 January – when Mother was hospitalised for what my father described as a nervous breakdown. He closed his letter to Huxley with the remark that had he been a bachelor, 'I could have won through'. He was saying that he would have settled in Manaus to complete his work if he had no family encumbrances. He could then have been single-minded and uninterrupted. What springs to mind is Birtwistle's initial advice about not to marry!

I wonder why he wrote to Julian Huxley in such a way – in 1950, more than a year after his resignation and departure from Brazil. Was it from guilt; did he want to clear his mind, put his record straight, cover his tracks?

I have not yet succeeded in finding out about what it was that Mother 'ratted' about. It must have been serious for him to consider resignation. 'Ratted' suggests that she divulged something he had done, that she betrayed or denounced him. It also implies his guilt.

I have also not discovered what were the 'sayings and doings' my mother and Molly had been spreading around in Cambridge. Whatever it was, it damaged his reputation, or my father would not have complained.

*

Here, I need to write about Molly and her possible role in our family situation, as Dona Heloisa's letter of 1951 states that immediately after Molly arrived in Rio at my father's invitation, my mother's attitude changed completely and plans were laid for returning to Britain.

All my attempts to engage Molly to discuss this period were spurned. She knew that I was researching and writing this book but was determined to draw a line under the past. In June 2009, during a visit to England, a meeting with Molly was arranged but a day or so before the due date she cancelled citing ill health. An alternative date was also refused – ill health again.

In 2010, Paul Tanner told me that Molly was getting frail and her memory was not good. In 2011, aged 89, she was in hospital and clearly more frail. I had asked Peter if there was any hope of her providing the evidence which she would have given to the divorce. No, that will go to the grave with her. And so it did. Molly passed away on 29 July 2012. She was the only one, I feel sure, who knew most of the circumstances leading to my parent's divorce and I can only draw conclusions from her silence although I am not remotely interested in placing blame.

In 2006, Marj Goodhue wrote in reply to my questions about the rumour I once heard that Molly had made a pass at my father.

> I really didn't know Molly at all so I can neither affirm nor deny the rumour. Let's face it – Sheila was the gem of that family. The rest of them were a bit odd (to my way of thinking) – sort of standoffish, if you know what I mean. They were more or less loners as I remember it. Sorry, I don't mean to criticise your relatives – they were mine too. However, none of them were ever as friendly and outgoing as Sheila. She was always the one to come and visit to see her grandmother and the rest of the clan at the [Prides] Corner. Dana might drop in for a few hours on his way to or from some place in connection with his work. Molly came once when she accompanied Sheila from California in 1947 and only stayed a few hours.

Thinking about all this jolted my memory and I recalled an incident when Belinda and I lived near Stourport. Molly came for a weekend and by Sunday afternoon we realised she was making no plans to leave. I asked her what train she was planning to catch but she said she hoped she could stay longer. After a chat where I, with as much tact as I could muster, made it clear that she would have to leave that day, she told me that she had discussed it with Belinda who had agreed to her staying on – to house sit. I was quite taken aback, and talking to Belinda learned that no such conversation had taken place. Molly attempted to drive a wedge between us. Was this what she succeeded to do with my parents?

On arrival in England we stayed for a while with grandparents Corner. Molly didn't join us; she went to the Eckersleys near Chelmsford. Mother, Christine and I then went to *Tilbury Hall* in Great Yeldham, Essex.

Thirteen days after returning to England, Mother met with Aunts Stephanie and Do and, as Aunt Stephanie's diary entry of 30 September 1948 implies, she told them the reasons why she had left my father in Brazil.

[D]own to Hyde Park Hotel by 2.40 – Do's sitting room bathed in sunshine & full of flowers – Sheila arrived at 3 & talk was easy working up to the things we most wanted to know – she was very sane & calm & told us her tale very convincingly – feel very sympathetic. Wish I could have had John's answers to it all.

*

My father wrote to me from Manaus on 13 November 1948. Attached to the letter were two pages of sketches of 'hunting (mushrooms) in the woods', which he sub-titled 'The Three Little Boys and the Ears of Wood at Manaus, 1948'. He thanked me for my letter with news of Lindsay, and asked questions about my sisters: 'does she cry a lot… is she little or big… do I talk to Christine?' He told me he was that day flying to Rio and that he hoped to come to England in January. He ended, 'Love and kisses to Mummie, Christine, the New One and yourself, DADDY'.

My father had been thrown out of the Niteroi house, yet he wrote 'Love and kisses to Mummie'. Surely he was trying to make sure I was not worrying about the separation. Indeed, I was not aware of things then as a sheltered child. Life, difficult as it was becoming for me, was normal; I knew no different. Perhaps he was missing us all, feeling some remorse, and wanting his wife to read it.

Mother wrote to my father on 1 December 1948 inviting him to *Tilbury Hall* for Christmas. In turn, he wrote to Dona Heloisa, marking the letter personal: 'A letter today from Sheila says that she invites me for Christmas to the house that she has in England. I think that Molly will be there'. He noted that the letter was written after my mother had spoken with her lawyer and with my uncle who is our family lawyer, and concluded: 'It seems to me, therefore, that I should use this opportunity without fail to gather my family together... If ever there was a time for me to go to help my family it is now'.

He informed Heloisa that the same day he received a letter from his mother saying that 'when Sheila had to move into *Tilbury Hall*, she ran upstairs and burst into tears, so that they had to postpone the day'. The Eckersleys, with whom my mother had been staying, had also written to Gramma Bailey to tell her that Mother was very run-down and ill and 'almost unable to cope with the new house and the three children'.

My father's letter turns to Molly's place in the circumstances. 'My sisters and friends in England cannot penetrate the barrage set up by Molly, but I think that Sheila is now appreciating the sad things that have happened, and she is bound to attempt to maintain an attitude of defiance and fortitude in support of her decisions last June'.

As far as he knew, Molly was to be married on Christmas Day and that at least 'Sheila knows that I will not sit at the same table with Molly, and there is hope that all our problems may be reconciled'.

He finished the letter by telling Heloisa that he had been expecting news like this which required another decision in a hurry, but that it was dependent on whether he received an invitation for Christmas; 'now, I cannot refuse unless I am physically prevented'.

That he knew Molly was to be married on Christmas day in Paris means that the plans must have been made many months before. The remark 'Sheila knows that I will not sit at the same table with Molly, and there is hope that all our problems may be reconciled' shows where my father laid the blame; he held Molly responsible and there appears no love lost! His implication is that after Molly had gone, things might again settle down, and I think he hoped for that.

At last, the events of early 1949 were falling into place. My father was clearly pleased to be invited to join us for Christmas – indeed, he was expecting it. He must really have hoped that with Molly gone, he could resurrect the marriage and there might again be a future for Mr and Mrs E. J. H. Corner and family.

*

I do not know when my father found out about an important point which was revealed to me in my correspondence with Leslie Audus in 2006. Audus wrote:

Your father paid me a completely unexpected visit in Stanmore where I had been living since 1948. The reason – he wanted me to help him (how I never understood) in taking divorce proceedings against your mother. Apparently a good friend from Singapore days had, after a number of years of silence, dropped in your father's ear the knowledge that your mother had been having affaires [his spelling] while he was a prisoner of the Japs in Singapore. I told him that I knew nothing whatever about your mother's doings and wished to do nothing about the matter since she was as much my friend as he was.

I discussed this with Belinda and she reminded me of something she mentioned many, many years ago and rightly guessed that I had forgotten. Indeed I had forgotten and, on being reminded, I remembered that I really didn't then want to know, when such family memories were painful and I was attempting to clear my mind of it all – my mother had admitted to her that there had been someone else.

Did my mother have an affair in 1942–1945? I think it likely, whilst working at the American Military Hospital perhaps. Cambridge was the only place where she was 'settled' while my father was in occupied Singapore.

However, an affair can mean much but must not be misunderstood without facts. She simply might have danced with the same person too often, been seen with someone frequently, formed a friendship, but none of that proves an affair in any serious way; most unwise perhaps and those were different days and difficult times. I'm not disbelieving it; simply there is nothing in the information I have which definitely proves it. The then attitude towards Americans in Britain surely did not help my mother. Not even the coming divorce named adultery, just desertion, and from the information I have, there is no reference, even by implication, to adultery – just "affaires".

My father learned of her affair from 'a good friend' in Cambridge who had known us in Singapore. Leslie Audus said he seemed 'to remember that he had been on the Singapore Botany [sic] Garden staff and had got away to the UK before Singapore fell'. Did my father check the story or was the innuendo sufficient? Leslie Audus certainly didn't confirm it and wanted nothing of it.

Then there were those from Singapore who resented my father and his war work and would be jumping at the chance, any chance, to scupper him. Who from Singapore was in Cambridge at that time, late 1942 to late 1945 when we were in Great Shelford, and knew my mother? He must have been a 'friend' of them both and I wonder now if 'he' was someone who had attempted 'that affair' with her, and was rejected, becoming a devil's disciple, something of a snake in the grass! Was the 'he' a 'she', who didn't like my mother, the wife of a friend? I have my private thoughts but without proof cannot point a finger. Yet my mother suggested to Belinda that there had been someone else – that is beyond doubt.

My father, like any other man, would not have received information about his wife's "affaires" without reacting. He must have confronted her but I have no evidence of anything that transpired.

*

Mother was in mental turmoil in early 1949. The circumstances of her marriage were taking their toll. She was reluctant to tell her family but Eva Eckersley and Grannie Corner could see her state of mind. My mother had been married just three years in a land far removed physically and culturally from her native America when she was forced by war to separate from her husband during which she had "affaires". Some three and a half years later, they were reunited, only to begin a completely new life in Brazil where her husband spent most of his time travelling for work. So the marriage struck the rocks of despair, and she chose to take her two children and a third soon-to-arrive to England. She was desperately lonely and completely worn out.

Mother's fragile mind-set at that time is clearly shown in two long letters from Gramma Bailey to her daughter. In 2010, Peter Tanner sent me the copy of *Rootabaga Stories* which I so well remember my American grandmother giving me, and reading to me in 1947.

In the leaves of the book, as if bookmarks, were the deeply personal letters from Gramma. I agonised about whether I should publish them, and concluded that I had no choice since they are central to this part of the story and they are wonderful letters. The first is this moving, caring and loving one from *Gunston Hall*, near Lorton, Virginia, dated 5 January 1949.

Sheila, my dearest Bravest One: Eva-Eck [Eckersley] has written me a note to give latest bulletins, bless her, and I hardly know how I should have survived without it! Just remember, when things get too difficult, that John [my father] is not himself and try not to hold any bitterness in your heart against him. If I could help, except by stupid parcels or worse letters, it would be a great comfort to me. But I have the greatest confidence in your wisdom, no matter what stress or provocation you may suffer. Happier times are coming, my dear Girl. I know it, tho' how is impossible to fathom!

I spent Kay's birthday at *The Mouse Hole*, and what a joy to be there! It is simply wonderful here [*Gunston Hall*], glorious food, cleanliness and comfort – but, I still adore my dirty little *Mouse Hole*. Much of the time was spent in thinking about you & Kay, though I was quite unable to write to him. I did send off a joint birthday cake by Air Freight on Dec. 21st, on Amer. Airline, with the first destination of London. If it ever got there perhaps Dana can retrieve it, somehow.

Did Kay go to Gt. Shelford with the Billing family? Eva-Eck speaks with such admiration of D. [Dorothy] Billing! I hope she [Dorothy] will write me soon. I had a beautiful Christmas card from Do, which is the only one from that source [the Corner side] in months. But I haven't felt much like writing either, so there!

Gramma B then wrote of the 'queer mild winter with an occasional cold spell' and of how her plants were coping with the occasional frosts. She mentioned her friends Miss Bish and Mrs Wigmore and their trips to the movies whereas she preferred to stay at *The Mouse Hole* to do odd jobs including the sending of

another pkg Air Freight last Friday, with various oddments for all of you. I sent it to Mollie so Eva-Eck could get it to you, as I don't know how you get about. (I do hope Dana will take some pictures of you & Lindsay as I am hungry for a glimpse of you both!). The pictures you sent me are my most precious treasures, looked at thousand times a day… Now I must dash to get ready for Mr Rice [the postman]. Hold your thumbs [we say fingers crossed]! Perhaps he'll have a letter from one of you! Well do I realize how hard it is to find time to write: I am such a wretch myself, with nothing to offer as an excuse. But just remember, my dear Child that I have the greatest confidence in you, a firm belief in the deep wisdom which you alone of my children have always shown, and a warm happiness in my knowledge of your courage and indomitable spirit, to carry through these dark days of anxiety & separation!

I hope Mrs Chaplin and her husband are to be with you full-time [at *Tilbury Hall*] from now on, and I rejoice in the report that she (Mrs C.) is devoted to you! Blessings come soon to my dear Bravest One and her Off-Spring! Better days are nearly here, my dear girl. Live one day at a time, and believe me I love you more than tongue can tell or heart can see, blessed child! Your devoted & most confident parents* – Muddie

What a letter! It not only so well illustrates my mother's most brittle state of mind in early January 1949, but also counters my father's suggestion to Heloisa and others that Mother had left him in the lurch.

The second letter, also from *Gunston Hall*, was written just a week after the previous one, and it seems not to respond to any particular contact.

Sheila, my dear, this is John's birthday, I know. It is also the twentieth anniversary of the death of your father. It is strange that birth & death should thus be linked so closely, but like love and hate, they are never far apart in our hearts.

At the risk of alienating you from me, I shall take courage to write

---

Although my mother's father was dead, her mother wrote for both, hence parents.

as I think Faddie would want me to do, to his best-loved child, the heart of his heart – and mine! It seems now, to you, that such a gulf of misery and misunderstanding and wrong treatment has swept between you and John that nothing & nobody [double underlined] can bridge it! That is true, my dearest Brave One, except for one thing. No one save yourself alone can walk that path of forgiveness; can struggle with the burden of that terrific job of rebuilding your life together. Say to yourself, as I have to myself, many times, in my times of utter misery. 'I will forgive him seventy times seven! And many more if necessary! I am not going to give lip-service only to my belief in the teachings of Jesus Christ. I shall live those beliefs daily!'

Of course, you will fail dishearteningly often, all humans do. But affirm your belief in yourself and your principles, my dear, for, somehow, it helps! And when you succeed in that most difficult task of all, setting yourself entirely aside, the results will be so astonishing and inspiring that your children will rise up and call you blessed. Mine seldom had occasion to do so, I'll admit, but the great happiness which Faddie & I achieved was not easily won by any means.

One time, when, as in your case, I was utterly worn out and discouraged; when my brake-linings on the wheels of my temper were perilously thin, and I lost my temper and lashed out frantically at the nearest object at the slightest provocation, Faddie told me if I continued to behave so he would have me declared insane and take my children away from me. Yes, he did, Sheila! He had no realization – few men have of the part he'd played in my demoralization or exhaustion. And I was too young to assess the load of anxiety and fatigue and discouragement which he bore, & give him comfort!

But, like me, you have three children to build your life upon, "troublesome comforts", as my grandmother used to say, and they are helpless pawns now, in your hands. No one can give them what you can, and be sure, no one will! Should you love them, in your own need for freedom, they must carry the double load of being part American & also abandoned waifs, to be pitied and suspected by others all their lives! I nearly left your father once, in a desperate moment, but returned to care for young Dana, knowing the pitiless censure to which others would subject my son if I left him. And Faddie & I grew slowly, together, to see and love each other very deeply, as you know.

One more thing: here is a third generation where the relationship between father and daughter may become a very precious thing! Nothing but death separated me from your father, or you from Faddie [died 1929]. Can you deny to Christy-Kit the ineffable joy of such a relationship for I feel, very strongly, that Christy and John may be the third generation where the bond will hold very closely and who could deny her that tremendous experience?

Faddie has great devotion to you, my dear, but he knew, even as an infant, that you were capable of being, as he fondly called you "a tyrannous tyrant"! You must guard yourself that you do not demand more of others than of yourself. I had that lesson to learn when you were young things. Hating many foods which I insisted my children learn to eat, I suddenly realised that I must learn to eat them too!

At present the prospect looks bleak and unbearable, but love can transmute any material into something glorious, given the slightest encouragement! And if you deal gently with John, no matter what the provocation, remembering him as a bitterly disappointed person whose failure with you has been a frightful shock to him; that he, too, faces an uncertain future in a dark world, and like all men, needs help and comfort far more than he dares to let you know or can express adequately; that he has many times tried to prove his love and devotion to you in various ways, not always acceptably perhaps, but with honest intention – Ah my dear Bravest One, many a woman has had a hard battle, like yours, which can only be won by inches! But what a triumph it will be, if you can go on; if you can steady your will and indomitable courage to the task of giving your children a calm, happy atmosphere where proper growth & development may be brought to full fruition, and you & John may weather the years proudly and with dignity.

You see, you are an American, by birth, and suspect therefore, in English eyes. It is a great responsibility and carries farther implications than either of us can vision! Can you rebuild your life, with determination and wisdom, those three, who never asked to be born but are now here, will go forth strengthened and armed for the battles & struggles which will one day be their fate!

Think it over well, dear girl, and be sure that I speak for Faddie as well as myself, when I write this! I shall love you always, from the depths of my being, decide as you will. Be sure of that! And you have never uttered a single complaint to me – a proud record! But your battle was once mine and has been met by legions of braver women than I for generations. Some of those have won through. God be with you. My love & devotion is unstintingly yours to command! Muddie

What moving letters, so well written with so much love, care and worldly wisdom – and so honest to life. These letters tell me what an extraordinary lady my Gramma Bailey was. She had borne her own share of marriage problems and could clearly empathise with what Mother was going through. Gramma encouraged Mother to draw from her inner strength and consider the impact of her actions. Drawing from her own experience, Gramma counselled, 'I nearly left your father once, in a desperate moment, but returned to care for young Dana, knowing the pitiless censure to which others would subject my son if I left him'.

I had no idea of any of this in January 1949 except that I was becoming most aware of a father continuing in turmoil and a sad mother. Gramma's last remark quoted here would ring true to the circumstances in which I was soon to find myself.

*

I have almost no recollection of my father returning for Christmas 1948, but I do have one vivid memory of him from that time which has never left me. *Tilbury Hall* had a little story, and a serious one, which both I must tell.

In 2007, Belinda and I called on the present owners of *Tilbury Hall* by arrangement and were made most welcome. After a tour of this elegant and historical house with beautifully tended expansive gardens, we told them of my project and that I had no idea why we had stayed there. They researched but could find nothing relevant except to prove that my recollection of a crooked stairs was right.

My vivid memory was about ambulance men coming to take my mother to hospital, on a stretcher, and having great difficulty in negotiating the crooked stairs on the way back to the ambulance from upstairs.

My father was very angry and shouted at them. I can never forget that, having witnessed and heard it all – and I knew about my father's anger. It was January 1949 but I can remember as if it was yesterday, mother being ill and my father shouting – and I mean shouting. I was in the hallway seeing their difficulty in negotiating the wiggly stairs. How they manipulated the stretcher around the sharp bend without spilling my mother I will never know.

On our visit to *Tilbury Hall*, we saw that the stairs were very straight but my memory of crooked ones was not to be deflected! During the tour of the house I noticed that the stairs from the first to the second floor, pointed out by the owner, were indeed 'wiggly' but they were not the ones I remembered. I was sure the wiggly stairs were the ones from the first floor landing to the ground floor hallway.

As we left, the owner said he would talk to the daughter of the previous owner, and some weeks later replied to me saying,

Caught Alethea Waller at a slightly more lucid time; her mother bought the house in Althea's maiden name (Ruggles-Brice) in 1947. Alethea married 8th May 1948 and moved to Tangiers. Her mother frequently visited her family in East Africa and would let the house for 2/3 months when she was away – to friends, friends of friends etc., not through an agency. She went away very shortly after Alethea's wedding. The staircase at that time was wiggly and Alethea's mother had it modified – apparently after you were here.

So my memory had not failed me. Yet, I had thought long and hard about the reason for the ambulance and believed, for many years, indeed up to Pandora, that it had been a possible miscarriage of Lindsay.

Lindsay was born in October 1948, christened Edred Lindsay Noel, and much earlier in my research I had assumed we were at *Tilbury Hall* late in 1948, so the timing was right for a miscarriage.

Then I received from Dona Heloisa Domingues, a copy of a letter written by my father on 24 January 1949 to Dona Heloisa Torres.

> Heloisa, Heloisa, here is the last [letter] in secret. Poor, poor Sheila tried an overdose of her sleeping tablets and has failed. She lies, recovering, in a mental hospital in Colchester. She is not mental, for she entered voluntarily, but she needs that prolonged rest with true care which I cannot give her with the children about.

My father said Mother entered a mental hospital voluntarily. In her then condition, I ask, how could that have been voluntary? I think my father directed her to one as a way to cover his guilt for I don't think it 'standard practice' that a suicide attempt be considered a mental case without further checks. He explained that her doctor thought it was a glandular disturbance resulting from the recent birth 'which makes her so embittered and impatient' (clearly my father's words not the doctors). He told Heloisa that it may take six months before she is fit enough to return to the family, 'so I must make my plans accordingly and find a house, a nurse and a house helper, until our Sheila returns'. He asked that Heloisa tell no one. 'I shall try to keep it most confidential in England', adding that he must be available to help the doctors and 'to keep off the friends of the other side who may make her think against her family'. He closed by saying that she was so down that she would not even feed her baby, but that 'after this abyss of despair, she will recover'.

This was a huge shock for I knew nothing of it until I read this letter, 60 years after the attempt. My poor mother, what had she endured? It is difficult even to comprehend. I was learning of her suffering in Brazil, indeed our suffering, but this was certainly caused by whatever happened in Brazil considerably aggravated by post-natal depression.

I can understand my father wanting to keep the attempted suicide secret; suicide then was not understood and society was intolerant. Yet was he somehow afraid that the truth would reflect badly on him? Did he feel guilty? Had he considered even for a moment that he had contributed to it? I think he had and his reaction of anger was, as I am learning, typical – that cover when necessary.

Marj Goodhue told me that my mother contemplated suicide in Rio and actually 'walked away from it (and the problems) for a while'.

I hesitate to dwell on this except to say that my mother was made of strong stuff. Well brought up in a strict but fair home environment, she learned independence and self-respect. She was always polite and courteous and taught us those standards. Whatever happened to her must have been overwhelming.

On 10 February 1949, just 17 days after this revealing letter, my father wrote to Heloisa again. In the second letter, my father said, 'she went to hospital on January 19th leaving me without any reliable help'. Knowing what I now know I am speechless. It shows my father's attitude in complaining that his wife, through a suicide attempt, left *him* without any help.

He continued by declaring that 'Sheila is determined to leave her family'. He had sought medical help and advice 'and I am trying to keep the "door open" for her return, which cannot be under six months because she is in such a poisoned frame of mind'. He wrote of his concern that 'she will only upset and destroy every effort that I make to take up a new appointment which they have very kindly engineered for me in the University'. This, he told Heloisa, is why he is using the University address 'so that you will not be bothered with changes'.

After more soul searching I have decided to include the following:

I am getting hard-hearted, though, because, after refusing to care for her children in the same house as myself, and refusing to communicate with me for over two weeks, Sheila rings up and asks me for the money to fly to the USA and back to see her mother who is dying.

He agreed to find the money at a most financially difficult time only to learn, he said, 'that the mother is not dying, and that it is not urgent for Sheila to go, and so she is staying on in England'.

She did promise to return any unused cheques, he said, and declared rather pointedly that 'one, who can go to see her mother, can also take the effort to care for her children'.

I do recall a little of that time: I remember my father talking of the 'flying to America' matter and being very angry. This was when he really started to vilify our mother and 'indoctrination' began. I don't doubt that money was sought, and for a visit to America, but I am doubtful of my father's interpretations.

I don't think my mother was ever the one to visit Gramma Bailey. She had been too ill and I feel sure her doctor would have banned her from travelling. It was, I feel sure, Molly who paid the RMS *Andes* fares and this was a way for mother to repay her.

In the end, it was Molly who flew to America to look after Gramma Bailey. Mother wrote to me about this on 8 February 1949:

Yesterday Shirley [Eckersley] and I went to London and saw Molly go away in an aeroplane, and tonight she is in Washington with Gramma again. Poor Gramma is not very well, and Molly has gone home to look after her.

This was written two days before my father's letter to Heloisa and only 20 days after Mother's suicide attempt. I have no doubt she was not fit enough to travel that distance; indeed, I wonder if the doctors were concerned that she should not be alone for a while.

After leaving hospital, my mother never again returned to her husband. We children had 'lost' our mother, our family and our happiness. She was helped initially by Tom and Eva Eckersley and then the Holttums and soon other friendships followed. Mother's brother, Dana, did some work with Tom Eckersley soon after the war, and from that our families came to know each other. As a result of this connection Gramma Bailey and Eva Eckersley became regular correspondents and Eva, being the person she was, took my mother under her wing, opened her house to her and was virtually a second mother. Without the caring help and compassion of Eva Eckersley and Ursula Holttum, Mother – at one of the lowest points in her life – might well not have survived.

As time went on, we children visited her at *Weatheroak*, the Eckersley's house, and enjoyed the large garden and the woods: for me a parallel to Gramma Bailey's garden and woods at *The Mouse Hole* where we were less than two years before – and what a hell of a two years!

I was sent away to school on 21 January 1949, two days after mother had gone to hospital. Twyford School was recommended by Uncle Anthony and Aunt Stephanie who knew the Wickhams who headed the school, and I believe they made these my initial schooling arrangements, of course with my father's approval. Mother had had long talks with her in-laws and realised that a settled school environment was important for me.

At Twyford, it was soon discovered that my schooling was seriously lacking; I was rather a timid boy and my writing and spelling was atrocious – and I still couldn't read.

Here is my first letter to my mother from Twyford, transcribed as I wrote it:

Bifor I cam to school Daddy Tok me to the sins [science!] Myusiam and I sor the bots and all the models iy was nis to go thear. I have told missis Wicam I don't think you wil not get a letr efery munde you wil get one ever day but I wil send you some letrs. I am luking fowrs to sey you. Love from Kay.

The school had a lot of work to do.

- XX -

MY LIFE AT TWYFORD SCHOOL

Twyford School is the oldest Preparatory School in Britain. There has been a school for boys in the Hampshire village of Twyford near Winchester since the middle of the seventeenth century. It moved to the present site in 1809, based in the elegant Queen Anne house that we see today.

Famous Old Pupils include Alexander Pope, Hubert Parry and Lord Douglas Hurd. My headmaster was Bob Wickham. He and his wife, Betty, played a considerable role in school life. They made sure that Twyford remained a Christian school with emphasis on good manners, high personal values and caring for others. In 1949 the school had around 70 pupils. Today, it is a small, co-educational, family-oriented school of about 350 pupils from ages 3 to 13 where every pupil is known by his first name and valued as individuals.

Bob Wickham's son, David, told me that 'After the end of the war my father was one of the first to see danger signs for "schools run for private profit" in socialist Britain'. Bob Wickham therefore called together an Advisory Council of three Old Twyfordians and three parents of then Twyfordians (including Anthony Hurd) which advised that the school's existence could be much better assured if it became a Trust with debentures issued to the Wickhams.

The Spring Term 1949 was my first. I had then lived with my mother all my life until she was sent to hospital on 19 January, two days before I started boarding school. I was just one year old when Mother and I left my father to evacuate from Singapore at the end of 1941. When he was reunited with us in England in December 1945, he was a father I never knew. For the next year or so, our family life was framed by his sorting-out his difficulties and legacies from the war and finding work. During our time in Brazil, he was not often at home and, when he was, it was normally just for short spells. Then we left him in Brazil, and the next I knew of him was his return for Christmas 1948. By then family life had all but broken down, life was strained and I never really got to know him even though I was eight and deemed ready to be sent away to school.

Boarding school daunted me: I was really afraid of it but it had to be. I remember buying school uniforms, a suitcase and trunk, taking the train to London – Liverpool Street station, crossing London to Waterloo station and then to Winchester before a change to the local service to Shawford for a ride of a couple of miles to the school. Aunt Do met me in London, and as I learnt, also Uncle Birtie, to see me onto the train. We arrived in the dark and I faced a discipline that was entirely new to me.

Although the welcome from Bob and Betty Wickham was kindness, I really felt that I was travelling into the unknown – and I knew nothing of my mother's illness and the consequences. Dormitory lists were posted, as were school lesson schedules and every afternoon we had games. We attended chapel twice a day. On Sundays after lunch, we were taken on walks into the surrounding rolling countryside and we were taught to write home.

My mother replied, from the Eckersleys' home in Danbury on 31 January 1949, to my letter. This was just twelve days after her attempted suicide – a sobering thought.

It was splendid to have a letter from you so soon, and I was so proud to hear that you were the first boy to settle down in the dormitory! Well done! I am glad too that you saw Uncle Birtie in London and enjoyed your train journey down to Winchester. As soon as ever I am strong enough, again, I am going to come down to pay you a visit.

She said that Molly, Enid and Shirley [an Eckersley daughter], sent their love – it surprised me on reading the letter from Pandora that Molly was there, knowing that she married in Paris on Christmas Day 1948.

'When I look out of my window', Mother wrote, 'I remember you and Christine playing in the garden and miss you very much'. In closing she told me that

Daddy is looking after Christine and Lindsay and James and Sandy [our dog and cat] and I expect he tells you all about them in his letters… Please write to me again soon… and I will send you lots of letters… PS Did you get my farewell telegram? I do hope so.

Although the letter was written to Twyford, the telegram must have been sent to Tilbury Hall before I left. I never saw it – my father did not show it to me or tell me of it – and not until I read this letter did I know of its existence. Did it contain the truth of it all? Unlikely, for telegram content then was brief. Was it simply a 'farewell' – the use of the word being in the American sense rather than its meaning to me as something final? I can't express my feelings.

How did my father get the letter addressed to me at Twyford? I must have kept Mother's letters and brought them home in the holidays, eventually to find their way into my toy box. He found and kept them, and placed them in Pandora.

Mother wrote again on 3 February 1949 from the Eckersleys:

Christine and Lindsay are both quite well again, and sleeping well at night, and out in the sunshine every morning. I expect Christine misses you very much indeed… I shall write to Mr Wickham soon and ask him if I may come and visit you one weekend at the end of February, or early in March?

She then referred to her condition:

I am getting better quickly, because Molly and Eva look after me so well. And just outside my window is a tree, where you used to put up your targets and build Indian teepees.

Aunt Stephanie wrote to Mother on 8 February 1949 saying that she had heard from Stephen that he and Douglas had visited me at Twyford. They had found me 'quite cheerful & happy' and whilst walking on the Sunday afternoon I had staggered them 'by enquiring as to the origin of electricity & jet power'. She told Mother that she hoped 'her family managed to keep their end up'. Stephanie continued, saying that she had invited my father for a visit and asked if my mother would join them, offering

the little car to go over & see Kay – I have had no reply [from my father] but I imagine he has been over to Paris or has been very busy but jog his elbow when you have the opportunity – love Stephanie.

This is a most warm and friendly letter from Aunt Stephanie who was aware of my parents' marital situation from her meeting with Mother in Aunt Do's flat on 17 July 1948. However, I am not sure she was aware of the seriousness of Mother's illness – it was written barely three weeks after the attempt. Aunt Stephanie was trying to be the peacemaker; my father didn't reply and Aunt Stephanie suggested Mother 'jog his elbow'. No such joint visit happened. Indeed, I know that Bob Wickham discouraged parental visits within the first two weeks and the last two weeks of term.

These times are well illustrated by the letters to me, Stephanie and Bob Wickham; the family situation shines through. In her letter to me of 8 February 1949, Mother said:

Poor Gramma is not very well, and Molly has gone home to look after her. Perhaps, next week, instead of writing to me, you could write and tell Gramma about school and football? It would make her very happy. I have put in an envelope for you to use.

On 14 February, Mother wrote to me again saying that she is missing us children very much and thanking me for writing to Gramma B. She closed, 'I am sure we will all be together again soon'. Was this for my encouragement? I don't think I shall ever know.

My father, in his letter to Bob Wickham of 18 February 1949, updated our situation with regard to my mother, moving house, his new job and his thinking.

He began by suggesting dates at which he would visit and take me out, asking if I might bring a friend, even friends. He said he would travel by train, not yet having a car, and his sister Stephanie would collect him. He then advised Bob Wickham that he had purchased a house at 73 Hinton Way in Great Shelford, the village where we lived during the war, and that

doubtless Kay will be sorry not to come back here [*Tilbury Hall*], but he has many friends at Shelford and he will be very happy there as it is in the country with a garden of ¾ acre. It is the part where my wife had been hoping to get a house and I think that she will like it too.

He told Wickham that 'she is still in a very run-down state of mind and I have been advised not to worry her with details as yet, but to try to get every thing in working order by the end of April or May'.

He hoped to move in around 25 March. In checking the date of the term end and the arrangements for my travel, he closed by confirming that he started his post at Cambridge University

on the auspicious day of 1st April [1949], but the professor says he does not want me to work before October, which is his kind way of allowing one who has been many years away from academic life to find his way back.

In sending his regards to Mrs Wickham he mentioned that he had copied the letter 'which I can show my wife'. I wonder if she received them, or was that good spin since there was poor communication between my father and Mother.

I am surprised at the personal details my father gave in his letter to a man he hardly knew, albeit my new headmaster. The picture he paints is almost of normality although he described his wife, a month after the suicide attempt, as being 'in a very run-down state'.

On 20 February 1949, my father wrote to me: 'Here is some great news.

Mrs Ruggles-Bryce is coming back into this house [*Tilbury Hall*] soon, so we have to move'. He told me that he had found a 'nice house' in Great Shelford and that it is on the other side of the railway line from our war-time house. He described the garden: 'many apple and plum trees and lots of room to play', and my 'nice little bedroom' for which he had bought a bed and furniture. 'Then you will be able to play again with all your friends in Shelford'. He closed by telling me he would visit the school to take me out soon – and his finish included 'love from Mummy'.

In Pandora there were two letters from Uncle Birtie and I will show the one dated 19 February 1949 from Skibbereen because it typifies him and his friendly style, and I have only fond memories of him.

'I have just had a letter from your Daddy and he says you are well'. He continued by warmly recalling his school days and that he hoped I was looking forward to visiting him at Easter.

> [W]e can go fishing and we may catch a salmon and some sea trout. We shall have an exciting time if we get a big salmon on our line. We may see an otter.

After telling me of the various wild animals I might expect to see he told me that

> we shall have to find a horse for you to ride and hunt the fox. My young IRISH friends are very clever at riding horses which jump high walls and banks. They go to shows and win prizes for jumping at Cork and Dublin.

In telling me that there will be 'many boys and girls about the same age as you, so you will have plenty of friends to play with' he mentions that

> we are near the sea and you can bathe and sail boats and catch fish. You will have plenty of fun and we can go for very jolly picnics and have plenty to eat... I am looking forward to seeing you and having a great time with you.

I visited as planned. How I wish I had been old enough to know more and talked about his time in Singapore, but that was not to be. Did Uncle Birtie ever remind my father of his advice not to find a wife? I doubt it for he was a compassionate man.

On 9 March 1949, my grandfather Corner wrote to his son: 'My Dear John, I got your letter & will pay the cheque when your mother returns home. That may be Sat. week'. He explained that Grannie Corner had his power of attorney and that she was away in Bournemouth. He further explained that his cheque was for the 'difference between the old & new terms, to Mr Wickham'. He was pleased that we moved into our house, '*Tilbury Hall* being completely unsatisfactory'.

Grandfather was blind by this time and clearly he was paying, or greatly helping with, my school fees. His letter makes no reference to the marriage problems. Did he know or was it being kept from him due to his condition or, with his wife away perhaps he didn't want to make any mention via a letter writer.

My father wrote a number of letters to Dona Heloisa Torres at the Museum in Rio (her UNESCO office) and on 10 March 1949 he told Heloisa that 'We (that is Kay, Christine and Lindsay the third) move into our new house (at the above address) on 9th March and I am to start work at the University on 1st April, but it won't be hard'.

He was to assume the post of lecturer in Taxonomy at the Botany School in Cambridge University.

In writing that his wife was staying with some friends at Chelmsford [the Eckersleys], where she had been since 25 January, and that it was the 'worst place she could be', he said that 'Sheila is hating everyone'. He informed Heloisa that Mother was seeing a psychiatrist weekly but he didn't think there was much progress. He hoped that when we were all settled in to the new house 'she may be able to rouse herself and see that we are not her enemies'. He then claimed that she did everything possible to hurt him, and either he must become thick-skinned 'or bleed to death'. He said that he had visited me at school and that I was 'very happy', adding 'he likes Brazil except for the black people!' In giving her my school address he said that I would love to get a letter.

I was slowly settling as a boarder and was becoming happier at school but was still having difficulty with learning. My concentration was very un-concentrated as was my reading, and in spite of my father's anger and my unhappiness, I was homesick. My father wrote of Mother: 'she may be able to rouse herself and see that we are not her enemies'. This is a most insensitive comment particularly having told Heloisa of Mother's attempted suicide. Was he continuing to set the scene with his friends in Brazil knowing he will soon need their help?

I am now sure that 'the barrage set up by Molly' to try to put in place justification for all that happened in Brazil was coming from the Eckersley house. Could she have been calling Aunt Stephanie, Aunt Do and Granny Corner, 'forcing the issues' on them, as well as 'the University'? Did she know of the suicide attempt, and her silence to the grave was to save me from knowing of it? Maybe, but I am not convinced.

My father was considerably helped with my school fees by his parents. (A term's fees at Twyford in 1949, without extras, were £78.) His letter to his father of 28 February 1949 – rational and sensible, respectful of his father and the circumstances, and appreciative – explained his financial position at that time, showing also the value of money in those days. He thanked his father for the offer to pay 'and I hardly know what to say... I do not want you to think that I cannot do so'. He told his father that he had already paid for my outfit, clothes, trunk, suitcase and the like for my first term. A considerable cost, but that he was financially hard-pressed having to find money for the house and furniture since his money in New York might take a while to transfer. This I guess was where some or all of his UNESCO salary was sent. In addition, he explained that UNESCO still owed him a lot of money and that they were always 'tardy in paying'. This was the money put on hold pending the resolution of the imprest account matter. He added that he had about five hundred pounds in Malaya but he didn't know how much tax he might have to pay on sums transferred to England. Continuing, he told his father:

> I have an Insurance policy to cover four years of Kay's education, 14 to 18, and, if I have not done so, I want to take out a life insurance policy for him and similar education policies for Christine and Lindsay.

He realised that he had more 'extras' to pay regarding the house so 'I am blest if I know what I should do. Let us compromise, if you like, and I will send you Kay's bills until I can get all my affairs in order and can see how I stand financially'. My father then confirmed that he would convert his savings to cover as many costs as possible and he hoped to pay off the house mortgage in two years or so, earlier if 'I get any war claim compensation from Malaya, but I do not count on this at all'. He closed by welcoming the offer of help 'in this difficult interim period', saying it would be 'very kind indeed'.

He wrote to Heloisa on 21 April 1949 stating that my mother was 'still away and fanning a flame that will not flicker with much lustre and time only will help us together'. That astonishes me; it was my mother refusing to return home not she 'fanning a flame' – more writing to suit perhaps – and it's important to understand that this letter is to Heloisa in Brazil whom before long he would need 'on-side' to write in his favour.

Mother did visit me early in March and her letter gave train details and the hotel where she would stay – the Norman Mede which I remember. It had a model of a World War I tank in the drawing room. She told me that we must buy Christine a birthday present (she would be two years old) and she hoped that I had 'a lovely time with Daddy'.

It concerns me that my memory of much of those times is thin indeed. Even though I was eight, I don't recall wondering why my parents were not living together and why they visited me separately. I was used to them being apart from the earliest age.

A few days later, Mother wrote again and thanked me 'for such a happy visit. I was so proud of your nice manners at the hotel and of your excellent improvement in reading and writing'. She continued, 'Eva [Eckersley] has written a poem about your goal! This is it… 'O Kay!

From Britain to the USA,
From Pole to distant pole,
The shout goes up: "Hurrah for Kay!
Three cheers! He's kicked a goal".
But listen! Is the referee
This world-wide joy dispelling
By calling "Off-side?" No! Whoopee!
It's "Corner" that he's yelling!'

Mid-April, my mother wrote again and told me that I was writing much better. She told me she was learning chess. (My father taught me in those days as he did Contract Bridge. I remember his losing it when, as my partner, I trumped his ace!) She asked after 'my new boat' which my father had carved for me and hoped Christine helped me to sail it.

Reading this letter again reminded me of something that worried me 'forever' – the request for photographs. 'Could you take a picture of Christine and Lindsay on your camera and send it to me?' my mother had asked. I don't think I ever took those pictures she asked for. Hate had arrived at 73 Hinton Way and even talk of my mother and her family and friends was much frowned on, nay, actively discouraged. Our indoctrination had begun – me aged eight and Christine not quite two; Lindsay only some six months old. I was even careful not to be seen reading my mother's letters. I felt guilty for some reason. Oh that I had understood what was happening between my parents.

These letters, with all the other Pandora information, and what I have learned from elsewhere, are throwing an entirely new light on those days. One only has to read my mother's letters to understand the attitude difference between her and her husband. In my mother's there is love with a direction, and mother never spoke ill of her husband to me, rather the contrary. What my father wrote in his letters to me and how he acted were two different things. His letters were warm and friendly, but they did not reflect the real man at home.

My father wrote to my headmaster on 19 April 1949 about our life in Hinton Way:

Here we are happily settled, save for our unhappy mother. Kay is full of life and now reads to me quite well every evening. We have an excellent Danish girl to help in all things.

Desperate for someone to look after us children, Father was temporarily lent an *au pair* by the Newmans – Helga Dinesen Søndergaard, the Danish girl – and the date of her arrival on the scene is important as she would play a big role in our lives.

Before Pandora, I had long shut my mind to those days of 1949 and the 1950s. When occasionally I thought about them I could only remember unhappiness – deep unhappiness – and I blamed Twyford for that and my poor performances. How wrong I was. It was Twyford, Robert Wickham and his team who recognised my predicament and carefully guided me through whilst showing me no obvious favour. What a challenge for them. I thank Pandora for enlightening me – Pandora being a euphemism for my father.

In May 1949, my father wrote again to Heloisa:

Sheila, poor Sheila, seems just to be biting her fingernails and I can do nothing to recover her sense of proportion. Time may heal, but where she is staying [Eckersleys] is not a healthy environment. Sister Molly returned to the USA in February and I have heard nothing since.

He followed up with another letter on 11 June 1949:

Alas, poor Sheila is still determined to believe that I am the most frightful monster that the world has seen, and so I have not seen her since the 19th January [1949] and she will not come back to see the children. We must go on hoping for the best, and that time will heal these unfortunate convictions. She must be very unhappy.

Why would my mother 'not come back to see the children'? She doted on us. Whatever she experienced, married to E. J. H. Corner, must have been dreadful for it kept her away and as he wrote these letters we children were becoming brainwashed against her and all her family and friends and I don't regret repeating that.

'We are having some beautiful summer weather', he wrote again to Heloisa on 21 June 1949, 'I wish I had time to enjoy it lazily, but I am very busy sorting out my luggage from Singapore. I expect that from Manaus any day now'. He continued that he hoped to sort out his scientific papers soon and would send her a set for the museum library and then wrote a strange sentence:

How often I think of those lovely days of last December in the fastnesses of Corcovado! We are all well & happy except for the unwilling Sheila who sits in sorry for hours long.

What did he mean by the 'fastnesses' of Corcovado? It was a strange comment which tested me somewhat. Dictionary explanations include: a stronghold, fortress, and a castle: a fortified or secure place: a remote and secluded place vacationed in their mountain fastness. Did he somehow feel safe at Corcovado?

I asked Roy Watling for a view on my father's use of the word, he having known my father well, and his reply was indeed enlightening: 'the safe haven's in nature, away from the hubbub of civilisation'.

This polarised my mind and I began to think that that was a driving force for my father throughout his life: the fastness of nature, away from the hubbub of civilisation, free to do as he wishes without the demands and scrutiny of others. There he was at his best and when his stammer left him. Might it be that he should never have married?

My father wrote another letter to Heloisa on 17 August 1949.

I have been frightfully busy, returning to academic ways! The children are very well. Kay has progressed a lot at school. Christine is very imperious and tries to embark on very long conversations which are quite incomprehensible as she makes up the words. And Lindsay, the baby, is now trying to walk… Alas, their mother is still away. I have not seen her since January. Sometimes I say horrid things to myself, but I am glad then that no one was listening, and I wish she would come back.

But he said many 'horrid' things to me about Mother and I particularly recall the comment 'your shit of a mother'. This shocked me for I had not before heard him swear in that manner. Times then were quite different and I was young. My school reports were not good and they produced regular berating and ugly scenes, with shouting, and the Jekyll at the fore.

It is becoming ever more apparent to me that my father wrote what he wanted people to read, when it suited him. I am coming to believe he was spinning a web for later – for it was becoming ever clearer that divorce was inevitable and he was preparing the ground, as was Molly's barrage for her sister.

My mother had visited his parents, and consulted her lawyer and also my father's uncle who was the family lawyer, so it must have been clear to my father that her side of the story was already known to the family. Could his written wish for her to come home be simply that the letters were to be available for use later in court as exhibits in his favour if necessary? Am I being harsh, too cynical, reading too much into it all? Or had he already taken legal advice – which so advised. Likely, I think.

Still, I have tried to imagine, as I do constantly, how difficult it must have been for a father, in 1949, to look after three young children, buy and settle into a house, and start a new job, having so recently returned from overseas, indeed two distantly-separated overseas. He was still concerned at getting back the many things he left in Singapore and he was attempting to sort out money matters with UNESCO and war compensation. Those were tough times for him of which one should not lose sight.

My mother wrote to me at Hinton Way during the holidays:

> Here is a picture of Daddy with two lovely dogs. I thought you might like to have it, to take to school or have in your room. I have sent all of Christine's parcels, for her birthday, this morning. She will be two years old on Tuesday and I hope you will see that she has a happy day and please give her a very special birthday kiss and hug from Mummy.

She was pleased that I had another new boat, again carved by my father who was very good with his hands. He made me wooden boats and taught me how, and I enjoyed the anticipation of them and sailing them on the pond which he later dug in the garden.

In the holidays I tended not to write to my mother. We would visit her but I was afraid of being caught writing as that would bring more trouble from the Danish girl, Helga, who would remind me what a horrible person my mother was and often make comments in that vein. I knew she searched my room so I was careful where I put letters; indeed, I tried to collect them before anyone else had seen the post delivery. I was frightened to mention my mother, and her friends, in any context for fear of more berating. Hate had taught me never to mention Mother at home, for fear of trouble. That was awful. I now much regret it, especially for not passing the kind messages which she had asked me to convey to my sisters.

Times were not all miserable; there were better moments but they could so quickly evaporate in some moment of occasion, then anger.

*

When I arrived at Twyford most boys of my standard were a year younger. The loss of a year, at that age, and no settled earlier schooling was significant. The more I research this period of my life the more I recognise that I owe an enormous amount to Twyford School. The fact that I was unsettled there in the earlier years was due entirely to my great unhappiness at home. Yet, I didn't like to be away from home even though life there was often miserable; quite a conundrum. I learned to shut out anything and everything which remotely reminded me of my unhappiness and this shutting-out unfortunately spilled over into things to which I should have attended – like lessons! My mind was often far away as my school reports in Pandora observed.

As 1949 progressed, I was still rather uncertain in school although many references by the headmaster do say that I was 'flourishing'. Academically I was still way behind, struggling with reading, writing and arithmetic.

On 25 September 1949, I wrote to my mother from school:

> When will you be coming back to the house we have got to know? Do
> you know who is coming to meet me at the end of term? Do you know
> when I am gowing out, can I bring a boy called Durham with me, will
> you writ and tell me when please?

This letter not only suggests the reality of my academic standard but
also, in asking when my mother would be coming back, that I seemed to
know nothing of events between my parents.

- XXI -

DIVORCE AND AFTERMATH

In January or February 1949, my mother sued my father for divorce on the grounds of cruelty. My father informed Heloisa of this development on 10 February 1949:

> I have been talking to my solicitor who is dealing with Sheila's action for divorce against me… stating that I did not cause them any bodily harm or cruelty, and that it was their obstinacy that lead to the unfortunate events.

His solicitor had asked if Heloisa would consider making a statement, on oath, 'concerning what you did during that eventful week, 13th to 20th June 1948' when my mother refused my father back into the house. Here is the request for a statement which I had been expecting!

The year between February 1949 and March 1950 was hard: I went away to school; life became increasingly difficult for me; my parents lived apart and we three children saw Mother only when we stayed with her during my school holidays.

Then in March 1950, my father wrote to Heloisa saying that he had meant to write to her in Portuguese but 'distress has driven all learning from my head'. He continued, claiming that my mother had become ever more hostile

> and has worked up such venom that she has decided that our family must be torn apart… poor little children… and so she has served me with a notice of divorce on preposterous grounds of cruelty.

He remarked that he has no option but 'put on the armour of righteousness and go out to fight my wife. Is it not horrible?' He told her that the situation was serious for the future of we three children who lived with him. As for my mother, he said she could live with him if she wanted to, but 'I cannot take any more risks or give way to her demands further'.

I hate to have to tell you all this, and I should not if it were only myself that were concerned, but I have no intention of letting such distress fall on the children.

He confirmed that all was in legal hands and he supposed divorce was the American way. He then told Heloisa that his problem was to find £500 to defend the case. He wondered if there was any hope of the IIHA Interim Commission refunding the money that he had 'advanced personally to Sr David Smith and Agenorde de Melo in Manaus', then added, 'But if there are no funds available, of course you are not to worry'.

'The armour of righteousness' – was he devoid of blame? 'It is I suppose the American way' – the culture difference showed its hand again. 'I have no intention of letting such distress fall on the children' – that leaves me cold because that is exactly what he did. Bob Wickham had warned my father against involving the children but he did and continued to do so, vil-ifying my mother to us. This letter, as much as any, tells me that my father wrote one thing and practised another: at least in this his most complicated private life. I think that he was despairing of those advances being repaid and, did he hope, by implication, that Heloisa might offer financial help?

And what of his statement that 'distress has driven all the learning from my head'? In 1950 he published a paper, a report and a monograph (see Appendix D)! Distress drove things from *my* head and impaired *my* learning.

Clearly, the lawyers were now dictating the pace and my father's had directed him to get statements from Brazil. His letter of 9 November 1950 to Heloisa advised her that the law was moving slowly but arrangements were in place to seek her statement in Rio. The statement was to include a number of things which my father listed specifically in his letter: The occasion and date of their first meeting '(May 1947 in Hotel Gloria, in our official capacities!)' and the circumstances of her becoming god-mother to Christine 'Sunday 20th July 1947 (you stayed for dinner with us in the evening!)'; and to confirm that they, my father and Heloisa, had discussed Manaus as a base for the IIHA, and 'your visit with the Brazilian delegation to Manaus – April 1948, to see the suitability of it: the Governor's offer to give accommodation for me & my family in his house. How I came to you on Monday afternoon… and told you what had happened'.

He certainly wanted Heloisa to tell of her discussions with

Sheila, Molly and Mr Valentine (Western Telegraph Co.) about turn-ing me out of the house & the desirability of accompanying me to Manaus… during the week of Monday June 14th (1948).

He recalled for Heloisa that she and Valentine tried to persuade my mother to let her husband return to the house but Mother refused and this was to be included in the statement. He stressed the importance of this because my mother was 'trying to make out that I voluntarily stayed away. Actually, she let me return on the afternoon of Saturday 19th June to pack my boxes, & in the morning of Monday June 21st to take them away'.

He then asked Heloisa for 'her conclusions' about his behaviour suggesting that she write that he 'followed your advice and that of Valentine, in the face of their [mother and Molly's] unreasonableness' and that the Valentines 'brought Kay to lunch with us on Saturday 26th June, & to say goodbye to me'. He ended by apologising for asking for all of this 'but if you could send me this account in Portuguese, (by air), it would help the lawyers. It does not matter how it is written, but it is so that they can draw up a statement here from you to approve'.

This is all I have of that letter but it includes the important matters. It seems to me, when re-reading it, that my father was leading Heloisa to what he wanted written.

Amongst the many copy letters I received from my researcher in Brazil was one from my father's lawyers to him dated April 1951. The firm was Cowan & Dalmahoy of Charlotte Square, Edinburgh. It reported that the lawyers 'have had yet another conversation with your wife's solicitor [Tom Baker] who informs me that the date for the hearing of the examination at Rio is still not fixed because no specific understanding has been reached with Mr Valentine as to the payment of his expenses'. My father's lawyers responded by telling Baker that the expense matter was resolved, and Valentine now understood. He continued, by advising my father that the other side are

threatening to have the evidence of Dr Boedener taken, and then apply to the court here in England for the case to be heard in the absence of the evidence of Mr Valentine and Dona Heloisa.

My father's lawyer confirmed that this was quite proper, 'but we must avoid this contingency at all costs'. He closed by asking, indeed urging, my father to contact Valentine quickly to make it 'quite clear that his expenses are guaranteed by you or Dona Heloisa'.

Dr Boedener was our family doctor in Niteroi and it looks as if his evidence was important. It rather looks as if evidence was not taken from him, and that may have been a big mistake. I think mother's lawyer 'missed a trick' here in not pressing matters by insisting on Boedener's evidence. Surely, in such a case, the doctor's evidence is crucial. Boedener could have known that abuse and mistreatment had taken place. Did my mother confide in him as patient to doctor, or was it obvious to the medical person – or both? What is crystal clear is that my father's lawyer advised that Boedener's evidence must be avoided 'at all costs'.

On the matter of Valentine's expenses, my father wrote to Heloisa on 16 November 1950:

> I wonder if you will write to Mr Valentine to tell him that you will pay his expenses on my behalf and with arrangement with Dr. Catta-Preta [my father's lawyer in Rio].

He told Heloisa that he didn't know what was happening but that 'it looks very serious'. He went on to ask if she would arrange for Catta-Preta to visit my mother's agent in Rio as soon as possible to find out why Mother's London lawyer was insistent that 'Valentine refuses to do anything because his expenses have not been guaranteed'. He guessed that mother's Rio agents must be in direct contact with Valentine and not via Catta-Preta.

With evidence needed from Brazil as well as England, the information and details were taking a long time to prepare. My father's lawyers recognised that if the case in London could be delayed further, then it would very much suit them – for if my mother was to be away from the family for more than three years then my father could counter-sue for desertion. The lawyers did slow things down as the letter to Heloisa on 3 November 1951 showed: 'I am glad to know how this miserable affair stands in Rio because Sheila's lawyers were trying to accuse us of the delay'.

He thanked her for agreeing 'to stand bursar' for emergencies and then explained that there was no longer a great hurry

> because in Feb. 1952 I shall be able to make a counter-petition for desertion against Sheila and this means that all my evidence can come out in the case, and none can be suppressed by her lawyers.

He continued by suggesting that my mother's behaviour over the past two years

> seems to have been highly questionable, but this is confidential. So please don't feel you must go out of your way to try to hurry matters now that we know how it all stands.

He wrote, without explaining: 'her behaviour in the last two years seems to have been highly questionable, but this is confidential'. Is he hoping the implication will further damn my mother and lead Heloisa in her thinking?

He closed by telling Heloisa that he was very busy writing a chapter on tropical trees for a new book planned by Julian Huxley, and that 'Kay plays hockey, second team, and football but is no good at arithmetic!'

I was not just 'no good at arithmetic'; my father clearly did not understand what I was going through. Sadly, he never encouraged me in sports;

he just continually berated my poor academic performances. Indeed, my performance at Twyford diminished; to be more accurate my academic performance went sharply downhill – from barely halfway up! The more I failed, the worse the reports became and my father's anger increased in some kind of proportionate ratio. I felt worse and began to lose my self-esteem. It was a vicious circle which, at the time, seemed to have no end. I didn't understand any of it and withdrew ever more, which only compounded matters at school because I didn't listen and concentrate in class.

All this while, he had been corresponding with the headmaster of Twyford School who gave clear and sound advice. The first of these letters is dated April 1951. My father had given him information on the marriage situation and that a divorce was likely. Bob Wickham replied:

As you know, I hate these troubles, because they always react on the children, and all I can say is do try to keep the children out of it all as much as you can. I think it is one of the biggest causes of Kay's present difficulties, as several of the staff here have remarked how difficult he finds it to settle to anything and in fact how little at peace with himself he seems; and I should say that this was far more noticeable last term than in any of the previous ones. No, I'm sure he's not a fool. He's actually an extremely quick learner when he really tries, but the amount of time actually given to concentrated work is a fraction of the time available. Normally his mind is far away or slips off over halfway through a piece of reasoning... No, I definitely don't think that the stick is the right solution. The boy has plenty of problems of his own and quite evidently [it] is not the moment, and it is not for us to add lack of understanding to them... But they are not the cause of the trouble. He has yet to learn how to learn before we can really blame him for rather feeble results, and he can't do this easily while family problems are his major worry. I promise to do all I can. I'm very fond of Kay and find him a most interesting problem; so far I've not begun to solve it, though, Yours v. sincerely, Bob Wickham.

A brave, honest and excellent letter. He clearly was aware of my problems and not daunted from advising my father. Yet, my father did not put that advice into action. Life at home continued under his rule, and after we children visited our mother during holidays, we were always cross-questioned on our return. This continued for years and became very traumatic for me and Christine; Lindsay never really knew her mother and was spoiled by Helga. Aunt Stephanie's diary of January 1952 records:

At 2.30 went down to Norfolk Street to meet John's lawyer & Mrs P – spent about ½ hour with him trying to remember details and impressions – Case comes off March 17th. Sheila is suing John for divorce on account of cruelty.

Did Aunt Stephanie tell my father of that meeting with Mother on 30 September 1948 soon after she returned to Britain and when Aunt Stephanie had wished she 'could have had John's answers to it all'? Knowing her absolute fairness in everything, I am sure she did even though it was over three years since. She constantly tried to mend fences and was very family-orientated. Of course the family would be loyal but then Mother was family too and she clearly was well liked by my father's family and relations. I wish I knew how my father had explained it all to his family.

The divorce was on 17 March 1952 and made absolute on 3 June that year. My father won the counter-suit for desertion and won the case, gaining custody of we three children.

Mother told Marj Goodhue once that she did not stand a chance of getting the children because she was American and my father was British and the divorce was conducted in a British court.

My father wrote to Dona Heloisa on 28 March 1952:

[T]he case is finished (26th March 1952) and I won! I have the custody of the children & I have a divorce on grounds of desertion… Her charge of cruelty was stopped by the judge. Indeed, the judge stopped the case after he heard Sheila's evidence & she had been examined by my counsel.

Further, he said that the judge had tried to stop the case at the beginning, the first day (24th March 1952), becoming annoyed 'at Sheila's insistence on prolonging the case'. He informed Heloisa that the judge wanted 'nothing to reflect on the children' and that the judge was determined to prevent Molly from giving evidence. '[H]e also wanted to prevent my ruination by costs'. My father thanked Heloisa for all her help, then he wrote something which surprised me.

[S]he accused me publicly & I have been publicly excused, where matters must rest without vengeance or acrimony.

Reading 'without vengeance or acrimony' leaves me absolutely astonished, dismayed, and cold. My mother was vilified by my father, before and increasingly after the divorce, and we children therefore grew to hate her. That was very wrong; it was evil. It was drummed into us that our mother had walked out on us – deserted us – that she wanted nothing of us.

*

Reading all of these letters, and I have included only a few, has been a trial for me; I have had to force myself sometimes but at last I am getting to the truth. I have to make my own judgements and comments because I have so little of my mother's side of things; but I try to be dispassionate. I can only throw comment knowing how things affected me and my sisters – and my side, our side, needs to be told, indeed must be told.

I am most grateful to my researcher in Brazil, Heloisa Bertol Domingues (not to be confused with Dona Heloisa Bertol Torres), for sending the letters to me. She was concerned about my reaction but she need not have been; they are the most important letters I have received on this tragic matter. Peter Tanner, my mother's second husband, summed up very well, and how difficult it must have been for him too when he wrote:

> The consistent violent abuse in Rio continued when they got back to England and finally after Lindsay was born your mother had a complete breakdown aggravated no doubt by post-natal stress. This is now classed as "domestic violence" – emotionally or psychologically (being told you are a bad person or worthless). She took refuge with the Eckersleys and he refused to have her back, if indeed she had the strength to join him again. Helga was immediately on the scene and I think had been lined up for some time. As he married her immediately after the divorce it was clearly not a "housemaid" relationship but highly compromising as he was living with her years before the divorce, although nothing was made of this in court. When the court case, at the Law Courts in London with Tom Baker her solicitor, came up the cards were stacked against her and she was cruelly put through the wringer.
>
> She was in court entirely on her own, had limited means, her counsel was useless and the judge entirely unsympathetic. Molly had come to England to give evidence on the extreme provocation caused by continual abuse she'd witnessed in Rio but she was in a separate room and never called. The judgement was therefore on the basis of desertion and because EJH argued that there was a risk that the children could be whisked back to the USA he was granted custody, with access.
>
> There was no alimony and only a pittance of support for the children whilst they were on holiday with her. This despite the fact that EJH had pocketed all the compensation for loss of property in Singapore, a good part of which (such as her family's silver and her own jewellery) was your mother's.
>
> The whole thing was a complete travesty of justice from which she must have emerged a total wreck and but for her tremendous resilience (and the support of the Eckersleys and Holttums) would never have got on her feet again.

Why was Molly not called? Why did Tom Baker, Mother's solicitor, not insist, I enquired. Tom Baker has passed away and I've been unable to find details of his practice but, so long after the event, I know there will be no chance of records being kept. It seems that record-keeping is inconvenient! Molly refused to talk about any of it; her evidence could still be presented through this book if only she talked. I despair because my mother deserves her story to be told.

As I dwell yet again on the case, I wonder at the judge ruling as he did in case my mother whisked us back to the USA. If that had been her plan then surely she would have gone straight home from Brazil instead of going to the UK. She could have left us children there while she came to England for the case – but no, Sheila Corner was an honourable person.

I am most surprised by the fact that nothing was made in court of the fact that Helga had been living in the same house as my father since early 1949, indeed for three years. In those days it was indeed *avant-garde*. I think my father gave it no thought; he was wonderfully naïve in such matters, but why did Mother's lawyer not make an issue of it? Was he that incompetent? No, not on this point, for how could he have known. Mother had left home before Helga arrived on the scene. I know when Helga arrived and that she lived-in, sleeping in the front right bedroom, from day one. I have no idea if anything untoward occurred; I was too young, but I do remember my father 'returning' from her room on occasions.

I also remember noticing that Helga searched my room while I was out and things started to go missing, particularly letters from my mother. I knew I had to hide some of these things so, one day, I selected a spot in the acre of garden and dug a hole, shored it with wood, and made it as waterproof as I could before hiding mother's letters and a 10 shilling note she had sent me, which was a lot of money to me then. When I came to collect the note all was gone. Clearly Helga had been watching me and had raided my hide – and stolen all! I said nothing, but never forgot.

I never liked her and I'm afraid that gradually, as I learned more of her, I hid my feelings less and less – the impetuosity of youth. That meant more trouble of course but I brought some of that on myself.

*

My father wrote a short letter to Heloisa on 18 November 1953, about five months after he married Helga on 8 April 1953. 'Compliments of the season to you, and just a little note to let you know that we are all well'. He told her that her god-daughter Christine was well and that I will go to Marlborough 'next autumn'. He told of Julian Huxley's invitation 'to write a book on tropical forests – so I am busy'. I didn't go to Marlborough, rather The Leys. And he was asked to contribute a chapter for Huxley's book, not write a book.

I don't remember anything of his wedding to Helga. The Twyford term had finished on 31 March so I should have been at home on 8 April 1953 – unless it had been arranged for us to be with Mother, which I think most likely. I don't even remember how we were told. My mind is a complete blank on all of that.

I constantly wonder when things really began to go wrong with my parent's marriage. Marj Goodhue wrote to me in August 2006 with most perceptive comments:

As to why the marriage went wrong, I honestly don't know. She never said much of anything against him. She did tell me once that he expect-ed too much from her. In Singapore he was well established when they married. She was expected to take her place in the community that she was a complete stranger to. She was expected to know all the ins-and-outs of the society and to entertain flawlessly – in other words, not to seat people next to each other who were enemies. I don't know if I am putting this very well but I think at that time she felt she was in way over her head and no matter how she tried she just couldn't please him.

With all that I have learned, I am sure that those comments are right; my mother really was on a 'loser' from the earliest days of her marriage and the time in Brazil somehow was the catalyst for final failure.

When I was researching to try to find the General Yamashita map, I found Yuki Hasebe, the wife of Professor Mitsuyasu Hasebe. She is the grand-daughter of the late Professor Teizo Esaki, one of the 'three profes-sors' who were on that visit to the Istana in Johore. I had some fascinating exchanges with Yuki and Mitsuyasu and in one Yuki told me of an incident when they visited my father in Shelford in 1993.

I and Mitsuyasu had got married and gone on our honeymoon to Eu-rope. We stopped by GB for visiting Dr Corner. At that time, Mrs Helga Corner had a problem in her health. That is why we met and had a lunch in the cafeteria of the Cambridge Univ. There was an impressive and unforgettable episode for me. When we had having a lunch, he said to me as follows: "Yuki remember, for a botanist, botany comes first, his wife second."

We kept having lunch and a talk pleasantly, but honestly speaking, his words were very shocking for me, and I thought about you and your mother. (I'd heard about your mother a little from my mother.) His words were absolutely unacceptable for a young newly-wed woman, but I believed firmly that it clearly express his belief and life. It seems that he regarded studying botany as his mission.

Yes, the studying of botany was always FIRST in my father's priority list – his mission. That was not a throw-away line. I believe he believed he was giving sound advice to the newly-wed wife of a botanist, from his own experience. That is what he did, and second is where he placed my mother – with tragic family results. Indeed, my father did not let the divorce proceedings distract him from his botany. In the year his marriage was dissolved, he published the second edition of his well-received seminal work, *Wayside Trees of Malaya*, and preparation for it ran tandem with the legal wrangle and breakup of family.

Yuki told me what her mother said of Yuki's grandfather's first post-war meeting with my father in October 1953.

> Esaki went to London to attend a congress. He met Dr Corner again and took a photo of them…. Dr Corner looked a mere shadow of himself. When my mother showed the photo to Dr Corner many years later [1989 in Tokyo], he just said that he couldn't remember the situation. He said he lost the memory of those days. I suppose the intolerable heartache, the split in his family, made him so spiritless and nerveless [sic]. Undoubtedly, it must be very hard time for you and your mother, but also for him I bereave [sic].

Yes, it was difficult for all of us. I am interested to learn my father looked 'a mere shadow of himself', and the photograph does show that; clearly the events leading to the divorce took their toll as they most certainly did on my mother. I think he did try to shut out those memories just as I tried so hard to shut out my bad memories.

*

Part of the divorce agreement was that we children must spend half of each holiday with our mother. She did not return to America because she wanted to be close to us. I was happy that this was so and I believe Christine was too. Lindsay enjoyed the visits until her stepmother's vilification of Mother took their toll. They failed with me, and Christine resisted but they were tortuous times. When Christine was locked in cupboards I let her out, and there was more trouble!

My stepmother, Helga Søndergaard, was on temporary loan as a maid from the Newmans; she stayed and eventually married my father, under pressure from her mother, on 8 April 1953 – just a year after the decree nisi. She was from farming stock near Mors in Denmark. Leslie Audus wrote to me in 2007:

> I remember a large square-framed 'nurse' from Denmark I think living in your father's household and looking after your sisters. The story

that came to my ears was that on one bright and sunny day the Corner household was invaded by another square-framed lady from Denmark, mother of the 'nurse'; she insisted that your father marry her daughter since they were living in the same house. This I believe your father did. I cannot remember ever meeting the new Mrs John Corner.

Was it a marriage of convenience and under pressure? I believe yes to both points; and Helga's mother clearly was more perceptive than the divorce court judge!

I wonder if his decision to marry Helga could in any way be likened to his comment about Alice Birtwistle. My father wrote that 'she brought happiness and comfort into his [Birtwistle's] spartan life'. Certainly Helga helped his comfort in that he could continue at his work and travels without a worry about the running of the home and his children; and his lifestyle was pretty spartan, when I knew it and that's a fact, not a complaint. This confirms the pressure to marry and I'm sure that he couldn't imagine the trouble of finding another housekeeper and carer. The decision to remarry suited him – but he didn't at all consider his young family. The botanist came first.

My father wrote to Heloisa on 27 October 1954:

Yes we are all growing up… Kay now at The Leys School, Cambridge as a day boarder where he is very happy… and I have married Helga who has looked after us since 1949 who makes the children happy, and puts up with me. She's Danish.

Had he forgotten he had told Heloisa about Helga on more than one occasion, and here again he reported that she 'makes the children happy'? The unfolding story will put the lie to that. And again he said I was 'very happy' too. How many times did he write that?

I can, with difficulty, recall a little of my life during these times and I have already written something of it. I know violence occurred to me, and I do remember having been hurled across the sitting room of 73 Hinton Way in the early 1950s. No doubt I had 'given lip' but violence is never to be condoned. I recall criticising Helga for something. It was not wise! It has been mentioned not infrequently by so many with whom I have contact that my father had a quick temper and was not good at suffering 'fools'.

I don't know for how long my mother stayed with the Eckersleys after her suicide attempt. She later moved to a lovely old farmhouse, *Gibbs,* with a big garden and deep in the country in the Essex village of Little Baddow; she rented rooms for income. She seemed contented when we visited her there in the holidays. She had many friends and worked locally, which included teaching at Heathcote School in the nearby village of Danbury.

Through this she met Rachel Catlow who became a life-long friend. Mother was unqualified in teaching so was 'hard up' and, not being able to afford a car, made good use of a bicycle. In later years, Mother sang in the choir of St. Mary the Virgin Church, Little Baddow, where she also was confirmed.

My memories of those days are few. However, I do remember William and Carene Hartop who I met when we were at *Gibbs*. They were one of the early tenants, as were the Robinsons and Thomassons.

William was in the German POW camp from which the Great Escape emanated; he was one of those vaulting the horse. After repatriation, he was part of Clarke's Shoes and became well heeled! In the 1950s he had a Bentley and my mother remarked that it was the only Bentley she drove. He took me to a Farnborough Air Show on 11 September 1953, the day before the test pilot John Derry crashed in his DH 110. I recall going to the Air Show every year in those days before it changed to biennial.

On 24 June 1953, Mother moved to Chelmsford to live in *The Limes*, a house owned by the Holttums and from which rooms again were rented to help with income. Deborah Holttum told me in 2011 that 'the house in Chelmsford was bought by my mother… specifically for Shelia, and which, at a later date, my sister was to inherit'.

I can remember my mother spotting my father lurking over the road while we children were with her. She pointed him out to me from a window. He was wearing his distinctive hat. What was his reason for lurking, for spying? I think he was trying to find ways of justifying to the court that we children should never again visit our mother. Was he looking for mistreatment of us by Mother? He would never have found that. All we got was love.

My letter to Mother of 21 August 1953 shows the tension we children lived under:

Thank you very much for your letter. No one asked me if they [my father and Helga] could read it. They didn't like Christine's hair [Mother had had it properly washed and cut] so they say "it will grow again". I am terribly sorry I could not come and see you at Pats or phone because Daddy smelt a rat and watched where I went for a bit. This may be of some use to you, today, (Monday) Daddy and Helga had a quarrel. Tomorrow I am going back to school. I can put a pretty safe bet on it now that the man you saw at the gate was Daddy; I can't explain now because it would take too long.

In an earlier letter, I had written a telling postscript: 'PS I won't write what I want to say because Daddy is going to read it'.

The house in Springfield Road, Chelmsford, was where my mother met

253

Lieutenant Peter Tanner RN who had then just come out of the Royal Navy from a short service commission. A physicist, he had joined Marconi in Chelmsford and lodged at *The Limes*. In her personal diary, Mother wrote on 15 August 1954: 'Mr Tanner moved in'. I recall much of my visits to *The Limes*: how I helped in choosing colours for re-decoration, the radio which Peter made for me and the continued encouragement in classical music.

In 1959, Mother moved from *The Limes* to an address in the Atomic Weapons Research Complex in Aldermaston where Peter Tanner worked. In 1962 they moved to Mortimer, Berkshire. Peter Tanner told me in 2006:

Before and after your Mother and I married, you and the girls came as usual for a few weeks in the holidays and we had very happy times together. However, Mum was then asked to attend a meeting in London (and I went with her) with a Miss Mathews (or a name like that) who was a social worker attached to the court with a responsibility I suppose of seeing that the terms of the divorce were complied with [It was a Miss Noel]. She said that the girls were so completely traumatised by cross-examination by Helga and EJH, both before and after their visits to Mum, that she thought it kinder if for a while the visits [to Mother] were discontinued. This ties up with their "furious" questioning of you after your visits. There was something paranoid about it. This Miss Mathews told your Mother she need not worry because when the girls were 16 they could make their own decision and would certainly want to maintain contact with their natural mother.

Mum pondered on this for a long time but then agreed to the ridiculous and unprofessional suggestion. Knowing only too well EJHC's ferocious tantrums she was always reluctant to do anything which would rebound on you children. In Christine's case it did work out that they [Mum and Christine] subsequently had a very good relationship but Lindsay has never come to terms with it. I'm sure she was told as a child her mother wanted nothing more to do with her and was never able to forgive her although Mum and Belinda also made a valiant effort to meet her [Lindsay] at one stage.

What a crazy decision. I had forgotten it until Peter's reminder. We children were being asked to stay with the very parent who was the cause of all our unhappiness and be denied visits to the one who gave us comfort. Yet, it was a courageous decision for Mother because it was to protect us children from my father's tantrums although it created a no-win situation for her. My sister Christine, like me, was old enough to suffer from the upbringing at home. She became deeply affected. My mother did her best, as time went on, to help and support her and certainly gave her the love she really never had.

The divorce settlement did rule that at age 16 we children could choose our parent. Sixteen in the late 1950s was very different from today. My father arranged for me to go on a skiing holiday, with the Worthingtons, co-inciding with my sixteenth birthday, so that I could make my decision and he made it clear to me that the holiday was for that purpose!

Griselda Worthington tells me she remembers

skiing in Austria with you a member of the party; you say in your emails this was 1957. I remember you did not seem happy and those life decisions you were supposed to be making are probably the reason. I think you were a learner skier and that Richard McConnell, a friend of my father, was a member of the party and he looked after you a bit and helped you with your skiing. Both your father and mine were super intellects and impatient of people they perceived as lesser mortals.

I remember this trip. It was also at age 16 that I had to decide whether to keep my dual American and British nationality or become British. Had I wanted to keep my American nationality I would have to spend six months a year in America and be available for the Draft. That was entirely out of the question because of education and other issues, so I became British although I recall having no part in the decision.

*

My father was most competent at writing what he wanted to think. I'm very sad that I don't have much of Mother's side to it all. Peter has recalled what he can, and I am grateful beyond words; it must have been most dif-ficult for him, but he has told me over the years that my mother rarely discussed these things with him. I can well understand her wanting to clear her mind of it all. She must have longed to consign it to the furthest recess-es, as I tried with my unhappy years – and it's nearly possible!

There is no doubt that there was fault on both sides. All I want is the truth, and for it to be told because too many still have incorrect and wrong information, but the truth has been denied me with Molly's refusal to tell what she knew, taking all to her grave.

Nevertheless, I do now have a much more balanced view of those days but my sister Christine passed on, soon after her father, in ignorance of most of it, just bearing a lot of the hurt. That is a most tragic affair as she was a lively and out-going person, and well liked. Her illness was a direct result of her ill-treatment at home in her younger years. That's desperately sad and so very wrong; I cried at her funeral. She left a husband, Douglas Cross, and three children, David, James and Helen.

My sister Lindsay knows almost nothing of it. She was naturally the 'child' of her stepmother (being only a few months old when they met, and

Mother had by then gone from the home) and I know she is bitter and feels that her mother badly let her down. Well, our father very badly let us all down and then he allowed, nay, imbued us with hate, to be a part of it and he shifted all the blame onto his first wife, her family and friends.

My mother never showed us feelings of hate; she never spoke in that manner and I never heard her speak ill of her first husband. She never deserted us children. She was forced out and E. J. H. Corner got away with it – until now.

I can much better appreciate now why mother would not talk about that past. That she didn't must never be thought of as an admission of any guilt. That would be most presumptive and extraordinarily wrong. She did talk a little to one of her lodgers at *Gibbs*. Mickey Gold Blyth, who was Mickey Robinson at Gibbs, told me in 2007:

Of course I only had Sheila's account of her marriage – when we first became close friends in Little Baddow; it was a very sad story, she told us that John had had her institutionalised and got custody of the girls – I was reduced to tears at times, as she was such a lovely warm person – she put down John's behaviour as the effects of prison camp and Dengue Fever – of course we never met him. We left Little Baddow in about 1954 and she used to come and see us in Barnes. Various men passed in and out of her life which pleased us, and was not surprising – she was so attractive and had a lovely sense of humour… I would say she had a slightly neurotic streak but we didn't find that strange considering all that she had been through.

So acrimony and misinformation remained with us for many years after the divorce.

TO THE LEYS

By 1953, when the divorce was past, I was coming to grips with things and starting to contribute positively to all things school. The school motto *Vince Patientia* – it's dogged as does it – is inspiring, and certainly Twyford taught me how to stick at things.

The period late 1948 to 1953 were some of the worst days of my early life, and whilst Pandora has led me through them again, I have found it extremely difficult; but there are lessons to be learned: of parenting, of good headmastership, of how to handle situations, of being responsible.

My father was not outwardly a religious man, yet his letters do suggest a clear belief and he did attend to the religious teaching of us children, me at least. My father insisted I attend church every Sunday. During Sunday lunch he would ask me to tell him about the sermon. I simply didn't attend to that and could only sketchily report on it and that always brought more trouble, which I hated; yet, try as I did, I somehow couldn't absorb what was said over the pulpit. One of his much-enjoyed extracts from the Bible is the riddle in Judges 14:14 – 'Out of the eater came forth meat, and out of the strong came forth sweetness'. It is most apt at this serious moment of my writing, for from bad must come good and out of all of this I was improved.

Here I pen something of an autobiography of my life at Twyford although this is essentially the story of my father. I include it because our stories are indelibly intertwined at this stage, and his handling of me – post-divorce – and my schooling shows some of his attitudes.

The following extract from Bob Wickham's reply to my father's letter of 29 March 1952, which informed him of the divorce twelve days after the *decree nisi*, is worthy of inclusion.

It is a little difficult to give advice on what exactly to say to Kay [about the divorce] without knowing what Mrs Corner is going to say. Most unfortunately I was laid up a week ago when she was here & so had no opportunity of discussing the matter. But all along I have besought her to keep the causes of differences out of any discussions she has with Kay, & concentrate on planning for his good, keeping points of difference in the background. Where these things are so fatal is where the parents conflict against one another for the child's affection. If they can be brought up to believe that both parents want the best for them, but that owing to circumstances they cannot live together, then not so much harm is done. I am quite sure you must explain quite clearly… incidentally, the facts of the situation in so far as it affects his holiday arrangements he has a perfect right to know, & an uncertainty of what the position is might be most unfair.

I do wish I could give you more helpful advice. Without having had a talk with Stephanie, or knowing what line Mrs Corner will take I do not feel that I can be more definite at this stage.

I wish I could remember how and what I was told about the divorce, but nothing – my memory is blank – except that he hammered home the message that Mother had walked out on us, deserted us. There is not a shadow of a doubt that my father's attitude and pressure was a disaster for me, as Bob Wickham warns – yet the warning went unheeded.

My school work deteriorated particularly from 1950 to 1953. However, during those tough years, I was able to find that I had an aptitude for sport and was much encouraged by those involved at Twyford School. At least this gave me some self-esteem, though at the time I was too young to realise this.

Bob Wickham summed up my academic status in January 1952, writing that 'It is a great pity that he has lost or never really had confidence in his powers of learning, which are not really at fault'. His letter of 2 May 1952 is self-explanatory.

My only answer is that any boy needs strict handling in the sense that he has to learn to do a job, whether he likes it or no, because it serves some useful end, or is a useful stage in attaining some desirable end. I would say that that is the big lesson of life. But I would issue a word of warning. A boy has to learn this lesson for himself as all other lessons, & you can overdo the forcing the pace. You cannot bully a boy into any desirable end. He will only react against it as soon as the pressure is released. All you can do is keep him face to face with the problem till it becomes his own problem. Kay is a person who has a natural tendency to shift difficulties. Possibly there are already enough emotional ones to have taught him to avoid them instinctively & I don't know. We shall have to be very firm with him. We could bully him into working. I'm sure that it would be wrong to do so. Kay is often unhappy as it is, & he's bound to seek compensations elsewhere. We should be committing a crime to take the bullying to the stage of making him unhappy.

You may think that I am being soft hearted. I'm not, I assure you. I'm just trying to look at Kay's whole character, & not merely his power to learn. I would suggest your discussing this with Stephanie who will, I know, back me up. You've got to be both mother & father to the boy now, unless you want to drive him into taking sides, & it's not going to be easy. We'll do all we can to treat Kay in the right way. I don't think we're very soft with him as it is. But he's a boy who'll need a lot of help, & one can only give him that so long as he knows that one is just, & that ultimately one is trying to help.

'You have got to be both mother and father to the boy'. My father struggled to be a father; he had no chance of being a mother, and I never thought of him as 'just' in those days but I should be careful for I was then quite young, 11, and very inexperienced. Yet, sadly, my father took little notice of this letter, written barely two months after the divorce. At this time, the pressure, ridicule and hate of all concerned with my mother, her family and friends, continued, even increased. We children were brainwashed.

Now that I have Bob Wickham's letters, his encouraging headmaster's summary concluding my report of March 1952 – stating that it is 'one of his best terms so far' – makes me appreciate his understanding of me during those difficult times. Yet, later in 1952, and completely unbeknown to me, my father wanted to take me from Twyford to a school in Cambridge. He told Wickham of this in a letter dated 6 September 1952. The headmaster replied:

I can't pretend to be anything but very sorry to receive your letter about Kay, & the possibility of his going to the Perse School. Nor can I regard it as anything but a sensible step. But we've come to be very fond of Kay, & though we get used to parting with boys in the normal course of events, a sudden departure like the one you contemplate comes as a bit of a shock when one had counted on having him as a member of one's family for more time to come. However, Kay's alternate future must be the only consideration, & if you can get him into the Perse, I'm sure it would be a wise step. I am finally somewhat doubtful about his being able to pass the entrance examination but I really do not know what they will expect.

So, he sent a character reference for me and hoped that plans work out successfully. Aunt Stephanie also wrote to her brother. By a process of deduction, I place it sometime in the summer of 1952 and before the letter just shown and before my father married Helga. She and Uncle Anthony were going on holiday to Bournemouth and called in at Twyford on the way. She wrote:

[W]e found them [the Wickham's] enjoying the last but one day of the holidays by their fireside – Betty busy darning dormitory blankets & Bob clearing his desk ready for the new term – they are a nice couple – here are some of the things Bob said about Kay.

He was one of the weakest workers in the school but his presentations were amongst the best. He was still having difficulty with concentration. However, once he did learn something he didn't forget it; 'there was no "in at one ear & out of the other" with Kay – when it went in – it stayed there.

Bob Wickham told her that I was a willing worker and that I was trying – no fool but the clue to 'all his troubles, as we know is that he wasn't taught to read and write when of an age to take to it easily and so is hampered and behind for his age. Only time & patience could help him make up for this'. Wickham confirmed that I would certainly become a senior and prefect if I stayed on and that I would make a good all-round athlete. 'His football had improved tremendously this term. He was playing with his head & fully deserved his colours'.

They discussed The Perse School and about my possibly going on to Marlborough and agreed that it was best for my father to be responsible for my education. Wickham was going to write to the headmaster of The Perse School to find out more about the 11+ papers. They are planned to be 'of an impromptu sort – set to judge a state of intelligence'. However, secondary school education prepared children for this exam whilst Prep school work covers 'more subjects with a Common Entrance for a public school as its goal & the emphasis is different'.

Wickham said most emphatically that if I failed in my 11+ to The Perse School 'which he might well do – it would be no sign of dullness or lack of intelligence in Kay, in fact he knew of one or two really bright boys that had failed – but really that at this still very early stage of educating he had not been prepared for his best'.

If I were to pass the 11+, then September 1953 would be the likely time for me to go there and if I were to fail, I could sit Common Entrance for Marlborough in a year's time.

Aunt Stephanie reported:

Bob Wickham said there was no reason at all why he should not pass & Mamma & ourselves have said that we should finance it – should Mamma die before Sept 1954 – Papa's money would be there to see him through.

She then turned to a rather different matter and asked my father if there was a boarding house at The Perse School.

I was just thinking, gloomily I grant you – but suppose Helga had to leave for any reason & you were without help for a time – could he board in? Or perhaps friends would come to the rescue – or would you consider him as a boarder if it were possible...?

What an excellent, thoughtful and most caring letter, sister to brother. If only my father had heeded her advice – but no, I was still rejected as lazy, a dullard; rather a no-hoper. My confidence was shattered. He took no interest in my sporting achievements, which were important to me and I suppose 'covering' for my lack of academic excellence. And he was good at sport in his youth – yet he never told me.

*

During the holidays in September 1952, my father took me to The Perse School to sit the entrance examination. The first I knew of this was in the car on the way to the school! The curriculum for such a school, as Wickham pointed out, was quite different from that of a Prep School and I had had no preparation. So I failed very badly, getting more trouble from my father and a lot of it! Amongst the many strong words, I was accused of being a dunce, hopeless and selfish – the last word he used to describe me on a number of occasions. He reacted severely and I was regularly berated. My confidence took more battering.

My father wrote to Stanley Stubbs, the headmaster of The Perse School, on 18 September 1952 and his whole attitude is well illustrated by his words to a stranger. After thanking him for his letter and 'great kindness in arranging this examination', he wrote:

I appreciate your help, and, though I must straightway apologise for the result, and for having wasted your time, I am very thankful to know, at last, the truth of my son's abilities. I am extremely doubtful, in view of his general disability to apply himself to anything other than play, that he will ever succeed in passing an examination, until he is many years older.

He concluded the letter by agreeing to take the Head's advice and discuss my case with the County Education Officer. I stress this closing sentence.

I must also discuss with his present headmaster, because I believe the boy is also a "psychological case", not in inhibitions from his parents' circumstances, but in his carelessness's and forgetfulness.

There it is: my father publicly exonerating the marriage circumstances as the cause of my considerable problems and blaming me to an unknown person in the University town of which he was a member of the Gown. Interestingly, he used the word 'disability' rather than inability. I was a psychological case.

My father also wrote to Twyford School. The letter illustrates how little he understood of my difficulties and clearly he was not, under any circumstance, going to admit even a part of the blame. 'As you well suggested, Kay has not passed the entrance examination to the Perse school. I am typing out the headmaster's letter'. He typed the letter in full, and continued:

Quite frankly, and perhaps too pessimistically, I do not see Kay passing any examination for many years, because he seems to have no ability to pull himself together and to apply himself. I have therefore to consider what is to happen to a boy who fails at examinations and for whom his father cannot bribe a way with high fees! Mr Stubbs suggested also that I should see the County Education Officer, which I must now do.

He told Wickham that he had talked to me but 'I become sullen and turn on him with some spiteful remark which I remember from his mother's lips'. He then asked the real question:

Do you think that I should find a medical adviser who can enquire into the boy's mind and see the reason of his difficulties…? I do not say psychologist because I mistrust the fangles of such people. *From his carefree behaviour, I do not think that his parents' battle worries him* [my emphasis]. He is just incapable of pulling himself together, and so he idles and fools'.

My father hoped that I would grow out of it but time was pressing 'and I am concerned at what is to happen to him in a year or two'. He continued by confirming that I would return to Twyford but for how long would depend on my efforts and 'what his grandmother can afford'. He told Wickham that he could not afford the present expenses – in fact, can only just make ends meet without the school bills 'owing to the alimony* which I have to pay. For the rest, I am ruined through having to prove myself entirely innocent'.

Wickham wrote to my father on 21 September. It is another important letter which I show in entirety.

I am very sorry to hear your news of Kay, though not unduly surprised. He is in no state to tackle any exam without pretty careful preparation. In the meanwhile, we'd better try to get him up to an examination

---

* *I was told by Peter Tanner that the alimony was a pittance.*

standard a year hence if you can manage to carry on like this. Incidentally, you could not "bribe" a way for him even with high sums at the moment. I'm told that approximately 1,000 boys a year fail to find places in the Public Schools at the moment!

No, most certainly I should not turn to a psychologist unless you feel forced to. Kay is a very sound little boy who had no early education, who has never learnt how to work, which is generally the result of a slow start, but who should make up the ground if he can only realise the necessity of hard work. I don't think you must be too hard on the boy or else you may easily lose his affection which is priceless, & it's not all his fault by any means. And you may well drive him entirely onto his mother's side. In any case, the boy deserves some sympathy for the home situations as the children always suffer.

No, I should try to talk quite quietly to him & suggest to him that he's got to take the lead among the other members of the family. He can only do that by a terrific effort, especially as this exam shows that there is a lot of leeway to make up. But he's no longer entirely a child, & he's got to realise that his future must rest on his own shoulders. So long as you can feel that he's doing his best, which you haven't always felt in the past, & which he must admit he's not always done, you mustn't blame him if he does not always come out on top.

You know, Corner, you've got a good son, whatever you may think of him at the moment, & one in which you may well feel proud one day. But he's a sensitive soul, just as Stephanie's children were, & if you try to drive him too hard, you'll have a disaster.

I'm afraid I've written bluntly and outspokenly. This is not because you have not my fullest sympathy. Indeed you have; as all boys are not easy to understand or to deal with. I don't know whether you have taken Stephanie into your confidence over this problem & of course I've said nothing to her. But I would strongly advise that you do so, & in fact would like to have your permission to discuss the matter with her, though I shall quite understand if you feel unable to give it. I think, in any case, the boy has probably had a shock & possibly a salutary one but none the less a shock. I don't suppose he had ever thought of the future apart from life here, where he is obviously very happy. And I think that you've got to be very patient & rather careful.

You do indeed have my deepest sympathy in your troubles. I shall be teaching Kay myself next term for Latin and History, & when I've seen a bit of his work again I'll write to Mr Stubbs or talk to him about his chances.

PS. Written in great haste as we were burgled on Friday night & my study was turned completely upside down!

In his reply, my father told Wickham of his attempts to help me with arithmetic, and cites an example of my hopelessness where all ends in tears and me threatening to go and live with my mother where I was happy. My father ended by writing:

> I told him that I would not try to help him any further, not even to say goodnight, if he could not be polite to me, but I would be very pleased to help him if he needed help. He said nothing.

I then locked myself in the upstairs lavatory. My father hand-wrote, in pencil, at the end of the copy of this letter:

> This boy has been spoilt. He needs slow, stern education now, or he will shirk all his life. But it is useless for me to go out of my way to help him make the effort, if the result is… that he will suggest he will go to live in his mother's house. So he tries to threaten me, as his reply to my efforts to make him make an effort.

I recall this incident, one of so many at Hinton Way, even though I was 11 years old. I don't remember any detail except the anger and the failed Maths. He was not the calm man suggested by his writing. This is one of the so many incidents that I tried to shut out. At the first sign of anger I learned pretty much to switch off thus shutting out almost everything. I went into some kind of auto-pilot, mental hibernation.

On 24 September Wickham replied to my father's letter:

> Thank you so much for taking my not very kind homily so kindly. I know you've got a terribly difficult problem, & have indeed my fullest sympathy. In telling me that Kay is difficult to teach, you only tell me what I know only too well. But judging by my own experience, a father always finds himself less able to do much for his son than anyone close… But you've had a rotten time, & I'm going to suggest what is probably a counsel of perfection that you forget for the time being your troubles over Kay; remember the roach fishing as those are the things which matter with one's children. After all, there is nothing which one can do immediately. In the meanwhile, he's really my problem & when I've seen a little more of his work than I have lately, & I shall see him for about 10 periods a week, I shall see if any solution presents itself. I may not be able to help. But you've enough troubles of your own, & even if he's a worry, you know Kay's a lad to be proud of in many ways. There is something of Julian [Hurd] in Kay, you know, & the only thing which could have helped him [Julian] would have been to try to get to the bottom of what was going on in his mind.

John Julian Hurd, born in March 1932, went on to Marlborough (from Twyford) and then National Service. Tragically, he found himself at odds with the teachings of war and committed suicide, age 19, in June 1951. My difficult years at Twyford (1950–1953) straddled his death. Bob Wickham was his headmaster and warned my father, 'Or you will have a tragedy'. This comparison with Julian Hurd should have hit home, but it didn't.

I must, after all this seriousness, include something of a more light-hearted note although it gave me a different kind of hurt! Betty Wickham wrote to my father on 14 December 1952 to say:

Just a word about Kay! Last night, haring through the class rooms [to the lavatories at the rear of the building before returning to the nightly chapel queue], he came into collision with another boy – Kay came off worst as his mouth met the other boy's head. I'm afraid it's knocked a tooth of Kay's out, but Miss Pursey [the school Matron] is pretty sure it is a first tooth – at the side. His front ones aren't very straight, and we can't remember if they were like this before the collision or not. However, I think it would be as well if he could see a dentist as soon as possible. I would have sent him there tomorrow, but ours is an expensive man (albeit very good!) & you may have a National Health one at home – & after all, a few days won't make much difference here or there. I only hope no damage has been done. It shook Kay pretty considerably; & this morning, when he, along with others, elected to come & attend the Communion Service, the effects hadn't worn off, & Kay had to go out feeling sick. I trust the day's interests will help him to forget the shock & we'll keep an eye on him.

In fact, the impact of my mouth on the forehead of the other boy had not only thrown the tooth, it had also cased a hairline fracture of my jaw above the front left tooth. That hadn't been realised by the school matron. My father took me to his dentist, Mr Farris – even now I remember his name! – in Cambridge, and the X-rays showed the crack.

He was pioneering a clear tooth-cover brace and after pushing out that front left tooth, for I could not properly shut my mouth, he placed the 'cover' over all my top front teeth to keep the straightened one in position. I had to wear that 'cover' for some weeks. Eventually the tooth died and the nerve was removed, which has left it darker than the others. Mr Farris did an excellent job for to this day I still have that 'dead' front tooth – and a painful memory!

My father was determined that I should sit the Perse exams again but, yet again, I knew nothing of those plans. Bob Wickham's letter to my father of 13 January 1953 tells all.

Stephanie Hurd very kindly looked in on us the other day & we spent some time discussing Kay's problems. She told me that for reasons of money you were very keen that Kay should go to The Perse School, if he could get his place, & with a view to finding out whether there was any special work we could do before the March examination, I wrote to the headmaster about this. His reply was frankly not very encouraging, & his letter ends 'I think I should say quite frankly that I am afraid Corner's chances must be regarded as slight in view of his performance in September [1952] & the fact that I have so many candidates for a limited number of places, which makes the examination very competitive'.

I think Kay might do better than he did last time, seeing that he would have had rather more warning of the examination; but I don't see him having much success where it is not a matter of passing, & he is up against competition, because one must admit that in competition he is below average. This raises the question of whether it is worth his while sitting the examination on March 26th. But if you wish him to sit & as the entry has to go through the Cambridge local education authorities, would you take the necessary steps for his entry?

I don't feel that there is necessarily any reason to despair of his entry into a Public School through the ordinary Common Entrance. He's still some way to go, but he is coming along steadily, if slowly. Stephanie was inclined to wonder if you were keen on Kay's going to Marlborough, leaving out the financial difficulty, which she says could be met, & would be met. It occurred to me that if you wanted Kay closer to home, would it be worth your considering The Leys School at Cambridge? I don't know much about it myself though in the past I've known some very nice boys who were educated there. There's not much in it in expense, except in travelling & visiting, £89 per term as against £87 at Marlborough & a small cost-of-living bonus. I just thought it might be worth your consideration. Stephanie wondered if you would prefer Bradfield, where the fees were, till quite recently 80 guineas. But educationally it is not as good as Marlborough, & possibly not in other ways.

Kay is in good spirits, & in so far as I've taken him for Latin & History, most willing to work. When you have had time to think things over, perhaps you could send me a line.

I never knew that it was Bob Wickham who suggested The Leys. He wrote again to my father on 24 January 1953 to say:

I'm afraid your letter has crossed one I wrote to you last night but too late for post, so I will enclose this with it. I cannot for a moment agree that a failure for Perse will be an incentive. They never are incentives & much more commonly produce that base of modern life the inferiority complex in which a boy lowers his faith in himself. Unless you think he has a chance of passing, I think it would be the worst thing he can do to note.

I should not worry too much about Agatha Christie. It's something for a boy to like to read, & with that in view we have all sorts of detective literature in the library, including one Agatha Christie! It's no good trying to keep it away from boys, & the best hope is to try to educate them to look a little higher as they grow older. Of course we may be the cause of the increase of juvenile delinquency, but that is still commoner among the cinema goers and illiterate!

I had a letter from Mrs Corner this morning, asking how the future reporting plans stood. Seeing that I am firstly [word could be 'primarily'] responsible to you, I feel that I must have your authority to pass on any information on this score. At the same time, she presumably has the right to know, & it puts me in a very difficult position to have to withhold information. So can I consider myself free to tell her what is finally decided?'

This letter was written ten months after the divorce and things remained bitter. It does show how my father involved a third party in the detail of his domestic matters. Thank goodness he did, for my headmaster's wise and determined advice no doubt saved me from – I hate to think what. The 'reporting' matter also illustrates how thoughtless my father was: he must have imagined that by 'winning' the divorce he could virtually forget his first wife and things of which she should be informed. This is why I question whether he sent copy letters to my mother.

I am learning more of my father's character from these exchanges; and clearly my mother, knowing well his tantrums, was hamstrung in that she had to show a softer side to me, natural for her, whilst encouraging me to stick at the academic work – a most difficult balancing act.

My letters to Mother from this period tell of the treatment we children had at home. On 4 November 1954, I complained: 'Helga still goes for Christine, more than Lindsay, and when there are visitors she always says Lindsay's good points and Christine's bad & she teases Christine about things she did in the past'. Christine, was then seven and Lindsay six. Another letter a month later said: 'As usual Helga is going for Christine much more than Lindsay, and whenever Lindsay does something wrong and Christine is nearby, Christine gets half the blame, partly because Lindsay tells Helga that it was partly Christine's fault'.

My mother was becoming increasingly concerned at the effect Helga's treatment was having on Christine. I could just about stand up for my sister and assured my mother that 'If I notice anything about Helga and the girls I will write and tell you immediately if serious'.

Meeting Mother became part of this cloak-and-dagger existence – 'I told Daddy that I went out to lunch with some friends and we went to a film in the afternoon, and he could not say anything against it'. How sad that I even had to hide from my father visits from my mother; I was afraid to tell him for the anger it would create.

In the years 1953 and 1954, my sporting ability blossomed and I played in the school football, hockey and cricket teams as well as learned tennis. I scored runs, goals, caught catches and secured wickets, and I was becoming a better learner – but not learned! Betty Wickham's letter of July 1953 to my father captured a moment:

Kay made 30 not out yesterday in a game of cricket & also made a very good catch. I thought you'd just like to hear that – these little tit-bits are apt to please us parents! Kay is a dear & seems to be getting on very happily. I'm glad you enjoyed Saturday [the annual sports day] – we both loved it. I feel a touch flat now!

My July 1953 report:

[M]uch improved compared to earlier days… still lets life rest rather lightly on his shoulders… up to a point he does well, but he lacks a sense of responsibility both in his work & outside activities. He is, however, always cheerful & willing, & much improved with earlier days.

On 4 September that same year, Bob Wickham ended a letter to my father: 'Kay is growing up very fast… he progresses in jumps, not only in character but mentally'.

'All seems very well with Kay & he beams whenever one looks in his direction', wrote Betty Wickham on 2 October 1953 to my father.

I was writing to know whether I might buy three new pairs of pants. His won't last more than a week or so & they've been well darned & patched, so I'm not being extravagant. Don't bother to reply if I may go ahead & buy them.

I know my stepmother taught me to darn and patch, for which I am grateful, but it shows how bad things were – no unnecessary expenditure until absolutely necessary. My underpants must have been holier than the Bible I was taught to study.

My games master reported on December 1953:

[A] very good inside forward indeed, with one weakness – a reluctance to shoot. He has ball-control, positional sense, and the ability to create and use an opening, and when he adds accurate shooting (and it is on the way) to these other assets, he will be outstanding. He has combined well with Paterson, and done much good work in defence as well as being the "brains" of the attack.

At last I was the 'brains' of something although Wickham had warned my father at that same time that I had to work very hard if I was to get a place at Marlborough.

Between 1953 and 1954, Marlborough had changed to The Leys and on 13 March 1954 Wickham wrote to my father:

[T]he thing I know I'm going to be asked, but which I can't answer, is what happens if Kay does not get his place at The Leys, which I gather they by no means guarantee. I gather you will have left for Holland by the time this arrives. Stephanie rang up as she hoped to take Kay out but was frightened away by one polio infection [the boy next to me in dormitory had contracted polio]. I'm a little puzzled as to what work to give Kay for the holidays. He's not the sort of boy to get much out of his work unless he is supervised as, in fact, he's all too likely to make mistakes which he won't detect & about which he becomes complacent. I've given him more history & anything else I can think of.

What my headmaster still hadn't fully appreciated was the reaction of my father, in spite of his many warnings. My father had again taken up the teaching cudgel that holiday, and was fierce and that didn't help at all.

I wrote to my father from school on 14 March 1954 thanking him for his letter and hoping he would have a good time in Holland. I asked if I was leaving Twyford that term or the next, and I told him that we would be out of quarantine [for polio] and would be playing games again. I reported on fourteen good marks and two bad marks, and said that I would bring my arithmetic and Latin books home. Concluding, I wrote that 'my journey instructions which I sent to you were sent to my mother and she sent them back saying that she didn't know where my trunk was going, so I sent them to you'. There was little or no communication between my parents and me.

In an undated letter to my father, but it has to be March 1954, I wrote that I was given a very good report again in the 'football characters' section of the school magazine, *The Twyfordian*, and that Mr Wickham thought I would be able to do a very good Latin paper in my exam. He expected me to get over 75 percent. When reading through my Pandora notes, I was arrested by a letter from Mr Humm to my father in March 1954. I remembered Humm and it in turn reminded me of the holiday cramming I then was receiving from him for my Common Entrance exam for The Leys. The moment when I arrived with some Latin homework, duly signed, he looked at my signature and said in a most critical and disparaging voice: "What is this signature? Coomer, Comer, Cooper? What is it? I can't read it." Since he was able to read something, although wrong, I resolved from thereon that my signature would never be decipherable and I changed it. Today, it remains much as the one to which I changed! He did help to 'learn' me more Latin and I achieved a good pass in the Common Entrance.

The year 1954 was to be my last at Twyford and academically it began nervously. Wickham wrote to my father dated 1 March:

> I enclose a letter from The Leys together with a rather cryptic set of marks! Now I must leave you to decide the next move. I would, however, say that Kay has worked like a brick. I've constantly brought him in, in the afternoon, to do an hour with me, and he's always appeared pleased to do it. He has also behaved quite excellently this term, entirely a different story from last, & he deserves a very firm pat on the back. I can only say that I would like very much to have him back next term, & think myself that that is the right course.

In my report for that term, the headmaster wrote:

> I cannot speak highly enough of his work in school, or of his helpful attitude out of school… I do not often tell a boy in advance that he has earned the position of "senior" [like prefect] but I have no hesitation in saying this in his case.

Pandora revealed a letter from the headmaster of The Leys, Dr W. G. Humphrey, to my father dated 13 March 1954 about my first attempt at the Common Entrance:

> Although your boy's performance in the February Common Entrance Examination was not brilliant, if he does equally well in June together with the kind of further improvement that another term of normal work at Twyford should ensure, he should be quite certain of reaching the standard we require for admission in September [1954].

He continued by saying that he could not absolutely promise – and yet offered a prospectus and registration form, then finally confirmed my place on 7 May 1954.

Having returned to Twyford, I wrote a letter to my father in April 1954:

> I am a Senior and head of a dormitory… I am sending my *Twyford-ian*. You must look at the Hockey characters. I have quite a good report on Hockey. Mr Wickham is enclosing Invitations to the Sports day in

this letter, so that you will be able to hire a car in plenty of time. I played cricket yesterday, bowled three boys and scored twenty-five not out, a good start for the season… We have started a model aeroplane club, with me at the head, we have got about eleven boys and we are going to try to put up a display for sports day. Give my love to Helga and the girls.

That's a better letter. And 11 boys out of the 70 – not bad! The Twyford School tennis team was entered to play in the Inter-Preparatory Schools Tournament at Wimbledon in the summer holidays of 1954. I wrote to my father in July to say:

For Wimbledon I need some white shorts and a pair of white socks. We have played two matches since sports day against Pilgrims [School, Winchester]. The first one I was run out again at 44, by a boy who went on to make 50 not out. Altogether we scored 111 for 3 declared, and I bowled their first two men out in the first over for 0 runs, but then it started to rain and the match was abandoned. The second match I scored 16, caught by a very good catch at short extra, when I off-drove a half volley over his head. He jumped up and stopped it with one hand and caught it on the way down, but we beat them. Mr Merriman [the tennis coach and English master] can't get the flat in London, but he has a friend in Chelsea, or we will stay with Tully's* sister.

Of the tennis, *The Twyfordian* of December 1954 records that 'all three boys did reasonably well in the eliminating rounds, but Corner was the only one to survive to the final day. The standard of tennis was, on the whole, high'. At least I did play at Wimbledon! In July that year, Bob Wickham wrote in my report:

Kay deserves quite full marks for the way he has put his back into many sides of school life in these last two terms. I can only say that he will be greatly missed both for this and his generally pleasant behaviour; we wish him every good fortune in the next stage.

He had written on 29 June 1954 to my father:

Just to put your mind at rest in case they have not notified you that Kay has passed into The Leys safely, & I enclose his marks which I should like to have back. This means the beginning of the end, I'm afraid, as

*Robert Tully was my great friend and brother of Mark who went on to an eminent career as a newsreporter and writer specialising in India. He (Sir Mark) was also at Twyford.

far as we are concerned, of our association with a very nice boy. He has been absolutely first rate in these last two terms, and he deserves full credit, which I hope you will convey to him. One small point; do you wish me to tell him, as I usually do to boys before they leave, about the facts of life. Someone certainly ought to at this stage. I don't in any way wish to trespass on the preserves of parents, but they do generally expect me to deal with this rather trying subject at this stage in their career.

My father clearly replied, for I did join the evening 'class' in Bob Wickham's study for instruction in the facts of life.

Betty Wickham wrote my father a delightful letter on 8 July 1954 saying:

I must write & say how very much Bob & I appreciated you writing as you did - & also to give thanks to you for one point of view – thank you very much for having sent him to Twyford in the first place – we're proud of the finished product & may he now go on from strength to strength. We shall all miss him greatly – it's hard to part with some of these children after five years. Thank you again. Yours ever, Betty Wickham.

Whatever I have had to write and record I must also say how pleased I am to see that my father wrote and clearly thanked the Wickhams for what they achieved with me. But sadly, he never told me personally what Bob and Betty Wickham had written about me. I learned of their kind and generous remarks only in 2006 when I unravelled the letters he included in Pandora. Better late than never, but had I known at the time I think my self-esteem might have taken a leap forward.

Looking back, I realise that I owe Bob and Betty Wickham more than I ever appreciated at the time. I owe them and their team at Twyford School enormous thanks for getting me through a time of trauma and putting me onto the lower rung of the ladder-of-life which I would never have successfully reached without their unflinching direction, compassion, teaching skill, determination and care.

So I went on to The Leys School in October 1954 as a day boarder.

- XXIII -

PROGRESS

The Leys was founded in 1875 by the Methodist Church for sons of lay members on a twenty-acre site – The Leys Estate in Cambridge. The Reverend Doctor Moulton, was appointed Headmaster and The Leys formally opened its doors on 16 February 1875 with sixteen boys from English Methodist families. Within two years this number had grown to 100 pupils. The setting for the popular novel and play *Goodbye, Mr Chips* is believed to have been based on The Leys where author James Hilton was a pupil (1915–1918). Hilton is reported to have said that the inspiration for the protagonist, Chips, came chiefly from W. H. Balgarnie who was in charge of the *Leys Fortnightly*, the school magazine where Hilton's first short stories and essays were published.

That Twyford had dragged me from a hopeless academic and timid boy to a level which was satisfactory is beyond dispute; but they were very aware of my difficulties at home and with that knowledge were able to help, guide and direct me from understanding. There was not that same level of exchange with the staff at The Leys – there was no need – and I was therefore very much more on my own. Still, the home difficulties were far from over and continued to affect me in many ways.

My housemaster on arrival at The Leys was A. McM. Buchanan, Buck as he was affectionately known, a well-respected man by all at the school. He had been a Scottish Rugby International in his youth. Sadly, he died in a car crash on the way back to the school from the Varsity Rugby Match (Oxford v Cambridge) at Twickenham in 1956. He had gone to see Geoff Windsor-Lewis, an Old Leysian, playing fly-half for Cambridge. He was succeeded in 1956 by Alan N. Pattinson.

Looking through the Pandora list, I noticed that most of my early reports from The Leys were there! In the first report, dated autumn 1954, the head wrote: 'he has settled down happily and has made a useful start on his work'. My housemaster reported for Lent term 1955: 'he continues to do well'. The class reports were satisfactory. The head: '…a term of steady work and encouraging progress'. For summer term 1955, my housemaster

273

noted: 'his behaviour is marked by good sense', and the head said: 'quite a satisfactory year's work... he must work hard to regain his rightful place next term'. My academics were finally on even keel.

In general, my upbringing at Twyford had seen me grow into a well-mannered and, if I may write it, a reasonably pleasant young man or, as my housemaster put it in my Autumn Term 1955 report, 'excellent and ever courteous'. I took one of my General Certificate of Education 'O' Levels a year early in 1956 and duly sat for history which the GCE results announcement form in Pandora advised a pass.

As things turned for the better for me, so too for my mother. Peter G. Tanner proposed marriage. When he wrote to Gramma B to tell her of his intentions, she replied:

After my (and her) experience with John Corner, it's perhaps understandable that I am terrified of a repetition of such a thing.... But I do want a full and happy life for Sheila, and Peter, I hope you (and she) can bring her to the realization of the wonderful potentiality which true happiness will mean. If you can do this thing my affection will know no bounds and the future, whatever it may hold, can be faced with serenity.

My reaction to the prospective marriage is recorded in a note written from Hinton Way, on a small torn-off piece of paper to Mother, soon after a visit with her. This was during another low moment in my life when I was desperately searching for love because I received almost nothing but 'exclusion' from Shelford, the home to which the divorce court consigned me.

I arrived back safely, but when I got in I had to wait before Helga would see me, then she only said "Hello". The only supper I got was two pieces of toast with cheese and a cup of coffee. This holiday was such a wonderful one [phrase underlined], I have never been so happy [underlined] before in my life. I did not know how to tell you, how pleased I was when I heard about you and Peter. If it comes off I think it would be wonderful; Peter is such a nice [underlined] man. Again I must thank you all for all you did for me while I was at home [Chelmsford]; I really love [underlined] you Mummy, more than anyone [underlined] else in the world.

These visits were usually followed by questioning by my father, accompanied with uncomplimentary remarks, as these extracts from my letters show.

The old atom bomb exploded tonight. There is one thing which Daddy said and he is quite wrong but I could not pluck up enough courage to tell him. He thinks that the house is [mother's house] a shambles, the garden the same, that I do no work there and I am not helped with anything which is quite, quite [both words underlined] wrong. You have done an awful lot for me and have made me so happy while I am not with you; you and Peter have helped me with no end of things and I am very, very [both words underlined] happy while I am with you. It is up to me to decide what to do when I am sixteen, and I am going to continue to come and see you, if I can, for more than half the holidays. I say this because you were right; Daddy decided for himself what I was to do [when 16], but he is going to get a shock, but the way in which he insinuated that I was living in a slum with you is shocking. I have never been so shocked in my life when he said what he thought I was living in. I am sorry to write such an appalling letter but I will always [underlined] be with you and Peter because I think you are a perfect pair and I am so happy [both words underlined] with you.

This morning I was cross-examined, through the newspaper [by my father]; he wanted to know everything [about the holiday] but before every question he said: "The girls told me that...." I did not give him any definite answers and I think he was very cross.

And on an unusual occasion I wrote, misquoting Churchill: 'guess what, no trouble when I arrived back!!! "Never before in the history of mankind has..." it ever happened like that'.

Peter Tanner and my mother married on 22 September 1956. My cowardice is evident in this postscript to a letter to Mother after the wedding: 'Have not said a thing about the wedding; I will leave the girls to tell Daddy – (hope he doesn't explode)!!!'

*

I remained a day boarder for all but my last year at The Leys in 1957, cycling five miles (8 km) each way, seven days a week, regardless of weather, for everyone had to attend at least morning chapel on Sunday (evening chapel was not obligatory for day boys).

My success at sport continued and I was active in most games at both house and school level. The Lent term report of 1957 has my housemaster writing, 'very good. He is an asset to the House' and the head, 'he has had, in every way, a good term'.

This all indicated that I was happy at school, working reasonably well and altogether continuing to develop as a young man. I wasn't arriving home from school before 9 pm each evening and sometimes later and with leaving home by 7.30 am each morning, often earlier, I felt happier. On 14 June 1955, I wrote to my mother about the consequence of my tennis practice schedule:

Lately, I have been getting back home later because I have been practising tennis, about the only time I get for tennis is in the evening, and
when I get home Helga and Daddy are very cross. I tell them that even
though I am a Home Boarder I can't get back early every night, and the
reason why I am practising is because I am being given trials for our
House tennis team, 4th pair. I told Daddy but it makes no difference,
and also when I get back later no one offers me any food at all, but instead they send me up to bed immediately. Now, I am disliking Helga
more and more.

I had little time with my father and that suited me. I'm not certain that
some of my teachers fully realised that I was still struggling academically;
I was well able, with hard work, to reach 'O' Level standard of GCE but I
think there were signs, in 1956 and 1957, that I would struggle at 'A' Level.
The GCE results form, dated 6 September 1957, confirmed passes in six
more subjects and with a re-take of one paper I ended with eight in all! My
overall reports continued to read well.

I was soon to be 16, the age when the court ruled I could choose my
parent. The skiing holiday took place; I didn't make the choice and continued the status quo – and suffered. How do you choose a parent even in
such a situation?

The time had come when I had to be thinking about my future – a
career – and I had hardly given it any thought at all. My father continued to
press me to become a medical doctor in his father's footsteps, and frankly,
the more he pressured me the more I resisted. How he could have imagined
that I could achieve it I don't know, and I do remember not knowing how to
tell him that I didn't want to be a doctor – and that troubled me.

Pandora had a card from my housemaster (East House) dated 5 September 1957, written to my father, clearly in reply to one from him. After welcoming my father's request that I board for my last year, Pattinson
wrote:

I shall certainly have a word with Kay about his future as soon as I
can. Now that the 'O' results are out it seems pretty clear from a fail in
Chemistry that his bent is not for science. Engineering with the RAF (a
year at Halton + 3 years at the University) seems to be the best solution.
The man from the Public Schools Appointments Bureau was very taken
with Kay and felt that he was cut out for that sort of training and career.
I'll look into it and report back.

I vaguely remember meeting the man from the Appointments Bureau
and being encouraged to the RAF; I didn't really need encouragement for I
was already forming a desire but I don't recall any approach to RAF Halton.

My reports continued well and it was only in the Summer 1958 report that my academic difficulties were commented on. My housemaster sagely reported: 'Excellent – though there is a need now for him to develop more positive drive' and the head: 'this report suggests that a very great effort will be required if he is to pass in certain subjects at the Advanced Level next July; since his future may well be affected by these passes, the effort is worth making'. I remember more trouble at home at this time which always ended in a big row – and slamming of doors even if partly metaphorical.

At The Leys, I joined Tim Williams, who I last met at the Great Shelford village school in 1945/46, and again became friends of his family who also lived in the village. Tim is six months older than me; he was at least a term ahead. Each term, I cycled to school, and mostly with Tim. We would meet at the crossroads in the centre of Shelford which we knew then as Freestones Corner, after the family-owned bakers shop on one side. The Freestones were family friends.

My friendship with Tim was to play a pivotal role in my life quite soon. His parents, Bill and Kate Williams, were building a house near Port Appin, north of Oban in Scotland, which was to be, and became, their retirement home. It was named *Am Bogha* after the bow shape of the bay right behind the house and to which their garden stretched to the shore of Loch Creran. The views were glorious, stretching to the twin peaks of Ben Cruachan and, if the weather allowed, to the mountains of Mull.

I first visited *Am Bogha* in 1958 with Tim. We hitchhiked from Stumps Cross, where his Uncle Norman dropped us off, south of Cambridge, to Glasgow where we stayed overnight at a youth hostel. Actually, we 'thumbed' a lorry near the Borders and enjoyed, as Tim wrote,

an excruciating lift up the old A74 in an ancient and noisy lorry that never went faster than 20 mph, ending up dancing about on the flatbed in the back. Four hours for 80 miles, and we only just got to the youth hostel by running for it before it shut for the night.

Tim was a member – I wasn't – so I had borrowed the membership card of a mutual friend and Leysian, Phillip Heywood. I spent time practising his signature and it was good enough on the day. The next morning we took the train to Bridge of Orchy where Tim's father picked us up.

We helped with the building and decoration of the house, did much gardening, moving of heavy rocks, and we walked and fished in those days when there were plenty of mackerel and sea trout in the Loch.

It was Bill Williams who introduced me to the oyster. We were strolling down the very stony beach late one afternoon (early 1960s, I think) and he was telling me about the oyster beds that he had seeded but due to disease had failed. Then he stooped, dug with his knife and out came an oyster which he immediately offered to me. I had never tasted one and, for some reason, thought they should be cooked – very naïve! In refusing as politely as I could, and knowing Bill loved them, I was, a few paces further, faced with the same offer for there was another of those shelled seafoods! I couldn't refuse again. It was shucked and in it went. To my amazement I liked it. That like stays with me right to this day.

As I got to know Bill and Kate Williams, I trusted them with my problems and they were sympathetic and properly neutral. I could talk to them and they listened. We talked often over annual visits, for I spent many holidays at *Am Bogha* and loved it all – happiness.

However, unhappiness continued at home. As I grew older I became argumentative with my father and stepmother, which helped not at all! I learned to drive in 1958 using my fathers' Humber Hawk, the 'Umber Awk' as some called it. I still remember the number plate – NLT 728 – and the column gearshift. He had bought it sometime in mid-1950 and I remember that he went to London to collect it; it was second hand, and on arriving back at our house he discovered the reason for the red warning lights – there was little or no oil in the engine. He was furious and it was gone for quite a while for repair. He certainly laid blame squarely at the door of the dealer who received a good ear-bashing.

As my later teens were approaching, I came, quite naturally, under frequent pressure to decide what I wanted to do after school. My real dream was to fly. At Twyford, I had set up and managed the model aeroplane club. Here was a natural interest. The Public Schools Appointments Bureau man was encouraging towards the RAF, and I was keen. My father was not – absolutely not – and Helga chided me. I really hoped to become a civil airline pilot but, with my father's resistance, there was no hope of funding the considerable training bills at the BOAC Training College in Hamble. The RAF was a way to learn to fly, paid by the government and after a short service commission in flying, I could then join a civil airline. A great theory.

In August 1958 I visited Grannie Corner. She recalled the visit in her letter of 25 August 1958 to her son.

> John, I congratulate you. You have a delightful son... one person said it's such a pleasure to see such nice manners & I found him very intelligent & well balanced. I don't think you need fear for his future. He has ideas, perhaps the confidence of youth, but thank goodness for that.

In 1958, the headmaster of The Leys, Dr Humphrey, retired and William Alan Barker was appointed the new head. I boarded for my last year (1959) and during that year I joined the 6th Form dancing class which was held weekly with the Perse School for Girls, located nearby. There I met Belinda Shaw.

I continued my Twyford sporting success at The Leys, being captain of the tennis VI in my last year and singles champion. I played in the hockey 1st XI in 1959, The Leys being well respected for its hockey: our coach was Neil White, a past British Olympic player who was much enjoyed by us all for his great humour and determined coaching; we were a successful team! I also was in the rugby 2nd XV and the small-bore (.22) shooting 1st VIII from 1956 to 1959. I went with the school full-bore (.303) VIII to Bisley in 1959.

When I began to achieve results at sport my father was neither encouraging nor discouraging. I can't remember him coming to see me play which would have been easy when I was at The Leys with his Cambridge office within short walking distance.

He did though expostulate rather forcibly when he saw on the school bill, in 1959, my purchase of a new tennis racket, a Dunlop Maxply: I was captain of tennis! I actually was afraid to ask him for fear of a 'no', but bought it anyway – and took the flak.

I joined the Corps early on in my days at The Leys and was Company Sergeant Major in my last year. I passed all the Corps exams, Certificate A parts 1 & 2 and post Cert A parts 1 & 2.

Something military seemed to suit me while my father continued to resist. I was determined about the RAF, thus more angst. What an environment in which to plan a career.

- XXIV -

FATHER AND SON ASUNDER

In my last year at The Leys, my learning skills were better though still not good. I continued to enjoy my sports and a freedom from home. I was probably subconsciously still pushing some things to the very furthest corners of my mind.

Looking back, I believe I allowed that freedom to spill over into my general attitudes and I'm sure I didn't apply myself to study as I should – I was still having difficulty in concentrating for any length of time. I don't blame the school but clearly they had no idea about what my problem was. There wasn't the parent-school exchange which so helped me at Twyford and to which my mother had contributed so much by her caring encouragement at all times and understanding of my difficulties. Neither do I belittle my father's contribution for he wrote most frankly to Bob Wickham.

In my last school holiday in the summer of 1959, I went to the RAF Assessment Centre at Hornchurch, Essex, having successfully applied for a Short Service Commission of three years. I kept the visit secret from my father. I passed all the physical and educational tests, taken over three days, and was offered basic training as an officer cadet at RAF South Cerney in Gloucestershire, the No 1 Initial Training School in a sixteen-week course in late 1959. I was graded A1 G1 – fit for anywhere in the world.

When I told my father of the results he was not supportive, and my stepmother was dismissive. But I pressed on and travelled to South Cerney where I learned the procedures of the RAF, discipline, and much more.

At our first gym session, the physical training instructor asked us all to take the circuit he had just shown us. As competitive young men we put in an effort and posted good times. At the end, the PTI said 'well done lads that is your benchmark; from now on you must improve on that time – every time!' A very good lesson was learned that day.

We had to write a diary daily, including current events as well as other matters of interest to each individual. The diaries were marked as part of our overall assessment and randomly, during class work, we would be asked to stand up and speak for five minutes on a subject of our choice or chosen for us. I mugged up on radar and that was the subject of my first talk. On the occasional weekends off I would visit my father but things there remained difficult – very difficult.

One of the character-building tests was that we had to spend a week under canvas, and for my Flight it was in the Black Mountains of Wales in January! This required many initiative tests and, looking back, it was invaluable for later life although not entirely appreciated at the time. We were teamed up with a friend and wearing RAF overalls with four old pence (for the emergency telephone call) in the pocket, we were expected to reach various checkpoints and to arrive at our camp within a tight deadline.

Public transport was banned; hitching a lift was also banned and no more than than the four pence was permitted. The schedule required travel through the night. My partner and I sewed paper money into our overalls and we secreted it well enough to pass the rigorous frisk as we set off. We were reminded that the various local home guards were out watching for us en-route and we must avoid 'capture'.

We arrived on schedule and undetected, having 'thumbed' three separate lifts, and began setting up camp. A separate tent was erected for drying our wet clothes and we soon learned that rather than cold shaving we could warm sufficient water in our mess tins by placing them on the paraffin heaters in the tent. This was strictly not permitted but then 'rules are made for the guidance of the wise and the obeyance of fools'.

During camp, I vividly recall that in the middle of one night, our officer, Flt Lt Barry sat bolt upright and said, 'Christ, I could pee like a horse' and out of the tent he went to pee right into the wind!

There were other amusing moments of young men behaving badly. A favourite was when being drilled while there was flying, we 'allowed' the jet noise to confuse some commands of the slave-driver NCO so that half the squad would turn right and the other left when a turn command on the march was yelled! This was trouble and one of the punishments was to sweep a hangar with a normal-size broom. The punishment started around 6 pm and, because an aircraft hangar is larger than one imagines, we swept well through the night but were expected to be on duty, immaculately dressed, for early morning parade.

After passing out and the formal parade (which my father did not attend), I was posted for basic flying training to RAF Syerston in Nottinghamshire, the No 1 Flying Training School in 1960. I was now an Acting Pilot Officer.

The course was a mix of half a day in the classroom and half a day (weather permitting) in the air learning to fly. I struggled with engineering which eventually let me down, but I did learn to fly, going solo in just over twelve hours and completing some thirty hours of flying, including cross-country.

My instructor was a young South African Flying Officer who had recently passed his instructors exams coming first in aerobatics. He taught me the finer points – albeit unconventional ones – of flying. If a loose object had been reported in one of the aircraft then we would find it by climbing to 10,000 feet then invert the aircraft for close to the maximum time of 11 seconds (for a Jet Provost) to see if the missing object floated to the cockpit canopy under negative G!

I particularly remember the day, soon after going solo, when I was doing circuits and bumps. I misjudged the flare height on one circuit and sensed a slightly heavy landing. The aircraft porpoised and after pushing the stick forward to try to keep the nose-wheel on the ground, I realised that things were definitely not improving! I opened up the power and went around again, landing very carefully. As I approached the hangar and the flying offices, I was hailed by the Flight Officer of the day, Flt Lt 'Bush' Barry (of pee-like-a-horse fame and also of the excellent moustache), and was requested to his office immediately.

"Tell me about that landing," he barked. "I thought it was a bit heavy –" and that is as far as I got. "You landed on the bloody nose-wheel you ***** and are fortunate it wasn't worse."

The porpoising reaction was explained to me and that whilst the natural reaction might be to push the stick forward to keep the nose-wheel down, it was in fact the opposite which was the remedy – stick back to keep the nose-wheel up until some speed had bled away. We were using the long runway, and fortunately I had plenty of distance in which to react. The next day, I saw the Jet Provost on jacks in the hangar. I sidled up to the mechanics working on it and enquired of the trouble. 'Some bloody idiot landed on the nose-wheel yesterday and bent the oleo – have a look'. I did and it was. How the wheel retracted for that last circuit I'm not sure.

On some weekends, I visited Cambridge and stayed with Belinda at her parents' house in Huntingdon Road, just to the north of the city. Things didn't improve between me and my father and, as time went on, I decided not to spend so much time visiting home. I wrote to him from the Officers Mess at RAF Syerston on 13 May 1960 telling him that my visits would grow less – a euphemism for I was leaving.

The two-page letter is in Pandora, and I notice a scribbled note on the first page, in my father's hand, saying 'to which I replied that at any time I was available to help'. I don't remember receiving any reply and I certainly don't recall that offer to help. The fact that he kept the letter and it found its way into Pandora surprises me.

I left the Air Force and I went home where there was a huge row, not surprisingly, because I had failed an important exam, the culmination of which was an ultimatum from my father.

I had arrived home and had a few days alone with Helga as my father was away. I do recall Helga pushing me to tell him of my plans as soon as possible, and I did so soon after his return. I realise now that Helga wanted me out and manipulated the situation to her advantage; I was still too naïve to realise where I had been positioned.

"You go to Australia or get out now." The 'get out now' was spoken loudly – almost shouted. I did not know where my father had returned from then because he never discussed that with me, but now I know that he had just been on the reconnaissance visit to Mt Kinabalu in preparation for the Royal Society expedition.

I had no idea why Australia but it was a hell of a long way away. I just assumed he wanted me as far away from him as possible. Some 48 years later, as a result of my research, I learn that my father had been in Australia and probably – certainly – had friends there. But he never told me that, never talked of it to me. Going to Australia was also a frightening thought as it meant that I would be far from my mother and Belinda.

My life had been made very difficult, particularly by my stepmother who I stood up to as I grew older. There were some awful battles resulting in violence from a father who was a real Jekyll and Hyde. Lovely when he was in the mood but quite awful and angry at many other times. I was frightened of him but usually stood my ground.

I left home early in the morning following that row. Taking a small case, I rode my bicycle to the bus stop at the Red Cross Hospital about halfway to Cambridge. From there, I took a bus to Belinda's grandparents' house where she was staying. Something of a Dick Whittington, but I was leaving. Many years later (probably the early 1990s), my father told his close friend Sir John Gurdon that he had 'turned me out'.

One day, not so long after my departure, I was in Cambridge and ran into Tim Williams who asked me what I was doing. We had a good chat and I explained all. Soon Belinda's father and Tim's father, Bill Williams, discussed my situation and, as a result, I stayed with the Williams for a while before moving to London. Bill, who was then Senior Lecturer in Geography at Fitzwilliam House, Cambridge, wrote in his diary on 22 October 1960:

Kay Corner came; he has had an awful row with his father; we have invited him here on Tuesday. KC came back from ? Norbury in very good form having got on well with his grandmother.

This was Grannie Corner but I don't know what Bill meant by "Norbury". It probably was Beaconsfield where she lived.

On 26 October 1960, I wrote to my father as encouraged by Bill:

I am extremely sorry about last Friday and I only hope you agree with

283

me when I say that the only way to mend the past is to bury it and forget it. Meanwhile I am staying with the Williams' as you may have gathered from the above address. Tomorrow I am going to see Mr Howard, the Careers Master at The Leys, and I hope to get some information on all varieties of careers… I'll let you know how it went.

The next day Bill wrote to my father:

I gather that Kay wrote to you last night to say that he is staying with us. It was arranged last Saturday when he was obviously much under the weather. He has told us something – all that matters to us – about the trouble that has arisen since he left the RAF. I am very sorry about it; so is he particularly that he has caused you, his father, pain and anxiety. I want to say no more now than that Kay, being a friend of our boys, is more than welcome to such help as we can give him. He can stay with us as long as he likes. If I can do anything to help you, please let me know. The last thing I want to do is to place myself in a position where I appear to take sides.

Kay is going to see Howard, the Careers Master at The Leys, tomorrow evening. He will let you know what transpires, and he has made quite clear to me that he wants your help and interest in this matter, and that he wants nothing more than that the former good relations between you should be restored.

Bill spoke to me about how he was to write to my father and we agreed to his general terminology. I didn't tell him that I really didn't want any more to do with my father – that was not a good thing to say when help was being offered – and I didn't mention the violence. Strangely I was afraid to. However, I am glad that nothing developed from the letter except that my father wrote a complaint to the Vice-Chancellor of Cambridge University about Bill. The Vice-Chancellor was an intelligent man, phlegmatic no doubt, and didn't get involved.

Having received no reply from my father, Bill Williams decided, with my agreement, to contact my father again and wrote to him on 21 November 1960:

I understand that you have been snowed under with affairs since you got back here, and I can only suppose that a letter which I sent to you by hand three weeks ago – to your department – either miscarried or got mixed up. I then wrote to tell you what Kay himself told you – that he was living with us. I know something of the difficulties that have arisen – though I am sure not all – I wish to take no sides in family differences; it has been possible for us to keep Kay, and he may stay with us as long as he wishes. Nothing would give us, or Kay, more pleasure than that we might help you as well.

The purpose of this letter is specific. This week Kay is going to have an interview with the Public Schools Careers people in London. I assume that when he has seen them – and possibly another person who, I understand, has ideas – he will have to consider where his future lies. Obviously such an important decision should be made with your guidance; certainly I will advise, but I should not dream of influencing any decision which might conflict with your views. My wife and I, while only too willing to help, realise very clearly that it would be wrong to influence Kay against your wishes. He himself is clearly anxious to please you and to consider you. I would be glad therefore if Kay could see you, or I on his behalf when he has been to London; and I should be glad, too, if you would let me know if there is any other way in which I can help. It seems most unfortunate that my first letter has gone astray, and I can only apologise for what must have seemed to you extremely off-handed behaviour.

My father replied to this letter. Peter, Bill's eldest son, in the course of researching for me, unearthed his father's diaries of the time. Bill wrote a diary regularly for most of his life. In searching the diary, Peter found the following relevant entry: 'Had a vile letter from Corner'.

I asked Peter in 2010 whether his parents had said much to him about those days. This is what he told me:

[B]oth my Ma and Pa were appalled at the way you were treated, and were prepared to do anything they could to see that you got the best help they could give in the circumstances. Initially, Dad considered your father not only disgracefully wrong in the way you were treated, but was very disagreeably surprised at the way your father dragged what was essentially a private matter before the Vice-Chancellor, in the professional field. He felt this was underhand and intemperate, and it was certainly a matter of conversation with me when I was at home. Years later, he came to find it quite funny, because his relationship with the Vice-Chancellor was friendly, and the latter simply thought of your father as a crank in this respect. He also considered Corner's conduct in Singapore as unworthy, but again came to recognise that there was such a degree of single-mindedness in C's make-up, that he probably was not good at seeing the wood for the trees, if that is not a lousy simile for a botanist! He always admired C's botanical expertise. I always think that a curiously academic trait; they admire the work but not perhaps the person.

Clearly Uncle Anthony and Aunt Stephanie were also aware of the situation and wanted yet again to help. She wrote to her brother – the letter was placed in Pandora.

Aunt Stephanie hoped that my father was seeing things – my circumstances – in a better light and offered help 'in any way'. She hoped that my father and I had been in touch for

> the most important thing, as we see it, & Anthony & I have had a long talk, is that Kay should be given all the backing we can give him to find another job – Banking if he so wishes it – preferably in a town near to Cambridge rather than Cambridge itself though surely Cambridge can hold the two of you.

She remarked that my mother would be unlikely to embarrass my father and that I could have my own accommodation and lead my own life.

> [T]here is no love lost between you but there must be fairness & strict business like dealings – you do Kay an injustice I think in saying this was all planned – & you show no understanding of the courage it took to face up to you on your return – the reason for the lack of greeting & the most inappropriate & hopeless moment to break the news.... I don't think it matters who is at fault – but I do know we should help Kay to find a new job & set him on the path of making a life of his own – & I expect you are feeling the same too now.

What could Stephanie have meant by Mother being most unlikely to embarrass my father? This reminded me of my father's comment about 'the sayings and doings of my wife and her sister'. Stephanie was probably a recipient of such talk but felt that since my parents had divorced, that threat was past.

There are always two sides to everything and I feel sure that both Aunt Stephanie and Uncle Anthony were playing exceeding fair. I would expect nothing different yet somehow they knew and didn't know my father although he was Stephanie's brother.

She also wrote 'you do Kay an injustice I think in saying this was all planned'. My father seemed to think that everything I did against him was pre-planned in cahoots with my mother. Nothing could have been further from the truth. I never spoke ill of him other than telling my mother frankly, as a child, what I was experiencing; I rarely mentioned him other than that, and I never criticised him to anyone else. Looking back, I realise, from what my wife and immediate family tell me, that I clammed up whenever an opportunity was given for me to talk of him. I never wanted to.

Aunt Stephanie continued her valiant attempt to bring us together and wrote again in November 1960. The letter began by saying that Grannie Corner and she were looking forward to visiting Burlington House (the Royal Society headquarters) to witness my father receive the Royal Society's Gold Medal. She then asked:

Will you get a ticket for Kay to come to Burlington House too? He would very much like to come and is free on that day – he is going to see the Public Schools Appointments Bureau on Weds and will write to you and report progress – he and Anthony had a long talk – I left them together. I thought Kay had had enough of females for the time being – He has written to the RAF for the testimonial they promised him and we assured him – from what you said to us – that you would back him in any reasonable career he chose... see you Wednesday week and do get Kay a ticket too – so that we can all rejoice happily together. Love to you and don't forget to count your blessings one by one when you want to swear most horribly!

I never received an invitation.

*

In Pandora, I found a note that I had written to my father on 11 November 1960.

There are one or two things which I would like to collect from the box in my old room. If it would be more convenient for me to take everything I will collect them by car at a time which would be convenient to you all? I would like to send my heartiest congratulations on the gaining of the Darwin Medal, a report of which I read in the *Sunday Times*.

I have racked my brains and I think I virtually emptied the box, which means that the contents of Pandora were accumulated after that. Or did he take some things before I came to collect? He wasn't there when I collected – left it to a hostile Helga – and the box was fairly empty. Many things had been removed, my stamp collection not the least!

On 4 December 1960, Uncle Anthony wrote to my father:

I hear you had a great time at the Royal Society on Wednesday. I am so glad all went well – and again my warm congratulations. Stephanie and I have been thinking a good deal about Kay since he was here a fortnight ago. I like him and if we can give him a hand in getting started on a business career we will gladly do so. You are wrong, you know, in believing that he is disloyal to you and the family. That was not his attitude at all. Say what you will, he has not had an easy time in the last few years. Now when he is trying to decide what to do you can help him better than anyone else, so I very much hope that in one way or another you will get together again in a normal way as father and son – and it is up to you.

Yet again, I learned of this letter only from Pandora. It produced nothing at the time it was written.

Aunt Stephanie and Uncle Anthony were always most welcoming and supportive and remained that way for all of their lives. I am extremely grateful to them for that, and for the support of Aunt Do and all the unbiased advice. I could have asked for no more from any of them and our many subsequent visits to their homes were memorable and happy.

I wrote to my father on 2 December:

I believe I said, when I last wrote that I was going to see the Public Schools Appointments Bureau in London. I was with them a week or so ago and the result was that any ideas of Banking were dispelled. That may sound rather a negative result but I told them of an opportunity that had come to light due to an old school friend of mine. This friend wrote to me saying that he could arrange for me to see his Manager who had been a member of the Student Guidance Council. This friend is working in the John Lewis Partnership and is at one of their Stores in London. I went to see the Managing Director and the interview was fruitful. I decided that I was interested in the Retail Trade as a future and he suggested that I work with them temporarily until Christmas to get the 'feel'. As I had nowhere to stay in London it was arranged that I should work with Robert Sayle [in their store in Cambridge] until Christmas which I am doing. Very soon I will be having an interview with the "big chief" of the Partnership and all being well I will be working in London soon after Christmas. The Public Schools Appointments Bureau also suggested this line to me and when I told them of the possible opening they were encouraging and said it was a chance not to be missed. I must say that from what I've read and been told the prospects in this firm seem very good indeed and I feel I must give it a try: thus the temporary work at Sayles.

I worked at Robert Sayle until Christmas 1960 before moving to Peter Jones in Sloane Square, London, where I joined the excellent Management Training Scheme.

John Cawley, my contemporary at The Leys, was already working at Peter Jones and we decided to share costs by finding a flat. This we did, renting a first floor, one-bedroom flat in Draycott Place, barely a three-minute dash to the staff entrance.

Pandora told me that I wrote to my father on 1 March 1961 from 34 Draycott Place. I told him I had 'joined up' with an old school friend to share the flat. Pandora also revealed another letter from me dated 25 October 1961 where I thanked my father for his letter and for opening an insurance policy for me. Although I do recall his telling me of the insurance policy, it bothered me that I couldn't remember those letters. Clearly I did manage to shut out most of those things.

On a lighter note, allow me to tell the story of the chamber pots. When I was placed in the China and Glass department of Peter Jones in that smart SW3 Chelsea district of London in early 1961, I was informed by the Department Manager, a large and booming lady and loved by all her staff, that they stocked chamber pots but they were never to be on display. If a sale was made they were to be brought to the department in a paper bag. How could a consumer make a selection and decide on size with nothing on show, I enquired of myself? So at Christmas 1962, just before the holiday, and then being a Section Manager, I – a little filled with Christmas cheer – created a beautiful display of all kinds of chamber pots right inside the main front door of that elegant and high-class department store. It didn't take long for someone to find me to tell me there was a call from the Managing Director's office. I took the phone to be asked to report to his office immediately. I did, only to learn that it was a jape (apologies for the old word for 'joke') concocted by John Cawley with the MD's secretary.

*

In July 1962 Aunt Stephanie wrote to her brother:

Dear Brother John, We had such a happy letter from Kay telling us that his engagement to Belinda Shaw is now officially announced – tho' we have not yet met Belinda – a niece of an old friend of ours at Chievely who lives at Cambridge knows the family well & says how nice they all are – they have been very loyal to each other & we hope they will be very happy. Kay is bringing Belinda to dinner with us next Thursday July 31st – if you are in London – join us at the House of Commons Lobby – 7.30. Love, Stephanie.

We dined and were encouraged and supported. My father didn't join us. My father, however, had met Belinda before, the first time at Hinton Way in 1959. She came again to a cocktail party with her parents, and visited several times up to when I left home. Belinda remembers Helga cooking Sunday lunch, which was tasty, and that Helga was friendly towards her. My father would have met Belinda on all these occasions, including the times when I gave Belinda driving lessons in Helga's car which was Grannie Corner's Austin 7!

Looking back on all of this, I don't think either the Williams or the Hurds realised how extremely difficult my father could be and that the split was so deep; they knew the Jekyll but not the Hyde. They knew not of the abuse I suffered. I wrote to my father on 19 July 1962:

> I am writing to tell you that I will be getting engaged to Belinda Shaw on Saturday 21st July [her birthday] – we plan to marry in about a year's time.

My father replied, and the letter in Pandora is marked 'copy' by him.

> Thank you for telling me of your engagement. I wish you both happiness. Do not forget that you have two sisters who, one day, may be Aunts. I can't remember Belinda's family, but I have a vague idea that she is the only child. Perhaps I am quite mistaken. But you should try to regain their confidence, and Belinda may be able to help. Your father.

Then a postscript:

> Invite your mother to the wedding and tell her that she will not see me, for I will not be there so that you will be assured of no embarrassment. I could not bear to meet one so unkind. Try, try to overcome selfishness: it is the cause of so much ill.

Why was it a copy? He must either have kept the original and instead of putting that in Pandora he hand-wrote a copy – or he never sent a reply and this is what he would have liked to have written. I don't remember any reply, but that doesn't mean he didn't send one. He tells me to try to regain my sisters' confidence and he accuses me of selfishness. What was that all about? With hindsight, I believe he was again juxtaposing me with my mother for he often accused her, to me, of selfishness – just as he not infrequently accused me of being a coward.

Bill Williams made a diary note on Sunday, 13 February 1962:

> [G]etting ready for a dinner party for Kay Corner's 21st birthday. [Actually after my birthday on 3 January.] There were 12 of us at table in the evening.

I remember that dinner so well which included excellent roast duck and good wines –a great evening. It was the first time I had experienced a 'grown-up' dinner party. Then on Sunday, 29 July 1963, Belinda and I were engaged.

Something quite unexpected happened one afternoon early in 1963. I was visited at the Peter Jones Store by the Assistant London Manager of Wedgwood, not unusual for he often visited on business. Over a cup of tea, he suggested that a meeting at his office might be useful – for us both. We met and an opportunity was presented to me. After thinking things over I called Uncle Anthony and asked if we could discuss the offer. We did, and he was encouraging and constructive.

The first non-family Managing Director of Wedgwood, Arthur Bryan, sat in at my final interview with Robin Reilly, the London Manager, and I so clearly remember him saying, "I know Mary Piggott (the China & Glass department manager of Peter Jones) very well… She will miss you if you leave them." I paused for a moment and replied: "I like to hope she will."

I got the job and joined Wedgwood in their London Office not long before I was to be married. A career change, in those days, was questioned – not to say shortly before marriage. I had a lot to explain to my in-laws to be.

*

Belinda and I married at the University Church, Great St Marys by the Market Square in Cambridge, on 17 August 1963. I had asked Tim Williams to be my best man. However, as his holiday dates prevented that, my great friend Roger Wagstaff took that position. Ushers were Douglas Hurd, Graham Papworth, Arthur Rose (Belinda's uncle) and John Cawley. Many friends from The Leys were with us. My father did not attend as he had indicated. My younger sister Lindsay also refused, saying that she didn't want to meet her mother. The rest of the family turned out in force and the invitation list shows ticks against Grannie Corner (then age 91), Anthony and Stephanie Hurd, Douglas and Tatiana Hurd, Stephen Hurd and Aunt Do.

During the service the heavens opened, accompanied by a loud peal of thunder. An auspicious start to the marriage! When we returned to Belinda's parents' house, the lawn was white with hail stones, but the sky had cleared – it was summer again – and we were given a wonderful reception in the marquee.

We drove to Southwold by the sea in Suffolk for our honeymoon at the Swan Hotel. That first night it was stormy and we were on the top floor. Water leaked gently onto our bed. I mentioned it to Reception to receive an apology and offer of another room – but it was two singles – no doubles available. We decided to stay in 'our' room and moved the bed!

At last I was finding a settled life and was beginning to understand what happiness really was.

*

On my first trip around 1964 to Barlaston, the factory and head office of Wedgwood, I arrived to find a most convenient parking space close to the main entrance. I parked, entered and was duly informed that I had parked in the Managing Director's place. It was suggested I moved – and quickly.

As the office junior, it fell to me to collect directors and senior management from Euston station, Heathrow airport, and the like, to bring them to the London Office or the company flat in Kensington. 'Don't lose your way boy', was the advice of Arthur Bryan after I did on my first trip! He excused that misdemeanour but told me that in the future, if it was a journey I didn't know, I must do a dry run so as to be absolutely sure of the route on the day.

Once, as I was bringing Mr Bryan from the flat to the office, and being the days of mini-skirts, he noticed me looking at one on the pavement. A hand came down firmly on my thigh with the remark 'you keep your eye on the road. I'll do the looking!' I did and he did.

In 1964, barely a year after I had joined Wedgwood, I had a telephone call from the General Sales Manager asking that Belinda and I visit Barlaston for a couple of days and join him and his wife for dinner at the Potters Club. During dinner, Bill Lydeard separated me for coffee and told me that there may be an opportunity coming to manage the Wedgwood business in Vancouver; was I interested? He asked for no immediate answer but did hope I would ring him within a couple of days. There was no guarantee as the office may be closed, but if it was decided to keep Vancouver open they hoped I would take it on. I replied to say yes, but it was decided that the Vancouver office would close.

One day, when I was at Wedgwood in London, Eva Eckersley made a surprise visit to the showroom. She asked for me and I came to reception. We spoke for a while and she suggested a confirmed date to take me to lunch. I agreed but on the day I pretended to be out. How rude I was, and what did I miss? This has stayed with me all these years and now I come clean, far too late. I was embarrassed to see her; it was so wrong. I wonder what she might have said about the days when she sheltered mother just after the suicide attempt.

In all, the ten years with Wedgwood were important and formative years for me. They were good days and at last I was growing up and away from the turmoil of home life in my father's house.

Arthur Bryan was significant in the progress of my career. When I decided to set up my own business, Astley International, in 1991 to bring fine china and crystal to the Far East focussing on Japan, I wrote to Sir Arthur (he had been knighted in 1976) to tell him; I wanted him to hear it from me and not via the grape vine. He replied and we met for lunch at the Potters Club where I gave him more detail of my plans. He was encouraging and asked that I keep him in touch with my progress. I did and we gradually settled into a routine of lunches two or three times a year when he gave wise words and support. So, when I learned that Sir Arthur had passed away on 11 February 2011, it was a sad moment for me. Now I recall my father's simple comment on hearing of the death of Carr – 'A wailing Pandan'. That came from the heart and I feel the same in losing a true friend and mentor.

I 'stumbled' on Japan by force of circumstance, being sent there to research business opportunities late in 1978, and the friendships I made there continue to this day. My father also 'stumbled' upon the Japanese by force of circumstance – the war and occupation of Singapore.

At our very different beginnings I don't think either of us understood the Japanese. The difference in logic in different cultures is neatly expressed in a poem by Gavin Ewart published in his book *The Learned Hippopotamus*.

White men in Africa,
Puffing at their pipes,
Think the zebra's a white horse
With black stripes.

Black men in Africa,
With pipes of different types,
Know the zebra's a black horse,
With white stripes.

My father came to like and trust the Japanese scientists because he saw things in their perspective and they had a common interest in science and the preservation of cultural heritage. Likewise, in doing business with the Japanese, I learnt that they have a different logic: for example, their format to formal meetings, and long pauses in negotiation. Like my father, I came to trust the Japanese and respect them for their professionalism.

I believe that my father and I almost crossed paths in 1983 in Tokyo. I was at the Lifestyle Europe trade show and had met Sir John Whitehead, the British Minister in Japan, as he made a tour of the British exhibitors. We supplied crystal to his home.

My father also visited Japan in 1983 to meet scientists who had been in Singapore during the Occupation, and had made an effort to pay respects at the grave of Professor Hidezo Tanakadate in Hokkaido. During that trip, he too met Sir John who either didn't connect the two Corners or was too discreet to enquire if we were related. Here was a moment in time which might have changed everything, but was not to be.

XXV

KINABALU

I did not know it then, but as I was charting my career in Peter Jones in 1961 and developing it in Wedgwood in 1964, my father was on the other side of the globe climbing a mountain.

He had also just stepped home from a reconnaissance trip to that mountain – Mount Kinabalu – in 1960 when I told him that I had failed an important exam and had to leave the RAF, precipitating my leaving home.

*

Fifty years after my father's expeditions sponsored by The Royal Society of London and The Sabah Society, North Borneo, I was to climb the mountain too as part of the process of finding the father I had lost.

I touched down early on 19 April 2011 at Kota Kinabalu airport and was met by Dr Ravi Mandalam of the Sabah Society. We made haste to my hotel and then to the Sabah Society Secretariat for the evening launch of the book *The Kotal Route Sketches*, which contains drawings by my father, to commemorate the Kinabalu Expedition of 1964.

The next morning, Ravi and his driver, Sadib Miki, collected me and we set off along the coast to the mountain. After an hour or so on a road where evidence of landslips and subsidence was evident, Mt Kinabalu loomed high, standing majestically, dominating all around her. Low's Peak was below some small clouds. We stopped, partially crossed a swaying rope bridge, and I took my first photographs. It was an extraordinary sight and most beguiling. I can fully understand my father's attraction to Kinabalu and his desire to climb and explore.

We reached our first stop, The Kinabalu Park Headquarters, after another hour. After a tour of the park museum and mountain garden, we boarded the vehicle again for the drive to the Mesilau substation. There, we were met by George Mikil who, as a youngster, had accompanied my father on the second expedition in 1964. As we left the substation for the Mesilau Cave, clouds began to burgeon.

Suddenly we were upon the cave, a cavern under a giant boulder which fell thousands of years ago, and where there was room for up to eight or so to rest. I paused, and recalled my father's story from the 1964 expedition.

Upon arriving at the Mesilau cave rock, my father took a stroll and noticed many large trees growing on the top of the rock, and one close to the edge. He wondered when the tree would fall down and felt that he should have it felled at once before setting up camp. Alas, he didn't and his premonition came true that very night.

His note to Professor Duncan Poore, a member of the expedition, written at 8 am on 20 March 1964 reads:

[W]e are all alive, but a ghastly thing happened. At 1 am last night Cr-r-r-r-r-ump, down came on a clear still night the big *Phyllocladus* on the Mesilau Cave rock. The head reached Askew's tent where I was sleeping. The six porters sleeping in the smashed tent ran at once for shelter under the rock and saved themselves or in a sec or two they would have been killed. Askew's tent was shaken with smashed twigs and leaves but undamaged. The path from the cave to Askew's tent is more or less blocked. I moved to Chew's tent by the river, but in my haste to jump up in Askew's tent when I heard the cracking, I knocked over a small hurricane lamp in the dark and the kerosene ran over the ground sheet.*

We continued, crossing the river and following the first part of Kotal's route up the hillside. It was steep and forested – in my father's days there was no track. Any lack of attention, a misplaced step and a fall downhill was almost certain.

We climbed on, passing the top of the boulder and to a height of around 1,920 m. We paused frequently to soak up the scenery and to look at the flora – pitcher plants and orchids, the smallest of which were in early bloom, including a slipper orchid unique to Sabah pointed out by our Dusun guide. The position of the Pinnacles of the East Ridge, hidden by cloud, was pointed out to me. They had prevented the expedition from reaching the summit in 1961.

At last, I could understand what my father experienced in his Royal Society expeditions; my visit to Kinabalu has been an important piece in the jig-saw of finding him. He was remembered by all, and George Mikil,

---

* In the folder of material given to me by Dr Janet West, there is the Story of the Broken Root. It comes in the form of a letter, from 9,000 ft [2,743 m] on Kinabalu, written to 'Helga and girls', dated 22 March 1964. My father asked that they keep the letter because he may want to write it as a short story, which I don't think he ever did. I have compared this letter to the note and though my father's story is written more flamboyantly, the truth is essentially the same. There is a picture of the Dusuns clearing that fallen tree in the 40th Anniversary Monograph.

known to my father as Mikin, spoke with warmth, admiration and affection for and of him. The Dusuns I met were quiet yet full of talk of the mountain, unassuming yet confident, with a wry wit and thoroughly competent climbers, so I can well appreciate my father speaking so warmly of his local assistants.

*

Kinabalu National Park was established as one of the first national parks of Malaysia in 1964 because of my father's initiative. It is Malaysia's first World Heritage Site, designated by UNESCO in December 2000 for its 'outstanding universal values' and the role as one of the most important biological sites in the world – or in my father's words quoted in the *Flora Malesiana Bulletin* of 12 January 1997, '[This] famous mountain... I believe [has] the richest and most remarkable assemblage of plants in the world'. It occupies 754 sq km surrounding Mount Kinabalu, which at 4,095.2 m, is the highest mountain on the island of Borneo.

The following account by my father, published in the Royal Society Expeditions *40th Anniversary Monograph* edited by Dr K Ravi Mandalam, G. W. H. Davison and Patricia Regis, provides a general understanding of the mountain, covering its geology and geography.

It is a granite intrusion into Eocene shale and older ultrabasic rock. Dense forest ascends its slopes to about 12,000' [3,657 m] and above this altitude there is the bare exfoliating granite dome tipped with a dozen major peaks. These rise as cones, flanges, and spikes of granite for several hundred feet to give the mountain its jagged head. The dome, however, is cleft on the north side into two parts by Low's Gully, which plunges precipitously for several thousand feet and has until very recently, defied exploration.

The 12,000' contour, therefore, is V-shaped, and the two arms represent Kinabalu West and Kinabalu East, joined by a narrow, very broken isthmus precipitous on both sides...

The ascent to Kinabalu West was accomplished in 1851 by Hugh Low, and it is from the west side of the mountain that our knowledge of its biology and geology has mainly been developed. Yet it is clear from its size and terrain that Kinabalu East must have as great, if not greater, interest. It has baffled conquest until a circuitous route round the north of the pinnacle region was discovered in 1963 by Dusun Kotal of Kundasan village. It was along this route that Kotal led me in 1964, but it is such an arduous and indirect approach, being in itself an expedition of at least five days from the base at 9,000' [2,743 m], that it must remain for some years a major undertaking.... No one, I believe, has yet crossed from Kinabalu West to Kinabalu East.

My father named this eastern route to the summit of King George Peak, Kotal Route*, after his enigmatic guide who, in my father's words, 'is the class of Dusun as silent, rugged and detached as a granite pinnacle'. By doing this, my father not only acknowledged and recorded the valuable contributions of a local guide, but ensured that Kotal bin Bondial of Kampong Kundasang found his rightful place in the history of Mt Kinabalu.

*

I did not know of father's expeditions to Kinabalu until Pandora inspired my interest. I have learned much from the *40th Anniversary Monograph* and Lord Medway's zoological report of the 1964 expedition.

The biological interest began after Hugh Low's climb in 1851. He had observed a huge lowland dipterocarp forest which is typical of the region and above, 'an island refuge of sub-tropical and temperate life'. He noted that above 9,000 ft (2,740 m) there were trees, shrubs and herbs which are 'allied to those in China and the Himalayas' and amongst them 'grow plants of Australian, Tasmanian, and New Zealand alliance'. Equally perplexing was the lower forest slopes with its wide variety of Australasian conifers and myrtles mixed with plants from Malaya, Sumatra, Java, and Mindanoa.

My father, in the 21 November 1963 *New Scientist* article titled 'Exploring North Borneo', stated: 'The mountain and its surroundings are among the most important biological sites in the world, with over 600 species of ferns, 326 species of birds, and 100 mammalian species identified. Among them are the gigantic *Rafflesia* plants and the orang-utan'. The parasitic *Rafflesia* plant, which has the largest single flower in the world (particularly the *Rafflesia keithii* whose flower grows to 94 centimetres in diameter), is found on Kinabalu.

In 1960, an initiative arose within the Royal Society with the formation of a North Borneo Committee, chaired by Sir Joseph Hutchinson, of which my father was a member. Approval for the study was obtained from the then Governor of British North Borneo, Sir William Goode, whom my father knew from pre-war Malaya. In August 1960, a reconnaissance visit was made by my father who became the leader of both expeditions.

On the way to North Borneo, my father stopped in Singapore and a party was given in his honour by the Director of the Gardens, Dr H. M. Burkill. Those present included Dr Chew Wee Lek, George Alphonso and Dr Ahmad Abid Munir.

---

* *Like Kotal Route, the names of many peaks and pinnacles on Kinabalu East, the eastern Plateau and the North and East Ridges, such as Gully Peak, Outpost, North Peak, Lion's Rock, Echoing Rocks, Rhino Horn, were given by my father. They remain in use today in mountaineering literature on Kinabalu and are referred to by climbers who frequent this mountain.*

Munir, a botanist and botanical artist, in a talk at the State Herbarium of South Australia on the occasion of his retirement in August 2001, recalled 'the rollicking return from Britain en route to Borneo of the famous E. J. H. Corner, the former Director of the Gardens and a global expert on figs, fungus, seeds and just about everything else'. He described my father as 'charismatic, jolly, friendly and knowledgeable', and said he was 'maliciously declared unfit for working in the tropical climate on a fictitious medical report (or certificate) by some controlling authority'.

Later on, according to Munir, my father was declared fit for work and was asked to return to Singapore, but refused, saying: "I would go back only if the same official and medical doctor give in writing when and how I was medically unfit and how or why I am fit now." Here was an interesting take on how the Colonial Office had my father medically boarded out after the war. It also explains how my father could have been offered to return to Malaya in early 1947 but by then was contracted to UNESCO in Brazil.

On the 1960 reconnaissance, the *40th Anniversary Monograph*, quoting my father, states:

> The first part of the programme was the ascent of the East Ridge from the neighbourhood of Poring village, where the road ends. It was hoped to reach the pinnacle-region about 12,000' [3,657 m] altitude, but the main body of the expedition was halted, as had been feared, by precipices at 11,000' [3,352 m].

> The second part was to traverse from east to west the Pinosuk Plateau, which had been made known geologically through the work of Collenette. This plateau is named after the village of Pinosuk which word means in Dusun, as I was informed, the forest retreat from mankind. It is conspicuous from the air as a fairly level plain of small-leafed forest of gloomy aspect in the south-east bay of the mountains, at 4,000 –6,000' [1,220–1,828 m] altitude. Geologically it is composed of an enormous mass of rock debris washed and fallen from the mountain, consolidated with fine detritus, and traversed by several swift streams in the characteristically deep gullies.

> For the third part, if time allowed, the soil studies begun on the mountain were to be continued in an area of high-altitude (c. 4,000') shifting cultivation, as practised by the Dusuns, as the beginning of an enquiry into the problem of natural regeneration. Then, throughout the journey, the opportunity was to be taken to consider the altitudinal limits which might be advised for the extent of the proposed national park. So much deforestation having occurred on the other sides of the mountain, up to 4,000' and 5,000' [1,525 m], the east side might give the opportunity of including in the park an extensive and uninhabited stretch of lowland forest continuous with the mountain forest.

My father's reconnaissance report for the Mamut Valley and Pinosuk Plateau is given in the *40th Anniversary Monograph*.

Our journey was the merest reconnaissance, but it has brought to light the need for much fuller exploration from the 4,000' contour up to the higher, precipitous parts of the Mesilau and Bembangan rivers at 8,000-9,000' [2438–2743 m]. Until this is done, we can have no adequate idea of the part which this unmolested stretch of country plays in the natural history of Kinabalu. An expedition could spend several months here on problems taxonomic, ecological, climatic, and edaphic. Thus I was surprised by the abundance of large woody epiphytes, many unfamiliar to me and most, unfortunately, sterile.… The plateau certainly has seasons, for the oaks and chestnuts had just finished fruiting when we were there and the gibbons were moving off. It is the least-known region of the mountain, richest in life and most deserving of fuller study.

*

From the beginning of June until the middle of September 1961, the Royal Society Expedition explored the east and south slopes of Mount Kinabalu. While it was considered unsuitable to organise a large party to investigate all aspects of botany and zoology, it was deemed desirable to invite as many scientists as possible from North Borneo, Sarawak, Singapore, and Malaya, where much of the previous records of Kinabalu are stored in herbaria and museums.

The plan was for an advance party consisting of Chew Wee Lek, Adam Stainton and my father – all botanists – to prepare a series of camps along the East Ridge. Stainton also served as expedition cinematographer and photographer. To arouse youthful interest, it was arranged that a patrol of boy scouts from Jesselton (now Kota Kinabalu) would join the expedition for ten days at the end of July. The progress of the expedition was transmitted via letters and tape-recordings to the Information Officer, J. M. Dinwiddie, in Jesselton who sent news to the local press which in turn relayed information to the papers in Sarawak, Malaya, Singapore, and Hong Kong.

Under the title *The Eastern Ascent Route*, the my father's account of the start of the expedition is also in the *40th Anniversary Monograph*:

From June 2nd till July 10th we were largely occupied by the making and victualling of the ascent-route; the narrow jeep-road north from Ranau ends after 10 miles at the Mamut River near the village of Poring. Here is a government roadhouse of bamboo, or rather a halting bungalow, beside the few small hot springs which issue so unexpectedly from the rocks at the foot of the mountain: (temperatures 55–60°C, according to Collenette [Mrs Sheila Collenette, a botanist from Sarawak], and fortunately too hot for mosquitoes. Our baggage, brought by chartered plane and land-rovers from Jesselton to Ranau, was transferred by land-rover from the Ranau resthouse to this halting bungalow where it was arranged into man-loads for the foot-slogging ascent. Only one slight incident occurred at Ranau. During one night cows came under the resthouse and ate the cardboard cartons of two boxes of tinned fish; next morning we found the tins scattered over the compound but, miraculously, untrampled.

The expedition first engaged Dusun carriers through the District Officer of Ranau. Later, when they came to enjoy the expedition, these Dusun got their kinfolk from villages many miles away to be substitutes when they had to return to village duties after one day to several weeks. Six Dusuns remained throughout the expedition and a total of about 120 were employed. To most Dusuns, an expedition to look for plants, animals, and soils, was a novel idea. However, they delighted in it as they enjoyed the activity and it employed their knowledge of wild things. Several became expert field assistants.

The expedition's Base Camp was established at 3,400 ft [1,036 m] at a place discovered by J. Singh and was therefore spontaneously named Singh's Plateau. Although by no means flat, areas were flattened for tents and for the erection of a Uniport Extended Oval, an aluminium hut which had been brought for the convenience of field work. The *40th Anniversary Monograph* quotes my father, saying that the Base Camp

lay at the upper limit of the dipterocarp forest and was supplied by two rivulets which rose in a nearby hollow and gave us the equivalent of two running bath-taps, except, that one stopped temporarily during a fortnight of dry weather. This lucky coincidence of ridge-site, water, and rich forest made Singh's Plateau a perpetual delight to the biologist, as it was the mainstay of our labours during June and July. Undergrowth was cleared but all large trees which were not dangerous were left except for some on the north-east flank of the ridge which we felled in order to obtain a view and to let in the sunlight.

By June 11th, the Uniport had been erected and named *Burlington House* [after the Royal Society headquaters in London]; it was an oval, 25 x 14' [7.5 x 4 m], to which had been fitted as many window panels as possible and four doors. The windows were fitted with removable frames of Windowlite to keep out the swirling rain and the nocturnal siege of insects. Thus it was airy and well lit… it is a transportable laboratory which, once set up, makes an invaluable work-room for all weathers. Everyone rejoiced in this luxury which G. L. Carson [Conservator from North Borneo] has so felicitously suggested. Rain, nevertheless, roars on the roof, and Bornean acorns make the report of a firearm.

In establishing the camp, most canopy-trees were left standing, and the camp, though a hive of activity, did not disturb forest life. The *Anniversary Monograph* records that at this 'refreshing altitude' there were not only trees, over 100 ft [30 m] tall, of the dipterocarps *Shorea*, *Hopea* and *Dipterocarpus*, but also trees of Meliaceae, Sapindaceae, Bursuraceae, Sapodaceae, *Durio*, *Neesia*, *Sterculia*, *Artocarpus*, as well as strangling figs, with a great variety of lianes and the rich undergrowth of smaller trees (Annonaceae, Myristicaceae, Guttiferae, Rubiaceae, Euphorbiaceae, etc.) of lowland forest.

Monkeys, squirrels, tree-shrews, and birds took little notice of us or came to feed on the crumbs, but the orang-utan, whose nests were on site when we arrived, disappeared. The gibbons began to whoop at 5 am. At dawn we could watch the sun rise over the lowland forest. By 10 am the site had warmed up, but the shade of the big trees prevented it from becoming too hot and glaring. Smythies [Conservator of Forests, ornithologist] re-named the camp *Burlington Barbetage* because seven of the nine barbets of Borneo here shout themselves hoarse and the eighth can be heard a little higher up the ridge.

The site deserves much more study and exploration. It is the region of orang-utan, gibbon, and the red-leaf monkey. Many plants of *Rafflesia* occur in the neighbourhood. … This is wild, aboriginal, steep forest. We found no evidence of strong winds on this side of the mountain. Dead trees, dead limbs, and dead lianes remain in situ and a chance knock or tug by the passer-by may bring them down. Where there are screes, particularly by the streams, the loose rock may be dangerous to walk over, even when covered with trees. A party of us, six strong, felt the forest-floor wobble on one occasion and very delicately we had to retire. The screes, however, are attractive for they have a rich growth of herbaceous plants and small trees not found in the dense forest; gingers, aroids, orchids, gesneriads, small palms, geocarpic figs, annonaceous treelets, *Elatostema* in great variety, and ferns predominate. They are the early stage in reforestation, and, as the steep slopes are ever falling down, screes develop at all altitudes with a characteristic succession of plants. They make one of the main reasons for the vegetational patchwork all over the forest-clad mountain side.

Besides major landslips, large and small rocks keep falling down. The larger smash their way through the forest to a standstill. We continually encountered them at all altitudes and called them 'erratic blocks', some being as much as 30' [9 m] high. In their wake arise new opportunities for regeneration. Having come to rest, often with an overhanging side, they make a cluster of new habitats in damp shade, dripping walls, and exposed top where epiphytes become saxicolus. According to altitude, again, they have their characteristic vegetation, even their own trees rooting from the top. Thus, between 4,000 and 6,000' the slender shrubby *Ficus setiflora* Stapf was generally to be found on these erratic blocks and nowhere else. The smaller rocks, however, may be caught in the branches of trees and care must be taken to watch out for them while climbing in stream-gullies full of things about to topple.

Camp 2, some 3½–4 hours climbing away from Base Camp, was at 6,500 ft [1,981 m], down a very steep slope beside a small stream. Because it was difficult to access, this camp was used 'chiefly as an emergency', although Chew Wee Lek studied tree-flora intensively and Smythies the ornithology, despite the area being too high for much bird life. Dense tangles of small-leaved bamboo hung in festoons on trees round the camp, on the ridge above, and on the slopes below. This bamboo, characteristic of the mid-altitude 5,000–7,000 ft [1,524–2,133 m], was encountered again at 5,000–5,500 ft in the Mamut valley. Unfortunately, all specimens were sterile.

My father recorded that some 500 ft [152 m] above Base Camp, the dipterocarp forest ceased and the montane forest of conifers, myrtles, tea-trees (Theaceae), *Drimys*, *Rhododendron*, *Vaccinium*, and the ever-present oaks and laurels began, with most of their common species being present to 10,000 ft [3,048 m] and more. *Podocarpus imbricatus*, *Phyllocladus*, *Leptospermum*, the orange-barked *Tristania*, *Schima* and *Agathis* formed 'the mossy forest in the dripping cloud-belt with thick raw humus, trunks and branches thickly covered with moss, liverwort, orchids, and twisted limbs of elfin-character in exposed places'.

This altitude introduces so many new features of the environment as increased wind, prolonged mist, diminished light, lower temperature, and cold soil as well as many new plants that it is not clear whether the climate or the soil conditions are the more effective in establishing the vegetation… Just below 5,000' on the ascent-route, rocks outcrop and the path took a steep turn to a knoll where we felled some trees to obtain a view to the east and into the Mamut valley. This… is an exhilarating place which gives access along its flanks to rich pockets of herbaceous mountain vegetation: unfortunately we had no time to explore these in any detail. The trees of *S. monticola* were in flower. Their cream-white crowns could be seen singly or in small scattered groups on the mountain-side and ridges marking exactly the 4,000 – 5,000' [1,219-1,524 m] altitude. Thus we could identify it on the ridge south of the Mamut River, where we subsequently collected material in verification. The species was discovered originally by Clemens on the west side of Kinabalu and is now known to occur also in Brunei and Sarawak. Together with the apparently new species, it occupies the highest altitude of any member of the dipterocarp family.

On a landslip near this knoll, my father found the only plants – again unfortunately sterile – of *Ficus endospermifolia* and *F. tarrenifolia* which he had earlier seen on the east side of the mountain, though both were common on the western flank. It was at the foot of this hillock where the new oak-genus *Trigonobalanus* Forman – the 'missing link' in the evolution of the oak – was found.

[T]he new genus (*Trigonobalanus*) of the oak family: it is a beech-tree with oak-leaves in tiers of three, and it develops beech-nuts in tiers of three to seven nuts on acorn-cups along a slender stalk. It is common at 4,000–5,000 ft [1,219–1,524 m] and it is now known that it also occurs in Celebes and Malaya, with an ally in Thailand. It knits the northern beeches, oaks, and chestnuts, in an unexpected manner and it draws in the southern beeches (*Nothofagus*) of South America, New Zealand, Australia, and New Guinea. Looking at the world-distribution of the oak-family, one would put a finger on Borneo as the hub of its radiation.

'I was thinking and searching on these lines', wrote my father, 'in the rich oak-forests of Kinabalu when Dr D. I. Nicholson, of the Forest Research Department of Sabah, picked up the beech-acorns of this missing link'. This was hailed as the great biological discovery of the 1961 expedition.

A little above the knoll, the mossy forest assumed its true character with impenetrable thickets of tough saplings and undergrowth interlaced with climbers and bizarre *Nepenthes lowii*.

At the bottom of a steep drop on the north side of the knoll was a small gradual valley where the important, but chilly and draughty, Camp 3 was set. Serving as the intermediate depot on the ascent-route, it was at 8,500 ft [2,590 m], six hours of climbing beyond Base Camp. A stream near the camp plunged in a vertical drop; such waterfalls and the gullies leading to and from them provided among their rocks many sheltered places where unusual plants like *Impatiens*, *Begonia*, and *Pentaphragma* occurred.

[T]he ridge at Camp 3 catches the tail-ends of the storms and cloud-wrack which drift eastwards from Tenompok. The stream valley plunges eastwards and catches, too, the ends of the storms from the eastern lowland. The forest in the valley was soaked in an immense profusion of dripping liverworts, mosses, and lichens. From this altitude onwards, so cold and damp were the evenings, so frequent the soaking of arms and legs in the wet vegetation that we practically gave up bathing, we donned sweaters and "heavy-duty trousers" over other clothes and slept, thus, in light sleeping-bags. The Dusuns complained also of the cold and wet. We supplied them with two blankets each, cotton pull-overs, and gym-shoes because in the wet moss the soles of their bare feet softened and cracked.* Indeed, in clambering among the steep mossy places, clutching wet stems, roots, and rocks, our fingers suffered likewise and we discovered a want in our otherwise copious supplies, namely hand-cream.

My father continued to record in his beautiful, evocative writing style:

Harrison reported hearing cicadas on a warm evening at Camp 3. At Base Camp their noise, as usual, was deafening, until our ears became accustomed, and, as usual, the succession of their trills told the time of day. Just before sunrise a long screech, which Stainton called the 'electric drill', aroused us. Then, with various alternating screechings of other species, as the day wore on, there came towards sunset the rasping honk and steam-whistles; through the night there was a ringing ting-a-ling until the drill announced the dawn. But, from Camp 2 upwards, there was silence at night except for the croak of a frog, the patter of rain, or the drop of fruits eaten by nocturnal rats.

*

After 20 days of ascent from Base Camp, Camp 4 was set at 2,865 m after crossing the shoulder which separates the Mamut Valley and Bemgangan River. Here was where the expedition had the first glimpse of the summit dome of Mt Kinabalu.

Then we came to the first of the two mountain-tops marked 9,025' and 9,450' on the map. They are covered with ridge-forest, resembling attenuated mossy forest, and to obtain a view we had to climb small trees of *Leptospermum*, *Podocarpus*, and *Phyllocladus*. We could at last see to the summit and north-eastwards to Gunong Tambuyukan. The Dusuns became enthusiastic and, studying the map beneath the outlook tree, put two dead horse-flies on the summit contour to mark the arrival there of their leaders Laminggu and Gelidah (who now styled himself 'orang gunung', or the man of the mountain). They were too optimistic. Nevertheless the horse-flies indicated that we were following animals, though footprints could not be found.

The saddle between the two tops was a dense mossy forest but around

Dr Egon (Sporax) Horak reported a story from his uncle, Saidin, who was a porter to my father in both the 1961 and 1964 Kinabalu Expeditions. It seems that during the prolonged stay on the slopes of Mt Kinabalu, my father's boots fell apart. It did not matter much – he continued to walk barefoot up and down the forest, cliffs and stony trails. Dr Horak commented: 'A tough guy, indeed'.

each summit were many paths made by animals and small open spaces covered with a thin layer of grasses. Fringing these places on dry rocks was the dwarf fern *Gleichenia peltophora* Copel. There were also small bogs, 15–25 cm deep, in which grew *Sphagnum* and numerous Cyperaceae including *Cladium*. After reaching about 2,400 m, the elegant jug-shaped *Nepenthes lowii* gave place to *N. edwardsiana* with its long symmetrical pitchers.

Water was found below the saddle on the north side. The descent, as usual, was tiresomely steep and the stream was a poor trickle in a dense glade of the urticaceous shrub *Pilea*; here, however, they met the giant bracken *Pteris wallichiana* Ag. which was a new record for North Borneo.

Camp 4 became the base for the expedition in July 1961. It comprised four two-men tents, a small tarpaulin for the stores and working platform, and a large tarpaulin for the Dusuns, 'who talked through most of the night round a smoky fire and grew more and more engrimed'. The camp was about three hours' walking from Camp 3 and, in terms of rice-transport, involved at least three days of exhausting portage. Thus, special rice-lifts were organised to cater for the line of camps.

A fairly common tree around Camp 4 was a species of *Talauma* (Magnoliaceae) with massive trunk and large leaves. The trunks were too wet and slippery to climb, so there was no choice but to fell a tree to collect the fruits. My father recorded that it took three hours to hew the 60 cm trunk. The undergrowth was of rubiaceous shrubs and small trees, 'all with characteristic manner of branching of the main stem'. The quantity, size, and variety of ferns found in the stream-gullies were 'truly staggering'.

He noted that at 9,700 ft [2,956 m] above Camp 4, the yellowish clay soil and the mossy forests with its thickets of rattan gave place suddenly to granite out-crops.

> The vegetation, which had been rather similar from 6,000' [1,828 m] upwards, now changed abruptly and we were able to walk about freely round and over the rocks and the leaning trunks.… I found a good way to collect by climbing out on the leaning trunks and gathering from the crowns of smaller trees which grew up to them, from lower down the steep slope. *Eugenia, Ilex, Eurya, Symplocus,* and *Polyosma* were common. On the ground was a thick array of slowly rotting, fallen trunks, branches and twigs, and underfoot the dark-coloured and strongly acid soil abounded in earthworms. Their castings were often formed into large turret-shaped mounds some 8" (20.3 cm) high. The rapid incorporation of litter into the mineral soil by these worms prevented the build-up of a thick humus layer as in the mossy forest.
>
> The oak-trees leant and twisted until they became prostrate, when they threw up new limbs, as if they could not die. Animal life seemed scarce except for the Mountain Blackbird (*Turdus poliocephalus see-*

bohmi), so tame and ignorant of men, as all visitors to the mountain have noticed that it sits like a giant robin with plum-coloured vest almost within arm's reach. The birds hopped around me as I turned over the logs in search of fungus and mistook me, I am sure, for a rhinoceros.

Indeed, it was here, on a 30m-wide ledge with coniferous-myrtaceous forest, grassy glades and shallow sphagnum-bogs below the crest of the 3,050 m ridge, that Ben Ensoll, the zoological collector from the University of Malaya, drew my father's attention to some tooth-marks on the bark of a tree. He identified them as those of rhinoceros, and pointed out the 'abundant evidence of their browsing'. This, Ensoll explained, was why the oak-wood was so comparatively easy to move about in. The narrow corridors were created by the passage of large beasts winding round the rocks and trees. Imagine! Rhinos at 3,050 m on Mt Kinabalu not too long ago!

My father continued:

As we sat on a log studying these tooth-marks a scurry announced a tree-shrew. One appeared, followed by another, of a kind which had not been trapped. Swiftly raising gun to shoulder, [Ben Ensoll] pointed at them through the dense undergrowth, twisting his body through three-quarters of a circle, while I ducked out of the way. Then, as the leader paused momentarily for a jump, the other caught up. There was a loud report and Ensoll fell over backwards in his unbalanced position, but we picked up two dead shrews. He knew exactly what to shoot and when to get two beasts with one shot.

Rhinoceros, wild cattle, sambar deer, and pig certainly frequented the high ridge. The horse-flies, again, proved that our arrival had driven them onward. To see them, of course, needs lone tracking. Our van of path-cutters would have disturbed them. Ensoll, in spite of his sixty years, made many lone clambers along the ridge-side, but was unsuccessful in seeing them. There can be no doubt, however, that on this 10,000' ridge, a few rhinoceros find a mountain refuge which connects with the undisturbed Pinosuk Plateau to the south and the precipitous Nalumad valley to the north, whence they may still have a mountain route to the Mount Templer Reserve.

Here is a place where the lingering ecology of the Sumatran rhinoceros should be undertaken. One would like to know what it lives on, whether it's coming and goings are connected with the fruiting trees and the quick growth of the myriad seedlings, where it may breed, and how it spends the time of almost incessant rain from October to December when the ridge would be inhospitable enough for the woolly rhinoceros.

Near the crest of the ridge the forest dwarfs, and one bursts with delight on to a stupendous view. *Podocarpus imbricatus, Phyllocladus,*

Leptospermum, Ilex [holly], *Symplocos, Rhododendron*, and *Vaccinium* become waist-high shrubs, intermingled with orchids, several species of *Lycopodium, Euphrasia*, and the dwarf *Nepenthes villosa* in place of *N. edwardsiana*. If it is still before 9 am, and the clouds have not gathered, the north tip of Borneo may be seen. Eastwards there is a suspicion of Sandakan. Southwards over the Pinosuk Plateau there is range after range of forest-clad mountains to the Indonesian distance. Westwards, and deceptively close, is the rocky dome of Kinabalu from which the jagged north ridge runs to Gunong Nonohan and the walls in the unbelievably steep and precipitous upper reaches of the Kinapasan and Nalumad rivers. Along this ridge we worked during July. We had no name for it, other than the 10,000' ridge.

Close to this ridge, at 2,895 m, Camp 5 was set up. There was no time to clear the site, so the place was dismal and gloomy. Tents were in short supply and the Dusuns found shelter under the overhang of a group of large 'erratic blocks'. Fires were made with difficulty because of the prevailing wetness, and plant collections were dispatched daily to Camp 3, where plant-drying was completed.

Listening to the drips, as I lay there on my camp-bed the first night, I heard continued drops which awoke in my memory a sound of Malaya. Small hard things fell and rolled. Next morning I verified my guess that they were the fruits of *Adinandra*-trees (Theaceae) partly eaten by nocturnal rats. There were two species, which have been identified as *A. impressa* Kobuski and *A. verrucosa* Stapf. One had reddish pink flowers, the other deep crimson.… In Malaya I knew them as having cream-white and, possibly, bat-pollinated flowers and bat-distributed fruits. In Malaya too, several species for this reason of distribution distinguish secondary forest. Thus, I discovered that Camp 5 was pitched in old, extremely dense, secondary forest of *Adinandra* on a large scree which had, in fact, been the cause of the difficulty of fixing up the tent the day before.

When my father ascended to the ridge again, he saw, about 90 m above the camp, the rock face from which the avalanche that had smashed the original oak forest (*Lithocarpus havilandii*) had come. While he deduced that that had permitted the invasion of *Adinandra*, he noted that small trees of *L. havilandii* were beginning to re-establish themselves in this secondary forest which would presumably revert to oak forest.

Many more immense 'erratic blocks' were found below Camp 5, and the remains of a recent camp fire was found at one overhang which could have sheltered about two dozen people. '[A] track lead past this block,' noted my father, and '[w]e hoped that it was not used for hunting rhinoceros'. Small plants of *Galium*, *Alternanthera*, and some composite grew round the erratic. As these plants were commonly found on open rocky banks of the rivers of the Pinosuk Plateau, it was deduced that their adhesive fruits may have been carried up by travellers.

Going westward along the ridge up to 3,230 m, a long, sloping rock ending in a precipice was encountered. It was thinly clad with bushes and orchids, as well as a fruiting bush of *Ficus deltoida* var. *intermedia* (= *Ficus oleifolia* subsp. intermedia (Corner) C.C.Berg), – the highest altitudinal record of the whole genus.

Beyond this rock rose a pinnacle which, from its shape, Smythies had dubbed the 'Matterhorn'. The Dusuns, however, called this point Gunung Mayabau, proving that they were familiar with the area. Yet, there was no sign of a track to the peak.

To scale the Matterhorn was possible only through the dense scrubby forest on its south side. To make the path up the 500' [152 m] to the top occupied our five leading Dusuns for three days; it was so steep and involved so much climbing by roots ('gardening', as Stainton informed me, was the Himalayan expression) that, as leader of the expedition, I declined responsibility for any who ascended. At the top there was the same superb view, yet grander from the proximity of the granite dome of Kinabalu. We scanned through the telescope the means of further ascent and decided that it should be possible by various detours to the southern side of the pinnacle-region, the northern being clearly too precipitous. Alas! Half a mile beyond, in very broken scrubby forest with trees 20–30' [7–9 m] high and emergent rocks everywhere, we reached the obelisk-like pinnacle about 200' [61 m] high which we called the Rhinohorn from its shape and its emblematic mark of the beasts. Around this pinnacle to north, west, and south were precipices which stopped our progress. Returning from this point on the first occasion, we encountered such a fierce north-east wind and cold rain that our fingers became numbed and we had considerable difficulty in hanging on to the rocks and trees to prevent us from being blown off or from falling into the numerous crevices.

Near Ranunculus col we found a fallen nest of the Mountain Black Eye (*Chlorocharis e. emiliae*). It was made, as Allen (head of the Soils Division of the Dept. of Agriculture, North Borneo) and Berwick have described (1958), from the aerial roots of an orchid, and lined thickly and softly with the golden stalks of the capsules of a species of moss. Smythies and I searched for the moss (as yet unidentified), but not till a fortnight later did I discover it by chance on the underside of a leaning rock where neither rain nor drips nor trickles could wet it. Thus the little bird knows where to gather the one dry lining in the region of mist.

It was then 23 July, and in view of the expedition programme, the difficulty with tentage and rice supply, as well as the monthly festival fair in Ranau the next day which would deprive the expedition for a few days of most Dusun labour, my father decided to call a halt and return to Base Camp.

Later, in early August, Peter Askew, the expedition's pedologist, and the geologist Peter Collenette would continue up the route to make a temporary sixth camp at 3,444 m. To the west of the Camp 6 plateau was a precipice which dropped to the head of the Mesilau River, and the roar of waterfalls and spouts on the precipice and also from the higher south-facing precipice of the main massif characterised this site.

In the early morning, before the mist and rain shrouded the views, the Rhinohorn, marking the end of the main ridge route, looked tantalizingly close but also one could see clearly the precipices which halted the further advance of this path. The plateau was thickly covered with the dwarf thicket forest of *Rhododendron*, *Leptospermum*, etc., characteristic of the crests of the 10,000' [3,048 m] east ridge. The forest was but 6' to 8' [2–2.4 m] high but this was sufficient to provide a welcome shelter from the strong and cold winds. The ground itself was much broken by rock outcrops and boulders so that the clearing of even a small temporary camp site was a hard task.

Camp 6 could be reached in less than two hours of strenuous walking from Camp 5 though porters with their loads needed another two to three hours to cover the difficult terrain. The path which ran through non-mossy forest along the base of the cliff on the south of the main east ridge was initially fairly easy. Then it left the contour and descended steeply to cross the headwaters of a main tributary of the Bembangan river. From the other side of the stream, the path climbed steeply out of the river valley to the flanks of the ridge which ran southwest from the Camp 6 plateau.

On the sides of this ridge the non-mossy oak-forest was often broken by large sedgy and glassy glades such as had been seen in some of the ill-drained hollows between Camps 4 and 5 except that here the glades were more widespread and not apparently confined to the wetter sites. It was probably not a coincidence that the appearance of these glades was associated with abundant signs of both pig and deer. The area was also criss-crossed by many hunters' tracks and clearly, unlike the forests adjoining the ridge to the east of Camp 5, this part of the high altitude forests of Kinabalu is much visited by hunters from Kundasan and the other kampongs along the southern edge of the Pinosuk Plateau. *Rhododendron lowii* was conspicuous as were tall raspberries with large yellow but sour fruits.

From here, a way was found westwards but progress was halted by either sheer rock walls or precipices. According to Askew, 'So intricate was the pattern of pinnacles that one's sense of direction is soon perplexed and then lost. One almost disbelieved the compass'. Further progress was doubtful, but Camp 6 was seen as an excellent base for the further exploration of the higher pinnacles and the north side of Kinabalu.

Thus, the expedition ended on 14 September 1961. On the night of 17 September, a joyous party was held in the market of Ranau. In attendance was the District Officer and other government officials, the staff of the Ranau Transport Company which was key in commissariat and financial arrangements, the Dusun expedition members, their families, and the constabulary.

My father and Askew then returned to Jesselton where they gave an expedition report to Sir William Goode. They also, by invitation of the Sabah Society, addressed a large gathering in Sabah College, including many school children, about the purpose and results of the expedition.

*

The results of the 1961 expedition were discussed at the Royal Society in November 1963. Since the 1961 expedition was stopped midway by steep flanks, precipices, gullies and pinnacles, it was decided that a second expedition would be organised running from 1 January through June 1964.

The objectives set for the 1964 Kinabalu expedition were three-fold. First, there would be a fuller exploration of the Pinosuk Plateau and the intensive study of the high-altitude oak forests at 4,000–10,000 ft as the mountain's forest appeared to be the hub of much of the eastern flora, including the 'missing link' in the evolution of the oak. Second, there would be another attempt to reach the pinnacle region by way of the Mesilau River. Third, a reconnaissance would be made to decide on the boundaries of the Kinabalu National Park.

To meet the first objective, the systematic collection of plants and animals and of ecological investigation would be conducted by Professor M. E. D. Poore as botanist and Lord Medway from the University of Malaya as zoologist. My father was again appointed leader of the expedition.

The routes to be explored were shown on a map hand-drawn by my father, and he would once more engage the services of Kotal, the Dusun hunter from Kampong Kundasang, as the chief guide. On this expedition, my father and his team succeeded in reaching Kinabalu's highest point, King George Peak.

In 1963, by way of preparation for the second expedition, the Forest Department had re-erected the Uniport Burlington House at Base Camp. Tents serving as combined workstation and sleeping quarters were set around this common facility.

There, Lord Medway discovered that my father used a rather unconventional method of describing fungi.

John Corner used 'taste' as one of his field characters in the identification of fungi. In the evenings, while working on my own collections in an adjoining tent, from time to time I would hear him cough and spit loudly, no doubt recording his latest specimen as 'peppery', 'bitter' or worse on the tongue.

My father had in fact discovered some 3,000 species of macromycetes within a mile of the Base Camp.

Lord Medway's report contains some other lighter episodes of camp life:

Inevitably, when a mixed team is camped far from home comforts, food became a preoccupation at Base camp. No doubt through much exertion in preparatory work in London, the expedition had been fully victualled by generous food manufacturers, concentrating on minimum weight and sound dietary planning. In this diet, dried egg powder was the main protein component plus one can of corned beef in each week's ration; vegetables were dehydrated flakes. Hereby arose two causes of resentment. First, Dr John Smart, entomologist and the only other Cambridge academic matching Corner in seniority, being allergic to egg, claimed all the corned beef – thereby depleting both variety and flavour in the meals of the rest of us. Friction grew and, ultimately, for reasons I no longer remember, Corner and Smart reached breaking point. I have been told that the two men were never reconciled. At one stage I was myself so hungry for variety that I scoffed most of a jar of peanut butter, originally intended to be rat bait – a lapse that left my professional conscience burdened by guilt…

The second issue also impinged on the people of Kundasan, through whose fields we had to pass on our way to and from camp. They were efficient growers, thwarted by an undeveloped and distant market. With a surplus of fresh produce, at bargain prices, they offered delectable substitutes for our wretched dried vegetables. In this case, agitation spread among the whole team. John Corner finally relented and, on a special day, bought some luscious fresh cabbages. The delighted Europeans made a large salad. But young Ho Coy Choke lamented to me the dreadful implications for the year ahead of having nothing better to eat than raw cabbage, on that day of all: for it was Chinese New Year, 1964…

[O]ne day John Corner and I were the only two in camp. After I had done the rounds of nets and traps, I thought of lunch, and asked my leader what he would like. 'We had porridge for breakfast, and there was some left over. That will do. I am very fond of cold porridge', was his firm reply. Aspiring for something more tasty I embarked on a culinary adventure: nicely fried onions, some salt and pepper, and into the pan I tossed slices of cold porridge – with disastrous effect. Thus did I learn that there are only two prospects for cold porridge: to be eaten as it is, or chucked.

*

I do not have a record by my father of his climb of the highest point of Kinabalu above its eastern plateau. However, Lord Medway's account and description of his climb to the top gives an indication of what my father would have experienced. Like my father, Medway was guided to the summit by Kotal, following the trail which Kotal had established in 1963. In Medway's log book was 'a pencilled guide to the path ahead given to me by John Corner, sketched in plan on one side and in profile on the reverse'.

On 9th April, I took this trail, over two summits of c. 11,200 feet, down into the Latingan gorge and up again the other side – a stage described by Corner as 'heart breaking'. I took my leader's advice and avoided Fuchs' camp site, and forged on to the next, named simply Ulu Latingan, at c. 10,500 feet altitude. At this height, the air temperature at daybreak hovered around 6.0°C; in the morning sun, dry bulb temperatures could rise to 20°C but, as the afternoon clouded, ambient temperature fell to around 10.5°C.

The Latingan camp was a truly beautiful site, high on the flank of the East Ridge, with wonderful morning views across a vast, forested landscape... In the afternoons, the cloud gathered level, below the ridge, and we gazed over an undulating grey sheet through which distant wildlife sounds were filtered. Our tents were pitched in ericaceous scrub on the relatively gentle slope of a landslip fan. At the head was a concave shelf of exposed bedrock from which the major part of earthy cover had slipped, leaving no more than thin pockets of soil. On each flank, the scrub (dominated by *Leptospermum* and *Rhododendron ericoides*) merged into open woodland, some 40 feet tall, identified by Duncan Poore as conifers (*Podocarpus*, *Phyllocladus*), *Eugenia*, *Schima* and *Prunus* spp., over a carpet layer of ferns, sedges and broadleaf herbs. The shrubs included a large orange-flowered rhododendron.

Here, at last, I saw the expected white-toothed shrews scurrying over the ground – probably the Kinabalu Shrew *Crocidura baluensis*... but, perhaps, the mysterious Black Shrew...

On 13 April, I pushed on to the Mekado camp (~10,800 feet) taking only 3 hours (against John Corner's predicted 3½–4 hours). The entire journey was shrouded in thick mist, which gave way to intermittent rain in the afternoon; air temperature 9.0°C. Occasional breaks in the cloud gave glimpses of wet, towering rock faces above and across ravines. After rain, the small stream near the camp was in flood, and the roar of falling water surrounded us in the mist.

Towards evening, the cloud lifted intermittently, to reveal sheets of rock running with water, white spouts and short falls. Opposite us, the long north-east ridge was silhouetted; above us, spikes and vertical faces of grey rock, occasional patches of soil on which woody vegetation grew to 15–20 feet. The only birds seen were an island thrush which roosted convivially in the tree overhanging the camp fire, mountain black-eyes and a flock of white-bellied swiftlets wheeling around a rocky point to the southwest (where David saw nests on 15 April). The night temperature was again 6.0°C. I set 59 traps in a patch of sodden forest, and caught two summit rats.

The following morning, after clearing my traps, I started for the peak at the civilised time of 06.35 h. I saw Lion Rock resolve into its two components, and at 08.40 h I was on the summit ridge (12,900 ft). On the bare rock, rooted in crannies and crevices, dwarfed, replescent *Leptospermum* was in flower. I also noted *Rh. ericoides* and other small, woody shrubs whose names I knew not, a rough grass, and small herbs including types familiar from Europe: an eyebright, a buttercup, a loosely creeping green-leaved *Potentilla* and an umbellifer.

Within 200 feet of the summit cairn, I appeared to enter a different vegetational zone, perhaps the region of regular frosts, characterised by a silver-leaved *Potentilla*. On the way I met only one bird: an island thrush, at 12,800 feet. I reached King George V peak (13,340 feet) at 09.35 h but, already, the view was completely concealed by cloud. A strong wind blew from ENE and the air temperature was 5.5°C.

On my return, I took the opportunity to visit the site of the 1961 base camp. Here… I experienced my one major disappointment of the trip. On 29 April, feeling unwell, I stayed at the camp while my companions went out into the forest. Thus I missed an encounter with a wild adult female orang-utan, with young. For an hour they watched as the ape angrily circled in the treetops, breaking off dead and living branches to hurl, by an awkward back-handed, under-arm gesture, at the intruders, her baby seated on the hip (*berdukung*). The following day, I hurried to the site. I saw two fresh nests and three old ones, closely grouped within a radius of some 100 feet, but found no signs of their builders.

No symposium was held after the 1964 expedition, and no joint collection of papers was published. Many participating scientists therefore published their findings in a variety of publications, but the Royal Society did not keep an inventory of this scientific output. The only record of the expedition in the Royal Society archive is copies of papers deposited years after the expedition by my father.

XXVI

SOLOMON ISLANDS

Without intending in any way to downgrade the importance of this expedition and my father's role in it, I will not report it as fully as those to Kinabalu but will endeavour to give the important facts. It was conducted from 20 June to 15 December 1965, and was the Royal Society's largest and logistically most complex biological expedition till then. The main purpose of the expedition was to explore the biogeographical diversity of the British Solomon Islands as set by the expedition originator, the late Professor Carl Pantin, when he was chairman of the Southern Zone Research Committee of the Royal Society of which my father was a member.

A large party of at least 23 on land plus the Marine Groups and visitors made up the Royal Society Solomons Expedition. My father led the expedition, and in addition, had special charge of flowering plants and fungi. Professor J. E. Morton was head of the Marine Party, while Royal Society member George E. Hemmen wrote most of the reports, and was in charge of organisation and cinematography.

*

In 1568, Alvaro de Mendana discovered the coral islands Ontong Java and set foot on Santa Isabel and Guadalcanal. Before the Royal Society Expedition, the only general scientific appraisal of the islands was by H. B. Guppy in 1882–1883 on the survey ship HMS *Lark*. Although there had been several smaller expeditions since Guppy's time, a great deal of special information was amassed by the Geological Survey and the Agricultural and Forest Departments of the Solomons. The Royal Society Expedition leant heavily on their foundations and borrowed their personnel. The late Dr T. Whitmore, the expedition's chief botanist, had already spent two years on the islands as Forest Botanist while Dr P. J. M. Greenslade brought his knowledge of agriculture and entomology.

The Solomon Islands consist of nearly one thousand islands covering a landmass of 28,400 square kilometres. The main islands of Choiseul, New Georgia, Santa Isabel, Guadalcanal, Malaita, and Makira have rainforested mountain ranges of mainly volcanic origin, deep narrow valleys, and coastal belts lined with coconut palms and ringed by reefs. The smaller islands are atolls and raised coral reefs, often spectacularly beautiful. The region is geologically active, and earth tremors are frequent. More than 90 percent of the islands were originally forested, but came under severe pressure from logging operations. The coastal strips are sheltered by mangrove and coconut palms. Luxuriant rainforest covers the interiors of the large islands. Soil quality ranges from extremely rich volcanic to relatively infertile limestone. More than 230 varieties of orchids and other tropical flowers brighten the landscape.

Little was known about the biology of the islands prior to the expedition, but the region was already then beginning to attract commercial interest in its timber resources. It was thought that the area might well provide a key to questions of biological distribution patterns between Southeast Asia and Australasia.

*

The work of the expedition fell into two parts – the marine and the land. As there were no regular boat services between the islands, and the possibility of local hire was remote or even non-existent, there was the need for an expedition ship to obviate the great uncertainty of local charter. Thus, it was auspicious that Captain S. Brown, who had great experience of Pacific and Solomon waters, put his ship *A. K. Maroro* at the expedition's service. The programme, therefore, resolved itself into short journeys of two to four weeks inland on Guadalcanal, San Cristobal, Kolombangara, Santa Isabel, and Malaita, with coastal work on Guadalcanal, New Georgia and the Russell Islands. The scientists all knew that the islands had not been studied thoroughly and that, if they may be lucky enough to return, they would prefer to study one island in greater detail. Thus, the land-party, undoubtedly, missed many pockets of peculiar vegetation waiting to be discovered in the rugged terrain only by chance.

There were various problems to be resolved and these included the over-riding one of the origin of the sea-mounts which the islands cap, all linked on a 1,000 fathom shelf. There were also the arguments for and against long-distance chance dispersal over the seas as a sufficient explanation of the present fauna and flora. In the use of the expression 'land-bridges', I was reminded of one of the few things which I recall about my father from those days before 1960. He had told me that in his study of the fig he was tracking the evolution of the world's landmasses by its migration. Have I remembered correctly, for this was long before the Solomons Expedition?

There was also the problem of the Malaysian element, and which parts of it are derived from, or have entered into, the Solomons' complex. There were the particular relations with Fiji, New Hebrides, New Caledonia, the

Bismarck Archipelago, New Guinea and Queensland, and the expedition realised that it should explore the New Hebrides.

'Then, I will point on the horizon to South America', my father wrote, for he was going to argue that *Heliconia* is a genus of about 100 to 200 species of flowering plants native to the tropical Americas and the Pacific Ocean islands west to Indonesia and which reached the Solomons from South America.

Finally, there was the obvious fact that because the islands were distant, they were thought of as marginal and irrelevant 'to the mainspring of life'. Although my father noted that there were no more-developed mammals than bats and marsupials, and the pigs were surely introduced by the islanders in their chance dispersal overseas, he pointed out that there were considerable botanical problems peculiar to the Solomons. In fact, he questioned whether the islands 'have not held in their isolation keys to the evolution of flowering forest'.

In the post-expedition summary, it was pointed out that neither the botany nor the coral reefs, so unexpectedly dead, seemed to fit the geological dating. I was interested to read the references to the dead coral. This was 1965 and I don't think that climate-change was the subject of the day!

The report concluded by stating that the Solomons, far away and untouched by industrialism, offer the most intriguing problems for the biologists. Rather, as an appetiser, the group had tasted and would like to return but surely in smaller parties. The problems to be pursued would be those of dispersal, speciation, phyletic evolution – the hypothesis was that species continue to adapt to new environmental and biological selection pressures over the course of their history, gradually becoming new species, and the sheer mechanics of existence before the onslaught of man obliterates them. Unfortunately, there were no further Royal Society sponsored expeditions to the Solomon Islands.

As part of the closing summary, my father expressed gratitude to the Royal Society and – most interesting to me – 'to the wives for having allowed us this freedom.' Of course he was thoughtful in thanking the wives, but I've never before or since read of him making such a specific thanks. Was the botanist suddenly second to his wife? And if he was thinking of his wife, the wife was then not my mother. Perhaps he had by then learned a lesson thirteen years after the divorce.

After recovering from a bout of malaria and on return to Cambridge, my father took the chair of Professor of Tropical Botany. He had in fact received news of his appointment in the Solomons as Ruth Kiew reported in *Flora Malesiana Bulletin* 12 (1) 1997:

[O]ne evening when Corner was sitting in camp, in pouring rain on a remote mountain several days from the nearest village, a runner appeared from the darkness and produced from his waterproof pouch a letter from the Vice-Chancellor of Cambridge University, which announced his appointment.

It was a deserving appointment for a most able and individual scientist who in 1966 became President of the Cambridge University Natural History Society.

- XXVII -

PROFESSOR OF TROPICAL BOTANY

As I look back on my father's life, I come to the conclusion that he was destined to be a professor right from his early days in university, and, as his life progressed, that of tropical botany was a natural: and where better than Cambridge University to finish his academic career where it had started. This was to be his full circle of life – his '*maru*' (丸, Japanese for 'circle').

In his student days, my father's mind was often ahead of matters-of-the-moment, like the missing of that scholarship exam paper, and he had little time for things which were absolutely not necessary for his advancement. One of those was not pursuing a PhD. I think he felt that the time needed to achieve it would have restricted his progress rather than enhance it.

Yet, to learn something every day, even a correct spelling, was something that drove my father. Amongst his favourite authors were Bunyan, Blake, Thackeray and Gibbon in particular. As a youngster, I can remember him reading me a number of books including *The Water Babies*, and I learned the meaning of 'Do as you would be done by' and 'Be done by as you did', both important values for life for all generations. He encouraged me to read, although he was dismayed when I found Agatha Christie at Twyford! He was a determined and single-minded man right from his very early days and he smoked his pipe long after it was fashionable, his books and papers bearing witness to that.

In 1949, when I was sent away to boarding school, my father was appointed Lecturer in Plant Taxonomy at the Botany School in Cambridge. His seed work began with a study of *Annonaceae* that same year in which he found four integuments in some taxa, followed by *Leguminosae* in 1951. Over the following years, he built up an impressive collection of seeds and he both sectioned and drew them, studying the development of their integuments and thereby building on the work of Fritz Netolitzky.

A number of my father's students have written to me about the teaching style of the 'kindly white-haired older chap' who leant on the lectern and spoke without notes. He would speak about 'a wide variety of vaguely botanic subjects of such depths of insight and lateral thinking that he polarised his audience into those who rapidly fell away and ducked his lectures and those who were inspired for life'.

Duncan Poore attended my father's very first course at Cambridge and found him

diffident and, I now suspect, extremely nervous. His lectures were fascinating, full of stimulating ideas and irreverent anecdotes – very memorable but quite impossible examination material! It was particularly in the field that he shone. A visit to the tropical houses in Kew – the nearest we could get to the tropical forest – was a revelation; so was an excursion looking at the fungi around Cambridge, for his studies of fungi were probably his most important scientific achievements.

Godfrey Curtis gave me fascinating information that speaks about the challenges my father liked to pose for his students:

I remember the first occasion he addressed us. Some twenty minutes into the lecture (it was about Allomyces) he drew on the board a sphere with a couple of lines on it not un-reminiscent of a cricket ball with its seam. We all diligently bent to our note books and assiduously copied the drawing as this was the first tangible thing he had happened upon up to this point. 'Aha!' I recall he triumphantly declaimed – 'you have all made a note of this and yet I have not explained what it is!!' We had of course all assumed it would be a spore of the fungus. 'This' he pursued, 'is the world distribution of the species – and these are the tropics of Cancer and Capricorn!'. In the corner of my eye I watched as several undergraduates silently crossed out the diagram! It was typical of his approach – to inculcate in us a sense of discrimination and to test what we were being taught – indeed to think for ourselves: two recurrent themes in this teaching.

David Crompton said:

He would probably have seemed fairly forceful to undergraduates who had not had the benefit of life with RSMs (Regimental Sergeant Major) or been through Officer Cadet School. I was willing to answer back or even challenge his assertions. Again I discovered later that he loved an argument; he thrived on verbal duels and would provoke outrageous discussions. Looking back, I cannot imagine that he was ever an easy research collaborator or team member, but I may be wrong.

The short poem by Elmer W. Smith, the talented botanical artist, best sums up my father's point of view in everything.

In matters controversial
My perception is quite fine
I always see both points of view
The one that's wrong; and mine...

In 1954, my father was elected to the Council of the Linnean Society on which he served to 1958 and then 1959 to 1961, becoming Vice-President in 1960. He was elected a Fellow of the Royal Society in 1955. He was critical of the probing procedures preceding such elections and simply refused to fill out the Personal Record form on appointment. After frequently and tactfully being reminded that it had to be done, he eventually did so in June 1990, completing the lengthy form in great detail by hand, 35 years late. In his letter to the Royal Society in which he enclosed his Personal Record form, he wrote: 'herewith this distasteful matter'.

My father served on the Royal Society Biological Expeditions Committee from 1956 to 1963, and the Pacific Science Committee from 1958 to 1971. He was also involved in forest conservation in New South Wales and Queensland, Australia.

In December 1958, he was the Royal Society's delegate to the Darwin-Wallace centenary in Singapore. This was a tough one for him because 'in sadness' he had left Singapore 13 years previously and was indeed reluctant to return. Yet, he did, and 'when I stepped from the aeroplane, the smell of durian, pineapple refuse, curry and joss-sticks in the warm air restored nostalgia'.

A remarkable revelation occurred during this visit. The scientific week was lively 'with local exploits and some ridiculous politics concluding with a great dinner party'. My father was placed next to the Chief Minister, Lim Yew Hock. At the same table were the Chairman of the Celebration and his wife – his old friends Dr and Mrs Sandosham, the Professor of Dentistry who my father taught elementary biology – and Professor and Mrs Gilliland.

At the conclusion of the speeches, when the applause had died away, Mrs Sandosham told my father that the lady opposite, the wife of the Professor of Dentistry, would like to speak to him with a particular question. My father moved to be seated next to her and, after a chat, she asked: "Were you ever in the General Hospital?" For a moment my father was surprised, then

a sheet of lightning lit the past. I took her small hand and kissed it, to everyone's astonishment, and said, "You are the ministering angel!"... "And you," she replied, "were the first patient that I nursed." Of course my heart is in Singapore.

This chance meeting was 24 years after my father was hospitalised for scrub typhus.

My father was elected a Fellow of Sidney Sussex College, Cambridge, in 1959 –'War and international responsibility led me to return to academic life', he said. From that year on, he kept mycology as a hobby and became Reader in Plant Taxonomy at Cambridge. He was not allowed to give mycology lectures at Cambridge although he was a famous mycologist in his own right.* In 1963, he became President of the Botanical Section of the British Association for the Advancement of Science.

Although I recall all the damning of Holttum by my father, he wrote to Holttum on a number of occasions from 1959 to 1962 as botanist to botanist, and the tone of the letters was friendly, not frigid.

His letter from the Botany School dated 15 November 1963 illustrates my point and provides interesting comment.

Thank you for helping so much with the splendid delivery of your contribution on ferns to yesterday's discussion. I am sorry that we had no time to discuss in detail, but it is never possible at these meetings.

He apologised for overlooking Holttum's contribution on the climbing bamboos of Kinabalu but asked for a copy, with illustrations, 'so that I can arrange for publication before I leave again for K [1964 Kinabalu Expedition]'.

In 1964, the year my father visited the Solomon Islands to plan for the Royal Society's expedition, he published *The Life of Plants* which elaborated on Church's work and his theories of plant evolution. Written for students, but suitable also for an enlightened general audience, it contained his own drawings and photographs, and was a bestseller.

Professor Dr David Hawksworth, Director of the International Mycological Institute, first encountered *The Life of Plants* on a book display rack in December 1964 as an undergraduate and was so captivated that he bought his own copy.

[T]here were the challenging statements flagged-up in the Preface: "A living thing is too complicated to be understood" (p. ix), "The most baffling problem is how plants came on to land . . ." (p. xi), "Trees need

---

*Although my father did not lecture on mycology, he did continue to contribute to the field and was well ahead of his time. IMA Fungus, the global mycology journal of December 2012, refers to a comment of the origins of fungi my father made in 1964: 'to judge from the great accumulation of plant debris which makes the Coal Measures, either they were not then established or they were unable to cope with the chemistry of those plants'. The journal, in its research update, states that 'comparative genomics have shown Corner was, as in so many aspects of mycology, spot on'.

fungus" (p. xi), etc.... As I avidly read the text from cover to cover, my excitement grew. The book was a maelstrom of ideas and concepts that were new to me: fungi originating by the loss of photosynthesis from seaweeds; Coal Measures being formed because fungi had not yet evolved mechanisms to decompose lignin; asci as aerially adapted aquatic sporangia; the resurrection of A. H. Church's ideas of lichens as transmigrants of life to land from 1921. And of course Corner's "Durian theory", postulating that the primitive fruits of flowering plants were arillate carpels or, in the syncarpous ovary, capsules – then still a 'hot' topic prompting either excitement or scorn amongst botanists depending on their perspectives. Corner later chortled to me he had quite enjoyed the angst his "little joke" had caused in the botanical establishment.

The Life of Plants includes insight into and understanding of evolution*, something which my father gave deep thought to throughout his life, and refers to in many of his writings. He gained some notoriety among creationist circles in those years for a frequently circulated quotation: 'but I still think that to the unprejudiced, the fossil record of plants is in favour of special creation'. Here is the fuller context:

> The theory of evolution is not merely the theory of the origin of species, but the only explanation of the fact that organisms can be classified into this hierarchy of natural affinity. Much evidence can be adduced in favour of the theory of evolution – from biology, bio-geography and palaeontology, but I still think that, to the unprejudiced, the fossil record of plants is in favour of special creation. If, however, another explanation could be found for this hierarchy of classification, it would be the knell of the theory of evolution. Can you imagine how an orchid, a duckweed and a palm have come from the same ancestry, and have we any evidence for this assumption...?

Whitmore, in his obituary of my father in the *Independent* newspaper, said *The Life of Plants* was 'full of his originality', but it was a brief reference in the same obituary to my father's 'scintillating appearance as expert witness in a court case on the issue of whether packet soup could be labelled mushroom (rather than toadstool) if it contained pore rather than a gill

---

* *When my father developed his theories of evolution, he tried to persuade his mother to accept them without particular success. On one occasion, she replied, 'Never mind dear, no matter what you say the Good Lord will still look after you.' That greatly annoyed my father. Darwin was less forceful with his wife, showing greater understanding of her views with compassion.*

fungus' which caught my attention.

I wrote to ask Roy Watling, one of my father's close mycologist friends about this and he replied, 'Yes I do know about this court case brought against Nestlé'. Further research led to Issue 6 of the 1959 British Food Journal that reported the case. The occasion was around the late 1950s or early 1960s, and the matter revolved round Nestlé's mushroom soup, sold as freeze-dried powder in packets. It was made of dried *Boletus edulis*, or the common mushroom (*Psalliota* or *Agaricus campestris*), a pored fungus which dries much better than the domesticated mushroom which, because of its chemical composition, goes black on drying, does not freeze well and looks unpalatable. The genus Boletus has several edible species which are commonly eaten on the Continent. It freezes and freeze-dries well, and produces a much better flavoured dried product. "This much I knew," said Janet West in helping me with this research. "What I had forgotten was that the word Boletus is derived from a closely similar word in both Greek and Latin which translates as 'mushroom'".

A food standards or honest trading agent of the West Sussex County Council at Chichester had taken Nestlé to court alleging that the soup was not mushroom soup. Nestlé hired Dr James Ramsbottom of the British Natural History Museum (author of the then main book about British macrofungi) to argue that, really, the names mushroom and toadstool were separated only by scientists – not ordinary people – and there was no case for prosecution. Without warning, the local government officer produced my father who said 'stuff and nonsense, they really are different'. My father argued that the cultivated mushroom did not cover the poroid fungus. Although the court, following the usage of people in the country areas where mushrooms grew, ruled that *Boletus edulis* was properly described as mushroom, Janet West wrote, 'I'm sure that John gave a scintillating performance'. So am I.

*

My father served on the Royal Society New Hebrides Committee from 1964 to 1966, and led the Royal Society expedition to the Solomon Islands. On his return, he assumed the professorship of Tropical Botany, Cambridge, and in 1966 became President of the Cambridge University Natural History Society.

My father's scientific life was back on track and he was able to disseminate the vast knowledge he had acquired in Singapore, Malaya, Brazil and his expeditions to Kinabalu and the Solomons. Indeed, he inspired not only his research students but all who were taught by him.

At Cambridge, he continued to develop his work on *Wayside Trees of Malaya*, elaborating a classification of the genus *Ficus*. Some of his type specimens are deposited at the Cambridge University herbarium. In concentrating on so large a genus he saw clearly, as he did in his seed work, the grades of classification and the importance of clades – the scientific classification of living organisms.

Palms were a group which had not been covered in *Wayside Trees*, and my father rectified it by publishing *The Natural History of Palms* in 1966. The book, which was described by the Whitmore obituary of my father as 'fine broad-brush treatment flawed by many small errors', was criticised by those whom David Mabberley, my father's last research student, called 'nit-picking specialists'. However, it remains by far the most readable account of palm biology.

Mabberley is an admirer of my father's style of writing which he said is 'an attractive almost seductive one', but he added that it is

a literary style not welcomed by many scientific journals today. Nevertheless, parts of *The Life of Plants* are reprinted in Bernard Dixon's *From creation to chaos – classic writings in science* (1989). Here, Corner rubs shoulders with Francis Bacon, Rachel Carson, Charles Darwin, Fred Hoyle, T. H. Huxley, Isaac Newton, Alfred Russell Wallace and H.G. Wells.

The opening of *The Life of Plants* illustrates the way my father so simply saw things and avoided jargon!

The Plant is a living thing that absorbs in microscopic amounts over its surface what it needs for growth. It spreads therefore an exterior whereas the animal develops, through its mouth, an interior. The definition is vague but it gives the reason why the limb of a tree ends in leaves, not fingers, and it helps to explain how in the long run of evolution a monkey came to sit on the tree and a cow to ruminate in its shade.

Some of the best of my father's writing can be found in his chapter *Evolution in Contemporary botanical thought* (1961), and in his papers *On thinking big* (1967), *Prototypic organisms XIII; Tropical trees* (1975) and *The Palm* (1981).

From 1968 to 1975, my father served on the Royal Society Southern Zone Committee but resigned his Fellowship of Sidney Sussex in 1973, over the question of the admission of ladies, never to return to that fold. He took a similar stance as a Governor of Rugby School (1959–1975) on the same issue. In his Royal Society records, he wrote that his resignation from Sidney Sussex was due to his 'refusal to agree the College becoming bisexual'! At a meeting of the Fellows of the College, when it became obvious that the debate was lost, my father rose, threw his college keys on the table in front of the Master, and stormed out. Moments later, there was a knock at the door and in walked my father to collect his car keys – still attached to the ring!

There was more to the resignation than just ladies. David Chivers from the Anatomy School at Cambridge told me that he had heard that my father

had a major, long-running disagreement with the Master, Professor Linnett. I then met him in the street and said that it was sad I did not see him any more at Sidney, that High Table was not the same without him. I said I gather that it was not the admission of women that caused his departure, but trouble with the Master. I said that he was not as good as his predecessor, David Thomson, historian, a great man who smoked himself to death prematurely. "Very sad," John said, "Yes, David Thomson A1, A1, present man G3, G3"!! I have never forgotten that; it summed up John's outspokenness so well.

My father also did not mince his words at Cambridge when things did not go his way. When construction began for a new building in the courtyard area of the Botany School, he began to lose 'his' parking space to others, much to his dismay and fury. He put messages under windscreen wipers, reported the matter to the principal and did all he could to discourage invasion of 'his' space. But it continued and this became one of the many frustrations that made him give up his room and work from home – an arrangement that continued right up to his passing. This incident well illustrates my father's ability to make a big decision based on such trivial matters. If he felt 'crossed' that was it – usually forever, as I well know.

I heard a variation of the 'keys story' from Dr John Dawson relevant to the parking space saga.

Corner finally complained about loss of parking space to the University Vice-Chancellor and on one occasion, when the VC was present, he complained again – said he'd had enough and was resigning. He threw his keys on the table and departed. On reaching his car he realised his car key was still on the ring and returned to collect it.

So often with good stories they become distorted with time – both are worthy of telling and the truth lies in both.

In 1968, my father was chief guest, in Sri Lanka, of the Ceylon Association for the Advancement of Science and, by special invitation, visited the Royal Society and Royal Geographical Society Expedition to Mato Grosso in Brazil, mainly to decide on whether it should continue. His arrival must not have been well announced and Dr Peter Askew, an expedition member who was also with my father on Kinabalu, recalled that 'neither Roy Montgomery nor I were "in camp" when Professor Corner arrived but either

David Moffatt or Peter Searl were there. No one knew, so I understand, that he was coming and he only made a fleeting visit. No one knew him so that, I was told by David or Peter, his remark "Do you know who I am" was subsequently much quoted'.

Here is an example of my father directing his anger when 'caught out' – in this case, not impressed by being unknown. His obvious success as a scientist brought about a certain impression of aloofness and I think that this, as with the return occasionally of his stammer, was due, certainly in part, to his continuing uncertainty about views of his role in wartime Singapore. In 1968, his story of that time was still virtually unknown, certainly by the general public. I don't think he was ever 'that assured man' which so many thought. He had to fight his inner feelings all the time and this his stammer betrayed. His anger was his cover when needed and behind which he sought sanctuary.

My father was elected President of the Cambridge Philosophical Society in 1970 and he was awarded the Linnean Society Gold Medal that year. He also travelled to Indonesia as the first Royal Society Leverhulme Visiting Professor but that, he felt, was a failure. He was on the Leverhulme Council and served, inter alia, the Leverhulme Scholarship Committee from inception in 1967 to 1970.

Dr John Dransfield, one of my father's research students, told me something of that visit to Indonesia and his impressions of my father as a tutor which show other aspects of my father's character.

During the period of my PhD research I found your father rather aloof and rarely approachable. I did not meet Mrs Corner [Helga] until the very end of my research, and that for three minutes. Not once was I invited to his home. At the time also, I was acting as tutor for undergraduates and so sat again in Corner's lectures, but found them much less substantial than I did the first time – charismatic yes, but I was much more critical of the content. This was around 1968–1970. In 1972, the Corners visited Indonesia as part of a Royal Society Visiting Professorship scheme. They stopped in Sri Lanka on the way where they were feted.

In Indonesia, conditions were very basic at the time and furthermore the Director of the Gardens had just changed, with the new director unaware of your father's eminence and not very sympathetic to a VIP visitor whom he did not know and inherited from the previous director.

The Corners, as part of the Royal Society scheme, were to be provided with accommodation. I desperately tried to get everything arranged before their arrival, and just managed to secure a spacious guest house in the garden. However, things were not like Sri Lanka, and Mrs Corner found the whole experience culturally shocking, and I took the blame – I know this, because she related all my iniquities to other people in the Gardens who promptly told me. I must say that I tried my best to help but they did not endear themselves to me – particularly in the disparaging remarks about the Javanese (Java man walks again, what Bogor needs is a sanitary inspector, not a Roy Soc visiting professor), and about me and my kind (grammar school boys rather than public school boys who were lowering the standard of Cambridge). Strangely this was the first time I experienced such prejudice in Cambridge circles.

Corner stomped off back to Sri Lanka in a fury, cutting short his professorship and then spent several years maligning me and even wrote letters to the Overseas Development Admin to try to get me sacked. Although I owe my career and enthusiasm for palms to your father this falling-out was never healed.

This is an example of a number that I have come upon, where my father did not forgive; indeed, he allowed that Dransfield incident to fester in his mind. It was a weakness in a clever man.

It is also the first time I have heard of the attitude expressed by his second wife. She came from basic roots, and there's nothing wrong with that, but the success of her husband clearly went to her head. Her comments were ill considered, high-handed and wrongly placed.

David Chivers had also heard of my father's poor treatment of those who crossed him. According to him, Tim Whitmore never got a post at Cambridge when my father retired because my father disliked him. Peter Ashton, on the other hand, 'must have been something of a favourite'.

C. X. Furtado was both a favourite and a friend because of my father's interest in palms. Once, some white botanist condemned Furtado for daring to put proposals in plant nomenclature. My father challenged the white botanist to a fight for insulting his friend. This challenge was witnessed by Henry Burkill who nearly dropped his index cards. No fight took place.

Like Furtado, Professor Kevin Kenneally, who is Honorary Research Associate, Western Australian Herbarium Science Division, Department of Environment and Conservation, was one of my father's favoured ones. Kenneally wrote to me in 2009 (after an electronic introduction by Jean Paton, a friend and neighbour of Judy Bryning, an *Orion* passenger – which illustrates how one contact often circuitously led unexpectedly to another in my research).

What Kenneally told me confirms that my father could be charming and cooperative to those whom he liked – in this case because of the nature of and approach to the botanical research involved.

On my 21st birthday in 1966, Arthur (McComb of the University of

Western Australia) presented me with a copy of your father's recently published book *The Life of Plants* – a book I still treasure. On graduating in 1973, I joined the staff of the Western Australian Herbarium as a botanist and began a series of flora and vegetation surveys of the Kimberley in WA. In those early days not much was known of the tropical flora of the Kimberley and duplicates of my material were sent to the Royal Botanic Gardens at Kew for specialists to identify. Many of my collections were figs and I started a correspondence with your father and he was exceptionally helpful and encouraging to a young botanist. I got the impression he admired people who did field work!

In 1975, I was given the opportunity to visit the RBG and meet many of the botanists that I knew only from our correspondence.

From that opportunity to visit the Royal Botanic Gardens he met many of the botanists, including my father, whom he knew just from correspondence. By then, my father was Emeritus Professor of Tropical Botany at Cambridge University.

I had let your father know I was working at Kew and he invited me up to Cambridge to meet him. When I told some of the Kew botanists of this they were rather surprised. They said your father could be quite irascible and difficult, didn't tolerate fools and was particular whom he invited to his home!

So when I went up to Cambridge I was not sure what to expect. I need not have worried. Your father and mother [stepmother] invited me to tea and they were very charming and gracious to this botanist from the antipodes. Your father was very interested in my work and we spent time chatting about his botanical career and his time in Singapore… It was a very memorable visit. Your father and I maintained a steady correspondence and he was always courteous and extremely helpful.

My father 'retired' from his office at the Botany School in 1975 and continued his work from home, with occasional visits to the university, the Combination Room mostly. He 'corresponded the world over', as he wrote, and worked to finish his last manuscript *Moments Botaniques*, which was never published. That was the year when he was diagnosed with glaucoma 'as with my father and younger sister', he wrote – and 'as with me', I write.

To celebrate his 70th birthday in January 1976, some of my father's research students planned to have an article, 'Tropical Botany', published in *The Garden's Bulletin*, Singapore. However, as H. M. Burkill said in his introduction to the 31 August 1976 edition where the article eventually appeared, 'the best-laid schemes o' mice an' men, Gang aft a-gley'.

The initiative for the article came from Dr Kenneth Sporne and Dr David Frodin and all was put together by Dr David Mabberley. In fact, Mabberley told me that as he finished his thesis in 1973, Sporne, who was his internal examiner at Cambridge, said to him that it was Mabberley's duty to prepare an article to celebrate my father's 70th birthday.

That year, my father's *Seeds of Dicotyledons* was published in two volumes. He was obviously still very productive as two years later saw the publication of *The Freshwater Swamp-forest of South Johore and Singapore*. Tim Whitmore mentioned these two publications in the obituary he wrote of my father for the *Independent*. He described the former as 'highly original' but was critical of the latter, saying that it 'studiously ignored advances in tree science since his own researches in the 1930s'.

The late 1970s was when the Japanese entered my father's life again. All this I gathered in 2007 in my exchanges with Professor Mikiko Ishii whom I got to know via Robin Miller and Deborah Holttum. In 1978, I began my business in the Far East, and from that my great interest in Japan blossomed.

From 1974 to 1978, Professor Ishii was researching Medieval English Religious Dramas in Cambridge. Let me allow her to tell the story:

It was in the spring of 1977 that Professor Corner came to see me at my office in the building of Oriental Faculty, Cambridge University, UK, with the letter of introduction from the Society of Philosophy of Cambridge University.

I was a lector of Japanese at the Oriental Faculty, working at the same time as a Research Student at the English Department, writing a PhD on medieval English religious drama. We introduced each other and shook hands. I found my hands clasped firmly by very large, strong, solid hands. His face had features of English aristocracy, a narrow, intellectual face with a high nose and large blue eyes; he was very tall and high. But his hands were of great contrast with the graceful physical features. They were the hands of a farmer or someone who was accustomed to working with the soil. He looked at me with gentle smile. I felt his warm humanity. That is how we met. It was the beginning of a great story.

He talked about his cooperation with Japanese scientists during Japanese occupation in Singapore during the war. Not only did they preserve the museum and the botanic garden but also did some scientific studies together and published them, including the *Wayside Trees of Malaya*, during the war. To tell you the truth, in the beginning I could not believe what he said about his experiences. He had a *curriculum vitae* of the Marquis Yoshichika Tokugawa with him and asked me to translate it into English. It was a simple curriculum vitae but covers the eras of Meiji, Taisyo, and Syowa. The modern Japanese history is reflected in his personal history. He was the last lord of the Tokugawa family in Meiji era, MP of the House of Lords [Tokyo], a famous biologist, the founder of Socialist Party, the president of the Tokugawa Museum in Nagoya, and a great patron of music and arts.

I translated the curriculum vitae… and called the professor. He came to see me again to take it. He read it in front of me with big smiles. One day he turned up again with his wife. He had a large bundle wrapped in a *furosihiki* (a big handkerchief) with him and placed it on the table and opened it. They were the materials from his days in Singapore and the letters from the friends in Japan. What he had said to me about his old days in Singapore is not a fairy tale but a true story. He told me that he would very much like to write a memoir about the days in Singapore, when he worked with his Japanese friends. But he lacked the backgrounds, had little information about his friends and did not know well what they had been doing after they went back to Japan. Most of the material from Singapore is written in Japanese which prevented him from writing a true story.

I presented myself as his translator and went to his house at Great Shelford to read the materials. In September, next year, I went back to Japan for good to take professorship in Shizuoka University. It was lucky for the Professor Corner that I came home, because I could actually visit his friends in Japan. I often met Dr Haneda, former closest friend and colleague of the professor. Dr Haneda told me his own story about the days in Singapore and I translated them and sent to the professor in Cambridge. Dr Haneda asked the mayor of Yokosuka City to build a museum for the citizens. He had a study in the museum. He realised his dreams about a museum in his own museum. He took me to the Tokugawa family in Tokyo. The head of the house at the time was the son of Yoshichika, Yoshitomo Tokugawa. He was awarded CBM for his lifelong contribution to the friendship between Japan and England. He was the president of the Society of Japan-British Society.

I was warmly welcomed by the family and one day I was invited to dinner. The son of Yoshitomo, Yoshinobu Tokugawa, a great historian joined the dinner and after the dinner he lectured me on the history of Tokugawa family of more than three hundred years. He was frightfully intellectual and knowledgeable. I recorded his talk and translated important parts and sent them to the professor in Cambridge, so that he could know how the very person, a scientist and politician who had great influence on the occupation army to preserve the museum and the botanic garden in Singapore during the war, was created. I borrowed some photos from the family, copied them with their permission, and some important materials concerning the family. They often invited me to their family gatherings and festivals as their close friend. Yoshinobu Tokugawa became the head of the family after his father died. Yoshinobu died of lung cancer a few years ago. He was one of the closest friends of the present Emperor and a great adviser. The Emperor misses him very much. In this way, without knowing it, I was involved in the unspoken high society of the present-day Japan.

In the summer in 1979, I went back to Cambridge with large amount of materials and gave them to the professor and we talked about them for days and for weeks. Eventually, he started writing a memoir. It was completed in 1980 and published by Heinemann Asia.

The Marquis: A Tale of Syonan-to, was published late in 1981, a year after my father contracted muscular paralysis which was fortunately caught in time. In 1946, my father had sent a resume of the events of his wartime experiences to *The Times* and other British journals to take his story but was rejected by them all. The editors considered his story as unbelievable. His 'short note' published in *Nature* magazine, however, 'struck some chords but the time was unripe for the truth', he wrote in *The Marquis*.

Something fired him to write *The Marquis* and I guess that those newspaper rejections were contributory, but I have a feeling that by the age of 74 or 75, he was tired of the sniping and decided the time had come to tell all, not as an article but in a book. Publication was after the passing of Tanakadate, Birtwistle and the Marquis.

I was struck by the content of the book. There are many inaccuracies and I conclude that my father was careful not to be too controversial in his recounting of the horrors of occupation because he didn't want to offend the Japanese who had by the time of its publication honoured him. The material was carefully selected to tell the story of his achievements and those of the Japanese men of science. The omission of Japanese atrocities like the massacre at Ulu Tiram was what infuriated the POWs and contributed to the criticism of my father after the war. There was also no mention of the risks Holttum took to help those interned in Changi Camp, for instance, by delivering letters which husbands and wives wrote to each other as he visited the internees. No wonder the Holttum family considered his book very one-sided, indeed incomplete in balance. I share that opinion.

I was also surprised at the order in which my father presented his book. It clearly had not commanded the attention to detail of presentation that such an author should find natural. It suggests to me that he found it difficult to present his story, was still uncertain of it, and the publisher released it much as it was written. Still, it does tell of the war experiences of an extraordinary man.

My father had given a copy of his manuscript to Mikiko Ishii and allowed her to write a Japanese version based on it for the Japanese reader.

She also wrote a children's book about friendship between enemies in wartime. Both books were published by distinguished publishing companies in Japan, the memoir under the name of my father with Ishii as translator. The children's book was credited solely to Ishii.

Ishii's version of *The Marquis* kept as closely as possible to my father's story and script but was restricted by space. According to Professor Togawa, Mikiko Ishii was 'uncertain whether she should include the Corner-Shinozaki affair and she sought Dr Haneda's opinion'. He replied saying:

> I met Shinozaki for the first time at Jurong Internment Camp in September 1945 [this was when the British had returned to Singapore and Haneda, with the other Japanese scientists, were interned]. I don't think Mr Shinozaki had an ill feeling toward Dr Corner. There was to other way [no other way] to act that way as part of his official duty. In the war time everyone was insane. Because the Japanese version is the translation of Dr Corner's book, the original text should be faithfully recorded. It is wise to narrate the incident with modesty rather than omitting entirely. I am sure Dr Corner and Mr Shinozaki will develop friendly relations.

The response to both books in Japan was sensational with many favourable reviews. Readers were all surprised, almost beyond belief, by the unusual friendship between enemies during the war. In Professor Ishii's assessment, 'The book gave a great encouragement to the people what to do, how to behave as a person in the time of crisis.' Twenty thousand copies of the memoir was quickly sold out.

In contrast, not many copies of Heinemann Asia's publication of *The Marquis* were sold. I don't think any serious marketing was done by the publisher, and I further learnt that Heinemann gave many unsold copies to my father which he gave away to friends and acquaintances. Whilst it can be read today in some libraries, the book is little known and copies are extremely hard to come by.

My father complained that 'Heinemann are rotten publishers', adding that the English edition had been a flop, and the book was on sale in England only at Heffers bookshop in Cambridge. He noted that the Japanese version 'has sold well'. Rather ruefully, my father remarked that 'it is the only book to show that there were decent Japanese in 1942–1945'. He reported that the reviews were mostly hostile and that 'had I written a book of endless horror, it would have been successful'.

By the time my father reached his later years, I think he realised that I had probably not read his book and this was why he put a copy into Pandora. He was right. I had not only not read it, I had not even heard of it. My father wanted me to know about his time in Singapore during the Occupation. I am pleased that he did because it inspired me to this opportunity to bring his story to a wider audience, which my father deserves.

Another person who had not read the book was Dr Jeremy Smith from Australia. My father had been his Botany Part II supervisor. He asked his brother Dr Tim Bayliss-Smith if he could find him a copy and Tim made enquiries in Heffers, the Cambridge bookshop, and discovered that it was out of print.

Tim telephoned my father, explained the problem, and my father said he would give Tim a copy. A visit was arranged and Tim drove out to Hinton Way.

Your father was watching Japanese sumo-wrestling* on television, and seemed completely engrossed. He asked me to wait until the end of the fight. After that he could not have been more charming, and gave me a copy from a large pile of the books which he had bought from the publisher when it was 'remaindered'. Emboldened, I asked if I could have another copy for myself, and he said yes, of course. We reminisced a little about my old college, Sidney Sussex.

The house seemed to be full of botanical work in progress – dried specimens everywhere, books and papers, the usual academic disorder. I seem to remember your father complaining about failing eyesight.

This was in the early 1990s and gives a snapshot of my father in his last years†.

---

* In the Royal Society Memoir of Emperor Hirohito my father wrote: 'anxious to learn more about the late Emperor's interest in sumo, my enquiries were rewarded by a photograph of the Emperor's Cup, given to me by the Japan Sumo Association through the hands of the Chamberlain Mr Naoru Tanaka'.

† Dr David Hawksworth, a British mycologist and lichenologist also recalled his visit to my father at his Great Shelford house on 26 January 1992: 'We met in a rather dimly lit room, and I remember red banners or signs with Japanese script, and many fading black-and-white photographs including Japanese soldiers. We had an immensely stimulating discussion, and despite him having made clear when the meeting was arranged that he would not have much time, he insisted that I stay and eat with them. His second wife Helga was there and prepared the meal – fried eggs, white bread, and tea. I do not know if that was a regular part of the diet, but if so might help explain why he seemed rather slim!'

XXVIII

REVISITING WAYSIDE TREES

During my research, I invited stories about my father to learn more about his complicated character, his successes and failures.

My father relied on a small coterie of friends, many of them distinguished in their fields, and was considered to be very right-wing but few indeed were able to discuss politics with him. "I never discuss politics," he frequently said. I think this was the politician's 'No' for I heard many times his outbursts about political people he thought were 'not doing good'.

My father certainly appeared to some to be something of a snob and this showed when he fell out with Dransfield over accommodation in Bogor. Whilst investigating this, I learned that he did have a high opinion of himself and gave the impression that he was above most of his colleagues; his intellect was greater and this shone out in *The Marquis* where he gave little or no recognition to his boss, Eric Holttum, which so deeply disappointed, indeed, much annoyed – infuriated – Holttum and his family.

His criticism and impatience with people who fell below his mark extended beyond scientific matters to routine work. Ho Coy Choke's story from the 1980s when my father was Visiting Professor of the University of Agriculture, Serdang, to prepare the third edition of *Wayside Trees of Malaya* illustrates this. On one visit to my father's flat, Ho found my father, with a wet face towel around his neck to keep cool, typing the revisions himself on an old manual typewriter. The university typist made too many mistakes.

Dr Quentin Cronk was another who responded to my invitation for stories. He was educated in botany at Cambridge University and knew my father.

[H]e came to my farewell dinner at Cambridge and said generous things (he could support tenaciously those he liked as well as be a formidable enemy to those he didn't). I think one of the main reasons I got on well with him was that I always made a point of devoting a polite degree of attention to his [second] wife Helga, who in old age was often incoherent and awkward to talk to (perhaps the forerunner of the dementia, I am told that later became full blown). Many other people merely ignored Helga, finding her too difficult to talk to, which EJHC thought dismissive and unkind (which it probably was). Actually, if one was prepared to take the trouble, Helga was full of interesting stories.*

Yes, Helga was always difficult to understand, from her arrival in the household in March 1949. It wasn't the dementia then, but there were many occasions, very many, when I had to 'translate' for friends and visitors to our house. I don't think she ever learned English, just picked some up as time went by. It was often embarrassing and I struggled to understand her rapid delivery of gobbledegook English.

Cronk said he once discussed family holidays with my father as Cronk had young children at the time and holidays seemed difficult to organise. My father mentioned that

when he had a young family he would start a holiday… by driving as far from Cambridge as possible, well into the night, and when he got tired he would pull into a lay-by, recline the seats and the whole family would sleep in the car, saving time and the expense of a hotel. I remembered this as I thought it was an interesting (if somewhat single-minded) approach.

I do remember that journey to the West Country when we 'holed up' not in the car but on blankets under the dripping trees of Savernake Forest in Wiltshire on the way to North Devon, Hartland Point!

In late November, my father wrote to Robin and Priscilla Hill from Tokyo saying that he and Helga had spent almost six weeks in Japan:

On 18th November I was granted an informal interview with the Emperor in his Biological Laboratory, hidden away among trees behind his official Palace. It was [scheduled] for 30 minutes but the Emperor was so intrigued he forgot it was 40 minutes which (I was told) was entirely exceptional.

---

* Quentin told me this wartime story recounted by Helga: 'She had quite a time of it as a girl in occupied wartime Jutland. As communications were difficult at that time she would deliver messages by bicycle, including to people in the Danish Resistance Movement – dangerous work. She told me about one close call when she and a friend were out cycling on one of their "deliveries" and nearly ran into a German military convoy. They threw their bicycles into the bushes at the side of the road and hid in the undergrowth for several hours until the coast was clear.'

My father gave details of this meeting in his *Biographical Memoirs for the Royal Society* on Emperor Hirohito:

> I was asked to explain the Durian Theory. I spoke about the long discussions I had on the subject with Professor Kwan Koriba and His Majesty became so interested in how enemies had managed to cooperate in wartime that our heads came too close across the narrow table and I had discreetly to withdraw. I described the noticeboard at the entrance to the Tokugawa Forest at Kiso which, after many injunctions, ended with the request 'And please talk to the trees'; His Majesty smiled.

Although my father wrote in an arcing one-liner – 'Of the British Embassy we have heard nothing, but understand it exists!' – he was told rather directly by the embassy that his visit was 'unofficial' whereas that of the President of the Royal Society, due shortly, was official and arranged by the embassy. 'So I shut up' my father recorded, although he did give the Emperor greetings from the Royal Society and Linnean Society 'which no one told me to, but I thought correct – and he was so pleased'. My father said that his informal audience 'was one great privilege, seldom granted to foreigners', and he was taken around the Imperial Biological Laboratory 'which so few foreigners have seen'. The Emperor's last words to my father as they shook hands were, 'I hope you will continue to promote Anglo-Japanese friendship'.

My father finally had to give up microscope work in 1983. It must have been really hard for him for even at age 77 he was far from retirement. Indeed, I don't think such a thing ever occurred to him. His inspiration was to drive himself to the end to bring science to the masses. He felt that if the young were inspired to nature they would show greater interest in conservation.

On 15 November 1985, he became the first recipient of the International Prize for Biology presented in Tokyo by the Crown Prince of Japan. The prize was established that year in commemoration of Emperor Showa's years of research in biology and his 60-year reign, with the intention of encouraging biological research around the world. The bestowal was an award of 10 million yen (around £35,000 in 1985), a medal embossed with an abstract design of the clathrozonid hydroid *Pseudoclathrozoon cryptolarioides*, and a silver vase embossed with the imperial chrysanthemum crest in gold. After the ceremony, my father was invited to a family dinner at the palace of the Crown Prince.

Professor Mikiko Ishii gave me the background of the award:

> As for the International Prize for Biology, I got a call from one of the members [committee]. He told me that they were thinking to nominate

Prof. Corner as the very first candidate. They highly appreciated your father's academic achievements but also your father's friendship and cooperation with the Japanese scientists during the war, keeping the Museum as it had been… Officially, your father was awarded the prize on his scientific achievements, but to get the very first one, behind the curtain, it involved Japanese government's appreciation for his activity during the war.

I think this was certainly just reward. His one-on-one informal meeting with the Emperor no doubt was reward too, and that was high honour indeed. Reward or not, my father was grateful for being recognised. Veronica Appleby, the daughter of Dudley Appleby, my father's old Rugby school friend, found a copy of my father's address of thanks from the award ceremony in her mother's copy of *Life of Plants*. My father wrote: 'The award of prizes ranges from incentives to the young to recognition of the services of the old. It is my category and I can say in words of my faith "Lord, now let'st thou thy servant depart in peace"'.

My father was honoured by the Japanese a second time in 1985 with the presentation of the Golden Key to the City of Yokohama. Mikiko Ishii, who accompanied him on the trip, did much of the planning and she told me that my father was scheduled to speak about his experience in Singapore. On the day, he caught a cold and was taken to hospital (he was 79). As invitations had gone out and the audience was to be considerable, cancellation was not a possibility. Ishii presented the speech on my father's behalf, without notes, and it took about an hour and a half to deliver.

My father was medically insured but not Helga who stayed in hospital with him. So he was expected to pay for the sheets she used and other costs. My father was furious. How could a hospital have the gall to charge him for his wife's expenses, even if she was uninsured? Ishii acted as mediator and persuaded the hospital not to ask for payment. She sorted it all out and remarked that 'I had a hectic time in Yokohama!' I bet she did.

My father made his last visit to Japan in 1989. This was to prepare the Royal Society Memoir of Emperor Hirohito. When it became known that the Emperor was gravely ill, my father was moved to write to the Crown Prince and Princess to suggest that 'someone should consider presenting to the scientific world the biological side of the Emperor's life'. He felt that although such material was beginning to appear in Japan, 'the West was still largely in ignorance or uncertainty'. That year, my father also spent a week in New Caledonia to study the unusual number of trees there which had accord with his Durian Theory. The year 1989 was also the first that he was listed in *Who's Who*. Interestingly, his first wife is not mentioned in the entry, only his second wife.

*

A third edition of *Wayside Trees of Malaya* was published in 1988 by the Malayan Nature Society. It almost did not happen because of a quirk arising from the disintegration of the British Empire and my father's stubbornness.

When my wife and I visited Singapore in June 2007, we met Dato' Henry Barlow, Honorary Treasurer of the Malaysian Branch of the Royal Asiatic Society and the Malaysian Nature Society. He had written to me about his meetings with my father and which included the following detailed account of the issues which almost scuttled the planned third edition of *Wayside Trees of Malaya*.

The second time our paths crossed was about 15 years later – I suppose about 1980, in connection with new editions of his *Wayside Trees of Malaya*. Unbeknown to me, Universiti Kebangsaan Malaysia (UKM – The National University of Malaysia) decided that it would be desirable to invite your parents [father and second wife] out to Malaysia for about six months to enable him to travel the country and write a new edition of his book…. So UKM provided car and driver, and accommodation at the University rest house for some six months, at the end of which a new draft was ready, and was indeed sent to the printers for proofing.

There then arose a problem of copyright. The first edition had been written in the 1930s when your father was a colonial officer in Singapore, the second edition in the early '50s, when he was no longer a colonial officer. Meantime, Malaysia and Singapore had parted company politically in 1965. There were thus three candidates with, in theory, a claim to part of the copyright: Malaysia, Singapore, and whatever Whitehall office dealt with such 'residue of empire'.

Whitehall was consulted, and wisely washed its hands of the whole affair, saying they wanted no part of the action. Let Malaysia and Singapore work it out between them. Malaysia and Singapore discussed, and came to the sensible conclusion that Singapore would waive all rights (having virtually no forest by then) in exchange for 50 free sets of the new edition, to be supplied to them by UKM on publication. UKM then not unreasonably advised your father of the upshot. However, your father disagreed most vehemently. There was never, he asserted, any question of Singapore having any claim on even part of the copyright. (I never heard his reasons for this assertion). Moreover, he would demand his royalties on the 50 sets to be given to Singapore – this could not possibly have been more than £200. He rushed to his lawyers and ran up some £700-800 in legal fees. UKM did the same, and I was told clocked up five to ten times as much. The first proofs were locked away in the UKM safe, and deadlock ensued, for some eight to ten years! Successive

British High Commissioners to Kuala Lumpur were invoked, to try to resolve the deadlock, to no avail.

As the early 1980s proceeded, your father realised that unless the deadlock was resolved, there was little chance of his seeing the third edition in his lifetime. Meantime, I had become aware of the situation, and as Hon. Treasurer of the Malaysian Nature Society (your father had been a founder member in the 1930s), with responsibility for the Society's publications, was watching the position with interest.

Dato' Salleh Mohd Nor, a good friend of mine, was President and close to the increasingly frustrated UKM authorities… How to provide a ladder down which your father could climb professional dignity intact?

So I suggested to Dato' Salleh that he should offer to the UKM authorities, and your father, that MNS would take over publication, to be paid for by UKM. And so it turned out, the responsibility for seeing the book through the press falling to me. I am no botanist, so I managed to contract out the technical editing to Dr Chang Kiaw Lan of Singapore, now deceased, one of your father's former pupils. She was under strict instructions not to communicate with your father till the very last moment, when all but the most difficult queries had been resolved, lest there be a replay of the UKM saga.

This indeed was how things turned out satisfactorily, and the book has proved to be one of the Society's most successful publications. At the end of the exercise I received a nice letter from your father, thanking me for my pains, but adding some rather critical remarks about the legal profession!

The late Roderick MacLean, MCS, OBE, went to Malaya in 1950 and held many important posts in government service before becoming Director of the Singapore International Chamber of Commerce. He told Audrey McCormick, who visited him in hospital on my behalf in December 2001, about his role in the publication of the third edition of *Wayside Trees*.

Malaya wanted to reproduce it, but Singapore claimed that as Corner was a government servant, they were the ones who held the copyright. I had to intervene, on the grounds that we in Singapore owed a considerable debt to Corner because he saved the collection in Raffles Museum from being sent to Japan, and probably being sunk en route or otherwise dispersed. I therefore approached the Singapore Minister in charge of the Govt Printer and pointed out that Singapore owed a moral debt to your father.

In due course, the moral justice of this was acknowledged in Singapore and Corner's book was allowed to be published in Malaya and the Singapore claim to copyright was completely withdrawn.

When the third edition was released, it was discovered that the cover picture for Volume 1 was captioned with the wrong name, *Alstonia angustifolia*, instead of *Alstonia angustiloba*. Chang Kiaw Lan wrote a personal note to my father to explain the mistake and a magnanimous professor replied:

I never supposed the mistake… was your doing… perhaps the photographer made the mistake. Anyhow, it is a battered old tree that has lost its top and not a picture that I would have chosen. However, old trees must not be scorned… I have always been proud of the book and Ed. 3 is your gift and more to SE Asia.

In 2007, Mikiko Ishii sent me two audio tapes from my father's 1983 trans-Japan visit which she said neither she nor my father had listened to. The transcript to follow, in which my father recounts the thinking behind the initial writing of *Wayside Trees*, is from his illustrated after-dinner speech in Tokyo. His guests included some of his Japanese scientific friends from the Occupation days, and Yoshitomo, the son of the Marquis Yoshichika Tokugawa, and I note that my father spoke in simple English.

This book on the wayside trees in Malaya was written by me in 1940. It took me many years to write and to get these photographs. I took nearly all these photographs myself; I developed them myself and I printed them myself and the blocks were made in London. I still think they are some of the best photographs which have been taken to illustrate trees.

I decided to write it because I wanted to give the people of Malaya a way of taking an interest in their countryside. In the old days in Malaya, and to some extent now, roads went through the forests and there were big forest trees by the wayside and nobody knew their names. There were big forest trees in the villages and nobody knew their names, except the Malays. So I had to collect all the Malay names and make some English names for them and then the Latin names.

The book is illustrated on the outside with a monkey on a branch of a tree, because the helper I had to collect the specimens from the trees was one of these pigtail monkeys with one of those little tails and this shows him standing on the branch of the tree. He has pulled off a twig which is falling down here, and here is the rope collar round his neck, and I am standing somewhere at the bottom around here, and he would get the botanical specimens for me… Mind you, I learned this all from the Malay villages.

Now in my copy of this book in England, on the back page, I have pasted a note which I received from the British Governor, Sir Shenton Thomas, which thanked me for giving so much pleasure to so many people in Malaya.

Later in his speech, my father claims that the book was also well received and known by the Japanese of Syonan-to:

> The second volume is all pictures which gives an idea of the countryside of Malaya. Many Japanese who came to Malaya and Singapore could not read much English, but they could see the pictures and read the names and see where they were. So this was of great interest to others. In fact, Professor Tanakadate used to say to me that after General Yamashita your name is better known to Japanese than anyone else in Malaya. Well, of course I knew he was only making a joke out of that.
>
> The second point is this book identified me as the author of something that was scientific and was not political. I never was political and never am political, but the countryside and the ways of nature and scientific research have been my interest all my life, so I was identified fortunately as a scientist and I was always introduced, even by Marquis Yoshichika Tokugawa, as the author of *Wayside Trees of Malaya* and that suited me quite enough.

In the same speech, my father tells a good story about the book and its 'little adventure' to Tokyo.

> Well, Professor Tanakadate returned to Tokyo from Singapore in June 1942 and he took amongst other things a new copy of this book on wayside trees which we had found in the government printing office in Singapore, and the object of it was he said he would present this to the Emperor of Japan. He also took a number of photos that I had of Singapore and Malaya, as good copies as I could get to present to the Emperor. Now, when Professor Tanakadate came back from Japan, we went to the director's room upstairs at the Raffles Museum in Singapore and he talked about his journey and his travels and the difficulties, and many ways and things in Japan. Then all of a sudden he got up, he turned very red and with a sweep of his hand he said, "Stand up", like this. So I stood up and he said to me, "His Imperial Highness, the Emperor of Japan, wishes me to thank you for the book on wayside trees of Malaya. It is the only book he has ever read in bed. Sit down." So I sat down very astonished at this brief announcement, which I have every reason to suppose is true and had not been invented because Professor Tanakadate was quite good at inventing some stories, but I don't think this one.

My enquiries have revealed a variation of this story and it seems it is not clear whether it was Professor Tanakadate who took the book to Tokyo, or Marquis Yoshichika Tokugawa. Professor Yoji Akashi of Nanzan University, Nagoya, told me that my father did have doubt as to whether Tanakadate told the truth or embellished the story. He wrote to me in 2009 and I quote, retaining his Japanese style:

> There is no way of ascertaining who, Tanakadate or Tokugawa present-ed *Wayside Trees of Malaya* to the Emperor. Tanakadate was known to be bluffing and show off himself. Tokugawa noted Tanakadate's charac-ter, describing that he took credit for everything that was accomplished. None of the scientists [Japanese] trusted him (*Tokugawa Yoshichika, Saigo no Tonosama, The Last Lord of the Owari Tokugawa*, Kodansha 1993 pp 186-189).

However, there is no doubt that a copy of *Wayside Trees of Malaya* was given to the Emperor – and he kept it in his bedroom. My father's address at that Tokyo dinner confirmed it:

> Well, years afterwards I came to the Pacific Science Congress in Tokyo in 1966. I was a representative of the delegation from the Royal Society of London and in due course all the delegates were presented to the Em-peror and Empress in the Imperial Palace in Tokyo, and we all walked by quietly in single file. We all shook hands with the Emperor and I think the Empress. But of course it was an official formal reception and very little notice was taken of anyone. I wished to have a few words if possible, especially with the Empress who seemed, I think, a very cheer-ful person, but we were pushed on and there was no opportunity to say anything. But I did inquire from a Chief Minister and he told me, 'Yes it is true that the Emperor had kept this book on a table by his bed'. Well, we got as far as that.

Dr Ruth Kiew, my father's penultimate PhD student, wrote one of the best hands-on praise for *Wayside Trees of Malaya* in the *Flora Malesiana Bulletin.* She refers to the book as remarkable

> because it is not only packed with accurate, original, and interesting observations but they are recounted in a vivid style that captures the in-terest of the amateur and professional naturalist alike. Many times have I been impressed, on comparing a living specimen with a description in *Wayside Trees,* at how accurately Corner has caught the idiosyncrasies of the plant. It is as though he made his description from the plant I hold in my hand! One that has stuck is the Midnight Horror (*Oroxy-lum indicum*), which he describes as follows: 'This grotesque tree fills us with astonishment…aesthetically, it is monstrous. The corolla begins to open about 10 pm, when the tumid, wrinkled lips part and the harsh odour escapes from them. By midnight, the lurid mouth gapes widely

as if filled with stink'. He told me he coined the name after staying at a rest house [in Malaya] where he was unable to sleep because of the terrible stench, which when he got up to investigate discovered was caused by this night-flowering tree, which grew just behind the rest house.

Not only did his vivid and lucid style set him apart, but also his characteristic line drawings. He always prepared his own illustrations as he believed that it required accurate observation and that, in addition, illustrations clearly show important features where a photograph in comparison can be just a mindless representation. He was therefore extremely annoyed when a reviewer criticised an illustration in his *Natural History of Palms* (Corner, 1966), as incorrect, when, as he indignantly said, it had been drawn from life. However, he was vindicated later when field observations in India proved him right.

I too have discovered the great value of *Wayside Trees of Malaya*, for the book helped me with deciphering the scientific names hand-written by my father. Talking of illegible handwriting, I recall that Sir David Attenborough once mentioned my father and his use of monkeys to collect from the jungle canopy in a talk on BBC Radio 4. Indeed, he suggested that the book *Wayside Trees* was compiled by a monkey! My father would have much enjoyed that.

Once, when Belinda and I passed a second-hand bookshopin Australia, in country New South Wales, we went in and I asked the owner if he had any books by E. J. H. Corner. He checked his computer which told him no, but he did have a request for a copy of *Wayside Trees of Malaya*.

I have since bought three copies of my father's famous work so that I can bequeath a set to son Andy and daughter Katie. The Corner family should always have a set prominent in the bookcase for all to see.

XXIX

OUT OF THE CORNER

Sadly, despite my father's standing and the respect he commanded as a scientist, and his sustained contribution to the vital importance of tropical botany, the subject ceased immediately in Cambridge on his retirement – indeed, in the choice word of Mabberley, it 'withered' – and the rich resources my father built were left unused. It is sad that the enormous experience, enthusiasm, research and teaching of this unique man have not been continued. I wonder if his hands-on approach to tropical botany can ever again be matched, not only because it demands the commitment and talent of my father's level, but also so many of the forests have gone, and more continue to go at a rapid rate.

My father considered his greatest botanical mentor to be A. H. Church. In his 'Recollection' in *Revolutionary Botany: 'Thalassiophyta' and Other Essays by A. H. Church*, he wrote:

> *Thalassiophyta* prompted the work on discomycetes; it led to *Clavaria* as the most seaweed-like of basidiomycetes, and to *Thelephora* as the clavarioid which reveals the deterioration into the bracket and resupinate form, not primitive as so often held. *Clavulina cartilaginea* and *C. gigartinoides* in the dense forest of Pahang, *Thelephora borneensis*, and *Paraphelaria* of the Solomon Islands have reminded me on distant occasions of the one who taught me botany.

He also considered as mentors C. E. Carter and Kwan Koriba during the occupation of Singapore, and eventually, as stated in his Royal Society notes, Emperor Hirohito of Japan. He valued greatly his research students and placed importance on their work, although he never built a research group.

Others of strong influence on my father were Humphrey Gilbert-Carter of the Botanic Gardens in Cambridge, Robin Hill, and Julian Huxley about whom my father wrote, 'If an ember still glows in UNESCO it is his vivacity'. Barton Worthington certainly was one of my father's closest friends and I had thought that to be life-long. Yet, there was a falling-out in the late 1960s after Worthington had criticised my younger sister who then was modelling. If that friendship was lost I have to be amazed, and it tells something of the man my father was. I note that Worthington did attend my father's funeral.

My father never really retired. He extended the back of his house with something like a conservatory and this became his study from where he gazed on his beloved garden. He continued to 'strum' on his piano which I remember being there when we moved into Hinton Way in 1949. He insisted I learned the piano, which I did or tried to when away at school, but I gave it up around 1953. My father was not happy and told me I would regret it in later life. He was right.

I remember quite a lot about that Hinton Way house: bittersweet memories but there had been some good times, although not many. We took morning coffee on the swing-seat in the side garden, accessed from the dining room, which became his office, where Cromwell hung and the damning of politicians mostly took place. There, in a cabinet, he kept his Madeira that I used to sample and liked! My bedroom was immediately above. The croquet played on the grass tennis court, always most competitive with 'local' rules. Helga was an able cook particularly with the simple food.

I learned to appreciate and enjoy classical music thanks to my father's encouragement and the gramophone given to him by his mother around the early 1950s. I was limited in listening time by Helga because, as she frequently said, 'electricity was expensive'. However, I grew to appreciate and enjoy the music of Beethoven particularly, as Grannie Corner remarked long ago.

Professor Jim Ginns, who was introduced to me by Roy Watling, wrote to me in 2007 with an observant description of the Hinton Way garden. Ginns had been awarded a sabbatical year and moved from his position as research mycologist with the Canadian National Mycological Herbarium, Ottawa, to the herbarium at the Royal Botanic Gardens, Kew. He was invited to Cambridge by my father who showed him and his wife, Anne, some of Cambridge before taking them to Hinton Way. Of Cambridge, Jim wrote that, 'it gives one the feeling that great accomplishments are possible here. But as Corner pointed out all one really needs is a small work space and a few books…!' Ginns continued:

Turning off Great Hinton Way into the Corner residence, I had the feeling of entering a tropical rain forest/jungle. The lane is in deep shade due to overhanging boughs of plants unfamiliar to a Canadian; all view of the road is obscured by trees and huge shrubs (much to the pleasure of the Corners). They recently (2 years ago) purchased the other half of the double – primarily to prevent others from buying the one acre and putting in additional houses. Now the Corner estate is two acres with much vegetable garden space. Eighteen apple, plum, pear and cherry trees (some nearly dead of old age); during a garden tour he offered me a ripe fig which I enjoyed as it was the first I ever had fresh (being used to the dried or canned figs). Knowing little about figs I made no comment on the plant and that was fortuitous as I later learned that Corner was an authority on the genus *Ficus*. I must admit that at the time of our visit, I knew little of his studies of green plants and was familiar with only some of his work on the fungi.

My father gardened until he could no longer see well enough to avoid damage both to the garden and himself.

*

Towards the end of 1995, in my father's 89th year, Professor Ishii visited him at his home. He was waiting for her 'together with souvenirs he had brought back from Singapore at the end of the war'. She observed that his tall frame was as upright as that of a younger man.

He unwrapped 'large strips of paper on which the words *Shonanto Hakubutsukan* (Shonanto Museum) and *Shonanto Shokubutsuen* (Shonanto Botanical Gardens) had been inscribed boldly in Japanese characters, handwritten in brush and ink'. My father also had 'a sheaf of brand new "Banana banknotes"...as well as a booklet entitled *Shokuyo Yasei Doshokubutsu* (Edible Wild Animals & Plants) which had been compiled under the orders of the Japanese army [by] British scholars of the museum and botanical gardens who conducted joint research'. My father had kept these 'artefacts of Shonanto' which the Japanese military government had attempted to destroy when they were defeated. He told Ishii that at some time he would donate these artefacts to the War Museum in London. I checked in March 2013 and he did not, although that's where they should be – as should the Yamashita map from the Istana Tower.

That year, a documentary film was made and broadcast across Japan called *Do You Know Shonanto**. Produced by Hachiro Ikeda, it took Japan Channel 7 TV Asahi over a year to make. It tells the story of the Japanese taking of Malaya and Singapore, from the Japanese perspective of course, and it includes something of my father, Eric Holttum, William Birtwistle, and features Japanese war photography. This was why Ishii visited – to assist and translate where necessary for the filmmakers.

Robin Miller, a retired freelance writer for radio, television and theatre was also planning a film about the Japanese and Singapore during the Occupation.

* *Shonanto is the phonetic pronunciation of Syonan-to, the Japanese name for Singapore. It roughly translates 'Light of the South'.*

My involvement with the Singapore story began when I spotted a tiny item about it in the *Times* here, many years ago*…. I ploughed away on and off, gradually assembling a few details, then more until the basis of an extraordinary story began to emerge. I saw it as a British-Japanese co-production TV drama or dramatised documentary, believing the Japanese would surely be interested since it was the only creative story I knew about in the whole horrendously cruel catalogue of Japanese occupation.

Viscount Hugh Trenchard, who worked in Japan in the financial sector, heard about the project and was very keen for it to succeed. He introduced Miller to 'the redoubtable' Professor Ishii who was confident that she could get Miller into the Imperial archives where surely a full account of the Emperor's involvement would be housed.

Miller wrote to my father who sent him a copy of *The Marquis*. They spoke once on the phone and he considered that my father might be difficult to deal with – 'either obstructive or insistent on being involved'. When he first contacted my father in 1987, my father 'was very cranky… bitter about the lack of success of the book and horrible about Professor Holttum who he clearly hated'.

Miller also approached Holttum (then stone deaf) who said he would help 'provided I don't have to work with Corner'.

Of course, for a dramatist, the situation between your father and Prof. H is full of tension and suspense but it must be v. painful for you. I worked as hard as I could, getting treatments and outlines to producers here and in Japan where the Hollywood mentality prevailed – 'where's the girl?' I realised I could not dig out the details unless I went to Japan, got a translator, got into the Archives, met the son (or grandson) of the Marquis, and in short spent a lot of time there and a lot of money on the necessary research which I just don't have. It was so frustrating because I do believe Mrs Ishii could have opened all the right doors.

"Where's the girl?" the producers had asked. Miller didn't know anything of my mother then. There's the girl. What a girl and what a story. The middle of the story, which Miller also couldn't know, is the breakdown of my parents' marriage and the effect it had on us all: a real family drama not to mention the 'oryx'.

**What Robin Miller read was a paragraph in the middle of an article under Tourism Singapore from* The Times, *14 September 1981: 'The horticultural gardens not far from the tourist area of Orchard Road are equally valuable. One of the few happy stories from the Second World War in Singapore, the gardens were tended throughout by one Japanese and one English professor'.*

In fact, Miller had asked my mother for an interview. I know my mother gave this deep thought but declined. Miller sent a long fax to Mikiko Ishii and on this matter.

> Unfortunately (if understandably) the first Mrs Corner has declined to be interviewed. The end of her marriage to Prof Corner was so unhappy that she cannot bear to awaken memories… I do know that she left Singapore with her baby son in her arms before the Occupation. She has not seen *The Marquis*.

In my various exchanges with Miller, he added to the reasons why my father and Holttum could not get along. He cited my father's intolerance of anyone who disagreed with him, and continued,

> [M]y personal opinion is that Prof. Holttum and he were two totally different men. Yes, the Quaker mentality (which I much admire) might have maddened him if he was of a different faith or none; smoking another annoyance for Prof. H no doubt.

Unfortunately, due to ill health, Miller never finished the project. However, I have been the beneficiary of his research. On Mikiko Ishii's suggestion, I obtained all the material she had sent to Miller. This mountain of documents was in Miller's loft and he had no way of reaching it with his rheumatoid condition. Deborah Holttum came to the rescue and spent two visits scrambling in his attic and sending me as much material as she could find!

*

My father was a member of the American Mycological Society, British Mycological Society, French Mycological Society and the Czechoslovak Scientific Society for Mycology. He became a Fellow of the American Association for the Advancement of Science and was a Member of the Botanical Society of America, the Royal Netherlands Botanical Society and became an Honorary Member of the Japanese Mycological Society. In 1958, he was the Royal Society's delegate to the Darwin-Wallace Centenary in Singapore travelling in Indonesia, Malaysia and across India.

His bestowals include the Darwin Medal of the Royal Society (1960), Patron's Medal of the Royal Geographic Society (1966), the Gold Medal of the Linnean Society of London (1970), the Victoria Medal of Honour from the Royal Horticultural Society (1974), the Allerton Award from the Pacific Tropical Botanical Garden, Hawaii (1981), the International Prize for Biology from the Japanese Academy of Sciences (1985), and joint winner of the first de Bary Medal of the International Mycological Association (1996). His CBE was awarded in 1972.

His medals are lodged in Cambridge at the Fitzwilliam Museum. These awards and recognitions speak volumes for the scientific ability of a special scientist. Wendy How, my father's housekeeper in his last years, was with him early in 1996 when he was sorting them out. She wrote to me about what had transpired in her inimitable style: 'his meddles they were in a safe in the kitchen. Prof had lost the key so I got a blacksmith to get it open for him. I layed them all out on the table so he could say ware they should go to. I rang his friend from the collage to come and sort them out for him and take them to Fitzwilliam'.

My father willed his expedition diaries and their accompanying material, including drawings, photographs and pamphlets, to the Royal Geographical Society, but none of these is in the Society's collection. Some type specimens are in the Cambridge University herbarium at the Department of Plant Sciences (the Botany School), and others are in the National Fungus Collection, Beltsville, USA. His complete mycological collection, including mycological drawings as well as his mycological library, was to have been received by the Department of Mycology at the American Department of Agriculture, Beltsville, Maryland, but they could not agree to his conditions so the collection went to the Royal Botanic Gardens Edinburgh at Roy Watling's request. Books, 'such as he may wish', my father recorded in his will, were to go to Dr David Mabberley, his final PhD student.

My father bequeathed his plant collections to Oxford University but for some reason they were never received. Watling explained to me that 'with David (Mabberley) then making a number of moves, the few plant specimens destined for Oxford, and the illustrations destined for Canada when David was there, are still in safe keeping in Edinburgh'.

My father's major work, *Flora Malesiana* about the figs of Malesia, was eventually published in two parts in 2006, ten years after his death. The 35-year delay was because he had fallen out with the editor, Dr C. G. G. J. van Steenis, Director of the Flora Malesiana Foundation, who he said 're-arranged the very complicated bibliography of many species to suit his convenience, with which I completely disagreed because it made nonsense.' Dr van Steenis, who my father regarded as a 'staunch friend', later apologised for what he had done, but the books remained unpublished in my father's lifetime. The review of *Flora Malesiana* in the *Edinburgh Journal of Botany* provides some juicy details of this:

A student of Corner's once said that argumentative letters with van Steenis even included derogatory name calling in Malay. The impasse seemed a sort of last colonial standoff in the botany of a region once divided between the Dutch and the British. After Corner's death in 1996 the manuscript that had languished in Leiden was passed to C. C. Berg who revised it so extensively that he became its primary author.

My father's research will no doubt continue to shed light on things botanical as this story from Dr Henry Noltie's book, *Raffles Ark Redrawn, Natural History Drawings from the Collection of Sir Thomas Stamford Raffles*, illuminates:

A retired colleague, who periodically unearths paper 'skeletons' at home, and returns them to the Royal Botanic Gardens, Edinburgh, had deposited some papers in my office. I didn't look at these at the time, but prior to a visit to London to select the drawings for this exhibition, I decided to clear my desk, and what should one of the skeletons prove to be but a foolscap typescript entitled *Paintings of Flowering Plants which Sir Stamford Raffles caused to be made in Bencoolen, Sumatra, March 1824*, written "*for private circulation to scientific institutions concerned with the botany of Malaysia*" by E. J. H. Corner, in 1957.

The timing could not have been more auspicious, for it would reduce the enormous amount of time required if the plants in the drawings had to be identified from scratch; moreover, they were the work of one of the greatest experts on the Malaysian flora. To make the identifications Corner had had to travel to Scotland, by train from Cambridge, as the drawings were then in the possession of Mrs Drake of *Inshriach* near Aviemore.

Dr Tim Whitmore, in the obituary he wrote of my father for *The Independent* a few days after my father's death, acknowledged that

E. J. H. Corner was the last of the titans (H. J. Lam, C. G. C. J. van Steenis, R. E. Holttum, P. W. Richards) who shaped tropical botany in the decades after the Second World War. In a long and colourful career he made significant contributions to the study and interpretation of higher fungi and flowering plants and drew attention to their wonders before television, when the world was a much bigger place than today.

Of his contribution to mycology, Roy Watling said: 'Corner's greatest contribution to world mycology was to draw attention to the vast diversity of fungi particularly the *Macromycetes* in the tropics, especially SE Asia; demonstrate how to study such an exceedingly variable assemblage and provide publications for those on the ground whose formidable inheritance is to study their country's mycodiversity.'

David Mabberley summed up my father's life work: 'His monographic work on *Ficus* and the elaboration of the Durian Theory whilst still in post; his monumental contributions to mycology, largely in retirement, are amongst his greatest achievements.'

Mabberley, in the biographical memoirs of my father for the Royal Society in 1999, made the important point that my father had interests much wider than just mycological; he made an early move from mycology to angiosperms which led him to be a conservationist – and the cause of rainforest conservation permeates his writing as does the importance of study in the tropics.

As a tropical botanist he was unique in performing research on both seed-plants and fungi: his knowledge of botany and its literature was prodigious. Underlying everything, he was a developmental biologist; the study of development, process rather than 'characters', was inculcated by Church. Corner's breakthrough in fungal systematics hinged on the development of the fruiting body. His seed work was ontogenetic; his work on tree-architecture was similarly so. In figs, his greatest alpha-taxonomic group, it was the development of the leaf venation that opened up new insights. His paper *Transference of Function* was published in both the botanical and zoological journals of the Linnean Society (1958); with succeeding work on totipotency, cloning and homoeotic genes, this pioneering work, based on a consideration of a wide variety of plants and leaning in part on the Durian Theory, bears re-reading by today's specialists in developmental biology.

Although a monographer of *Moraceae* and the gigantic genus *Ficus* in particular, Corner kept up interests in all groups of plants, as is witnessed by the range of topics that his research students studied, from Palms to Compositae. Yet he never proposed a new system of angiosperm classification. He believed that all the systems then in use were flawed because of the rank parallelism in angiosperm evolution. However, in *Seeds of Dicotyledons*, he outlined major criticisms of those systems, basing his arguments on seed structure and, later, Dahlgren's system in particular, although less successfully, in a paper (1981) rather more full of rhetoric than science. It has taken the use of sophisticated DNA sequencing techniques to bring order to what is known; it is astonishing to see how much was foreshadowed in Corner's seed work.

Indeed, my father's interests and realm of knowledge exceeded his specialty areas. Ho Coy Choke had described my father's personal research – which involved field collections and detailed descriptions with drawings – on higher plants, *Ficus*, palm and fungi as 'par excellence', and considered my father's choice of *Ficus* 'for deep study' was brilliant. The species include geocarpics, cauliflory and stranglers.

I must add fig wasps to the list to illustrate that he had knowledge much wider than just botany or his particular science. I am finding a man who was enormously inquisitive in diverse directions: expected of a scientist of course but the breadth of my father's inquiring has surprised me.

My father had written an article in the *Biological Journal* in late 1985 on figs and fig wasps, and had corresponded with Professor William Ramirez of the University of Costa Rica and Dr F. Martin Brown of Colorado Springs, USA, about the insect. To Ramirez, he wrote:

> [A] point which seems to have been overlooked is how the fig-insects find their hosts. They cannot detect styles from the outside, and I am sure that they do not recognise the botanical details which distinguish species of *Ficus*. Hence, I conclude that it is by smell of which we know practically nothing... When I grew *F. carica* in Singapore, it attracted several kinds of beetles which had certainly never encountered this species of *Ficus* before, and even I could detect its smell. Unfortunately, this was before I had any detailed knowledge of fig-insects, and I failed to note if any entered the receptacles. And those beetles eventually killed my plants!'

Amongst the papers and letters sent to me in January 2011 by Professor C. C. Berg of the University of Leiden and joint editor of *Flora Malesiana*, there is an extraordinary exchange in April to July 1989 between The Rt Hon J. Enoch Powell (better known as a politician than a professor), my father and Professor I. Galil from Tel Aviv University, Department of Botany, concerning figs. Powell, in examining the variety of meanings of certain Biblical texts and sayings, pointed out that there may have been a loss or change of meaning in the translation from Greek to Hebrew and vice versa. This led Powell to investigate certain sayings in Matthew's gospel about ficus. He was directed by Radcliffe-Smith at Kew to contact my father as an acknowledged expert.

A long and convoluted correspondence followed and, in April 1989, my father wrote to Powell: 'I am growing rusty and problems of the edible fig-tree *Ficus carica* always trouble me because it is so varied and I am not an expert on it'.

By that time, my father was 83, and his last paragraph of the same letter to Powell is intriguing.

> It is strange how, in the course of life, circles close. Here I am trying to answer your problems of Jesus as a botanist. I realised in 1926 when as an undergraduate, I said in a discourse to the Natural Sciences Club at Cambridge, 'Reconsider the lilies of the field! They do toil as they do spin, but with so little ostentation that even He was deceived by His Father's cunning' (perhaps, I should have said 'craft'). Jesus was not a botanist, nor were the writers of the gospels. But, these problems are intriguing as we look far, far back on how people thought and spoke.

I am sure my father enjoyed such intelligent distractions, like the mushroom soup matter. For me, this correspondence highlights the difficulty in aligning botanical knowledge with biblical, of believing in evolution and balancing that with the biblical texts, and reaching explanation for surely there always will be one. My father was a great 'evolutionist', supporting Darwin's theory, but I see in this exchange a serious attention also to the biblical writings. I am pleased to learn of this and to read of his seriousness in this matter.

The Professor of Tropical Botany, with many notable achievements, also shone in occasional amusing moments. I am grateful to those who have contributed for I knew almost nothing of his scientific work and even less that there was a sense of humour lurking beneath that spiky exterior! Oh, that I had found the sense of humour for the spiky exterior was ubiquitous to me!

Shelagh Worthington wrote, 'John was my godfather – not much god about it – but a highly amusing and wonderful person to have around. His brilliance went with a child-like humour and naughtiness'.

Mabberley told me that the Fellows of Sidney Sussex College would be reduced to fits of laughter by my father's after-dinner jokes.

His way of telling an anecdote was inimitable: with head slightly thrown back and index finger prodding the air (and sometimes a disconcerting flick-up of the lenses of a Japanese pair of spectacles he wore, allowing him not to take them off while using a microscope).

Dr David Chivers of the Anatomy School, University of Cambridge, introduced to me electronically in 2010 by Gathorne-Hardy, recalled that 'He was really entertaining – life and soul of the party – every time, having the company in fits at times'.

One of my father's colleagues, Professor David Crompton, said he was 'scintillating company'.

He loved dining in on Wednesday and Friday nights and was wonderfully stimulating after dinner when we gathered in the Senior Combination Room. He sucked happily on his pipe, which had a very small bowl, and captivated us with opinions and stories. The greater the argument, the more he enjoyed himself. I soon learnt that he did not always want to be taken seriously; he wanted everyone in earshot to have a memorable evening. Exaggeration, wit and sarcasm, interspersed with an extensive vocabulary, were the hallmarks of his performances after dinner on Wednesday and Friday, especially on Wednesday when the same group gathered for what became known to some of us as 'Professor Corner's night out'.

Of my father's other personal traits, David Mabberley wrote in the Royal Society Biographical memoir:

John Corner was a man of imposing bearing. He did not suffer fools and could be stubborn or irascible; he fell out spectacularly with some colleagues and even some of his own research students. He could be remarkably formal; all the time that I was his research student (1970-'73) he referred to me as 'Mr Mabberley', even when I arrived, trembling with my latest offering, for his fortnightly meeting about my work. With his back to the door of his room off the herbarium in the Botany School, his body hunched over his old brass microscope, he would be cutting sections of seeds by hand ('To embed in wax, Mr Mabberley, is to embed in obscurity') and would grunt a 'Come in' without turning round.

Clearing his desk, he would start reading my efforts, and then exclaim, 'Yes, that reminds me of this... or that... plant, or that place... or so-and-so's work'. Idea spilled out after idea, insight and revelation; I could not (dared not?) write it down, but left the room enervated, inspired... Corner expected loyalty and generally got it, but those felt to be ungrateful or letting the side down, in being less uncompromising than him, were consigned to outer darkness. He kept up a vast worldwide correspondence, usually writing letters by hand; he was a loyal supporter of those he thought worthy or worth encouraging. He had little time for narrow specialists and especially decried what he saw as retrograde trends in biological teaching and research, notably in North America. The removal of living plants from young people's experience particularly irked him: with fewer and fewer having practical experience from school or being brought up in the country, he would encourage them to get their hands dirty, to grow plants: in his book, gardening was a definite plus for a botanist. He also deplored the use of photography rather than drawing, rightly asserting, 'To draw is to understand'.

Bureaucracy was an anathema to him: in his view it hindered scientific progress. His anti-establishment stance led to his celebrated campaign against the erection of a grand entrance to the University Botanic Garden in Cambridge which was to have incorporated a public lavatory (Clochemerle-sur-Cam) next to the World War I memorial; his impassioned rhetoric prevailed against the University authorities and it was never built.

Mabberley's Biographical memoir shows my father as the scientist that he was, devoted to his work to the exclusion of almost everything else. He was aloof, even arrogant, yet to many most kind and approachable. He was often misunderstood but cared not a jot for that. He had little time for mere mortals of a lower intellect and really should never have been a family man.

To a man, his research students had great respect for him and there is no doubting the eminence to which they all have achieved.

As a lecturer, my father, according to Peter Ashton, was much discussed but rarely seen by the freshmen. However, all the freshmen

of whatever subspecies of biologist, were at once enthralled. His approach to botany and his perspective on nature were novel, often quite startling, and enthralling. Listening to him addressing the evolutionary significance of fruit structure, in which he set the fruit and its tree in vivid context of the jungle life in which it prospered, and illustrated it with his clear and stylish draughtsmanship, was inspiring.

Mabberley agreed, but adding that my father was 'sometimes shy in new company… when his stammer would be more evident. He was a brilliant conversationalist when at ease'.

His lectures, with occasional stammer, were spellbinding, and student visits with him to the Botanic Garden and University Library to see the treasures there were unforgettable; the lectures, like his writing, were original, iconoclastic and highly entertaining. Professor Corner was one of the most colourful biologists of the century.

Professor Bruce Ing had a close encounter with this colourful biologist during his undergraduate days in Cambridge. He recalled a foray to Chippenham Fen, near Newmarket. It was led by my father who pointed out a specimen of *Amanita phalloides* (the death-cap fungus) and asked Ing if he would like to taste it. Ing responded, not being quite as green as the fungus, "after you sir!" Ing told me another tale of my father's wit:

I approached him in my capacity as Secretary of the Cambridge University Natural History Society… to give a general lecture on 'The natural history and evolution of the fig'. Your father replied that the title was not very inviting and, after a few moment's thought, he suggested, 'The fig leaf and what's behind it'. The lecture was brilliant, the hall packed and the evening a great success.

Ing further recalled that my father, when at Sidney Sussex, took a real objection to the idea and the membership of the Pitt Club, essentially the Young Conservatives Club for the rich, chinless wonders, as my father described them. His room at Sidney Sussex overlooked the front door of the Club and he took great delight in using it and the arriving members for target practice with his air rifle! 'The feat endeared him to generations of undergraduates', wrote Ing, 'and demonstrated his impish sense of fun'.

Griselda Worthington, one of Shelagh's sisters, told me of the time when, as an undergraduate, she walked through the college court and found my father banging on a window to attract her attention.

I didn't study Botany so I didn't attend his lectures but… I was a mediocre student and terrified of his intellect (and he could be sarcastic as well). John once took my sister Shelagh and me out to a curry meal* in London. We were semi-grown up so it was probably the early '50s when our parents were still in the Belgian Congo. He let us order unbelievably hot curries and I remember hardly being able to speak, gulping water with sweat pouring down my face and feeling a right idiot.

David Chivers shared another story about my father and his domain:

On entering the cluster of buildings known as the Downing Site the first to be seen is the Botany School (where was the window of EJHC's office). He looked out over a well-kept lawn. One day, builders erected portacabins and he flipped!! He organised opposition and I fully expected him to chain himself to something or go on hunger strike. There is the story of his having broken down the door into the store in the Botany School after the store man had locked the door for his lunch break and refused to open it until he had had his lunch.

Ing remembered passing my father's room in the Botany School when a book flew out of the window! The volume contained a review of a new book by Ron H. Petersen with whom my father aroused heated debate on the subject of the structure of fungus fruit bodies, especially with claveroid and bracket fungi. Their correspondence was frequently published and often vitriolic, and Peterson's just-published book was not complimentary to my father. No doubt his temper fuelled that missile. However, I believe he acted sometimes for effect, and why not!

I know my father's temper and can believe this story. When he lost it, he really lost it, and if I hadn't been sometimes somewhat cowed I might have found some amusement in the tantrums; but I never did!

But some at the Botany School surely did, for on a pillar near the door to his office from where he could survey all, the one from which he spotted Griselda Worthington, and through which window the offending review was launched, some wag had put up a notice: Beware the Dangerous Corner!

After hearing of the disagreements and written arguments (for they

---

* I remember this restaurant – Veeraswamys in Regent Street and still there. It was one of my father's favourite restaurants and he took me just once, sadly long before I learned to enjoy good Indian food!

never met) between my father and Ronald H. Petersen – and intrigued by the Bruce Ing story – I decided to try to find the author who inspired that flying book to discover what happened, and why.

Dr Petersen responded in a most courteous way and confirmed that he never met my father:

> I invited him to speak at a symposium at our university in 1968, but he was otherwise occupied in an expedition. Our second chance came when I was visiting in The Netherlands in 1970. I wrote him as to whether I could visit with him, thinking that perhaps we could "bury the hatchet" eye-to-eye. He wrote back a note saying that he would take no pleasure in meeting someone who so criticised his work. Thus was the long-distance (geographically and personally) relationship perpetuated....
>
> One of my most influential mentors was a mycologist named Marius Anton Donk [a Corner critic], a citizen of The Netherlands, but a resident of 'The Dutch East Indies' (now Indonesia). During WW II, he was imprisoned (separated from his wife, also imprisoned) and tortured by the Japanese. Understandably, he survived the war period loathing the Japanese (he never spoke to a Japanese mycologist again). Again, understandably, he had deep misgivings about your father's relationship with the Japanese occupiers and considered your father's postwar cordiality with Japanese workers suspect... My impression (from Donk and others) was that EJH wrote and illustrated his '*Monograph of Clavaria and allied genera*' while in Singapore. It was finished by war's end (or shortly thereafter) but was not published until 1950. The manuscript (and figures) must have been rather bulky, and the story of its transportation back to UK and subsequent publication must be an interesting saga.

The manuscript of *Clavaria and allied genera* did return to England with my father although I remember him telling me that he lost everything in Singapore and his making quite an issue of telling me about his beloved MG sports car that he never saw again. All the many drawings and photographs contained in the substantial book were done or taken by my father. Petersen went on to say that my father

> took up the clavarioid fungi in about 1964, and one of my first tasks was to take the extant keys and try to extrapolate Corner's concepts. I found it relatively easy to learn his genus concepts which were brilliant and useful, but when I tried to use his species concepts, they fell apart rapidly. It was then I learned that his descriptions of American species were based on memories of Cambridge (and some Kew) specimens and the literature. These shortcomings served as the basis for my first

doubts about his work, and soon thereafter to published questions. At first, he was kind enough to send me some specimens of his own so I could see with my own eyes his descriptions and conclusions, and those specimens were (and are) invaluable. But when I raised doubts about his species concepts he was short-tempered and blasted my conclusions in print. Technically, EJH relied on study of living specimens. Following the accepted Code of Botanical Nomenclature, taxa are based on selected specimens called 'type specimens'. It is the obligation of the monographer to ferret out type specimens or to designate them. EJH had learned the European species 'at the knee' of the authority who described them, but EJH also felt that if a species was confusing (its name had been used in multiple ways), the name should be discarded. My conclusion was that the name should be typified and re-described so that it could assume some rightful place. It was on this divergent philosophy (in print) that our relationship soured.

I learned that one of the big problems between the two was the return by Petersen to my father of the specimen samples mentioned earlier. They arrived in a damaged state and my father was indeed not pleased. I asked Ron Petersen about this incident, and he replied:

I don't remember the incident specifically. Surely, in the opinion of EJH, the specimens had left his hands UNdamaged, and when they arrived back in his hands, they had suffered some level of damage. I can empathise with his anger – all herbaria have such incidents. Now, EJH penned at least one paper attempting to explain why his collections were not (perhaps) up to the standards usually desired by the mycological community. His reasons were absolutely on target – collecting and preservation conditions in the tropics were abysmal, so some of his collections were preserved in spirits and others were mal-dried (but to make up for this, he executed excellent watercolours of many collections). With this as background, he understood the difficult circumstances under which collections were made, and to receive damaged specimens back from loan was understandably aggravating; most of we curators would have sighed and put a mental asterisk next to the organisation returning the specimens (if the damage seemed to emanate from them and not from postal wear and tear). Apparently, EJH reacted with anger – but he doubtlessly already had some negative baggage for me before this incident. This must have been just the latest in (for him) a long list of transgressions.

Ron Petersen told another story which rings true, one which originated from Dr Derek Reid who was a curator of fungi at Kew.

During some earlier time of his life, EJH visited the herbarium at the Royal Botanical Gardens, Kew. There (at that time) the conventional wisdom was that the day began at 9 am and ended at 5 pm (with, of course, due time for morning and afternoon tea and some lunch). Weekend work was forbidden. Corner could not abide by this, but the stout iron fence and gates were closed appropriately so access was prohibited. One Saturday, he was caught trying to scale the fence and promptly banned from further work in the herbarium. Whether this ban persisted I do not know.

My father was certainly not one who was shy of making sure his views were heard and could take 'real objection'. Dr Peter Grubb of the Department of Plant Sciences, told me about his affirmative action to the proposed new gate for the Cambridge University Botanic Garden in 1962.

[T]he Botanic Garden Syndicate drew up a plan for a new gate and a public lavatory nearby. This plan was approved by the Council of the Senate, then the relevant highest body of the University, and published in *The Reporter* of 10th December 1962. The proposed lavatory, a cylindrical building, was to be paid for partly by the City Council, who had also agreed to maintain it for 99 years. Unfortunately, it would have been opposite the pointing finger of a young man on the War Memorial who had survived WW1 and was pointing to the future. There were to be seats around the Gate where one could ponder.

My father opened the discussion on the subject on 22 January 1963 and I must extract some of his speech if only to give just a glimpse of his style which Grubb described as 'a typical speech of sarcasm, wit, eloquence, lavatory humour and seriousness'.

We are now offered in this Report a low grille, receded it is true, but leading in a hard and un-botanical line by a gate that will normally be shut – unlike the welcome of other University gates – to a Cambridge brick turret that, as a public lavatory in the form of a pygmy gasometer, will block nearly one half of the forecourt and ruin with its insolence both aspect and retreat. Then, for fear lest common speech associate the name of the great benefactor with this redoubt, of which the most that can be said is that in decency it turns its back on the scene, there is proposed a nameless gate, to be dubbed surely the 'Lavatory Gate'- the 'Lavatory Gate to the University' – just as the redoubt itself will be styled the 'War Memorial Lavatory'. The gate is to cost a fraction of what was formally deemed worthy of University, City, and Botanic Garden, and a conspicuous part in the front is to be leased to the City on a peppercorn basis, because nothing more exciting, apparently, can be thought of to confront a new University gate than a public lavatory. We are supposed to take this plan seriously. We are asked to let off for nothing the most prominent part of the site where we should have made our best effort in planning. We are asked to put the first entrance to botany behind a public convenience; and I emphasise this catastrophe because I have often heard, looking into the future, how the Botany School must gravitate more and more to the Botanic Garden.

In all my devotion to science, I have never felt so openly ashamed. Tragedy there is, and comedy – tragedy because the fine intention is foregone, and comedy because there will spring up in this public spot a well of mischievous humour. There must be something wrong, as the Report senses, when the Cory benefaction, intended for the capital improvement of the Garden, is to be used to build the gate, but the name of Cory cannot be set on the capital.

The place for a public lavatory is the centre of the Garden. If this is not obvious, then let the questioner enter the Garden from the War Memorial roundabout and discover for himself. If the Garden has succeeded, as we all believe, his interest will be aroused, his purpose diverted, and his stay prolonged. He will seek conveniently the central lavatory, small and obviously in need of improvement with the space and seclusion to do so. Then, he may continue in his enjoyment of the Garden. He does not want to go outside in order to come back.

I was amused by the metaphors that lie almost almost undetected. Tim Whitmore, in his obituary of my father in *The Independant,* described the loo issue as droll. I think not, but what a plot for a Gilbert and Sullivan operetta – 'The Redoubtable Convenience or Clochmerle at Hand' – with a little music of Brahms inspired by Listz! Clever men are often controversial by accident, intention, or both – and my father was certainly very clever.

Professor Ho Coy Choke of Universiti Malaysia, Sabah, who as a young man was on the Kinabalu expedition with my father, recalled that he could be dismissive of those he considered below himself.

Corner was a master at creating biological hypotheses and expounding them to others… Surprisingly he was not so receptive to the novel ideas of others. In Kinabalu I tentatively developed a scheme for the evolution of the shapes of acorns of various oak species. He dismissed my hypothesis with instant contempt.

His conceit was not only for those his junior. Dr Egon Horak, one of the very few whom my father engaged in joint-research, wrote to me about an incident in the herbarium at Bogor Botanical Gardens when my father examined the paintings of C. van Overeem, the Dutch mycologist and curator at Bogor in the early part of the last century.

At one occasion I discovered that EJHC made pencil-written comments and corrections at the back of the paintings, eg 'wrong!', 'common in Malaysia', 'also observed in Singapore' etc.

In the *Flora Malesiana Bulletin* of January 1997, Ruth Kiew tells another story which shows how dismissive my father could be.

Corner also had an alarming reputation for unpredictable irascibility and indeed, as a student in Cambridge, there were many anecdotes in circulation. One was of a student who planned to do a PhD under Corner's supervision but who, on getting a third class degree, asked Corner what he should do as he was no longer eligible for a scholarship. The reply, so the story goes, was 'I don't care...as long as I don't see you again'.

Bruce Ing received no such treatment:

[W]hen I graduated in 1960, I asked your father to sponsor me for membership of the British Mycological Society and also the fellowship of the Linnean Society of London. He graciously agreed to do both and wrote some flattering comments on my behalf. They have become the two most important societies for me throughout my career. I probably would not have been such an enthusiastic mycologist without your father's encouragement. Since 1960 I saw much less of him but we did bump into each other at conferences and it was always good to see him and listen to his talks. You can probably deduce from the above that your father will always be my hero and role model and I should like your family to know how much I admired and respected him.

My father also had high regard for Professor Roy Watling. In 1993, three years before he died, my father wrote: 'To Roy Watling, my successor in Malesian mycology, and may he find a companion – even a monkey'.

The admiration and respect was mutual. Watling said that as a lecturer, my father was 'charismatic and spell-binding; there is little wonder he swayed many an impressionable undergraduate.... Although often argumentative, and radical to many... (h)e was always there to encourage and share his experiences and material for which many will be truly grateful'.

Once, after a lecture in Edinburgh given by my father, Watling and he were chatting when Watling commented that he didn't agree with a particular point. After a pause, my father replied, "Roy, you know that, and I know that – but they don't." This story shows a moment of confluence of the type my father would only accord to those whom he respected.

David Chivers wrote of my father's work and achievements as

Absolutely outstanding – the breadth and depth of his research – a real pioneer, who inspired so many, communicated so widely and effectively..... Lord Cranbrook will have more insight into these aspects.

Gathorne Gathorne-Hardy, the 5th Earl of Cranbrook did, as he expressed to me in 2009:

I think that during my time at Cambridge as an undergraduate (1953–56) your father was not yet Professor, but only Reader in Tropical Botany. However, his lectures were the most inspiring of any that I attended during my Part I in Natural Sciences. Long before I discovered the seductive delight of the durian, I knew that it was ramiflorous, pachycaulous and arillate, and hence (in Corner's contested opinion) a primitive among flowering plants.

I can't be sure in retrospect, but I feel that his infectious enthusiasm for his subject was one of several influences that made me receptive, just before I graduated, to Tom Harrisson's invitation to come to Sarawak to work at the Museum – a totally unexpected and unplanned jump into the dark, which turned out to be fundamentally significant in directing the whole course of my subsequent life and career. I thank EJHC for this.

Yet, Lord Cranbrook who was on Kinabalu with my father in 1964 said, 'after the expedition, he remained a friend for life; while in many ways personally ascetic, he did not avoid controversy and could be reactionary, and irascible'.

Professor Duncan Poore in his *Memories of Kinabalu 1961–1965* (*the 40th Monograph*) confirmed that assessment.

Corner was an idiosyncratic leader. Without doubt, he was a wonderful and stimulating companion in the forest but he could be difficult and intolerant: on one occasion he almost left someone stranded in the highest camp by withdrawing the lower camps too fast.

Part of my entry on August 1st, my first day, reads: 'Stainton came back in evening reporting a route down the Mamut River. C [Corner] extremely critical of most of his fellows! Meijer [botanist from the Forest Department] sent off with a rocket. Camp filthy and organisation rather sporadic, I think, but everything seems to work and no doubt a lot is being accomplished'. A later entry of August 12th reads: 'C got a letter from Mrs Collenette and is raging about her as usual. She seems quite unaware that she has raised all this storm around her head: and Chew has been told to put her in her place'.

Ho Coy Choke agreed that my father 'can be equally rough' with women. He continued by saying that my father could be tough on those he disliked. He excluded W. Meijer from the two Royal Society expeditions to Kinabalu. Meijer was an extremely prickly and opinionated Dutch botanist, employed in North Borneo, who wrote a cyclostyled monograph on vegetation in Mount Kinabalu for a UNESCO Symposium in Kuching, Sarawak, before the Royal Society expeditions of 1961 and 1964. My father, in his last letter to Ho in the 1990s, complained that Meijer refused to return his photograph of an apparently new species of *Rafflesia* found in North Perak, Malaysia.

Was that, I enquired, why he was refused a place on the Expedition? David Mabberley replied in the negative.

[Meijer's] work has been described as being, 'in general, of a mediocre or worse calibre'… and I am sure this is why he was excluded; simply not up to scratch, but not returning a photo was a 'hanging' offence!

Ho summarised my father's character with a telling comment: 'Corner is like the *Tualang* tree… hard & towering often with a hive of killer bees in its crown'. *Tualang* was van Steenis' nickname for my father.

In Mabberley's incisive assessment, my father's individualistic style was a hallmark of his research, and he instilled that independence of thought into his research students.

Like Church before him, Corner never ran a research group in the modern sense of that term. He let his students range where they would and he was never joint-author of papers based on the student's own research. So esoteric was Corner's style that, on his retirement, tropical botany withered in Cambridge; however, to compare his contribution with the equipment-heavy research groups of today, justified by the amount of grant money thrown at them, is misguided. His tools were cheap, but his mind was great. Like a philosopher, or other thinking academic, he instilled ideas and freshness into generations of young people and, through his research students and their research students, generations more, just as his mentor Church had done before him. The 'school' is in the enlightened.

Dr Scott Redhead, Curator, National Mycological Herbarium, National Research Scientist, Biodiversity (Mycology and Botany), Agriculture and Agri-Food Canada, sent me a summary which describes well my father and his early work leading to the publication of '*Clavaria and allied genera*' in 1950. I include the following long excerpt to provide a view of the science of E. J. H. Corner.

E. J. H. Corner early in his career demonstrated an acute ability to observe the finest detail combined with the eye of an artist, to intellectually piece together original observations, to put aside established thought, and to draw his own conclusions but especially to develop his own theories. It is clear to me that he was first and foremost a biologist (not a taxonomist as many view him) and very much a philosopher.

His first six papers on cup fungi (Discomycetes) in 1929–30 are amazingly detailed and reveal all of these abilities. For the larger fungi, that include mushrooms and bracket fungi (mainly the tough or woody polypores), it was his persistence (perhaps patience and attention to detail) in trying to see how the tissues were constructed that allowed him to see what others had missed. There was that plus the fact he was on site in the tropics where fresh material was at hand and materials often had to be preserved in liquids, rather than just by drying them. All of this led to his discovery of the different types of fungal hyphae that are involved in the construction of fruit bodies. With his 1932 publication '*A Fomes with two systems of hyphae*' a light bulb of an idea went off in his head.

His philosophy is outlined clearly in the first two paragraphs of the introduction to his 1950 book, '*A monograph of Clavaria and allied genera*' – to study the fungi 'in terms of hyphal properties, to trace phyletic lines through homoplastic levels' and to 'facilitate systematic mycology in the tropics' because 'to omit the tropical element is certain failure'. Note also in his acknowledgements written a year after the war, his sense of history, respect and gratitude to the great past, contemporary and upcoming mycologists, and on his more humanistic side (rather than a purely scientific side), his thanks to three prominent Japanese figures who personally helped to protect him and his research materials… these same types of trails through time (the names and dates of his list, recorded in the 1950 monograph, of the localities of new species' type specimens that he EJHC personally collected) can be deduced from his other publications as well, but if there are collection books they might be better recorded in them…

My point here, is that a considerable amount of work was done during the war it seems, mainly based upon collections made before the war, but some that continued during the occupation, supplemented by some upon return to England and a few made before leaving England for Singapore. He just never stopped working.

The 1950 monograph classification was largely based upon his newly perceived importance of the tissue structure. The taxonomic key to the taxa begins with the first couplet asking about the tissue (whether dimitic or monomitic) and continues on in that vein. He strongly defended this opinion of the importance of tissue structure again and again when examining these tissues which was not [then] accepted taxonomic practice. The 1950 monograph was well received by an appreciative G.W. Martin (review in *Mycologia* 43: 384-385. 1951) who predicted that adoption of Corner's methods 'will lead to a much clearer understanding of the larger fungi'.... It must then have come as quite an affront and shock for EJHC to read the review by Maxwell Doty (Taxon 3: 227-230. 1954), a researcher who had worked on *Clavaria* in the western USA in the 1940s, and to whom EJHC had apparently given a copy of his monograph. Doty's article was focussed on nomenclature and specifically on type citations, and probably should have been written with greater sensitivity to the circumstances involved with the writing of the book during war time occupation. The new, at that time, International Code of Botanical Nomenclature had just been published (1952) resulting from the International Botanical Congress meetings in 1950 (notably the same year as your father's book was printed and a full four years after submission of the manuscript). Doty, who at that time was proposing changes to the next edition of the International Code of Botanical Nomenclature, was probably caught up in a narrower vision of the world. He heavily criticized E. J. H. Corner for his position on types (a nomenclatural issue) while on your father's side, there was such pride and relief that the book, manuscript, and specimens had all survived [the war] and gone forward. E. J. H. Corner said, 'I have informed Dr Doty, who thinks the world is perfect. It was an unbelievably good turn of fortune's wheel that spared the Singapore herbarium in 1942. Does science rest on good luck or good reporting? By which I mean that did the publication of my monograph depend on Japanese goodwill to the effect that, if my collections had been lost, I should not have written it?' (Taxon 4: 7.1955).

EJHC continued with his studies on fungal taxonomy and anatomy (and biology in general) leading to another monograph in 1966, '*Monograph of cantharelloid fungi*', a mere 255 pages, rather than the 740 pages for the '*Clavaria and allies*' tome. Yet this book caused even more problems and upset for him than happened for the first. Continuing with his research theme into the anatomy of fungal fruit bodies and moving onto another group characterized by gross morphology, he realized that not only were tough, woody fruit bodies composed of different types of hyphae, but that fleshy fungi also had different anatomies, and in doing so noted what he called sarcodimitic construction. Bearing in mind that virtually nobody prior to then was looking at, let alone using such tissue differentiation, to help identify or to classify fungi, EJHC again boldly went where others dared not to go. Again he focussed on firsthand observations and things that were difficult to determine from dried herbarium specimens. Three heavily critical reviews were written the following year (by R. W. G. Dennis [at Kew, England], by D. A. Reid [also at Kew], and by A. H. Smith [Univ. Mich., USA]) each acknowledging the strengths of the monograph but then lighting into EJHC for perceived shortcomings. Your father responded the next year (*Mycology in the tropics—apologia pro monographia sua seconda*. New Phytol. 67: 219-228. 1968)…

Admittedly, from an outsider (me) when reading the reviews, the monograph, and the rebuttal, I can't help but see enormous amounts of posturing. There were truths on both sides but every one of them could have been expressed more objectively. As a young student looking at these printed words, a certain amount of fear and trepidation is created, lest anything one might publish might draw such articulate wrath (the likes of either the review authors or your father). The greatest criticism in the reviews was reserved for EJHC's manner of presentation (which reflected his philosophical stand that studying fresh material was more important than herbarium materials, and that tropical studies were required) followed by criticism of his taxonomic redefinition of what he called *Trogia*, based primarily on soft tissues composed of what he called sarcodimitic tissues. Here it seems he ran with an idea far too far and raised many an eyebrow. It seemed unrealistic (then and now) to lump all the taxa he called *Trogia* together because of their diversity outside of the presence of this type of tissue, and by going out on the proverbial limb, EJHC lost support of many fungal taxonomists. His ideas were dismissed, but in doing so I think taxonomists ended up throwing out the 'baby with the bath water'…

Nobody has ever taken up *Trogia* in the sense of your father, and virtually nobody working on mushrooms (Agaricales) bothered to examine tissue anatomy of fleshy fungi with a view to correlate differences taxonomically, except for checking microchemical reactions (which notably EJHC did not regularly check). This is in remarkable contrast to the taxonomists working on leathery or woody bracket fungi who had embraced the study of tissue types earlier coined by EJHC, i.e. monomitic, dimitic, trimitic. Generic redefinitions were often based upon such constructions, and EJHC's early contributions were widely acknowledged as pioneering; to quote, (Gilbertson, R.L. & Ryvarden, L. 1986. North American Polypores Vol. 1, p. 15, under Micromorphology), 'Corner's fundamental work (1933) on the hyphal system at once gave mycologists working with polypores a complete new set of tools, and his discovery was a major step forward for a more consistent and reliable classification of this group of fungi.'

Of his critics Dennis and Reid, my father felt that neither really understood fungi. According to David Frodin, taxonomist, Honorary Research Associate at Kew, and one of my father's research students, to my father, the 'Kew approach' was superficial. He considered that there was a certain arrogance shown then by the Kew mycologists assuming the view that they knew best particularly as they '…looked at the relationships of fungi in mainly a "spatial" sort of way, rather than with a deeper understanding of their forms and their evolution'. Frodin continued with the most perceptive remark:

> [T]oday, however, evolutionary frameworks have come to be constructed using gene sequences – but it is quite brilliant if morphological reasoning is found to be more or less congruent with the more recent genomic evidence. I have been fortunate to have had that experience. Students should learn both ways; but scientists often have a problem with history. I am not sure if anyone has done a correlation of your father's *Seeds of Dicotyledons* with the recent gene-sequence phylogenetic system of flowering plants, of which the most recent, relatively definitive version appeared in 2009.

This chapter would not be complete without listing the key discoveries of E. J. H. Corner, the Professor of Tropical Botany. When I set out to write about my father, I was determined not to be drawn into science and associated terminology because the reader I target is not so much the scientist but the common man, who I want to understand what I am writing and be excited by botany; however, this proved impossible and I make no apology. How naïve I was in thinking I could so do! I am learning and trying to understand, and having some success too thanks to my father's use of English and avoidance, at all costs, of jargon.

1928. Discovery of Neotiella crozalsiana and neoteny in the evolution of the fungus fruit-body from the algal soma. This was the discovery of a microscopic disc-fungus, its development leading to ideas on interpreting relationships within the fungi. Roy Watling commented:

> John emphasised the large number of micro-fungi which would be found with bryophytes, a fact which took over fifty years to be appreciated throughout mycology. He also demonstrated that fungi go through stages of development which reflect earlier stages in their evolution cf. the human foetus with tail etc. etc. and shows the relationship with their former algal ancestors (something not supported by modern researches but as always food for thought!).

1932. Hyphal analysis in fungi in the new words monomitic, dimitic and trimitic. It took 33 years to 'cotton on' to the importance of hyphal analysis in mycology, c.f. the work of G.H. Cunningham, (New Zealand). The discovery, with Cunningham, that bracket fungi, which have similar anatomical construction, are related. The mitic system is now a fundamental part of the established classification of the bracket fungi and has been applied successfully to other groups.

1944. The meaning of the durian and so to pachycauly, a non-mycological contribution emphasising the evolution of the pachycaulous tree-form from more simple thinner stemmed ancestors best demonstrated within the single genus *Ficus* – figs, and of dicotyledons: the idea of the pachycaul tree being central to the evolution of the rainforest, both woody plants and forest animals. The durian has a large spiky fruit which splits when ripe revealing seeds covered with pulpy aril, a feature he argued to be primitive.

1950. *Clavaria* as the origin of the Basidiomycetes. My father compared the clavaroid fungi with the development of algae and demonstrated a fundamental yet simple similarity in pattern suggesting the club fungi were ancestral to many of the other groups of higher fungi. We are now aware that the clavaroid fungi are more a group of parallel lines of evolution than a homogeneous one bringing together a number of elements all with a simple, branching system strongly showing an ancestral parameter. My father, drawing parallels with the algae, considered the club-shaped mushroom as the primitive from which other forms evolved.

1950. *Polypores*, to expose the richness of the fungus flora of SE Asia. His ideas are still expanding even today. He was correct in the richness of species in the tropics of SE Asia representing endemics; species from northern climes, circumpolar tropical species etc, a mixing pot.

1961. *Trigonobalanus verticillata* – the beech-oak (Kinabalu); a genus of *Fagaceae* which joins together several important temperate genera such as beech and oak, and possibly reflects an ancestral taxon. 'This is a group of arborescent plants and so I am unable to comment on whether the phanerogamic botanists still think this is the case', says Watling.

1966. *Trogia* as the still misunderstood genus of the tropics. 'They are still misunderstood although the concept of sarcomitic hyphae fundamental to *Trogia* is now regularly used in defining a group of xeruloid genera. *Trogia* however, in John's extended concept, is not acceptable. It covers many separate genera some not really closely related' (Watling). My father expanded a genus, already described from the tropics with few species, into

My father studying mushrooms.

Top: *My father photographing the staff ablutions facility, Kinabalu expedition,1964.*

Bottom: *Dusun porters, Kinabalu expedition,1964. [Both courtesy of the Royal Society]*

Right: *My father's sketch of the tree that fell during the 1964 expedition (see page 295).*

Overleaf: *(from left) Lindsay, Helga, my father striking a classic pose and Aunt Do in the back garden of Aunt Do's house, Sheet, Hampshire.*

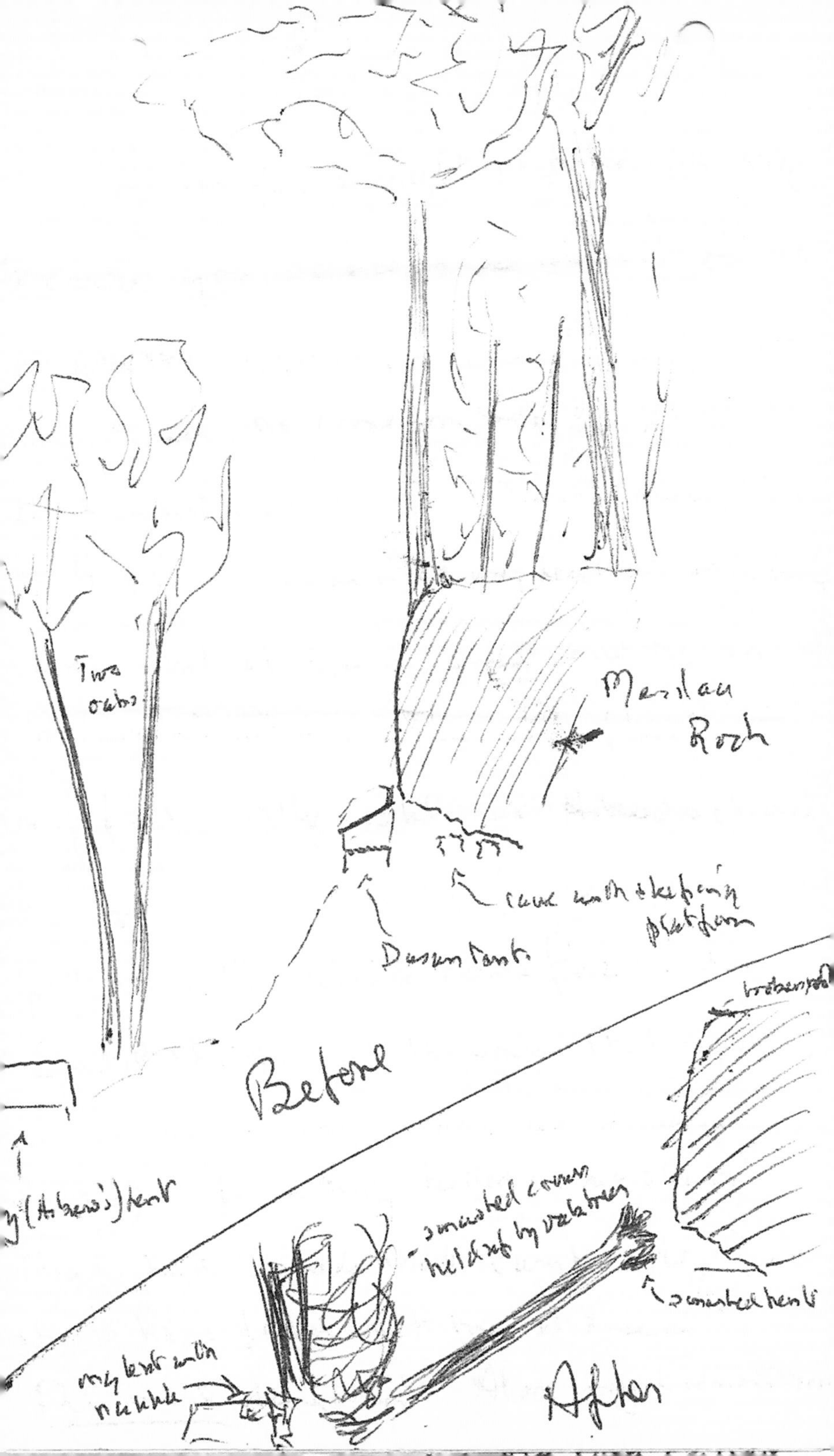

Two
oaks

Merlau
Roch

Descent track

cave with sleeping
platform

Before

y (Andrew's) tent

tree barspoon

smashed canoes
held up by oak trees

smashed tent

my tent with
rucksack

After

Left: My father's medals at the Fitzwilliam Museum.
(Top row, from left) The Darwin Medal, The Patron's Medal of the
Royal Geographic Society, The Linnaean Medal, The Victoria Medal of Honour,
The Victoria Medal of Honour badge.
(Second row, from left) The International Prize for Biology,
The Golden Key to the City of Yokohama, The Robert Allerton Award for
Excellence in Tropical Botany or Horticulture.
(Third row, from left) The de Bary Medal, The International Botanical Congress Medal,
The Colloquia Botanicorum Medal, coin marked: 'Brazil, Peter II, 2000 reis, 1889'.
(Fourth row) Commander of the Most Excellent Order of the British Empire.

Top: My father receiving the International Prize for Biology in Tokyo in the presence of
the Crown Prince and Princess of Japan, 15 November 1985.
[Courtesy of Japan Society for the Promotion of Science.]

Top: Department of Plant Sciences in 1904, then called the Botany School. My father's office was to the left of the door on the left.

Bottom: My father in his sitting room at 73 Hinton Way, Great Shelford, around 1993. [Courtesy of Wendy How.]

Top: 73 Hinton Way, Great Shelford.
Bottom: Wendy How and myself, 2007.

Top: *Belinda and myself, 2003.*

Bottom: *Our six grandchildren, photographed by our son, Andy, in July 2013.*
(From left) Ella Corner, William Buckley, Annabel Buckley, Alice Buckley,
Josh Corner and Zach Corner.

Top: Corner's fig (Ficus microcarpa) near the jetty at Mawai from which my father embarked on many botanising trips. [Courtesy of Tony O'Dempsey]

Bottom: The tree at the bottom of the Hinton Way garden under which my father's ashes were scattered by Wendy How in 1996.

My father and his sketch of a Russula found on Bukit Timah.
The sketch is dated 16 January 1941, thirteen days after my birth.
[Russula sketch courtesy of Prof. Roy Watling, RBGE.]

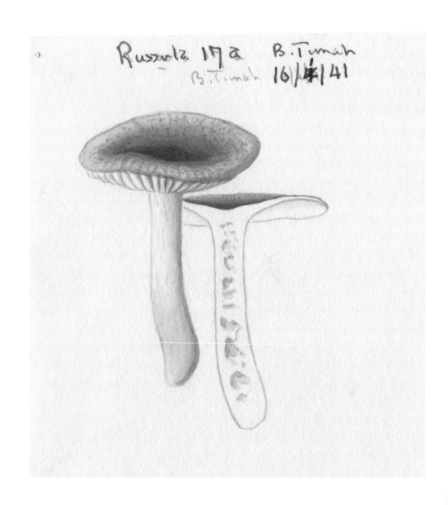

a large genus which contained mushrooms, cup-shaped forms and smooth crust related forms.

1966. *Paraphelaria* as the *Clavaria* analogue. 'Jelly fungi are quite a separate group of Basidiomycetes with origins in common with the early rust – and smut – fungi ancestors. John found this club-fungus in the group having all the external appearance of a true clavaroid (Homobasidiomycete) fungus. There are now known to be many parallels between the jelly and non-jelly fungi' (Watling).

- XXX -

THE LIFE OF ANCIENT TREES

Although, after retirement, my father wrote: 'as with judges, so with bot-anists, the older the wiser', this extra wisdom didn't extend to finding me; trying to re-establish a relationship; finding his one and only son, from which the family name would, indeed does continue; responding to even one of my many approaches over the years, or those of others on my behalf. Should I have forced the issue? I chose not to after all the no replies. Both my father and I lost something from that. Once in the 1970s, when Chew Wee Lek, one of my father's research students, visited the Shelford house for dinner, Chew asked about me and was told that I was in London and probably earning more than he (my father). At least he did know I was in London but clearly he hadn't mellowed even after my being gone for 17 years!

I made many efforts to reconcile with my father. We always told him of the arrival of children and house moves, but never got a reply. We sent pictures of the children from time to time and I kept him abreast of my career, but again never a peep. When I started my own business in 1991 and had become more knowledgeable of Japan and things Japanese as part of my business, I told him but received a deafening silence.

A most important story to tell is the one about the day in 1975 when Belinda, with our children Andy and Katie in the car, turned up at Hinton Way to deliver some things from my late Aunt Do's house. Belinda was Aunt Do's executor as was Aunt Stephanie, and in clearing Aunt Do's house, they discovered many things, including books, that my father had obvi-ously given to her. A ruse was concocted, to try to help reconciliation, that Belinda should turn up unannounced at Hinton Way, with the children, to return them and hopefully find a more receptive reception. I knew nothing of this.

Belinda parked on the road outside the house and leaving the children in the car, she walked down the drive. Andy was nine and Katie seven. Be-linda saw my father in his well-worn, regularly worn, wartime khaki shorts near the front door. He asked, "Who are you?"

Belinda replied, a little taken aback because they had met on a number of occasions before we married, saying, "Professor Corner I am your daughter-in-law and I have brought some things from Aunt Do's house."

He still looked baffled so she said, "I am Kay's wife."

That did it!

"Go away! GO AWAY!" was all he said in a very firm and loud voice, before himself turning his back and walking away.

Belinda was staggered, indeed shattered, never having been spoken to like that before and returned to the car with everything. My children, who heard it all have never forgotten this incident and that is how they remember their paternal grandfather. Katie was magnanimous as the years went by and I think would have liked to meet him but Andy was put off for life. That was the closest they came to meeting him. I think my father really didn't know how to handle such things and his quick temper was a front behind which he so often hid from his uncertainty.

In the early 1970s, Belinda's father once found himself standing next to my father at the urinals in Sidney Sussex College! It was, of course, unplanned; Belinda's parents had gone to attend a lecture. My father-in-law took that moment to remind my father that he had two grandchildren who would surely, one day, like to meet him. He received a brief, non-commital reply.

I have often wondered what would have happened if I had turned up at Hinton Way and faced up to him. I wish now that I had. I realise that my attempted contacts were always by letter and I think that Helga must have intercepted many, if not all, of them. There is no doubt she helped orchestrate my leaving the household and I believe that my father would do nothing to upset her. He was afraid to upset her – for the sake of his life. She gradually took precedence even over his real family. She had an eye for the main chance but he seems not to have realised that, always too busy with his work. Or did he understand it but her convenience outweighed the inconvenience – I think this more likely. It was of his own making. As I reflect on this and without wishing to justify my action, or inaction, I have to say that I don't think my father felt he could do anything with regard to me while Helga was alive.

My father should never have remarried. All he needed was a good companion/housekeeper to manage his house and meet his daily needs, allowing him complete freedom to travel, write and continue his work unhindered.

Douglas Hurd, in his autobiography *Douglas Hurd Memoirs*, wrote about his mother:

> She came from a family… which never questioned that the men took the important decisions, but only after listening with respect to the opinions of the clear-minded women whom they had married…. She

was the peacemaker of her own side of the family, particularly in trying to reconcile the disputes of her brother John Corner with his wife and children.

That Aunt Stephanie came from a family 'which never questioned that the men took the important decisions' gives me a better understanding of my father. His dealing with matters difficult and family was very different to that of his sister. She had advised her brother that despite my leaving the family home the most important thing was that father and son kept in touch. Sadly, that advice was never heeded.

As I write, and learn more, I begin to understand the man better, indeed I find I care about finding out about him, and some explanations come to mind, but I can never excuse some of his actions which destroyed his family, my family – and nearly me.

The newspaper liner to Pandora is the *Cambridge Evening News* of Monday, 30 September 1974: that was about a year before Belinda had called to deliver Aunt Do's books. All the time he had been collecting and keeping letters and documents to go into that suitcase – or was he – and when did he start? Perhaps it was a decision taken much later. I think the 'later decision' is the more likely but he must have kept most of my things from after my walking out. Had Helga found them, she surely would have destroyed them, so my father had kept them from her prying eyes. But I never saw my stamp collection again. My father had letters from all over the world and my collection grew rapidly. It was in a red stamp-collecting album with gold-block wording. Where did that go?

Was Pandora his way of explaining, of saying sorry? Was it a kind of absolution for him, to find something to leave me? Perhaps, and I take some solace in the fact that he intended it to reach me. What a hell of a legacy.

What did he hope from me, for him or for me? Was it his sop to me as was the child's set of art materials by the Japanese to him? No, he was a complicated man and, on much reflection, I am convinced that it was his way of giving me something. He saw gifts in a different way from the norm, for he had his particular logic too.

No matter, I find it very hard to say thank you. Yet it is leading me to finding the man, my father, and exposing the truth of so much. Had he hoped I would accept the challenge and find the truth? In the curious way of his logic I just think he did.

In his last years, he was musing over the past and I believe he was regretting some things, some actions, that had had such an effect on all his family, and him. Did my father reflect on his first love, his first wife, his lost family and all the troubles of earlier years? His work was over, he would never have considered it finished, yet I think he was feeling a little morose, reflective, and lonely – but it was too late.

*

I don't think it ever occurred to my father that he would give up, or retire fully from his work. Around 1990, he had reduced his work load, due mainly to his worsening health, and he had long since moved away from his Cambridge office which meant a certain loss of daily contact with botanists and scientists which had an important value and contribution to his life. In spite of this, he continued his worldwide correspondence and worked on the manuscript of his last book, his biography; he continued his regular forays to the Combination Room where his presence was clearly much enjoyed. His Bluthner piano was regularly strummed.

I was long gone, though he did have visits from his daughters but they became fewer and, as far as I can establish, mainly because neither daughter could get along with his second wife. Deep down, his children were a little afraid of him and all in all he was not a good father. Still, he would welcome family and I have photographs of him, with some of his grandchildren – those of Christine and Lindsay – in that lovely garden of Hinton Way, with his dog, and clearly they were good moments. He generally was not unfriendly but was never really at ease in social settings and he could lapse into anger or frustration at a moment's notice. Looking back it was as if he always was anxious to get back to his work.

From time to time his nephews, Douglas and Stephen Hurd, would visit. His close friends, especially those who lived nearby like the Gurdons, the Switzers and the Evans, were also most supportive. They were pillars of strength, as was his housekeeper Mrs Wendy How and his loyal gardener Bill Langstaff.

*

My father died on 14 September 1996 in his Hinton Way house.

News reached me of his passing, and after much thought, I decided, in 2000 or thereabouts, to find out if I could contest the will which clearly had no mention of me as no one had contacted me about it.

Looking back, I was angry that he had treated me the way he had, ignored all the attempts at reconciliation, and completely ignored his son and heir. It was not the money but the fact that he had visited his troubles on me and made me feel responsible, guilty; a gesture of good faith in his will would have helped – but silence to the end.

I consulted a solicitor whose advice was that if I did contest the will it would be expensive. I dwelt on this and decided that I really didn't any longer care. I was not going to seek something that was not intended for me. My father had decided to leave me nothing except that suitcase.

I continued with my life hoping to keep the past right at the very back of my mind. I had not then seen his will and had no idea of its contents and I had not opened Pandora. I still wanted nothing of any of it, and put it in the loft out of sight and out of mind.

Around 2000, during a visit to England by my daughter Katie from Australia, I took her on a tour of Cambridge to see The Leys School, the Botany School, *Southernwood* – the house where the Williams had lived – and of course Hinton Way. As we walked down the drive of Hinton Way we saw a portacabin in the front garden and introduced ourselves to the resident. He told me he was refurbishing and developing the houses and later was to build in the back garden. He explained, clearly with some pride, that the house had been owned by Professor E. J. H. Corner. I responded by telling him that I was the professor's son.

We were allowed to look around the houses and I was able to tell Katie all about those darker times, show her my bedroom which overlooked the side garden where we had tea and coffee, elevenses as it was then known, and the large garden now very overgrown. I told her the story of the 'hide' that Helga had found and went to exactly where I had dug it. We saw the grass tennis court where we played our competitive family version of croquet, and the vegetable patch where I had once been directed by Helga to do some digging where my father had recently sown! Bittersweet memories but there had been some good times, although not many.

In October 2004, Belinda and I emigrated to Australia and settled close to our daughter in the eastern suburbs of Melbourne.

In 2006, when I did acquire a copy of my father's will as part of my research for this book, I noticed it was drawn on 25 July 1994 and a codicil was added on 22 May 1995. His first wife, my mother, was specifically named and excluded. There was no mention of me. After much thought, I have concluded that he purposely didn't exclude me. He never did anything by accident. I think at least two of his executors believed, nay still believe, that I had walked out on my father and was the one at fault. They didn't contact me. It was as if I didn't exist.

I noted that a Mrs Wendy How was a beneficiary of the will. An address was given so I decided to write, some 13 years after the will was drawn up, hoping she might still be residing there. I did not hold my breath, but she replied by email. Wendy How was my father's housekeeper and carer. She knew there was a son somewhere although my father never mentioned me.

We visited the Hows at their home near Cambridge when we visited England in June 2007. We also visited the Hinton Way house again and it was in its new redeveloped form. I was able to show Belinda my bedroom, the front lounge where I learned to enjoy classical music and where the Bluthner piano had been. This was the room in which I had been hurled, from one side to the other, in the early 1950s. It was also the room in which I played many a game with my lifelong friend Tim Williams, listened to classical music, particularly Strauss, Beethoven and some Nielsen, under electrical restrictions by Helga! The stairs were as they were in my time. The sombre brown paint was gone and through the new canvas there was cheer. It had been tastefully renovated, was much brighter – but I shivered a little.

*

Wendy How and her husband Raymond worked for my father from 1993, in the last three years of his life, and her information is fascinating and important to the understanding of my father in those final years.

When Helga contracted Alzheimer's around 1992–93, she began to shun her husband, became difficult, and demonstrated all the characteristics of dementia. My father employed a housekeeper but she didn't last. The second and indeed the third failed to make the grade too and finally along came Wendy How from the same agency. She started part-time, soon becoming full-time. My father was so disgusted with the agency that he arranged for Mrs How to be released from contract so that she could work permanently for him. He paid her the same weekly wage plus the commission which would have gone to the agency, and backdated the increase. Although Wendy was well paid, she worked hard and very long hours.

In November 2004, my father wrote to Lindsay about Wendy: 'I could not get on without her – so cheerful, willing, kind and helpful in every way. I trust her completely and ask her advice on many matters'.

At my behest, Wendy wrote for me her memories of starting to work for the Prof, as she calls my father. She began by telling of the time she worked for local government in areas near to Cambridge; she liked that work very much but declined to stay on because her department was moved to another office in Cambridge and she had to brave bad traffic in the daily commute.

This was when she returned to care-work and was sent to look after Helga Corner at Hinton Way. On her first day she had difficulty in finding the house, it being well screened by high hedges. She found my father standing in the drive waiting, pleased to see her. Wendy recalled: 'I had no idea what was expected of me only what the agent had told me that the job was to look after Helgas* needs as she had altsimers. I had looked after altsimers before'.

By then, Helga had reached the stage where she really didn't know what she was doing, and Wendy How quickly realised that she needed 'to keep Helga amused so Prof could spend time in his study'. She also needed to prepare meals for my father and do a lot of cleaning. Wendy How noticed

> that there was nothing much to eat in the house as I think they had been living on packet soup and cheese; they must have been living like this

---

Wendy How's quotations are as she wrote them. Occasionally, words in brackets have been added for clarity.

for a long time as the kitchen was in a bad state; black cobwebs hung from the cooker and all the pots and pans were rusty or burnt, but I managed my first week.

My father told Wendy to go and buy whatever was needed. During the second week, her week off duty, the agency called to ask that she return quickly to Hinton Way because the relief carer had again walked out. For about a month, these events were repeated. Eventually my father had a row with the agent who decided that no more carers would be provided. Wendy How elaborated:

When I returned to Hinton Way to start my week on I found that the carer had left on the Tuesday and Prof had rang his younger daughter and she sent two carers from London to spend the rest of the week with them; the bill that he got from the London agents I think it was about £800, that was for four days work.

Wendy remarked that after all these troubles, 'Prof had a slight hart attack he was in such a state that I promast [promised] him that I would not leave them again'.

My father recalled those times in a meticulously written scientific description of the stroke which I found in the Janet West folder, saying that he had been worried for some two weeks, 'deeply perplexed and worried about housekeepers – more so than in the last six months – and Helga was a constant trial and interruption'. He said that such a minor stroke was a warning caused by worry, but 'Wendy has stayed & says she will – thank god! And that I must not worry anymore'. After a side-swipe at housekeeper/carer agencies he ended by confirming that his speech returned in about six weeks.

'Helga was a constant trial and interruption', my father wrote. He was 88 and still could not muster the compassion to be supportive of his second wife who was by then very ill, his botany still coming first.

It was soon apparent that Wendy needed to live in and her job certainly became what the modern world calls 24/7. Access was built into the semi-detached house which my father had acquired next door and a flat was created for Wendy and her husband, Raymond, who at times stayed with her there. There was structural work to be done although the Hows did all the decorating at no cost to my father. Having no furniture, Wendy remembered that 'I got some from my home and Prof gave me some from his side and jean gurdon gave me some that had come from a flat that they had sold'.

Wendy purchased a mat with a hidden alarm to put outside Helga's bedroom so that she would be alerted if Helga left her room in the night. In the end, the outside doors had to be locked to prevent Helga from wandering off.

My father took Helga to the Combination Room at the Senate House in Cambridge for lunch twice after Wendy became a permanent carer but stopped because Helga would wander off.

After that he went on his own until Helga went in to a home then I went with him. It was very nice going into what the Prof called it the combination room very grand, prof also took me to see some of the collages and the gardons, and we went to visit some of his colleges [colleagues] that he worked with, and he would introduce me to his friends that came into the combination room.

My father, accompanied by Wendy How, usually shopped once a week in Cambridge, visiting his favourite shops for tobacco, razor blades and the like. She recalled that on Wednesdays, 'Prof would ring for a taxi… prof would go off to do his shopping, and I would go around the market'.

[H]e also would visit his wine shop that was not far from the collagers [colleges], he would order cases of wine for his friends and family at Christmas and birthdays and there was a stationery shop he visited.

The shop was Heffers which had sold copies of *The Marquis*. Wendy remembered an altercation with the shop assistant there. That day the bill had come to around £100 and as my father went to pay, the young assistant asked to see his cheque card. My father's response was angry: "I have been coming into this shop for fifty years and I have never been asked for my card before." According to Wendy How, 'he was speaking at the top of his voice and all the customers could hear him… the young man said I am sorry sir but I still have to see your card. Prof gave it to him with bad grace'. Wendy told me of another similar occasion:

Once when we were visiting one of the collage gardens we had to walk across a side road and there was a car coming along fast. Prof let go of my arm and walked into the road and the lady had to brake, he said to her 'madam you are going too fast'; she called him a stupid old man and should be locked away. After she had speeded away we continued across the road, prof smiled and said 'well I had my say'.

For Wendy How, looking after my father and Helga had become a 24-hour job as my father's health was declining. He never had had to look after himself and required much attention. Although his mind was clear and sharp, he was having heart trouble as well as problems with his eyes. By late 1993, Wendy was doing everything: housework, cooking, shopping, driving him to meetings, sometimes escorting him to events and functions, and even entertaining. She looked after the finances for all of this which my father checked every Monday when plans were made for the forthcoming week. Hers indeed was a responsible position in every sense of the word, and my father must have trusted her.

It was soon clear that Helga had to go into a home for round-the-clock care. I learned that on one of my father's early visits to her in the care home, she didn't recognise him and told him to go away. He did and, I believe, never visited again.

Wendy told me that after Helga had gone to the home, my sister Christine rang my father and asked if she and her family could come and see him.

> He asked me and I told him that it was ok with me and he handed the phone to me to speak to her…. They had an hour with Prof; then we had our lunch; after lunch Prof went off to his study and I was left to entertain them.

Wendy asked that they come again and Christine told her that she wouldn't come to the house when Helga was there as they didn't get on. Now that Helga was away, Christine and her family did visit again several times. My father even made special arrangements for Christine's birthday.

> Prof paid for us all to have dinner at the Garden House hotel, Prof staid at home, By that time we had some of the bedrooms decorated so they staid the night and went home after brecfast.

I never knew my father as what I would imagine a family man to be; perhaps he had mellowed, but not sufficiently to respond to me! I had been consigned to outer darkness! In recent years, since I began the challenge of this book, I have thought a lot about this and with my memories of him I can only think that he would have found it extremely difficult to acknowledge me after all that had happened. He simply was not good at apologising, and my troubles with him were not of my making although I was never a 'perfect' child! He blamed me as a reflection of my mother. He accused me not infrequently of acting like my mother, indeed being influenced by her.

As for Lindsay*, she visited less frequently after Helga went to the care home, and her visits tailed away. She was spoiled from very early days and was the only one of us that Helga had any chance of winning over. This was not of Lindsay's making nor fault, and I have no doubt that she, like me until recently, has no idea of the truth of what went on. I hear that she

---

* Lindsay was the girlfriend of Syd Barrett, the leader of Pink Floyd. They were at school together. She later married Piers von Simson.

seems not to realise what a successful scientist her father was. That is sad but I didn't either for a long while. She closed her mind to it all, just as I did, but perhaps her 'suitcase' has not yet arrived.

*

My father suffered a second stroke around 1994 when he and Wendy visited my sister Lindsay at her house near Bath. This is Wendy's account:

It was a Saturday and when we arrived only the children were there. They showed us the cottage in the grounds that was ware Prof and I was to stay. It was grand on its own; there was a heated swimming pool and a stable bloke [block].

They settled in and as Bath is not far from where my father's nephew Stephen Hurd lived they decided to visit him. Lindsay remained away until the following Monday and that afternoon she went to visit them.

'Next day Prof was taken ill', Wendy How wrote. Lindsay was away again 'So I called an ambulance. They took Prof to Bath hospital'. Wendy stayed behind and contacted Lindsay and also the Hurds. Lindsay returned and drove Wendy to the hospital where they were told that my father had had a heart attack and would be given a pacemaker. When they returned to Lindsay's home, Lindsay told Wendy that she had to go to London for a few days but would keep in touch. She offered the use of her Land Rover for visits to the hospital. Wendy visited every day for about ten days, then she and my father returned to Hinton Way where 'we went about the days as before'.

One day, my father told Wendy that he had asked his solicitor to call to see him again about his will.

I don't remember the date he had come to the house before [July 1994 is my guess from the Will date] but I remember before that time he asked me to drive him to Cambridge to see the solicitor that jean Gurdon uses.

I learned from Wendy that she drove my father to visit this solicitor, by appointment, but were kept waiting, indeed for so long that 'in the end we left before seeing any one'.

Prof said to me that was a waist of time and that he had made an appointment for the solicitor [a different man from the same firm] to call at the house. And he did.… The last time he had an appointment with the solicitor it was to [two] young girls* [who visited him at his home].

* *The trainee solicitors were there to witness my father's codicil dated 22 May 1995 which increased the amounts for Wendy How and Bill Langstaff.*

After they left Prof came through for his tea and he said to me it would have been better if he had put his will on a fag paper.

Wendy continued that the days went by

in rutean [routine] fashion going through the bills on a Monday. Bill calling to do the garden… in the mornings after brecfast prof would spend time in his study, when it was time for coffee he would come through to the dining room, the days that Bill the gardener was there he would have coffee with him, they would be chatting away.

It was around this time that my father employed extra help for Bill in the garden and also a lady to do some housework so Wendy How would have more time to 'help him with his manuscripts'.

In one of many exchanges, Wendy, in reply to a host of questions, told me of the day my father had asked her to get the wheelbarrow to help him take old papers and files to a bonfire – 'a bunfire' as she delightfully wrote – to have a good clear-out. As she was doing this she realised that she would like to have some things as keepsakes, so she asked, and was told to take anything she wanted.

The things which she kept, and many of which she subsequently gave to me, were useful and important to this story. Initially, I didn't fully appreciate the importance of some, but they proved to be 'part papers' which completed the material I already had from Pandora and Janet West. They were essential pieces of the jig-saw puzzle.

Wendy How understood my father so well and wrote:

When Prof Corner was a child he was looked after by his nanny and servants, when he went to rugby school he was looked after by his fag. When he became a tropical botanist and lived in the jungle he was looked after by native boys. When he married the nanny of his children [Helga] he was looked after by her, when she was ill he had no one, his family did not come to help so he had to find help from agents. As a very hard man to please they did not stay. When I came to look after them in 1993 I was asked to live in every other week but that did not happen, his wife was so bad then she took a lot of looking after, she was sometimes violent sometimes very loving. at times would wonder of [wander off], she would us [use] her bed and shoes as a toilet, if she went into the kitchen she would turn on the gas take food from the fridge to her bedroom put her clothes down the toilet walk about all night, at times she would lay into me with her fists and slap my face when I gave her a bath then after she would hug and kiss me as if nothing had happened, all this going on in the house and not able to get eny

[any] help and Corner *san* [Note the use of the Japanese honorific.] having a row with the agents & social services, he had a slight stroke. When he asked me to stay what could I say but I would but at the same time I would try other agents to help but they did not stay, his doctor came to see him and said that his wife should go into a home for [the good of] his self and mine. So that is what happened, that meant he could write his books and letters and spend time working in his garden. I would help him with his manuscripts… At times, we would go out a lot. He would show me around the colliges grounds & gardens and have his frends to the house from all over the world. He new he did not have much time to go so he lived it to the full.

Thank heavens my father found Wendy How. He wanted to provide for her after his passing and mentioned this to close friends including the Gurdons, the Wests, and the Ashtons. Peter Ashton and his wife visited my father regularly in these later years and he wrote to me about this, concluding: 'On our last visit, Corner was being well looked after by a couple who lived next door. He was brought into the garden, blind, to briefly talk with us. He took particular pains to express his affection and gratitude to the couple (when out of their presence), and told us that they would receive his house as their reward'.

My father wrote to Lindsay to that effect around April 1995, the letter being hand-delivered to her at her house in Bath. Wendy How was there, saw it opened and heard the expression of agreement. My father was concerned at what might befall the Hows 'who have done so much to improve 89 Hinton Way without cost to me, and to master the garden'.

He then suggested two options and it is clear that the saving of his garden and providing work for the Hows were paramount for he wanted to reward Wendy for the time and devotion she had given him at almost total loss to her social life. He recognised that without her he could not have managed.

The other reason being that he had spent a lot of money doing up the house preparing it for use, after his passing, by visiting scholars to Cambridge. Wendy How said 'he wanted me to stay on & run this he gave me money to put in an account to start it off'. A new bank account was started for the purpose and it contained a substantial amount at my father's passing.

The intention was for Wendy and her husband to continue to live next door to manage the house for as long as money allowed. As a business, it would yield income to pay the Hows and also to put towards Helga's expenses, and vitally to keep Hinton Way from the developers, for a while at least. Essentially , the arrangement was to reward the Hows for their selfless support and attention.

Recognising that his health and failing eyesight would soon curtail his travelling, my father introduced Wendy to his Cambridge bankers.

Prof asked me to come to his bank with him; when we got there [West-minster Bank] he spoke to a young lady that worked in the bank that he seemed to know well and introduced me to her and the bank manager and said that he would like them to remember me as there may come a time when I will need Wendy to do my banking for me.

It was around this time that my father doubled Wendy How's wages to £500 a week, backdating the increase to when she started full-time with him – a substantial four-figure sum was banked by Wendy. This was in ad-dition to the backdating of the agent's commission which my father passed on to her. This meant that he had to find some £26,000 of back-pay. He explained to her that to avoid going into his capital he would pay it in por-tions as and when his income allowed. He advised her to invest it wisely in high-interest accounts and introduced her to his stockbroker.

Around then, unbeknown to Wendy, my father increased her legacy to £40,000. This amount would yield both capital and money for investment after his passing. My father had calculated that Wendy How would need a minimum of £100,000, at his death, to complete the planned refurbishment of 91 Hinton Way and have money to live on until the rental business was up and running. He had therefore put in place steps for that sum to be achieved.

It was also around this time when my father had his eye operated on.

When Prof had to go into Adam brooks [Addenbrooks in Cambridge] Hospital to have an eye op: I visited every day that he was there because he made so much fuss about the food; I had to take flasks of soup and sandwishers every day he was there. The day I went to pick him up from the hospital he was sitting on the side of the bed, when he sore [saw] me arrive across the word [ward] he said in a loud voice 'thank god you have come to take me away from this terrible place and the people in hear are so uncouth'... I was glad when it was time to take him home.

Wendy remembered happily that in the summer they had more visitors and that my father consequently spent more time in his garden. Perhaps, there among the greenery, he contemplated the passing of seasons as he did when writing to Edwin Schild, an amateur mycologist whom he had befriended: 'Spring is here! I never like the winter, for I became so used to the latitude of Singapore that I am a "tropicalist". But I always marvel at the beauty and joy of spring'. Wistfully, Wendy recalled:

I would make them sandwiches and cake some times strawberry's and cream; and a glass of wine... on Profs Birthdays he invited his close friends to join him for dinner at the collage restaurant in Cambridge.

Wendy said that in January 1996, 'he was not well at that time to have a party at the restaurant but he agreed to his friends coming to the house'. She invited all his close friends and because he didn't like too many people at a time around him she arranged the party in her side of the house, 'then all his friends could go through one at a time to visit him'.

By 1996, my father was not fit enough to do much gardening.

Raymond did the digging for the veg and I set the seeds and weeded. Prof would potter about doing what he could do… without damaging himself or the garden… When the weather was good Prof and I would sit in the garden and I would read his manuscript to him and now and then he would tell me to alter a word.

She recalled his telling her about his time in Japan, about how they called him Corner-san. 'That is when I said that would be a good name for his house as it didn't have a name. He thought that was a splendid idea, so I got a name plate made up and fixed to the front gate'.*

'The last few months before prof died dug less herd [Douglas Hurd] came on a visit and had tea with him,' Wendy remembered. 'It was very exciting as out side was his body guards and driver, and there was a car on the road blocking the drive way'.

On occasion, Wendy had lunch with my father and his banker.

Prof also invited his banker that dealt with his shares to come down from London and have a meal at the garden house hotel [Garden House Hotel by the river Cam] in Cambridge, I went with them twice, the last time Prof invited his banker to lunch Prof was not very well that day so he asked me to take him. So I did.

To allow Wendy How to take his banker – I think she means stockbroker – to a meal shows how much my father valued her ability, her judgement and bearing: confirmed also by his taking her to the Combination Room – for he was rather a snob.

'Then there was the time that the Japanese TV came to interview Prof', recalled Wendy. 'He did so well sitting there so at ease, it made him tired afterwards.' This was for the TV film *Do You Know Shonanto*. After that 'Prof was invited to go to Japan for a visit and had asked me to go with him but when the time came he wasn't well'.

In 1949, when we moved into the house, it was called Brenelle. *I remember my thoughts when one day we were driving past the house and I noticed the new name. I thought it very ordinary, even a bit tacky, but then I didn't know the background.*

Wendy continued, 'Prof deteriated fast and he couldn't get up the stares [stairs] so Raymond and I got his bed down into the dining room so he could look out into the garden'.

She would walk my father down the garden but as he became more unsteady on his feet she put a bench halfway down the path, and another at the bottom, for him to rest. She well remembered the day when they were sitting on the first bench and 'chatting away' when my father went quiet.

I looked round at him he had past out, I didn't have a mobile phone at that time so I had to run back to the house to phone the doctor.

My father had come round by the time the doctor arrived so between them they helped him back to the house. From then on, my father never again went into his garden. He would instead sit in his armchair, gazing on the plants he loved, and sometimes Wendy How or friends who were visiting would read to him. The doctor visited daily but soon the time came when my father simply didn't want to get out of bed.

[S]o that meant bed baths and I had to turn him over at regular intervals so I wasn't able to go to bed... I would sleep in the arm chare in his room and set the alarm so I could wake to turn him. He wouldn't eat solids so I had to get him vitamin drinks.

Once, when Wendy was persuading my father to take his vitamin drink, he said that he would not have been alive as long as he had if it had not been for her. He added that, at that stage of his life, she was the only one that he had to worry about. Wendy replied that he had better stay with her then – 'to which he gave his usual chuckle'. I had no idea what Wendy How had done – how much she had done – even beyond the call of duty and without complaint.

The day came when the doctor told her that she needed help. Wendy rang Lindsay to tell her and asked if she may arrange for a carer to be with my father at night so that she could get some sleep. This was agreed to but when Wendy asked if she was coming to see her father, she said she didn't want to see him in that condition.

Wendy How called the Red Cross hospital – where I had left my bicycle that day I left home in 1960 – and borrowed a hospital bed and all the equipment that was needed. Then she rang a firm of carers for help at nights. Christine and her husband did visit.

*

E. J. H. Corner, the Professor of Tropical Botany, died on 14 September 1996 in his Hinton Way house.

Most poignantly Wendy recalled receiving a telephone call giving news of the death of the author, Peter Plantagenet Fry:

[T]he day that Prof died the phone rang, it was Peter Fry's wife telling me that peter had died and would I tell john. We had a chat for a time then when I rang off I went into ware prof was in bed and the doctor told me he was in a comer [coma]… he died not many minuets after that peacefully in his home. That was what he wonted.… I just needed to keep bissy.

It was a Saturday and Wendy began to phone my father's friends and family. 'I started with Lindsay but she was out, then I rang Christine and Steven herd [Hurd]. Then Profs friends; I couldn't get his solicitor as there wasn't any one at the office'. Amongst the many who Wendy rang was the family of Marquis Tokugawa. Wendy worked through my father's address book and tried to call everyone listed in it. Wendy got through to Lindsay that evening.

[S]he said that she couldn't get over so I will have to do what was needed and to arrange the funeral as she wouldn't attend the funeral as she didn't want to see her sister or her mother.

I had left him; his elder daughter could not get along with his second wife and in his later years his younger daughter, who also could not get along with Helga, visited him less and less; and the two daughters sadly also didn't get along.

It could be thought that my father had brought it all upon himself but I think that that would be a harsh judgement. My father deserved better but made it difficult indeed, by his stubbornness, for his children to respond. There was, mostly, little or no warmth. Wendy How made all the funeral arrangements.

So on the Monday [after my father died] I rang the solicitor and told him what Mrs von Simson [Lindsay] had said [about the funeral and arrangements]. He told me to do what was needed and let him no when the undertaker would be calling… The doctor gave me the death certificate and I took it to Cambridge and got it registered. The undertaker arrived and asked what hymns I wanted. I wasn't expecting this but I thought of Prof and out of my mouth came 'Fight the good Fight' and 'Abide with me'. [Excellent choices.] The solicitor arrived soon after and the undertaker gave me a book of coffins to look though; the solicitor made a comment that 'a fifty pounds coffin would do'. I stared at him and chose a more suitable one… I gave the undertaker the clothes that Prof loved to ware and was best known in, his dear storker hat and the jacket he always wore with it.

One of the carers who helped with Prof at night volunteered to help with the food for the wake... there was a lot of Profs friends at the funeral, and some of them came to the house afterwards'.

My father's ashes were scattered by Wendy How under two trees at the bottom of his beloved garden. An important and simple memorial.* Wendy told me my father's last wishes:

To finish his last book (*Momont Botanic*) [*Moments Botaniques*], and he did; to put all his plant collections and manuscripts in order for Prof David Mabaly [Mabberly] to take over, and he did; live in his house till he died, and he did... to make preparations for his house to be made ready for overseas visitors from the college, and for me to stay on as housekeeper to them to save his garden from being bilt on for a time... The last few weeks of his life he lived and slept in his dining room that had French doors looking out over his garden and I would tell him what was growing and read the books that he had written, to him. He would tell me about things on his mind and *the mistakes he had made: about the bad time he had with his first wife* [my emphasis].

*

I have learned that there is no tablet, writing or any form of memorial at the Cambridge Crematorium where dust returned to dust on 20 September 1996. Not even a plant with plaque to commemorate a fine tropical botanist.

My father deplored the naming of plants after people and only once did this himself, commemorating C. E. Carr; however, others have risked his wrath by naming species after him. Would he really have been angry? After all, such naming honoured him and there are many plants *corneri* now! (See Appendix E for full list of plants and fungi so named).

Bruce Ing assured me that

the botanical world in the UK regards him as a hero for carrying on his work during the Japanese occupation and it was typical of his determination to carry on with important work without 'annoyance' from

*When Belinda and I visited the Hinton Way house in 2007, we found two bungalows under construction in the rear garden. My father would have been horrified had he known this was to happen to his beloved garden. Belinda and I found the trees at the very bottom of the garden under which Wendy How had scattered my father's ashes. During our March 2011 visit to the Hows, we called again at Hinton Way to find the bungalows all but finished. The trees were horribly diseased. When these trees are gone, E. J. H. Corner's last resting place will be lost forever.

'trivial' circumstances. It is difficult to estimate the vandalism that may have ensued if he had not been somewhat co-operative. Some things are more important than politics!

I did consider proposing a Research Studentship to provide a lasting memorial to my father in Cambridge, the place where he worked the longest, where he graduated and where his life ended, and of course to help the continuation of research into tropical botany. However, when I learned of the amount of money required to set it up I had to back away even though, had I contributed, I know many of my father's research students would have helped financially and no doubt in other hands-on ways. Such a studentship was alluded to in my father's will, but the 'hint' fell by the wayside.

In the Singapore Botanic Gardens, the E. J. H. Corner House still stands, leased as an excellent French restaurant. This was where my father lived when he worked in the Gardens, and where we all lived as a family in 1941–42 before the war and disintegration of our family life. The entrance to the Gardens nearby has been named the Corner House Gate. Three cannonball trees (*Couroupita guianensis*), grown from the seeds collected by my father from Peradeniya in 1934, still thrive in the Ginger Garden. Three *Dryobalanops aromatica* (Kapur) [Dipterocarpaceae] on Lawns E, H and O stand tall, and were planted from seeds which he collected from the east coast of Malaya. The fine specimen of *Inocarpus fagifer* (Tahitian Chestnut) in the Gardens' Bukit Timah Core is also a form of memorial to him. The Kapur and Tahitian Chestnut trees have been designated heritage trees by Singapore.

With the wonderful benefit of hindsight, I think that that war was both my father's saviour and undoing. What chance did the marriage have when my parents were, so soon after their wedding, divided by nearly four years?

My father's treatment, by many, at the end of the Japanese Occupation must have been soul-destroying, yet he kept that to himself and drove himself ever more to his work, realising greater achievement. He must have suffered and the family certainly suffered, but did he really care, did he notice?

I am encouraged to read that so many who knew him had deep respect for his work; I too have acquired a respect for the scientist my father was. What a complicated, difficult yet brilliant and hopeless man – accurate in science and yet so inaccurate in his family life.

EPILOGUE

Henry Ward Beecher wrote that 'books are the windows through which the soul looks out'. I believe that this book has been my window – but I have looked in as well by necessity.

Before the arrival of Pandora, my knowledge of my father was thin, but the journey it has brought me through his life has told me much. Yet, I continue to be struck by the muddle of Pandora by a tidy man. It appears that in the earlier days of its creation, my father was methodical in his placing of material. Later, that order clearly became disorder. The letters were all in neat bundles, enclosed in old envelopes and tied with string, but they were not in any obvious order or arrangement. It took me many weeks, sitting on the same floor where it all began, to sift through them and place them in date and subject order, and then type them. Deciphering all the many letters was a challenge in itself (Bob Wickham's handwriting was awful), and very time consuming. Photographs were usually subtitled but those with people were not. At first I accepted the missing pages and incomplete stories without thought – until I learned more and became driven to fill those gaps.

Then the June 2007 visit to England brought me to Dr Janet West and the file she had promised. There were the piles of paper which Wendy How saved from those 'bunfires', and other documents from my father's close friends sent to me at various times. I looked through the many papers and I began to realise that some missing parts of material in Pandora were there, while some were duplicates, and others were new material relating to nothing in Pandora. Still some gaps remain. I wonder how much more material might be in lofts or in the back of desk drawers, thought not to be important? In isolation, they may not be but, with what I have, they might be invaluable. I have surprised myself that I have done what I have done, though the more I find out the more I want to learn.

Let me not suggest for a moment that it has been easy. Having never written a book, I was faced with countless new challenges, and at times – many times – I wanted to walk away from it. Yet I persisted, and without a determination which comes from a tough early life and good schooling this would not have been accomplished, nor would it have been possible without the patience of my dear wife.

In my correspondence with my boyhood friend Tim Williams in 2007, we discussed some of our earlier days. I told him of the background to Pandora and of the note that was placed on it, the full text being 'to be given to Kay wherever he may be'. I am disappointed that the note was lost. Tim wrote:

> I have been haunted by your father's line: 'To be given to Kay wherever he may be'. As if he didn't know how to find you if he made any real effort; as if you were just a black sheep who had deserted him, rather than him being the one who failed to find a way of helping you at a crucial time, and then did not even acknowledge you and your family's existence; or as if back in 1974 he is somehow facing what his personal life has amounted to – not his professional life, which has always been given his priority – and leaves you to put the proud, sad pieces together (which is what you have been doing) though without being capable of bending his pride to a message of love. It's extraordinary! It's an act of angry defiance that is also one of trust; it's both hurt pride and inarticulate love, from an emotionally lost old man who has decided to go to the grave like this rather than try to unbend. And it makes me wonder what his childhood was like, that he learnt to wall himself off so seemingly impassively.
>
> What a burden of emotional baggage to inherit and open up! But in the end it is yours and your family's, I suppose – and all credit to you for lifting the lid of Pandora's box and clearly really getting down to it. I'm sure there is a lot to be really proud of as well as fascinated by, and it must be strange to re-encounter this man – your father – through his old students and colleagues. I think back to Hinton Way days, and his emergings from his study to play a cunning game of croquet then go back to his preoccupations, while the girls tried to get some kind of attention too, and confused Helga struggled inadequately in the background. Not easy for any of you. Thank goodness you found Belinda when you did! I sense that she has been wonderfully consistent in her love.
>
> How did EJHC and Helga meet? I'd always imagined she was little more than a housekeeper/convenience for your father to look after his house and children, and never picked up a sense of companionship between them – until a brief encounter years later that I may have told you about (and will do so again later). She always seemed anxious and insecure, and yes I do recall her weird meanness over the electricity as we played 'Air Attack' interminably to Strauss waltzes and Chopin. I think there were two occasions when she produced her special Danish biscuits and chocolate cake for tea with what for her was a flourish; otherwise she seemed a shabby, somewhat downtrodden and very iso-

lated figure. But when she precipitated the crisis between you and your father (didn't she?), she seems to have found a very determined malevolence....

When I encountered them together one day in Woollards Lane [Great Shelford] some years later (it must have been very close to when we left *Southernwood*, around 1966), I remember several things: first, my surprise at seeing them both out together, seemingly companions; then their smiles to me, polite, constrained, a bit wary, but on your father's part I felt linked enough to a shared past for me have a go. So I said that I would like to give them news of you if they would like to hear it. At this they continued to smile but began to demur and had to be off, and off they walked together. Years later, at Andy's wedding, when chatting with Douglas Hurd (whom I'd met slightly elsewhere) and he mentioned that he went to Hinton Way from time to time, I asked him if he thought he could talk to EJHC about all this, and he clearly thought it was beyond his powers of diplomacy, or else he couldn't face it: which suggests to me that your father's pride was so strong that no one wanted to struggle with it, including himself.

I continued my exchanges with Tim and he wrote again:

It occurs to me that EJHC may well have had uneasy relations with colleagues and 'authority' in his time at Cambridge, and may have found it difficult to get the full acknowledgement that he would have liked for his extremely distinguished work. I remember you once confiding that he had a 'filthy temper' – and he certainly lost it with WWW [Tim's father, W.W. Williams] when you took refuge at *Southernwood*, writing a letter of formal complaint to the vice-chancellor! But I think you'll know much more than me about this incident. I suppose that what I am fishing around in is something about his extraordinarily brilliant immersion in the world of plants, his undoubted charm at times, and something quite lacking, even dysfunctional at key moments, in his closer relationships – but there was always the sureness of his own world-class expertise to have recourse to/retreat to. No shortage of esteem there – though possibly some full recognition (eg, university chair) was still not quite his when your crisis with him happened. It's profoundly pathetic that he could confide to his housekeeper that he felt it was "too late" and couldn't bring himself to unbend.

But unbend he did. Wendy How, in one of her insightful letters, wrote about my father's confession: 'the bad times he had with his first wife'. I asked her what she meant and she resisted. A year or two later, on my persistence, she reluctantly replied, giving details – reluctantly because she is intensely loyal to my father and didn't want to hurt my feelings as she knew, from me, of my hard times with him. Wendy was sitting with my father in the garden.

The things he told me about his mistakes he didn't go into fully just as if he was thinking out loud with the look of regret, with the tips of his fingers together. He spoke about your mother as if her going off was partly his fault and would have done differently now, I think the bad times was having to go though the legal wrangle to keep you children together, he spent too much time on his job and not the things that matted [mattered]. then when he got custody, to find some one to look after you children, then there was Helga's family pressing him to marry her because it wasn't right for her to be living in the same house on her own with a man, and I do think he regretted his stubeness [stubbornness] about not getting in touch with you but he new he had left it too late, that showes in the way he saved all thoughs [those] things for you, and the regret about Steven herds [Hurd's] brother killing himself he felt he should have done something about it at the time. He told me about how his mother wonted him to follow his father's profession and how that put a lot of presher on him and made him stutter at times.

Well, there it is – as close to an apology and admission of some failure as I think was ever possible. But why so late – too late? Was he so proud?

He was successful in the divorce but, deep down, I think he knew that he was losing me, and probably, even then, Christine. Then it reached a point when, in 1960, I could take no more and went out into the world a rather shaken young man, and took a long time to recover, to find my self-esteem. Christine was so deeply hurt that she never recovered from her treatment, rather mistreatment. She died young.

Lindsay's hurt was different. She felt rejected by her mother, and was encouraged to this view by her father and stepmother, as were we all – and she was far too young to recognise anything different. Rachel Catlow, who wrote to me in 2007, said, 'your mother was devastated by Lindsay's rejection and later when you decided to cut yourself off from her'. What no one understood, indeed had no chance then of understanding, were the deep scars of hate left in us children by a fierce father and a determined stepmother. I have called it indoctrination. I did not 'cut myself off' from my mother; I simply visited her rather less often. Mother and I did get together in her later years and overcame the hatred that was sown.

*

In files which came to me late in 2011 from Robin Miller, I found some handwritten notes of a conversation the writer, who must remain anonymous, had with the late Dr Tim Whitmore about my father. The date is 19 March 1997.

> Genius but v. vindictive; had to have a whipping boy. Mycologist – brilliant book on Trees, given ex-gratia payment to rewrite book – new edition came out – huge sum of £s demanded. Charismatic raconteur – brilliant lecturer – Holttum's work will last – written work will last, Corner's work won't… Corner sailed close to the wind – collaborator… Corner on wharf – for raspberries! Fell out with family – threw all the children out – Danish housekeeper – married her. Several children did not turn up to funeral – Corner's young housekeeper put funeral together – priest drunk – fumbled funeral service…

There followed some remarks by a deceased Cambridge professor, who must also remain nameless, saying he was equally bitter about my father, and a young scientist in Botany wrote: 'vindictive, terrible man, serious flaw'. Mrs Paul Richards in a letter to Miller of April 1997 recognised that

> John Corner was a much more complex character and very easily took offence about very minor things… I remember that Paul refused to quarrel with him about some matter connected with the Kinabalu National Park… he remained on good though not close terms with him to the end of his [my father's] life.

When I read these, I pondered, for I don't want to portray anything biased about my father. The giver of the first lot of comments did have a falling-out with my father and no doubt was somewhat bitter. Yet his comments in the main ring true to the man that I have found and I remember. However, I don't agree one bit with the view that my father's work 'won't last'. That's wrong, for the proof of that is in the success today of his many writings. The man was also wrong about my father being a collaborator. I am convinced of my father's wartime motives. I have yet to read a book on Singapore and those times, and my bookshelf is full of them, which properly recognises my father's part in the saving of so much. The actions of Holttum, my father, Birtwistle and the Japanese men-of-science seem to have gone almost unnoticed. I have highlighted the tremendous job of conservation which they achieved in those dark days of the Occupation.

As I learned about my father's life in wartime Singapore, one of the things which I became absorbed by, and which still challenges me, is the existence of General Yamashita's battle map of Singapore. My father made efforts to find it after the war. My cousin, Douglas Hurd, has been helping me locate that map but on 3 April 2013, after receiving another letter from the UK Ministry of Defence, he feels this is his end of the line. I have made efforts and to date have also failed but I have no doubt it existed, indeed exists; unfortunately 'no doubt' is not proof of existence.

In 2009, I made an effort to find either a photograph of, or some official reference to, the map. I contacted, through Henry Barlow, Patricia Lim, a retired librarian whose published bibliographies have been useful to scholars researching the history of the Malaysian region. She suggested that the charcoal sketch 'may still lie covered by plaster'. Indeed, in her book, *Johor, 1855 – 1957: Local History, Local Landscapes*, published in 2009 before I exchanged with her, she refers to 'the battle plan that was found drawn on the parapet of that tower'.

I have searched in depth and have established that a photograph does not appear in the records of Dr Tadamichi Koga. Yuki Hasebe asked her uncle who has Teizo Esake's diaries. However, after a thorough search, no reference or photograph could be found. I asked the same of Mrs Yukie Kanae, the daughter of Dr Yata Haneda. She told me that her father's diaries were sent some years ago to Harano Agricultural Museum, in Amami Island, but the island was considerably damaged in October 2010 by a storm and the museum remains closed with much material lost.

Boris Hembry, in his book *Malayan Spymaster*, commented that the British Military Administration 'even in the short time they had been in Malaya, was already gaining a reputation for maladministration, extreme arrogance and high-handedness, and corruption'. So the map could have been lost to the void of the BMA: yet the War Office informed my father in 1946 that a photo had appeared in some secret document.

*

During the last chapel of each term at Twyford School, the headmaster, the Reverend Bob Wickham, to whom I owe so much, read from Ecclesiastes Chapters 11 and 12.

Chapter 11 opens with: 'Cast thy bread upon the waters: for thou shalt find it after many days'. And it closes: 'Therefore remove sorrow from thy heart, and put away evil from thy flesh: for childhood and youth are vanity'.

Within Chapter 12 are these sage words:

Vanity of vanity saith the preacher; all is vanity. And moreover, because the preacher was wise, he still taught the people knowledge: yea, he gave good heed, and sought out, and set in order many proverbs.

The preacher sought to find out acceptable words: and that which was written was upright, even words of truth.

I have sought out acceptable words, not easy at times, and I hope that what I have written is upright and they are words of truth.

I have found a man passionate about tropical botany, the wonderful forests of Malaya and conservation; he was a relentless botanist and a good and fearless leader. Outwardly he was an assured man but he was uncertain in some circumstances of life. He could be complicated and was undoubtedly aloof to those whom he saw as beneath him in science. However, he sits proudly with the best of those seeking to establish the evolution of all that is around us; Professor E. J. H. Corner was an inspiration of scientific discovery in the 20th century. His commitment to botany was complete, as illustrated by his telegram to his good friend Barton Worthington: "'Cave oppidians natura sylvicola' ie, beware the towns folk, or those who dwell by preference in big and artificial places, for Nature loves the woods – biologist pleading to another lest he should forsake his calling." He was married to botany and should have remained single in life as another close friend, William Birtwistle, advised.

My relationship with my father can be likened to that of Karl Beethoven to his uncle, Ludwig van Beethoven. Karl was a sensitive child and intelligent young man, with a brilliant yet angry father. Ludwig, who changed the course of classical music forever, was his surrogate father. To understand this, and the composer Beethoven, one must know something of all his music, the enormous variety, but especially the contrasts between his *Missa Solemnis* and the wonderful and inspiring *Choral* symphony; the Razumovsky string quartets and the piano trios, particularly the *Archduke*; the *Moonlight* and *Hammerklavier* piano sonatas, so very difficult to play in their different ways – as was my father to get to know; his Jekyll and Hyde music – but wonderful music available to those with the patience and ability to be inspired, play and understand.

Karl Beethoven attempted suicide; Bob Wickham warned my father, in a simile with Julian Hurd, that if he persisted in his treatment of me, he risked the same.

The composer, Joseph Haydn, remarked with a sigh when attending an early rehearsal, perhaps the first, of Beethoven's 3rd Symphony – the *Eroica* – 'the symphony will never be the same again'. My father brought a new interpretation to tropical botany, his *Choral* symphony was his contribution to the sciences for all people.

His later life dwelt in a more sombre fashion as did the string quartets of Beethoven; his piano though, that Bluthner, brought him cheer as did the music of Brahms – so much written in the minor key.

I have no doubt that his discoveries have changed much botanical thinking, yet he failed with his family as did Beethoven. Could that be a hallmark of excellence?

To understand my father, one must know something of his science – and that I did not. So many have written that he was a very private man. His unhappy childhood led him to seek solace in marriage, and a family, yet in both he failed miserably. His temper kept him at a distance.

He tried hard with me in the years 1948 to the early 1950s, as the letters in Pandora illustrate, but the loss of my mother and the arrival of Helga never gave that a chance. He ceded his responsibility to we three children. He backed himself into a corner – beware the dangerous corner!

I have no doubt that he loved us, but didn't know how to. It is a tragedy of life that wisdom comes with age. Had I been blessed with wisdom in my youth I might have acted differently and not left home.

I look back with sadness that my early life was so unhappy. This was what affected me most and I went through many periods feeling angry about it, sometimes most depressed. I wanted desperately to hide it all, forget that past of which I felt so guilty, was ashamed of, and hurt by. It is only time, and maturity, which brings one to realisation, and in my case, also a suitcase – 'To be given to Kay, wherever he may be'.

In Pandora, I found a story which meant little to me initially, but re-reading it a few times brought me to the appreciation of the botany, and its messages, botanical and otherwise. Sadly, pages were missing although I found one in the Janet West file. My father's skill in writing and passion for conservation shines through, as do other messages – a metaphor of his life. It has no title but tells 'the lives of ancient trees', to which I add a subtitle: 'the wisdom of plants'.

My father's enigma, like Elgar's, is hidden in some key phrases of his remarkable story. The message is overwhelming.

Talk about children! Why you're so old and aloof you don't know if you've got any...

'Lawyer', they say! 'I can mind my own business', he sighed...

How I dislike men. They have no dignity and behave like a horde of big ants...

Am I really so intolerant? Yes, I do admit...

It was the penalty of the monarch to be out of touch...

Sooner or later, his stroke would fall, just as befell his forebears...

'Lay off!' shouted Terap, incensed by the continual aspersion. 'Lay off with your abuse and refinement. I'm sick of your airs and contumely. As if you weren't just a bit of timber like the rest of us! Lofty scaffolding! You're growing more like a gargantuan skeleton every day, and you know what's coming. I'm going to lead the revolution that will destroy the forest and burn you up. Even the honey isn't all yours and you're good for nothing else. His words were drowned by distant snorts, as if un-muffled motor cycles were tuning up.

Are these pointers to the key of the door to the life of the tropical botanist? Do they summarise the threads which run through my story?

In this story too was heard the sound of the chain-saw rising in creeping crescendo above the soft and natural sounds of the gentle rustling of the leaves of those marvellous forests of the Land of the Dendrons – my father's paradise on earth. This too is a story about the conservation of forests.

There are wonderful descriptions of forests in Pandora which are to me the memory I want of my father, the one I never knew. Through my father's descriptive writing and simple use of words, I have become taken by botany and all the sciences which enthralled him. He so wanted, all his life, to enthuse others with the study of plants, animals and indeed evolution and he tried with me but that failed, and now I wish I had had a different teacher in him.

At first, as the sun set there was a pillar of cloud to the north; its crest was ghostly white, its west was a soft emerald azure, like a dream of night, its east was faintly gilded. As the sun set, the full moon rose and both at once cast their light on this cloud, and what material in all the universe can draw and reflect light like a cloud? Then when the moon was up, silvered burgeons loomed round, with distant rolls of thunder yet all the valleys were swathed in mist and the mist mounted up in fantastic heights so that it seemed to touch the clouds, and all glowed in silver beams. Then there came a gentle breath… and the mist moved… and while it lay in the valleys, the hill-tops and the tops of trees became visible.

What are those like giant steps mounting up? Whose hand is that, thrust out? I think they are the boughs of trees that cloud the slopes. What is that brow so frowning? Whose are these silver locks? Hush, they are the winds of clouds, and the raiment's of mist. Do you think tonight the deer will sleep? Do the moonbeams reach through the forest? Does the full moon stir the beasts as it stirs the soul of man? Drip… drip… drip… everything that is living is weeping tonight.

He weeps as much for the sadness of the loss of his children as the hillsides becoming barren. And I weep for not having known the author of these words.

My father rarely lost a chance to stress the call for forest conservation but few listened and fewer acted. He wrote in the early 1930s: 'The trees depart in flames, and nought remains to clothe our ignorance'. In August 1957, my father wrote to the Linnean Society about *Education and Nature-Protection in the Tropics.*

It is acknowledged that in temperate countries the care of scenery and of wildlife is beholden to the public conscience. In the tropics, where nature is grander, I find no public exertion and no educational drive in school or university to this real patriotism.

He comments on the increasing tendency in the tropical countries to accept that exploitation of the natural resources for financial reward is natural and therefore acceptable. To counter this, he encouraged the teaching of landscape and natural history 'not biology, geology and geography' which were 'partial and cramped with technicalities', and ended by saying:

> Then, I believe, the problem of nature-protection in tropical countries will take its proper place in public administration: and civilisation will have progressed by this measure of sentiment.

Have I found my father? I think so but not the kind of father that I had hoped to find.

Am I proud to be the son of Professor E. J. H. Corner? I very nearly am. But I can never forgive him for the hate which he engendered in us children of his wife, our mother, and her friends and family which became indelibly deep-seated – that was evil.

Yet, when I contacted the Forest Research Institute of Malaysia, the institute's immediate reply bowled me over and humbled me:

> We are greatly honoured to be in communication with the son of the renowned EJH Corner. Your late father's work has brought light to many mycologists in the Malayan region and also the world. As a tribute to your late father, we would like to present the two books related to your father which were published recently by FRIM.

That places everything in context and it confirms, if by now I need that confirmation, my father's position in science and that it is not forgotten.

I have acquired a great respect for my father; I have found an admiration for his scientific work and I now understand why he was so awkward in his family life. I come close to loving him. I am proud to have the Corner name and the values so associated and am thankful to have learned the peace and enjoyment of classical music and to have been touched by his passion for conservation.

Va pensiero.

Adieu.

I have found a father.

Appendix A
The Durian Theory of the Origins of Flowering Plants

The Durian Theory was first published by the Linnaean Society in 1949. My father's premise, of which he was passionate, was that tropical plants are at the centre of importance to plant evolution. He claimed to have identified the ancestral plant. His theory was not universally accepted, but it made him known in the world of tropical botany and immediately stimulated debate.

Of the impetus of the theory, Dr Peter H Raven, President Emeritus of Missouri Botanic Garden, St. Louis, told me:

I'd say your father thought of the Durian Theory because of his great imagination and intelligence. Confronted with the tropical rainforest he wanted to try to see how it could have fitted into the origin of flowering plants, and what particular features would have been important there that didn't occur in the temperate region.

My father put it this way:

[T]he durian theory is like the rijstafel with many side-dishes to which you may help yourself. The main course needs capacity! If it can be digested, there will be a revival to enlighten, and thrill every fibre of botany.

In his book *The Freshwater Swamp-forest of South Johore and Singapore*, my father wrote that on a visit to the forest south of Seletar reservoir with Professor Kwan Koriba during the occupation of Singapore, he 'found the fruits of *Sloanea javanica*, and the durian-theory began'.

However, the ideas of the theory had been forming much earlier for he concluded his letter of 10 August 1931 to Barton Worthington by remarking that, 'This is the beginning of durianology for it revealed the problem of what was the durian doing in the forest'. In the 'Recollection' which my father contributed to *Revolutionary Botany 'Thalassiophyta' and other essays by A. H. Church*, he wrote: 'I drew, of course, on all the writings of Church and carried on where he had stopped at Pteridophyta by means of the Durian Theory which is, indeed, the demonstration of Churchian robustness'.

I found in Pandora an untitled and undated roughly typed document – it is my father's recount of the theory written in simple language so that it is most understandable even to a non-specialist.

Without a moment for the Durian my writings would not be complete! That it is a big and smelly fruit of the Far East, with an acquired taste, is the popular notion. It has brought to me a whirlwind of thought. Chance had directed me and I have built a Durianology about the evolution of the tropical forest, about the evolution of flowering plants, their fruits and their seeds; and of course the natural history of those forests up to the descent of man.

The durian is a large and evergreen tree which fruits seasonally, twice a year around June to July and then December to January. It is often seen in the Malay kampongs, indeed in those of SE Asia. The flowers open early afternoon and disintegrate by around 2 am the following morning.

They smell of milk, which is an indication of bat pollination, and it is generally held that they are pollinated at night by small fruit-eating bats.

My father believed that bees – the evening bees – were also involved in pollination. The fruits are large and spiny; they take over three months to develop and can be the size of a human head. As they ripen they fall to the ground with a thud and begin to split. It is at this point that they start to smell! There are countless descriptions of this smell and drains, sewers, and the Singapore River at low tide are amongst them.

The smell resides in the husk; the Durian-eater pays no attention to it and, for the elegant, the seeds are served separately.

Their taste* is also difficult to define but strawberries and raspberries, caramel – indeed cream – are amongst those often used. The fruit is able to be eaten for only a few days after falling for the pulp soon turns rancid.

Its presence is forbidden in hotels and public transport. Yet, the demand is unsatisfied. If I were rich and inclined to business, I would own Durian orchards and a fleet of aeroplanes to meet external markets, and finance botany from the proceeds. The taste is acquired.

My father told of the repellent look of the slimy seeds but he persisted and came to enjoy durian although it never was his favourite.

If I had to choose the best fruit in the world, I would hesitate between the best mango and the best peach; the Durian lacks their subtle acidity. Those fruits are products of cultivation. The Durian seems to me to be a product of natural selection or, as I often prefer, natural perfection.

The name, durian, derives from the Malay *duri*, meaning 'thorn', so durian means 'thorny thing'. My father wrote of botanists having little interest in it, which he found curious, and his ever-enquiring mind asked

why the coppery scales on the leaves, the slender twigs, the ramiflorous [flowering on the branches] habit, the nocturnal flowers, and the monstrously delicious fruit? Why thorns and why such extravagance?

* *I first tasted the durian in Singapore many years ago. I tried it again, as a dessert melange in Australia, as did Belinda, and we think we liked it.*

My father recalled his re-learning of botany when he first arrived in Singapore and that he became fascinated by the variety of fruits in the forest, usually fallen to the ground. He found them poorly described and consequently little understood, with specialists even being cagy at identifying them from dried herbarium specimens. In studying these fruits, he noticed that a conspicuous kind was usually round or oblong, about the size of an apple

> that ripened red, pink, orange or yellow and split open to display black or dark brown seeds more or less surrounded with red, yellow, or white pulp (botanically, the aril) as if that apple had split open to reveal small plums.

These fruits, he noticed, occurred in various genera of various families. If they were mentioned in books it generally was to imply 'independent evolution in response to seed-dispersal by animals. How or from what was unexplained'.

I have already written of my father's botanising with Kwan Koriba near the Seletar Reservoir in Singapore. In a part of the forest my father had rarely visited, they stumbled on fruits of the description just given but with variations in detail. My father was unable either to recognise it or find the tree from which they had come. The next day, whilst 'searching' in the herbarium, he found 'that it was yet another genus in another family, namely the tree *Sloanea* in Elaeocarpaceae, and *Elaeocarpus* had fruits like plums'. Why did so many different genera and families have this spectacular fruit, my father pondered, and he realised that the durian was another example for

> there were red Durians with black seeds and red and yellow pulp. The Durians were heavily armoured and traces of this armour occurred in such fruits of other families. The horse chestnut (*Aesculus*) was a durian without pulp. Nutmegs were one-seeded durians without thorns.

And suddenly the light shone – 'that this kind of fruit, the fleshy arillate capsule or follicle, was not a freak of modern delectation but a primitive kind from which others, indeed all others, had evolved'.

This was revolutionary indeed, for it 'had all manner of consequences concerning the evolutionary history of leaves, flowers, twigs, and trees themselves', my father wrote. He immediately put his mind to the problem and debated it with Koriba and raised issues as they came to him. Koriba, senior in age and most experienced, 'criticised and improved, and I like to think that, as we sat upstairs in the laboratory, he at my desk and I sat at the window seat overlooking the herbarium, he was my first convert'.

My father recognised that the fruiting plant, indeed the flowering plant, had effectively introduced the era of vegetarianism and that the durian was a strong signpost. Noticing that most wild animals ate the pulp and the seeds when they could, he carried out an experiment with one of his botanical monkeys. He placed the pulpy durian seeds on a plate and offered it and in a flash the monkey filled its pouches, the back and front of its mouth and even held seeds in both hands, indeed it had so much it couldn't actually eat them!

After the war and when back in Cambridge in 1946, he told of his findings at a lecture to the Cambridge University Botany Club. At the conclusion, Harry Godwin suggested he call it the Durian Theory and that it became. Godwin was his third convert for Geoffrey Herklots was the second.

Besides being published by the Linnean Society in 1949, The Durian Theory was published in the *Annals of Botany* also in 1949; a French translation by S and F Halls appeared in *Adansonia* in 1964 with a preface by Professor G. Mangenot for *Les durianologistes français*. The theory was criticised both for and against – it was received with scepticism from its outset, but was admired for its ingenuity, breadth of vision, and novel insights – although my father tells of finding 'no really adverse criticism' in the many years since he first published the theory 'and that his faith remains'. Its alternative aspect as the origin of the modern tree has been greatly expanded by Professor F. Hallè of Montpelier University, by Dr P. S. Ashton in his works on tropical ecology and the tree-family of *Dipterocarps*, by Dr D. J. Mabberley in his account of '*Lobelia* and *Senecio*', and by Dr E. C. Bate-Smith in his biochemical and systematic researches on leuco-anthocyanins.

My father wrote that he found support for the theory in the Malesian species, *Ficus*, which he had summarised in his book *Seeds of Dicotyledons* (1976). He suggested that botany took little notice with its preponderance of research on temperate floras leaving little time 'for the overwhelming tropical floras'.

Dr Ruth Kiew in an article in the *Flora Malesiana Bulletin* of 12 January 1997 pointed out that the substance of the Durian Theory was not new.

> [T]o tell Corner that his Durian Theory was not original and had already been published long ago was not a chance most people would have taken, but this Dr. G.C. Evans did and lived to tell the tale. As predicted, Corner bridled at the suggestion but on being shown the evidence, agreed that it was so and indeed quoted the reference in a later paper where he acknowledged the pre-eminence of its author (Corner 1980); "Hence the man of the large mind abides in the thick not in the thin, in the fruit not in the flower'"; Lao-tzu (circa 6th century BC); Tao Te Ching XXXVIII 84a.

*

My father attended the Centenary and Bicentenary Congress of Biology in 1958, held at the University of Malaya, in Singapore, from 2 to 9 December, and amongst his presentations was a repeat of the first presentation of the Durian Theory at the Cambridge University Botany Club in 1946.

It was written up in *The Proceedings of the Centenary and Bicentenary Congress of Biology Singapore in 1958* and published by the University of Malaya Press. My father opened:

> This is a theory of the evolution of broad-leafed (angiospermous) tropical forest. It sprang from a detail, namely the aril, which invests the seeds of several tropical fruits among which the durian (Bombacaceae, *Durio zibethinus*) is a familiar example.

He explained that the theory is important to botany simply because it presents the evolution of the flowering plant in the tropics.

It presents both the reproductive and the vegetative evolution, which has been overlooked in the orthodox approach from temperate vegetation (Ranales, Amentiferae). It makes one realise the importance of the new vegetation cover, superseding the palaeozoic, which the angiosperm introduced and it directs attention from academic botany to the urgency of field-work in the tropics…

I can hear my father stressing this, 'the urgency of field-work' because he was passionate about that: you must go and see for yourself was his direction always.

To the zoologist the interest lies in the effect of the evolution of this vegetation. In place of the relatively non-putrescible and inedible palaeozoic vegetation (fern, gymnosperm), there arose, not once, but by age-long degrees, the putrescible and edible modern vegetation into which the myriad animals now fit.

Again he stressed that the theory becomes the evolution of tropical natural history:

The evidence is derived from living tropical plants. Fossils do not exist. But, if we are to understand flowering plants, the immense diversity of the tropical forests must be read, and the story seems to be this. Initially plants like cycads (pachycaul) with their low, smothering habit, established themselves and reproduced by black or brown seeds invested by red or yellow, edible arils. These plants were not heavily lignified, but they may have been spinous. Whether they had flowers distinct from fruits is debatable, but the palm, the *Victoria amazonica*, and the papaya (*Carica*) are such angiospermous derivatives. From this kind of plant, low in stature, but massive in construction, there gradually evolved the lofty, much branched tree with slender twigs (leptocaul), lignifying with secondary thickening into trunk and limbs, yet bearing much simplified leaves, flowers, fruits and seeds, befitting the slender growing points.

Early stages became embedded in the lowest layer of the heightening vegetation, or pioneers in vegetational succession, or epiphytes: and thus these evolving forests built up the immense framework of tropical biology. Stages in tree-evolution occur in many families and, even, in different genera of the same family. This means that floral or reproductive evolution, defining families and genera, preceded vegetative. Fossils show that from early Cretaceous the flowering plants have scarcely changed. For their origin we must go back to the beginning of the Mesozoic period, if not boldly into the Palaeozoic. And, if true of plants, so must it be of animals, which evolved from them. The botanist must doubt the avian and mammalian chronology, based on age of fossilisation, and put their beginnings much earlier than usually accepted. I note recently that Croizat (Panbiogeography, 1958) also argues for this long-term view, and that mammals (Triconodonts) are known from the Triassic (Kermack, Proc. Geol. Soc.n.1533, 1956, 31-31). There have been several objectors to this theory. None has met its argument, and no alternative for the origin of tropical forests has been offered. (See appendix F, Corner, E.J.H. The Durian Theory extended. Phytomorphology, 3 (1953), 465-476; 4)

Dr David Mabberley wrote about the Durian Theory in his Royal Society obituary of my father:

The Durian Theory is an extension of the ideas of Church, carried through to the development of the angiosperm vegetation. Faced with the range of tree morphology in a single monophyletic group, Corner asked the question, 'Which came first?', the stumpy little-branched form with big leaves (pachycaul, a word he coined) or the tall much-branched tree with slender twigs and small leaves (leptocaul); his argument hinges on the probability of the rising height of the angiosperm forest in taking over from other seed-plants, so that the pachycaul form is seen as primitive. The fundamental importance of the interaction of animals as pollinators and seed-dispersal agents in the success of the angiosperms led him to ponder whether the arillate form of seed, seen in a wide range of unrelated groups, with its "reward" for dispensers, was primitive or advanced. He argued that the convergent evolution of such an elaboration of the seed, a third integument, developing in exactly the same way in monophyletic group after monophyletic group, was an unreasonable assertion, so he took the arillate seed, associated with a dehiscent fruit, as the primitive condition.

Such a 'reward' is in the seeds of the durian (*Durio zibethinus*), and when Corner gave a lecture on his theory at the Cambridge Botany Club (1946) Harry Godwin suggested it be called the Durian Theory – although the durian, with its notoriously smelly, but delicious seeds, is a leptocaul tree.

From Corner's consideration of tree architecture comes the associated notion of reduction of leaf-size and complexity from pinnate to simple, from many veins to few, from apical growth to intercalary growth, to give the range of form seen today. From seed studies comes the simplification of the aril, its loss and its functions being taken over by other tissues of seed or fruit, to give the range of form seen today. To Corner, the primitive angiosperm was something like a terrestrial *Victoria amazonica*, with large insect-pollinated flowers, arillate seeds taken by animals, and massive primary construction: massive stems, buds and leaves. It is of interest to note that recent theorists have come to similar conclusions on 'palaeoherbs' from different evidence. Moreover, although criticised in detail, there has yet to be a theory of the origin of angiosperm vegetation as all-embracing as the Durian Theory.

Crucial are Corner's ideas on the co-evolution of animals and plants and of the 'transference of function', which are now today's orthodoxy. It was the spur for looking at temperate groups of plants in the context of the tropical woody ones, notably the pachycauls; from it came general principles of plant construction, schematised by Hallè in France (the theory has been translated into French) and Oldman in The Netherlands, and now known as Corner's Rules. The unbranched palm-type of tree 'architecture' in Halle and Oldman's scheme is known as Corner's Model. A basis for understanding forest structure and leaf stratification generally followed through the work of Henry Horn in the USA.

In 2007, Belinda and I visited the Australia National Botanic Gardens in Canberra entirely unannounced but were made most welcome. Dr Heino Lepp met us in the herbarium and I asked about the Durian Theory. He kindly agreed to send me his 'version for the layman' which I now gratefully reproduce.

In the durian fruit the case is spiny and the seed is wrapped in a colourful fleshy edible surround, called an aril, so you can call it an arillate fruit. The durian also falls to the ground and splits open when mature. Your father noted that such arillate fruits were uncommon but were found in a number of different families of plants.

Plants have a hierarchic classification. Low down is the species, next up is genus then there's family and there are another few rungs. The idea of such a classification is that related species are grouped together in a genus. Related genera (the plural of genus) are grouped in a family. To say that two plant species belong to the same genus is to say that they have a reasonably close relationship, whereas if the two species are in the same family (but in different genera) the relationship is more distant. A rough analogy is to say that you're closely related to a sibling, but more distantly related to a cousin – though there's a definite biological connection between you and your cousin as well. In this, very rough analogy, you and your sibling represent two species in the one genus, while your cousin is in a different genus – but in the same family.

If you see a feature common to a number of disparate plant families there are two possibilities. Either that feature has evolved independently in each family or the feature must have been present in the more ancient plants from which the modern families evolved. Going back to the human analogy, suppose you and your cousin share some striking physical feature. The two of you might have acquired that feature independently or you might both have inherited it from some common ancestor. Suppose you both join some society that, as part of its initiation ceremony, creates a scar on the right forearm of each new member. You each have that scar, but it's clearly a case of 'independent evolution'. On the other hand, suppose you both have a particularly distinctive shape of jaw (think of the Hapsburg Jaw) and neither of you have ever had any illness or injury that could have caused such a shape. Then it's very likely to be a case that you both inherited this feature from a common ancestor.

When your father saw arillate fruits in different plant families he surmised that this feature was not a case of independent evolution, but indicated a feature that must have been present in the ancient plants from which modern plants evolved. It is called a 'primitive' feature or condition. Your father went on to surmise that many different types of fruits found in modern trees have been derived from the arillate fruits by different modifications in the aril. He gave arguments for the derivation of different types of splitting and non-splitting fruits, fleshy to woody and fully arillate to non-arillate fruits from a durian-like ancestor. He also noted that the seed of the durian fruit is made for animal dispersal – the colourful, tasty flesh attracts animals of various sorts. He therefore proposed that animal-dispersal of tree seed was a 'primitive' feature. Before falling and splitting, the spiny outer would be deterrent to eating.

In the scar versus jaw example you will have noted that once you've observed a common feature, you still need to do some detective work (sometimes a lot of detective work) before you can come up with a believable cause of that feature. So your father looked at many examples to gather the evidence to support the durian theory.

Note that primitive means 'earliest, from which other variants have evolved' and does not mean that a plant showing a primitive feature is poorly adapted to its environment. Note also that the Durian Theory does not say that other trees evolved from the durian. The Durian Theory says that the primitive tree had a durian-like fruit. The durian theory would allow the modern durian tree to have undergone its own evolution from a primitive durian-like ancestor but the modern-day durian, in its fruit, still shows a primitive feature.

Since 1949, advances in science and continuing studies in plant evolution have proved that the Durian Theory is untenable although, according to Professor Roy Watling, the theory '[a]s your father explained it originally, and held to the idea, it has never been challenged'. Dr Peter Ashton told me that both fossil and molecular-biogeographic evidence now favours small trees or even herbs of the seasonal tropics, South America and Africa, as the origin of flowering plants. David Mabberley states that 'any modern book on plant evolution will not include the Durian Theory' and I learned from Dr John Dransfield that the Durian Theory is rarely cited these days.

As a student I found the theory inspiring but in my own palm studies for my PhD the basic principles of the theory did not seem to be borne out by my results. These days, botanists use cladistic methodology to analyze huge data sets, largely comprising molecular information, to develop hypotheses of evolutionary relationships and directions of evolution. I suspect only very rarely do the results in any way coincide with what would be suggested by the Durian Theory. Morphology has shown to be so fickle, with unusual traits evolving in parallel many times over and that molecular data seem much more reliable in indicating relationships.

Dr David Frodin believes that a number of principles of the theory may still hold good, particularly in relation to 'pachycaulous' plants.

A major test has come about with the rise of molecular (genomic) evidence for plant relationships and their widespread application (though sometimes there is too much dependence on it to the diminution or morphology, particularly where we don't necessarily always know what controls what). What we should look for is any potential 'relicts' in a phyletic series and see if there is potential evidence which is more or less congruent with the principles of the 'Durian Theory'. There are some papers where such has been expressed, but not that many – as many botanists still receive a largely 'orthodox' training (and in some places potentially narrower than before). We may not have moved on that far from 80 years ago.

In contrast, Peter Raven was firm in his conviction that The Durian Theory is no longer supported or quoted.

[I]t would be fair to say that no one who is in touch with modern scientific evidence accepts the Durian Theory for the origin of angiosperms now. It was a perfectly plausible hypothesis that did inspire a lot of thought and discussion when he proposed it, and I do think that would have had a lot to do with his reasons for proposing it. But it is clearly not the story of the way in which angiosperms originated, and it would be best if you simply said so… and at the same time appreciating all the discussion and hypotheses that followed.

And so I have 'said so'. Yet, as David Frodin wrote:

His Durian Theory may have relied strongly on rhetoric, but this was as much asset as liability. It was posited to provoke, to express a point of view at a time when our understanding of the tropical forest was little more than rudimentary. It was not necessarily to be taken at face value… One day someone should write a paper "The Durian Theory Revisited" in an attempt to see [if] is it still worthwhile as a thought-system; are there any underpinnings or otherwise from the now-substantial array of results from gene sequence analyses measured against the rate of substitutions over time, on which molecular phylogenies are based; and more evidence from macro- and micro-morphology.

I can now better understand the Durian Theory and find a curious coincidence that my father studied the durian because I see a remarkable resemblance in him – a hard and prickly fruit, a thorny thing, but when opened up the 'evil smell' gives way to a delicious soft-centre that many were still afraid to try!

Appendix B
Selected Contents of the Suitcase

I now think the suitcase was the one on the back of my father's MG sports car on 1 February 1939 in which he drove mother on honeymoon. He took that suitcase to Singapore in 1939 as he did that MG. When I set out on this story, I thought that the suitcase was the one bought for me to take to Twyford, but as time went on, I recalled that that case had my name imprinted in capitals on the top.

The suitcase contained many pages without title or description, and in note form. This all gives the impression of casual collecting but the father I knew never did anything by accident – always by intention – he was a meticulous man.

The full list of the Pandora contents, with all the letters copy-typed, fills 125 pages of A4 paper typed in 12-point Arial.

My father must have kept that case well hidden from his second wife and for so many years. She surely would have destroyed it and its contents if she had known the intended destination.

The newspaper lining the suitcase is the *Cambridge Evening News* dated Monday, 30 September 1974. This suggests, but is no proof, that my father began assembling the contents from that date, around 14 years after I had left home.

Many photos of Singapore/Malaya, some in negative form.
Two photo albums of people and scenes in Singapore and Malaya before 1942.
Photos by my father and latterly my mother.
An aerial view of Lajes airport in the Azores.
AA Maps of Singapore/Malaya, pre-war.
The British School Niteroi; a few of my school books.
My school reports, school bills and memorabilia from Twyford School and The Leys.
Twyford School magazines, *The Twyfordian*.
The Leys School magazine, *Leys Fortnightly*.
A Twyford School prospectus dating around 1948/49.
Many letters from the headmaster of Twyford School (The Revd R. G. Wickham) to my father, and some to The Revd Wickham, 1949–1954.
Letters from my mother to me at Twyford and after, and from me to my mother.
A letter from my father to his new mother-in-law in New York dated 1 March 1947.
Some of the seaweeds collected and dried in Niteroi by my father and myself, bright as the day they were dried and mounted.
Sketches by my father in Niteroi, in letters to me from 1947–1948.
The RMS *Andes* Passenger list, menus and memorabilia.
Pan Am 'Crossing the Line' certificates issued to me and my sister Christine.
Many used and un-used gift greeting cards, mostly American.
Scrap books of the birds and wildlife in Virginia compiled by me with help from Grandma Bailey, circa 1947.
One of my trainspotting books from 1948, by Ian Allan Ltd., *The ABC of British*

Locomotives with the numbers of those I had seen duly ticked off.

A story about the formulation of the Durian Theory.

A copy of *The Marquis, a Tale of Syonan-to*.

A story about Jim and Pen Landon.

Some of my father's writings and stories: 'The SGH/Care at its Best'; 'Monkey Business'; 'That once was beautiful'; 'The Lives of Ancient Trees'; 'Penelope Landon'; 'The Blue of Elaine'.

Mint copy of *The Kings Messenger*, the magazine of Kings School Singapore, Michaelmas Term 1941. It includes 'Monkeys' by S.K. and E.J.H. Corner.

An obituary notice, of my American grandmother, Dorothy Kavanagh Bailey.

Appendix C
Awards given to E. J. H. Corner

The Darwin Medal of the Royal Society, 1960. It is bestowed for work of acknowledged distinction in the broad area of biology in which Charles Darwin worked, notably in evolution, population biology, organismal biology and biological diversity. It is awarded biennially (in even years) and was created in memory of Charles Darwin, FRS, and was first awarded in 1890. The citation states that the medal was awarded to my father 'in recognition of his distinguished and strikingly original botanical work in tropical forests'.

The Patron's Medal of the Royal Geographic Society, 1966. The Gold Medal is the most prestigious of the awards presented by the Royal Geographical Society. The Gold Medal is not one award but consists of two separate awards: the Founder's Medal 1830 and the Patron's Medal 1838. The award is given for 'the encouragement and promotion of geographical science and discovery', and requires Royal approval before an award can be made. The awards originated as an annual gift of fifty guineas from King William IV, first made in 1831, 'to constitute a premium for the encouragement and promotion of geographical science and discovery'. The RGS decided in 1839 to change this monetary award into two gold medals: Founder's Medal and the Patron's. My father was awarded the Founder's Medal, the citation reading; 'for botanical exploration in North Borneo and the Solomon Islands'. The exploration in North Borneo refers to his leading of two expeditions to Mount Kinabalu, in 1961 and 1964, sponsored by the Royal Society and the Sabah Society. The Founder's Medal, designed by W. Wyon, is engraved with the recipient's name and the date of the award. One side of the medal displays the bare head of King William IV and on the reverse side is the figure of Minerva standing in front of a globe, holding a wreath and a scroll. A sextant and other surveying instruments lay at her feet.

The International Botanical Congress Medal, 1969. It was presented during the XIth International Botanical Congress, Seattle as an Honorary Vice-President of the congress. The medal was struck by Medallic Art Co., New York; inscribed 'E. J.H.CORNER VICE PRESIDENT'; struck bronze 63 mm.

The Linnaean Medal (formerly the Gold Medal) of the Linnaean Society of London, 1970. It was established in 1888, and is awarded annually alternately to a botanist or a zoologist or (as has been common since 1958) to one of each in the same year. The medal was of gold until 1976. The Medal is awarded by the Linnaean Society Council as an expression of the Society's esteem and appreciation for service to science. Any biologist, irrespective of nationality, who is not at the time a member of Council, is also eligible to receive the Medal, which is presented at the annual Anniversary Meeting by the President.

The President of the Society, in his presentation address, taken from the 'Record of the Proceedings of the Linnean Society of London for the Session 1969-70', in: Biol. J. Linn. Soc., 2, pp. 322-324, concludes with: 'John Corner, the Fellows of this Society admire immensely your capacity to take some "sordid botanical object and to revivify it durianologically", clothing it in red and black, flavouring it with strawberries and cream and placing it on a phylogenetic pinnacle within some gorgeous tropical forest of a bygone age, whose luxuriance and diversity would be unimaginable without your help. I am happy that it should fall to me to present you, by the authority and in the name of The Linnaean Society of London, this mark of their appreciation of your distinguished scientific work.'

Interestingly his Cambridge research students Professor Dr David Mabberley, Dr Peter Ashton and Dr John Dransfield are also awardees of The Linnaean Medal.

Commander of the Most Excellent Order of the British Empire (CBE), January 1972 under the New Year's Honours List of Queen Elizabeth II. It is given to award an achievement or service in a leading role at a regional level making a highly distinguished, innovative contribution with a wide impact.

The Victoria Medal of Honour from the Royal Horticultural Society, 1974. This medal was established to confer conspicuous honour on British horticulturists resident in the United Kingdom. The award, published in the February 1974 volume of the *Journal of the Royal Horticultural Society* contains no citation but I have been provided a copy of the original typewritten extract from the proceedings of the 170th Annual Meeting of the Society on 19 February 1974 which contains the citation delivered by Lord Aberconway, the President of the Society. It reads: 'Professor Corner, though originally a mycological botanist, has become the world's greatest authority on tropical plants, and especially those of south-east Asia, which he got to know during the sixteen years he spent in Singapore, in the gardens department of the Straits Settlements. Subsequently, Professor Corner, I understand you travelled extensively in the tropics in several continents, wrote widely on tropical plants, and became Professor of Tropical Botany at the place of your original technical education, Cambridge. I am sure that all the people whom you have encouraged to grow stove plants in Britain are much more happy at this award than they are at the prospects of getting fuel to keep those stove plants warm'.

The Colloquia Botanicorum Medal, 1975 was awarded to my father for his presentation at the XIIth Colloquia Botanicorum, inscribed 'E.J.H. Corner'; struck bronze, square 55 x 55 mm.

The Robert Allerton Award for Excellence in Tropical Botany or Horticulture, 1981 was awarded to my father and Dr Harold St. John. This award was initiated in 1975 and is given either for a specific achievement or to reflect an entire career in science. The records show: Dr Harold St John (1981), Bishop Museum, Honolulu, specialist in Hawaiian flora; and Dr E. J. H. Corner (1981), Rijksherbarium, The Netherlands, world specialist in the large and taxonomically complex genus *Ficus* (the figs).

The International Prize for Biology, 1985. The short official citation of the inaugural award says 'for Taxonomy or Systematic Biology'.

The Prize was established in commemoration of Emperor Showa's (Emperor Hirohito) long-time devotion to biological research. The booklet *The Ten Years of International Prize for Biology* states: 'The establishment of the Prize was brought to realisation in 1985 by the earnest desire of Japanese biologists for an international prize to be awarded in systematic biology and other fields of fundamental biology as well as the concerted efforts of the Japan Academy, the Japan Society for the Promotion of Science and other relevant institutions and organisations... A considerable monetary donation is given to the winner'.

It is pertinent that I report Professor Mikiko Ishii's comment which came to me in May 2013. 'As for the International Prize for Biology, I got a call from one of the members [committee]. He told me that they were thinking to nominate Prof. Corner as the very first candidate. They highly appreciated your father's academic achievements but also your father's friendship and cooperation with the Japanese scientists during the war, keeping the Museum as it had been. The gentleman who called me asked me to collect materials concerning Prof. Corner as much as possible and present them to him. I called Prof. Corner immediately and told him the story. He was delighted with it and helped me greatly. I was invited and involved in every celebration, including the ceremony. Officially, your father was awarded the prize on his scientific achievements, but to get the very first one, behind the curtain, it involved Japanese government's appreciation for his activity during the war'.

The Golden Key to the City of Yokohama, 1985. Professor Ishii writes: 'as for the golden key, when we visited Dr. Kihara (late emperor's friend scientist) at his institute in Yokohama, we were invited by the mayor of Yokohama at his office in Yokohama. The professor was then given the key and a handkerchief with the pattern of port Yokohama'.

The de Bary Medal of the International Mycological Association, 1996 for an outstanding mycological career. The citation reads 'for lifetime achievement in mycological research, particularly, contributions to ecology and the systematic of wood-decay basidiomycetes'.

A coin marked: 'Brazil, Peter II, 2000 reis, 1889' was given to my father in 2000. I have not been able to trace any background to this.

Complete list of Publications of Professor E. J. H. Corner,
and his scientific journeys, including key events of his life

I obtained some of these lists from the Archives of Sidney Sussex College,
Cambridge; the original has a date of 27 November 1952 and was forwarded to
them by H. Hamshaw Thomas. Others are from the Singapore Botanic Gardens
and Professor David Mabberley. Forest Research Intitute Malaysia most generously
sent me 'Checklist of Fungi of Malaysia, Research Pamphlet No. 132' by S.S. Lee,
S.A. Alias, E.G.B. Jones, N. Zainuddin and H.T. Chan, and 'Revision of Malaysian
Species of Boletales s. 1. (Basidiomycota) Described by EJH Corner (1972, 1974)'
by E. Horak and from both I was able to check publications and dates. Dr David
Frodin sent me lists up to 1976; Professor Roy Watling provided some others. List
of fungi are from the Plant Sciences Library (Cambridgeshire). Other records were
gathered from the research for this book.

I am most grateful to Roy Watling and David Frodin for checking the list – a
herculean task. All errors though are my responsibility.

1921–1930
1921. Began his studies on the anatomy and development of discomycetes.
1927. A cytological investigation of a sport in a plant of the Garden Stock. *Proc.
Linn. Soc. Lond.* 139: 75-77. This paper was written after university and before
leaving for Singapore in 1929.
1929. Arrived in Singapore as Assistant Director at the Botanic Gardens; papers
from 1929 to 1939 given in Singapore.
1929. A Humariaceous Fungus parasitic on a Liverwort. *Ann. Bot.* 43: 491-505.
1929-1931. Studies in the Morphology of *Discomycetes*, I-V. The marginal growth
of apothecia; *Trans. Brit. Mycol. Soc.* 14: 263-275, 14: 275-291,15:107-120, 15:
121-134, 15: 332-350. Drafts were started before Singapore and completed after
arriving in Singapore.

1931–1940
1931. Became a Fellow of the Linnaean Society.
1931. The identity of the fungus causing Wet-Root Rot of Rubber Trees in Malaya;
Journ. Rubber Res. Inst. Malaya; Vol. 3, pp. 1-4, 120-123.
1932. The fruit-body of *Polystictus xanthopus. Ann. Bot.* vol. 46; 71-111.
1932. The identification of the Brown-Root Fungus: *Gardens' Bull. Straits
Settlements*: 5:317-352.
1932. A Fomes with two systems of hyphae. *Trans. Brit, Myc. Soc*: 17: 51-81.
**1933. First home leave: He arrived in England on 9 or 10 June and returned to
Singapore arriving March 1934. Met the 'oryx'.**
1933. A revision of the Malayan species of *Ficus: Covellia* and *Neomorphe. Journ.*

Malayan Brit. Roy. Asiatic Soc: 11: 1-65.

1934. An evolutionary study in Agarics: *Collybia apalosarca* and the veils. *Trans. Brit. Myc. Soc:* 19: 39-88.

1935. Observations on resistance to powdery mildews. *New Phytol:* 34:180-200.

1935. *Cassia* in Malaya. *Agri-hort. Ass. Mag:* 5: 37.

1935. The fungi of Wicken Fen, Cambridgeshire. *Trans. Brit. Myc. Soc:* 19: 280-287.

1935. A *Nectria* parasitic on a liverwort: with further notes on *Neotiella crozalsiana Gardens' Bull. Straits Settlements* 8: 135-144.

1935. The seasonal fruiting of agarics in Malaya. *Gardens' Bull. Straits Settlements* 9: 79-88.

1935. Pamphlets on Malayan botany published in April 1935 referred to in *The Annual Report of the Director of the Gardens*, 73.

1936. *Hygrophorus* with dimorphous basidospores. *Trans. Brit. Myc. Soc.* 20: 157-184.

1938. Second home leave. He meets Sheila Kavanagh Bailey.

1938. The systematic value of the colour of withering leaves. *Chronica Botanica* 4: 119-121.

1938. *Annual Report of the Director of Gardens for the year 1937.* Singapore: Govt. Printing Office.

1939. 1 February, marries Sheila Kavanagh Bailey at St Peter's Church, Barton village, Cambridgeshire.

1939. Articles on botanical monkeys; *Annual Report of the Gardens Department, Straits Settlements.*

1939. *Zoo Life 1*, 89-92. See 1946 (Refers to use of monkeys for botanical collection in tropical forests).

1939. A revision of *Ficus*, subgenus *Synoecia. Gardens' Bull. Straits Settlements*, 10: 82-161.

1939-1941. Notes on the systematics and distribution of Malayan phanerogams, I-IV. *Gardens' Bull. Straits Settlements* 10:1-55, 56-81 and 239-329. 11:177-235.

1940. Became a Fellow of the Association for the Advancement of Science.

1940. Note: the larger fungi in the tropics. *Trans. Brit. Myc. Soc.,* 24: 357.

1940. Botanical Monkeys. *Malay Agri-hort. Ass. Mag.* 10: 147-149.

1940. *Wayside Trees of Malaya* 2 vols, pp 1-772: text-figs: 260 plates 228. 1st edition: Government Printing Office, Singapore.

1941–1950

1941. January 3rd, son John Kavanagh was born at the Singapore General Hospital.

1941. Notes on the systematics and distribution of Malayan *phanerogams* IV. *Ixora. Gardens' Bull. Straits Settlments* 11:177-235.

1941. The flora of Singapore. *Malay. Agri-hort. Ass. Mag.* 11: 59-62.

1941. Further notes on the Moreton Bay Chestnut. (*Castano-spermum australe*): *Malay Agri-hort. Ass. Mag.* 11: 151- 154.

1941. A naturalist's companion. *Malay. Nat. J.* 2:.11-14.

1941. December 31st, his wife and son were evacuated, travelling to Australia, America and eventually to England arriving February 1943.

1942. February to November 1945: War years in Singapore; much botanical work achieved for later publication, notably his research which led to the Durian Theory and he began his serious study of seeds in microscopic structure.

1945. He was repatriated to England in November.

1946. The need for the development of tropical ecological stations. *Nature* 157: 377.

1946. Tropical Biology: an international problem. *Biol. & Human Affairs* 12: 53-57

1946. Suggestions for Botanical Progress. *New Phytol*; 45: 185-192.

1946. The pig-tailed monkey as a plant-collector. *Zoo Life 1*: 89-92.

1946. Centrifugal stamens. *J. Arn. Arboretum* 27: 423-437.

1946. Japanese men of science in Malaya during the Japanese Occupation. *Nature* 158: 63.

1947-1948. Principal Field Scientific Officer, Latin America, UNESCO, starting in Rio de Janeiro and later as Secretary Hylean Amazon Project (UNESCO) based in Manaus.

1947. Daughter Stephanie Christine was born on 19 April in Hanover, New Hampshire. In late June, his family moved to Niteroi, over the bay from Rio de Janeiro.

1947. Variation in the size, and shape of spores, *basidia* and *cystidia* in Basidiomycetes. *New Phytol.* 46: 195-228.

1948. Studies in the Basidium. 1: the ampoule-effect, with a note on nomenclature. *New Phytol.* 47: 22-49.

1948. *Asterodon*, a clue to the morphology of fungous fruit-bodies: with notes on *Asterostroma* and *Asteromella*. *Trans. Brit. Mycol. Soc.* 31: 234-245.

1948. Report on the progress of the Hylean Amazon project (1947-1948): (Paris UNESCO 1948).

1947 to 1948. Travelled extensively in South America ending with six months in Amazonas based at Manaus.

1948. October, Second daughter born in England. Named Lindsay Mary Dorothy (originally christened Edred Lindsay Noel), later changing to Dorothy Lindsay Helga.

1948. June, excluded from the family home in Niteroi.

1949. Returns to Cambridge from Brazil, arriving late December, in time for Christmas. Appointed Lecturer in Taxonomy, Botany School, Cambridge. He wrote that Mycology was still a hobby and 'finalisation' of work on Ficus.

1949. The Annonaceous seed and its four interguments. *New Phytol.* 48: 332-364.

1949. The Durian Theory or the Origin of the Modern Tree. *Ann. Bot. New Ser.*, 13: 367-414, translated (1964) as 'La theorie du Durian ou l'origine de l'arbre modern'. Adaption française par N. & F. Hallè. *Adansonia* (N.S.) 4:156-184.

1950. Report on fungus-brackets from Star Carr, *Seamer*. pp. 123-124 in F.G.D. Clark; preliminary report on excavations at Star Carr, Seamer, Yorkshire (Second season 1950); *Proc. Prehist. Soc.* 9 (1950): 109-129.

1950. Descriptions of two luminous tropical agarics (*Dictyopanus* and *Mycena*). Mycologia.42: 423-431.

1950. A Monograph of *Clavaria* and allied genera. *Ann.Bot. Mem* 1:1-740, plates 16, text-figs. 298.

1950. Marriage with Shiela Kavanagh Bailey broke down.

1951–1960

1951. Obit. Prof. H. Tanakadate. *Nature* 167: 586.

1951. Lectotypes in Mycology: a taxonomic proposal. *Nature* 168:1031-1032.

1951. The Leguminous Seed: *Phytomorphology* 1:1 - 34.

1952. *Wayside Trees of Malaya* 2 vols., 772pp: text-figs. 260 & plates 228: 2nd edition, Government Printing Office, Singapore.

1952. Addenda Clavariacea, I Two new pteruloid genera and *C. deflexula Ann. Bot. NS*:16: 269-291. *Pterula* & *Pterilicium Ann. Bot. NS*:16: 531-569 & (1953) Ann. Bot. NS:.16: 531-569.

1952. Durians and dogma. *Indones. J. nat. Sci.* 5-6: 141-145.

1952. Generic names in *Clavariaceae. Trans. Brit. Mycol. Soc.* 35: 285-298.

1952. 17 March, divorce nisi granted and made absolute on 3 June.

1953. The Durian Theory extended. I. *Phytomorphology* 3: 465-476.

1953. Proposal No. 10, principles for stability of nomenclature (VIIIth Int.Bot. Congr.prop.10). *Taxon* 2: 101. And L.E. Hawker (1953): Hypogeous fungi from Malaya. *Trans. Br. Mycol. Soc.* 36: 125-137.

1953. The construction of polypores – I. Introduction: *Polyporus sulphurous, P. squamosus, P. betulinus* and *Polystictus microcylus. Phytomorphology* 3: 152-167.

1953. 9 April, married Helga Dinesen Søndergaard from Mors, Denmark.

1954. The classification of higher fungi. *Proc. Linn. Soc. Lond.* 165: 4-6.

1954. The Durian Theory extended – II. The arillate fruit and the compound leaf: *Phytomorphology* 4: 152-165.

1954. The Durian Theory extended – III. Pachycauly and megaspermy – conclusion: *Phytomorphology* 4: 263-274.

1954. Evolution of the tropical rainforest; a chapter written for *Evolution as a Process*, Pp. 34-46: J.Huxley, A.C.Hardy & E.B.Ford (eds): Allen & Unwin London.

1954. Further descriptions of luminous agarics. *Trans. Brit. Mycol. Soc.* 37: 256-271.

1955. Botanical collecting with monkeys. *Proc. Instn. Gt. Br.* 36: (no 162): 1-16

1955. Epilogia [*sic*] pro monographia sua. *Taxon* 4: 6-8.

1955. Elected a Fellow of the Royal Society.

1956. Taxonomy and tropical plants. *Proc. Linn. Soc. Lond.* 168: 65-70.

1956. A new European *Clavaria: Clavulinopsis septentrionalis* sp. nov. *Friesia* 5: 218-230.

1956. The Clavariaceae of the Mussoorie Hills (India) II with K.S.Thind & G.P.S. Anand: *Trans. Br. Mycol. Soc.* 39: 475-484.

1957. *Craterellus* Pers., *Cantherellus* Fr. and *Pseudocraterellus* gen. nov. *Festschr. F. Franz. Petrak: Sydowia. Beih.* 1: 266-276.

1957. Some Clavarias from Argentina. *Darwiniana* 2: 193-206.

1957. The Clavariaceae of the Mussoorie Hills (India) VIII with K.S. Thind & Sukh Dev: *Trans. Br. Mycol. Soc.* 40: 472-476.

1957. Paintings of Flowering Plants which Sir Stamford Raffles caused to be made in Bencoolen, Sumatra, March 1824, written 'for private circulation to scientific institutions concerned with the botany of Malaysia'.

1958. The Clavariaceae of the Mussoorie Hills (India) IX. *Trans. Br. Mycol. Soc.* 41: 203-206.

1958. Transference of function. *J. Linn. Soc. Bot.* 90: 33-40 & *J. Linn. Soc. Zool.* 44: 33-40.

1958. An introduction to the distribution of *Ficus. Reinwardtia* 4: 15-45.

1958. Malayan and Sumatran Discomycetes, with Cash E.K: *Trans. Brit. Mycol. Soc.* 41: 273-282.

1959. Vegetation of the humid tropics. *Nature* 183: 795-796.

1959. The importance of tropical taxonomy to modern botany. *Gardens' Bull. Singapore* 17: 209-214.
1959 to 1975 Member of the Governing Body of Rugby School.
1959 to 1973 Fellow of Sidney Sussex College, Cambridge.
1959 to 1965 Promoted to Reader in Plant Taxonomy at Cambridge.
1960. Taxonomic notes on *Ficus* Linn, Asia and Australasia; I-IV. *Gardens' Bull. Singapore* 17: 368-485.
1960. The Malayan flora in R.D. Purchon (ed.), pp. 21-24. *Proc. Centen. & Bicenten. Cong. Biol.* 1958, (Singapore).
1960. Taxonomic notes on *Ficus* Linn, in Asia and Australasia. V-VI. *Gardens' Bull. Singapore* 18: 1-69.
1960. Reconnaisance visit to Mount Kinabalu.
1960. Son, John Kavanagh, leaves home later in the year, never to return.
1960. Awarded the Darwin Medal by The Royal Society and became Vice-President of the Linnaean Society.

1961–1970
1961. Impact of man on the vegetation of the humid tropics; *Nature* 189: 24-25.
1961. Agnes Arber. *Phytomorphology* 11: 197-198.
1961. A tropical botanist's introduction to Borneo. *Sarawak Mus. J* 10: 1-16.
1961. Taxonomic notes on Ficus Linn., Asia and Australasia: Addendum *Gardens' Bull. Singapore* 18: 83-97.
1961. Introduction in J. Wyatt-Smith & P.R. Wycherley (eds.), pp 1-7; *Nature Conservation in Western Malaysia.* Kuala Lumpur: *Malay. Nat. Soc.*
1961. Evolution in A.M. McLeod & L.S. Cobley (eds.), pp. 95-115. *Contemporary Botanical Thought: Oliver & Boyd*, Edinburgh, UK.
1961. A note on *Wiesnerina* (Cyphellaceae). *Trans. Brit. Mycol. Soc.* 44: 230-232.
1961 Dimitic species of *Ramaria* (Clavariaceae) with K.S. Thind; *Trans. Brit. Mycol. Soc.* 44: 233-238.
1961. Led the Royal Society Expedition to North Borneo, in conjunction with the Sabah Society; he took the first photos from the east summit of Mount Kinabalu.
1962. Botany and prehistory in [UNESCO]; *Symposium on the Impact of Man on the Humid Tropics Vegetation, Goroka* 1960. pp. 38-41. Printed in 1962 but probably not distributed until 1963. Copy received at RBG Kew 10/10/1963. 'The mace of regalia…' quote from Mabberley; Biog. Mems R. Soc. Lond 45: 77-93 (1999). See p. 85 for Mace quote.
1962. The Royal Society Expedition to North Borneo, 1961. *Emp. For. Rev.* 1962: 224-233.
1962. The classification of Moraceae. *Gardens' Bull. Singapore* 19: 187-252.
1962. Taxonomic notes on Ficus L., Asia & Australasia; Addendum II. *Gardens' Bull. Singapore* 19: 385-415.
1962. Corner EJH & Bas, (1962); the genus *Amanita* in Singapore and Malaya; *Persoonia* 2: 241-304.
1963. The tropical botanist. *Advmt Sci. Lond*, 20: 328-334.
1963. *Ficus* in the Pacific region in J.L. Gressit (ed.), pp. 233-249; *Pacific Basin Biogeography. Bishop Mus. Press*, Honolulu, USA
1963. A criticism of the gonophyll theory of the flower. *Phytomorphology* 13: 290-292.

1963. A Dipterocarp clue to the biochemistry of Durianology. *Ann. Bot.* (N.S.) 27: 339-341.

1963. Studies in the flora of Thailand 16. Moraceae, *Dansk; Bot. Ark.* 23: 19-32.

1963. Wrongly shown as 1936 in some summaries, Exploring North Borneo; *New Scient.* 366: 488-490.

1963. Royal Society Expedition to North Borneo 1961: reports. *Proc. Linn. Soc. Lond.* 175: 9-32 (General Report): 37-45 (Special Reports).

1963. Why *Ficus*, why Moraceae? *Fl. Malesiana Bull* 18:1000-1004.

1963 17 August, John Kavanagh Corner married Belinda Mary Shaw in Gt. St. Mary's Church, Cambridge.

1964. Led the second Royal Society Expedition to North Borneo, in conjunction with the Sabah Society. The two expeditions were instrumental in the establishment of the Kinabalu National Park.

1964. A Discussion on the Results of The Royal Society Expedition to North Borneo, (1961) organised by E.J.H. Corner, *Proc. R. Linn. Soc. Lond.* B161: 1-91 (Commentary on the general results: pp. 3-6; Conclusion: pp. 90-91.

1964. *The Life of Plants.* 315 pp + 41 pl. Weidenfeld & Nicholson, London, UK [Also trans. *Leo Dile as La Vie des Plantes* (1964), and trans. Lucia Maldacea as *La Vita delle Plante* (1972), both with additional pp. after p. 316 by P. Coursin].

1965. Check-list of *Ficus* in Asia and Australasia with keys to identification. *Gardens' Bull. Singapore* 21: 1-186.

1965. Mount Kinabalu East. *Sabah Soc. J.* 4: 170-187.

1965. Led the Royal Society Expedition to the British Solomon Islands.

1966. A monograph of Cantharelloid fungi. *Ann. Bot. Mem.* 2: pp.1-255 + 5pl.

1966. *The Natural History of Palms.* pp. 393 + 24 pl.: Weidenfeld & Nicholson, London, UK.

1966. Debunking the New Morphology. *New Phytol*; 65: 398-404.

1966. Species of *Ramaria* (Clavariaceae) without clamps. *Trans. Brit. Mycol. Soc.* 49: 101-113.

1966. Kinabalu. *Straits Times Annual* 1966:

1966. On *Clavaria inaequalis* Fr. *Nov. Hedw.* 12: 61-63.

1966. The clavarioid complex of *Aphelaria* and *Tremellodendropsis. Trans. Brit. Mycol. Soc.* 49: 205-211.

1966. *Paraphelaria*, a new genus of Auriculariaceae. *Persoonia* 4: 345-350.

1966. Clavarioid genera and *Thelephora* from the Congo. *Bull. Jard. Bot. Etat* 36: 257-279.

1966. Awarded the Patron's Medal of the Royal Geographical Society and appointed Professor of Tropical Botany at Cambridge.

1967. *Ficus* in the Solomon Islands and its bearing on the post-Jurassic history of Melanesia, *Phil. Trans. R. Soc. Lond.* (B) 253: 23-159.

1967. On thinking big. *Phytomorphology* 17: 24-28.

1967. Notes on *Clavaria. Trans. Brit. Mycol. Soc.* 50: 33-44.

1967. Clavarioid fungi of the Solomon Islands. *Proc. Linn. Soc. Lond.* 178: 91-106.

1967. Biological expeditions. *May & Baker Lab. Bull,* 7: 90-92.

1967. Moraceae. [Bot. Rep. Danish Noona Dan Expedition]: *Dansk bot. Ark.* 25: 64-67.

1967. *Clavaires et Thelephora* with P. Heinemann. *Flore Iconographique des Champignons du Congo* 16: 309-321.

1968. A monograph of *Thelephora* (Basidiomycetes), *Beihefte zur Nov. Hedw.* 27: 110 pp + 4 pl.

1968. Mycology in the tropics *Apologia pro monographia sua secunda*; *New Phytol* 67: 219-228, 1968.

1968. Conservation – future prospects. *Biol. Conserv.* 1:21-26.

1968. Became a 'corresponding' member of the Botanical Society of America, and a 'corresponding' member of Koninklijke Nederlandsa Botanische Vereniging.

1969. Notes on Cantharelloid fungi. *Beihefte zur Nov. Hedw.* 18: 738-818.

1969. A discussion of the results of The Royal Society Expedition to the British Solomon Islands Protectorate, 1965, organised by E.J.H. Corner. *Phil. Trans. R. Soc. Lond.* (B) 255: 185-631. Introduction: 187-188: *Ficus*: 567-570; the botany of Jaagi Is, Santa Cristobel: 571-573; Mountain flora of Popomanusen, Guadalcanal: 575-577; Larger fungi of the Solomon Islands: 579; Summary of the discussion: 621-623.

1969. The complex of *Ficus deltoidea*; a recent invasion of the Sunda Shelf. *Phil. Trans. R. Soc.* (B) 256: 281-317.

1969. *Ficus* sect. *Adenosperma. Phil. Trans. R. Soc.* (B) 256: 318-355.

1969. The conservation of scenery and wildlife; *Proc. Ceylon Asst. Advmt. Sci.* 2: 220-231.

1969. Ecology and natural history in the tropics; *Proc. Ceylon Asst. Advmt Sci.* 2: 261-273.

1969. With Watanabe, K. *Illustrated Guide to Tropical Plants.* 1147 pp.: Hirokawa, Tokyo, Japan.

1970. Awarded the Gold medal from Societas Linnaeana Optime Merenti Carolus Linnaeus. This same year he became a Fellow of the Association of Tropical Biology.

1970. *Ficus* subgen. *ficus*; Two rare and primitive pachycaul species. *Phil. Trans. R. Soc.* (B) 259: 353-381.

1970. *Ficus* subgen. *Pharmosycea*, with reference to the species of New Caledonia; *Phil. Trans. R. Soc. Lond*: (B) 259: 383-433.

1970. New species of *Streblus* and *Ficus* (Moraceae). *Blumea* 18: 393-411.

1970. *Phylloporus* quel. and *Paxillus* Fr. in Malaya and Borneo. *Beihefte zur Nov. Hedw.* 20: 793-822.

1970. Supplement to 'A monograph of *Clavaria* and allied genera'. *Beihefte zur Nov. Hedw.* 33: 1-299 + 4 pl.

1970. *Ficus* (Moraceae). *Ident. Lists Malaysian Species* 537-648 in *Foundation Flora Malesiana.*

1971–1980

1971. Merulioid fungi in Malaysia. *Gardens' Bull. Singapore* 25: 355-381.

1971. Mycological reports from New Guinea and the Solomon Islands, 4, enumeration of the Clavariaceae. *Bull. Natn Sci. Mus., Tokyo* 14: 423-427.

1972. Awarded the CBE.

1972. New Taxa of *Ficus* (Moraceae). *Blumea* 20: 427-432.

1972. Studies in the basidium – spore spacing and the *Boletus* spore. *Gardens' Bull. Singapore* 26: 159-194.

1972. *Boletus* in Malaysia 263 pp + 23 p.; Singapore Govt Printing Office.

1972. *Ficus* (Moraceae) from India, Burma, Thailand, China, Korea, Japan, Ryukyu [Islands, Japan], Formosa [Taiwan] and Hainan. *Ident. Lists Malaysian Species*: 735-784: *Foundation Flora Malesiana*.

1972. Urgent exploration needs: Pacific Floras. *Pac. Sci. Assoc. Inform. Bull.* 24: 17-27.

1973. Resigned his Fellowship of Sidney Sussex College over the admission of ladies.

1973. Resigned as a Governor of Rugby School also over the admission of ladies.

1974. Became Emeritus Professor of Tropical Botany at Cambridge University and in this same year was awarded the Victoria Medal of Honour by the Royal Horticultural Society.

1974. *Boletus* and *Phylloporus* in Malaysia: further notes and descriptions. *Gardens' Bull. Singapore* 27: 1-16.

1975. New *taxa* of *Ficus* (Moraceae) 2: *Blumea* 22: 299-309.

1975. Prototypic organisms XIII. Tropical trees: *Theoria to Theory* 9: 33-43.

1975. The evolution of *Streblus* Lour. (Moraceae): with a new species of sect. *Bleekrodea. Phytomorphology* 25: 1-12.

1975. *Ficus* in the New Hebrides. *Phil. Trans. R. Soc. Lond.* (B) 272: 343-367.

1975. A Discussion on the Results of the 1971 Royal Society-Percy Sladen Expedition to the New Hebrides with K.E. Lee (eds.): Royal Society, London, UK.

1975. Memorials and Reminiscences in J.S.L. Gilmour & S.M. Walters (eds.), pp. 4-5 *A memorial volume Humphrey Gilbert-Carter*: Cambridge University Botanic Garden, Cambridge, UK.

1976. The climbing species of *Ficus*: derivation and evolution. *Phil. Trans. R. Soc. Lond.* (B) 273: 379-386.

1976. *The Seeds of Dicotyledons*. Vol. 1: 311 pp; Vol 11: 552 pp. Cambridge: Cambridge University Press, Cambridge, UK.

1976. Further notes on cantharelloid fungi and *Thelephora. Beihefte zur Nov. Hedw.* 27: 325-342.

1976. A new species of *Paratocarpus* Baillon (Moraceae). *Gardens' Bull. Singapore* 28: 183-190.

1976. On the clavarioid *Ramaria stricta* (Fr.) Quel in Borneo. *Persoonia* 9: 149-150.

1977. A note on *Gomphus. Mycologia* 69: 431-432.

1977. The tribute 'Tropical Botany' was published in the *Gardens' Bulletin, Singapore* to mark E. J. H. Corner's 70th birthday.

1978a. *The Freshwater Swamp-forest of South Johore and Singapore. Gardens' Bull. Singapore*, Suppl. I: ix, 266pp. (1976 in press).

1978. *Ficus dammaropsis* and the multibracteate species of *Ficus* sect. *Sycocarpus. Phil. Trans. R. Soc. Lond.* (B) 281: 373-406.

1978. The inflorescence of *Dillenia. Notes R. Bot. Gdn. Edinb.* 36; 341-353.

1978. *Dacrydium* in Malaya. *Malayan Nat.* J. 32: 103-104.

1978. The plant life in D. M. Luping, C. Wen & E. R. Dingley (eds.), pp. 112-178. *Kinabalu, summit of Borneo*: Sabah Society. Kota Kinabalu, Sabah.

1979. Became an Honorary Fellow of the Botanical Society of Edinburgh.

1979. Conservation of the plant world – purpose, action, education, maintenance. *Proc. Int. Bot. Congr* 12: 65-72.

1980. *Boletus longipes* Mass, a critical Malaysian species. *Gardens' Bull. Singapore* 33: 290-296.

1980. *Entoloma* (Fr.) Kummer in the Malay Peninsula. *Gardens' Bull. Singapore* 33: 297-300.

1980. *The palm*. T. T. P. Gunawardana, L. Prematilleka & R. Silva (eds.), pp. 116-122. P.E.P *Deraniyagala Commemoration Volume* Colombo: Lake House Investments.

1981–1990

1981. Received the Tropical Botanical Garden, Hawaii, Robert Allerton Award gold medal, for excellence in tropical botany.

1981. The Agaric genera *Lentinus, Panus* and *Pleurotus*, with particular reference to the Malaysian species; *Beihefte zur Nov. Hedw.* 69: 1-169.

1981. Recollection [of A.H. Church] in D.J. Mabberley (ed.), pp. 1-8. *Revolutionary botany*. Clarendon Press, Oxford, UK.

1981. *The Marquis: A Tale of Syonan-to*. Heinemann Asia, Singapore.

1981. Angiosperm classification and phylogeny – a criticism. *Bot. J. Linn. Soc.* 82: pp. 81-87.

1983. Ad Polyporaceas I. *Amauroderma & Ganoderma, Beihefte zur Nov. Hedw.* 75: 1-182

1983. The clavarioid *Ramaria* subgen. *Echinoramaria*. Persoonia 12: 21-28.

1983 The myristicaceous seed. *Blumea* 28: 419-421.

1983. Visited Japan to meet the scientists who had been in Singapore from 1942 to 1945.

1984. Ad Polyporaceas II: *Polyporus, Mycobonia*, and *Echinochaete, Beihefte zur Nov. Hedw.* 78: 1-129.

1984. Ad Polyporaceas III: *Piptoporus, Buglossoporus, Laetiporus, Meripilus* and *Bondarzewia. Beihefte zur Nov Hedw.* 78: 133-222.

1985. The botany of some islets east of Pahang and Johore (Malaysia). *Gardens' Bull. Singapore* 38:1-42.

1985. *Ficus* (Moraceae) and Hymenoptera (Chalcidoidea), figs and their pollinators. *Biol. J. Linn. Soc.* 25: 187-195.

1985 Essays on Ficus. *Allertonia*, 4: 125-168.

1985. Ficus (Moraceae) and Hymenoptera (Chalcidoidea): figs and their pollinators. Biological Journal of the Linnean Society of London, 25: 187-195.

1985. Awarded the inaugural International Prize for Biology, in Tokyo, and also received the Freedom of the City of Yokohama with the Golden Key to the City.

1986. The agaric genus *Panellus Karst.* (including *Dictyopanus* Pat.) in Malaysia. *Gardens' Bull. Singapore* 39: 103-147.

1986. The genus *Clavulina* (Basidiomycetes) in south-eastern Australia. *Austr. J. Bot*, 34:103-105.

1986. The tropical complex of *Mycena pura*. *Trans. Bot. Soc. Edinb.* (150th anniv. suppl.): 61-67.

1986. Acceptance address. K. Iwatsuki, P. H. Raven & W. J. Bock (eds.), pp xii-xiv. *Modern aspects of species*; biological thoughts in *Modern Aspects of species*, pp. 3-8: University of Tokyo Press, Tokyo, Japan.

1987. Ad Polyporaceae IV: The genera *Daedalea, Flabellophora, Flavodon, Gloeophyllum, Heteroporus, Irpex, Lenzites, Microporellus, Nigrofomes, Nigroporus, Oxyporus, Paratrichaptum, Rigidoporus, Scenidium, Trichaptum, Vanderbylia* and *Steccherinum. Beihefte zur Nov. Hedw.* 86: pp. 1-265.

1988. *Wayside Trees of Malaya*, 2 vols, pp. 1-772: text-figs.260 plates 228: 3rd edition, the Malayan Nature Society in conjunction with the United Selangor Press, Kuala Lumpur, Malaysia; [the original plates are now preserved at the Rijksherbarium, Leiden].

1988. Higher fungi. In *Malaysia: key environments* (ed. Earl of Cranbrook), pp. 88-101. Oxford: Pergamon.

1989a. Ad Polyporaceaes V: the genera *Albatrellus, Boletopsis, Coriolopsis,* (dimitic), *Cristelloporia, Dicanthodes, Elmerina, Fomitopsis* (dimitic), *Gloeoporus, Grifola, Hapalopilus, Heterobasidion, Hydnopolyporus,Ischnoderma, Loweporus, Paramastomyces, Perenniporia, Pyrofomes, Steccchericium, Trechispora, Truncospora* and *Tyromyces: Beihefte zur Nov. Hedw.* 96: 1-218.

1989b. Ad Polyporaceaes VI: The genus *Trametes: Beihefte zur Nov. Hedw.* 97: 1-197.

1989. Again visited Japan and spent one week in New Caledonia.

1990. Biographical Memoirs of Fellows of The Royal Society. His Majesty Emperor Hirohito of Japan, K.G., 29 April 1901 – 7 January 1989, elected F.R.S. 1971, (Cambridge 1990): *Biogr. Mem. Fell. R. Soc* 36: 243-272.

1990. On *Trigonobalanus (Fagaceae). Bot. Journ. of the Lin. Soc.* 102: 219 – 223, with 1 figure.

1990. Became an Honorary Member of the British Mycological Society.

1991–2000

1991. Ad Polyporaceas VII: the Xanthochroic Polypores: *Beihefte zur Nov. Hedw.* 101:1-175.

1991. The active basidium: *Mycologist.* 5:69.

1991. Rokuya Imazeki: *Trans. Mycol. Soc. Japan* 32: 311-313.

1991. *Trogia* (Basidiomycetes). *Gardens' Bull. Singapore*; suppl 22: 1-99.

1992. *Botanical Monkeys*: Pentland Press, Edinburgh. UK.

1992. Additional resupinate non-xanthochroic polypores from Brazil and Malesia: *Beihefte zur Nov. Hedw.* 55:119-152.

1992. Notes on the development of the fruit-bodies of four Malayan species of *Amanita* (Basidiomycetes). *Gardens' Bull. Singapore* 44: 43-45.

1992. The development of the fruit-body of *Marasmius cornelii* (Agaricales) and of a new species of *Marasimus* sect. *Gloeocephala: Persoona* 14: 395-405.

1992. The pachychalaza in dicotyledons: primitive or advanced? *Bot. J. Linn. Soc.* 198:15-19.

1993. 'I am part of all that I have met' (Tennyson's *Ulysses*). In S. Isaac, J. C. Frankland, R. Watling & A. J. S. Whalley (eds.), pp. 1-13. A*spects of tropical mycology.* Cambridge University Press, Cambridge, UK,

1993. Ad Polyporaceas explicanda: *Beihefte zur Nov. Hedw.* 57: 143-157.

1993. Obituary of Dr. Yosio Koyabashi, *Trans. Mycol. Soc. Japan* 34: 295-298.

1993. *Psathyrella* (Agaricales) with ornamented spores in the Malay Peninsula. *Gardens' Bull. Singapore* 45: 337-357.

1993. August, Mrs Wendy How became carer and housekeeper to E. J. H. Corner and Helga Corner.

1994. The development of the gills in *Amanita rubescens* (Fr.) S. F. Gray. *Beihefte zur Nov. Hedw.* 58: 1450152.

1994(b). On the agaric genera *Hohenbuehelia* and *Oudemansiella*; Part I: *Hohenbuehelia. Gardens' Bull. Singapore* 46:1-47.

1994(c). On the agaric genera *Hohenbuehelia* and *Oudemansiella*; Part II:

Oudemansiella. Gardens' Bull. Singapore 46: 49-75.

1994. The structure of *Piptoporus betulinus. Mycologist* 8:138-140.

1994. Agarics in Malesia I: Tricholomatoid II Mycenoid; *Beihefte zur Nov. Hedw.* 109:1-271.

1994. *Peat swamp forest in the Malay Peninsula. Malayan Nat. J.* 47: 373-374.

1994. *On general botany* in *The ten years of the International Prize for Biology* (ed. Committee on the International Prize for Biology), p. 15. Tokyo: Japan Society for the Promotion of Science.

1995. The polypore genera *Henningsia* and *Rigidoporus. Mycologist* 9: 127.

1996. The Agaric Genera *Marasmius, Chaetocalathus, Crinipellis, Heimiomyces, Resupinatus, Xerula* and *Xerulina* in Malesia. *Beihefte zur Nov. Hedw.* 3:1-141.

1996. E. J. H. Corner's autobiography, *Moments Botaniques,* completed but unpublished.

1996. Joint winner of the inaugural de Bary Medal of the International Mycological Association.

1996. 14 September, died at home in Great Shelford, near Cambridge. Probate was granted on 14 November 1996 at net value £604,383. There is no memorial to him except EJH Corner House, now the French gourmet restaurant, Les Amis Au Jardin in the Botanic Gardens in Singapore. His ashes were scattered under two trees at the bottom of his garden at 91, Hinton Way, Great Shelford, Cambs by Mrs Wendy How.

1997. January, elder daughter Christine Cross died, age 50.

1999. 23 January, Helga Corner died in Symonds House near Cambridge (Linton). Probate was granted on 30 March 1999 at net value £573,701.

2001–2013

2005. 23 November, his first wife, Sheila Kavanagh Tanner (née Bailey), died near Reading (Pamber Heath).

2005. After years of disagreement with van Steenis, and long after E. J. H. Corner's death, immense work on ficus culminated in the publication in *Flora Malesiana* in two parts, with Part 2 published first in 2005: *Flora Malesiana ,* Ser. I, vol. 17, part 2. Leiden: National Herbarium Nederland.

2006. *Flora Malesiana ,* Ser. I, vol. 17, part 1. Leiden: National Herbarium Nederland.

2013. *My Father in His Suitcase: In Search of E. J. H. Corner, Relentless Botanist* by his son, John K. Corner, published by Landmark Books Pte. Ltd., Singapore.

Plants and fungi named after E. J. H. Corner

Adinandra corneriana Kobuski (Theaceae, Malay Peninsula).
Alpinia corneri (Holtt) RM Smith (*Cenolophon corneri* Holtt., Zingiberaceae, Malay Peninsula).
Alseodaphne corneri Kosterm. = *A. paludosa* Gamble (Lauraceae).
Anisophyllea corneri Ding Hou (Anissophylleaceae, Malay Peninsula).
Argyreia corneri Hoogl. (Convolvulaceae, Malay Peninsula).
Artocarpus corneri Kochummen (Moraceae, Borneo).
Barringtonia corneri Kiew & K. M. Wong (Lecythidaceae, Malay Peninsula).
Bauhinia purpurea L. var. corneri de Wit = *B. purpurea L.* (Leguminoseae).
Begonia corneri Kiew (Begoniaceae, Malay Peninsula).
Bulbophyllum corneri Carr (*Epicranthes corneri* (Carr) Garay & Kittredge) = **B. vesiculosum J. J. Sm.** (Orchidaceae).
Calamus corneri Furtado (Palmae, Malay Peninsula).
Cinnamomum corneri Kosterm. (Lauraceae, Borneo).
Cornera Furtado = **Calamus L.** (Palmae).
Dysoxylum corneri M. R. Hend. = *D. grande* Hiern (Meliaceae).
Elaeocarpus corneri Weibel (Elaeocarpaceae, Borneo).
Freycinetia corneri B. C. Stone (Pandanaceae, Malay Peninsula).
Globba corneri A. Weber (Zingiberaceae, Malay Peninsula).
Henckelia corneri (Kiew) A. Weber (*Didymocarpus corneri* Kiew, Gesneriaceae, Malay Peninsula.
Homalomena corneri Furtado (Araceae, Malay Peninsula).
Licuala corneri Furtado (Araceae, Malay Peninsula).
Lithocarpus corneri S. Julia & Soepadmo (Fagaceae, Borneo).
Maesa corneri Sleumer (Myrsinaceae, Bouganville).
Medinilla corneri Regalado (Melastomataceae, Borneo).
Melicope corneri T. G. Hartley (Rutaceae, Malay Peninsula).
Morinda corneri K. M. Wong (Rubiaceae, Malay Peninsula).
Nisophylla corneri.
Pandanus corneri Kaneh.
Pentace corneri Kosterm. (Malvaceae s.l./Tiliaceae, Malay Peninsula, Borneo).
Platyscapa corneri.
Plectomiopsis corneri Furtado (Palmae, Malay Peninsula).
Rhaphidophora corneri Furtado ex P. C. Boyce (Araceae, Malay Peninsula).
Schismatoglottis corneri A. Hay (Araceae, Borneo).
Schoutenia corneri Roekm. (Malvaceae s.l./Tiliaceae, Malay Peninsula).
Sonerila corneri Nayar (Melastomataceae, Borneo).
Ternstroemia corneri Keng (Theaceae, Malay Peninsula).
Tetrardisia corneri Furtado = Ardisia denticulate Blume (Myrsinaceae).
Thrixspermum corneri Holttum (Orchidaceae, Malay Peninsula).
Timonius corneri K. M. Wong (Rubiaceae, Malay Peninsula).

The Research Students of E. J. H. Corner

Emeritus Professor Vernon H. Heywood, 1927– ; research student, 1950–1953. Vernon Heywood spent five years in Spain at the botanic garden and Instituto A.J. Cavanilles, Madrid, after leaving Cambridge, then held the chairs of botany at Liverpool and Reading where he was also Dean of Faculty of Science. He took early retirement to become Chief Scientist (Plant Conservation) of IUCN (International Union for Conservation of Nature) and founder Director of BGCI (Botanic Gardens Conservation International); then Executive Editor, UNEP (United Nations Environment Programme) Global Biodiversity Assessment and consultant to World Bank, FAO and other international organisations. He is a world expert in plant taxonomy and systematics, and has specialised in Mediterranean flora and vegetation, biodiversity assessment and conservation, genetic resources of wild species of economic importance, especially crop wild relatives, and invasive alien species. He has published 69 books, including *Flowering Plants of the World*, *Flowering Plant Families of the World* and over 400 papers in scientific journals.

Dr Brenda Slade (née Shore), 1922–1993; research student circa 1952–1954. Brenda Slade was a student at the University of Otago, 1944–1948. She took her PhD studying leaf anatomy at Newnham College, Cambridge, graduating in 1954. She was on the the staff of University of Otago as lecturer from 1945 to 1982, eventually being promoted to Associate Professor in 1971 which, at that time, made her one of the few women to have attained this rank in a New Zealand University Science Department.

Dr Frances M Jarrett, 1931– ; research student, 1953–1956. Frances Jarrett's PhD thesis at Newnham College was titled 'A revision of artocarpus and allied genera'. She took an MA in 1957. She monographed Artocarpus for her doctoral dissertation; this was revised for the later publication *Flora Malesiana* of which she was joint producer with C. C. Berg and E. J. H. Corner. She was head of the Fern section at RBG Kew from 1960 to 1981.

Dr Chew Wee Lek, 1932– ; research student, 1957–1960. Chew Wee Lek was Botanist, Keeper of the Herbarium in Singapore Botanic Gardens, 1960-1970 and later, Director of the Botanic Gardens, Singapore. From 1970–1975, he was Botanist, then Senior Research Scientist at the National Herbarium, Royal Botanic Gardens, Sydney, Australia. He was Conservationist and Regional Officer at the International Union for Conservation of Nature & Natural Resources at Morges then Gland, Switzerland, 1975–1982, and Consultant Botanist on the Flora of Australia, Sydney, 1983–1988.

From 1989 to date, he is a Solicitor & Barrister of the Supreme Court of New

South Wales, Sydney; in private practice in Sydney from 1989 to 2000 then in Chatswood, NSW from 2000 to date.

Dr Gordon deWolf, 1927– ; research student, 1957-1959.
Gordon deWolf has an interest in plant identification, particularly orchids and, professionally, horticultural plants. While pursuing a Master's degree at Tulane University in New Orleans, he won a Fulbright scholarship to the University of Malaya to study under R. E. Holttum, resulting in a MSc (1954). While pursuing a PhD program at Cornell University, he applied to Corner, and became his research student at Fitzwilliam College, Cambridge on American figs.

From 1959–1961, deWolf was Senior Scientific Officer (Colonial Staff) at RBG Kew. He was Associate Professor of Biology and Professor of Biology, Georgia Southern College, 1961–1967, and served as Horticultural Taxonomist (1967–1969) and Horticulturist (1970–1974) at the Arnold Arboretum, Harvard University. From 1975 to 1990, he was Coordinator, Horticulture Program, Massachusetts Bay Community College.

He joined the New England Botanical Club in 1949 and sat on its Council from 1972 to 1978, and was its President, 1976-1978. deWolf was made a Felllow of the Linnaean Society of London in 1960.

Dr Peter Ashton, 1934– ; research student, 1960–1962.
Peter Ashton gained a BA in 1956, MA in 1960, and PhD in 1962, all from Cambridge University. He was forest botanist to the Brunei and then Sarawak governments, 1957–1966, and lecturered at University of Aberdeen, 1966–1978. From 1978, he has been associated with Harvard Univerity: Director of the Arnold Arboretum and Arnold Professor of Botany (1978–1987), Professor of Dendronlogy (1978–1991), Faculty Fellow, Harvard Institute for International Development (1990–2000), Charles Bullard Professor of Forestry (1991–1999), Faculty Fellow, Center for International Development, Kennedy School of Government (1998 to date), Charles Bullard Research Professor of Forestry (1999–2004), and Charles Bullard Professor of Forestry, emeritus (2004 to date).

He was co-founder of the Centre for Tropical Forest Science in 1991, and was President, Centre for Plant Conservation, 1988-1993, and President, International Association of Botanic Gardens and Arboreta,1987-1993.

Dr Ashton was awarded Hon ScD, U. Peradeniya in 2001, and Hon Sc D, Ripon College, Wisconsin in 2008. He was co-recipient of the UNESCO Sultan Qaboos Prize for Environmental Preservation (1997), Fairchild Medal for Plant Exploration (2008), Japan Prize Laureate (2007), and the Linnaean Medal of Botany (2009).

Dr Timothy Whitmore, 1935–2002; research student circa 1957–1960.
Timothy Whitmore was a Major Scholar at St John's College, Cambridge, from 1954 to 1957. Inspired by Corner, he specialised in tropical plants, and for his PhD (1961) studied trees in Malaya. For his work on bark development, he was awarded the Rolleston Memorial Essay Prize at Oxford. He was also elected a research fellow at St John's, Cambridge, and appointed a lecturer at Southampton University.

He joined the Oxford University Expedition to Ecuador in 1960 and was Government Forest Botanist in the Solomon Islands, 1962–1965, and a Colombo Plan Forest Botanist in the Forest Research Institute of Malaya, 1965–1972.

Following that, he was Principal Research Fellow, London Natural History Museum, 1974–1976, Senior University Research Officer Oxford Forestry Institute, 1974–1989, and he was visiting scholar and affiliated lecturer in the Department of Geography, Cambridge Univeristy, 1990–2002.

Dr Whitmore was awarded the ScD degree from Cambridge in 1977, Hon. Dr. Ehime, Japan, 1992, Dr Hon Causa Toulouse, France, 1998, and Dr Hon Causa, Vienna, 2001. He was a past President of the Malayan Nature Society.

He edited Volumes 1 and 2 of *Tree Flora of Malaya* and is the author of *Palms of Malaya* (1973), *Tropical Rain Forests of the Far East* (1975), and *An Introduction to Tropical Rain Forests* (1990).

Whitmore's name is commemorated in the tree genus *Whitmorea*, which he discovered in the Solomon Islands, and in 18 species of *whitmorei*.

Dr Chang Kiaw Lan, 1927–2003; research student 1962-1964.
Chang Kiaw Lan read botany and philosophy at the University of Malaya, 1953–1958. She was appointed Botanist to the Singapore Botanic Gardens Service in 1959 and as Keeper of the Herbarium in 1970. Her first field trip was to the Sedili. She was based at the Singapore Botanic Gardens for most of her career and for 17 years edited the *Gardens' Bulletin*.

She was awarded a British Commonwealth Scholarship (1962–1964) for a PhD in Botany at Newnham College under the supervision of Corner. She returned to the Singapore Botanic Gardens in September 1965. In 1966, she attended the 11th Pacific Science Congress in Tokyo presenting a paper. In 1965, she collected fungi in the Cameron Highlands, Malaysia, with Corner and Dr Chew Wee Lek. In 1967, when the beginning of the Singapore government's Garden City programme was becoming significant, she was in charge of the Tree Planting Campaign. In 1977, together with David Mabberley, she edited the *Corner Festschrift Tropical Botany Essays* presented to E. J. H. Corner for his seventieth birthday (*Gardens' Bulletin* Vol. 29.)

Dr Chang was treasurer or committee member of the Singapore Branch of the Malayan Nature Society, 1970-1980, and Branch Chairman, 1976–1977. She served on the committee of the Alliance Francaise de Singapour as member or treasurer 1971–1980. In 1976, she was knighted by the French government in the National Order for Academic Excellence. In 1988, she indexed the third edition of Corner's *Wayside Trees of Malaya*. In the 1990s she took positions in taxonomic botany at the Singapore Botanic Gardens. She remained steadfast in her role as Keeper of the Herbarium and is a fixture in the affairs of the *Gardens' Bulletin*. See her Obituary in *Gardens' Bulletin Singapore* 55 (2003) 309-315.

Dr Engkik Soepadmo, 1937– ; research student from 1963–1966.
Engkik Soepadmo was Research Fellow at the National Herbarium of the Netherlands, the University of Leiden Branch, Leiden, the Netherlands in 1966 to 1968. From 1968 to 1978, he was lecturer in the Department of Botany, Faculty of Science, University of Malaya, Kuala Lumpur and from 1978 to 1993, Professor of Ecology at the same university. From 1993 to date, he is the Coordinator and Chief Editor, Tree Flora of Sabah and Sarawak Project, at the Division of Tropical Forest Biodiversity Centre, Forest Research Institute Malaysia (FRIM), Kepong, Selangor, Malaysia. Professor Dr Engkik Soepadmo, an Indonesian, was one of the three

recipients of the 2012 Malaysian Merdeka Award for 'Outstanding Contribution to the People of Malaysia' category.

Dr John Dransfield, 1945– ; research student 1967–1970.
John Dransfield gained his PhD in 1970 with a study of two Malaysian palm genera, *Eugeissona* and *Johannesteijsmannia*. He went on to devote his working life to palm research, working first in Indonesia for four years on rattans and other palms, and then at the RBG Kew until his retirement in 2005. He continues his palm research as an Honorary Research Fellow at Kew. He received the Engler Silver Medal in 1988, the Founders Medal (Fairchild Tropical Botanic Garden in 1988), and The Fairchild Medal for Plant Exploration in 1998 and the Medal for Botany from the Linnaean Society of London in 2004, and was created Cavaliere delle Palme by the City of San Remo in 2001. He is the author of several books on palms and numerous scientific papers.

Dr David G. Frodin, 1940– ; research student 1967–1970.
David Frodin joined the University of Papua New Guinea as a lecturer in 1971, served as senior lecturer, 1978–1982, then Associate Professor, 1983-1985. He was a botanist at the Academy of Natural Sciences of Philadelphia, 1986-1990, and was a freelance botanist, 1990–1993.

In 1993, he joined RBG Kew as a botanist until compulsory retirement in 2000 (due to an age limit then in force), after which he was a freelance botanist till 2009. From 2003 to date, he is consultant taxonomist, Chelsea Physic Garden.

Dr Ruth Kiew (née Evans), 1946– ; research student 1969-1972.
Ruth Kiew started at New Hall moving later to Darwin College from where she did her PhD, this being approved in July 1972 for a thesis entitled 'Taxonomy and ecology of Iguanura (Palmae)'. She graduated MA and PhD in 1973. She lived in Cambridge, and was a guest at Corner's birthday parties, pre-1960, at Hinton Way. She went to Southeast Asia in 1969 to research for her doctorate.

Dr Kiew was Professor of Botany at the Agriculture University of Malaya, after which she was Keeper of the Herbarium of the Singapore Botanic Gardens. She is now coordinator of the Flora of Peninsular Malaysia at the Forest Research Institute in Kepong.

In 1997, her work included 'hunting for new specimens' and going on at least two expeditions in the region every year; when not in the field she lectures frequently. In 2002, she received one of her field's top honours for discovering more that 50 species of plants, the Fairchild Award for Plant Exploration, from a leading botanical garden in Florida. The *Begonia* Dr Ruth Kiew is named after her.

Prof Dr David Mabberley, 1948– ; research student 1970–1973.
David Mabberley is a botanist and writer. Among his varied interests is the taxonomy of tropical plants of the family Labiatae, Meliaceae and Rutaceae, particularly citrus. His name is one of the best known in botany because of his plant dictionary, *Mabberley's Plant-Book, A portable dictionary of plants, their classification and uses.*

At Oxford (1967–1970), he was greatly influenced by C. D. Darlington, the then Sherardian Professor of Botany, and Mabberley developed a profound interest in the relationship between plants and humans. He moved to doctoral work under

Corner whose publications had inspired him to the conviction that plant evolution had to be seen in the light of work on tropical plants. This has led him to devote much of his scientific life to tropical botany, notably economic plants, especially the mahogany family, teak family besides citrus, and also to the evolution, systematics and nomenclature of, among other groups, grapes and apples, the latter with his Oxford tutor Barrie E. Juniper.

He has written some sixteen books and was President of the Society for the History of Natural History (1993–1996).

At Oxford, his research was broad based with research students and post-doctorate researchers from many parts of the world, but, in 1996, after profound disagreement with the then Head of Department, he resigned his university post to concentrate on undergraduate teaching and writing at Wadham College, where he was for many years Dean, before emigrating to Australia.

He has held positions in France, Holland, Australia, North America and latterly in England at RBG Kew where he was Keeper of the Herbarium, Library, Art and Archives. He returned to Australia in 2011 to become Executive Director of the New South Wales Botanic Gardens Trust, managing The Royal Botanic Garden and Domain (Sydney), the National Herbarium of New South Wales, The Australian Botanic Garden (Mt. Annan) and The Blue Mountains Botanic Garden (Mt Tomah).

Among the awards he has received are the José Cuatrecasas Medal for Excellence in Tropical Botany and the Peter Raven Award (by the American Society of Plant Taxonomists to a plant systematist who has made successful efforts to popularise botany to non-scientists), both in 2004. In the same year, he was appointed to the Orin and Althea Soest Chair in Horticultural Science at the University of Washington. He was awarded the Linnaean Medal for Botany (2006).

A Modern Tom Brown's Schooldays, Michael Scott. London: George G Harrap.

A View from the Summit. The story of Bukit Timah Nature Reserve, Dr Shawn Lum and Ilsa Sharp, eds. Singapore: National University of Singapore and Nanyang Technological University.

Achievements and Reminiscences, Hidezo Tanakadate. Unpublished manuscript.

Biography of Dr John (Jack) Reid from *Mosquito Systematics*, Vol 19/2 1987 pp 173 to 183. See web mosquitocatalog.org/files/pdfs/MS19N02P173.pdf.

Botanical Monkeys, E. J. H. Corner. Edinburgh: Pentland Press.

British Documents on the End of Empire, Malaya, the Malayan Union Experiment, Series B Volume 3, Edited by AJ Stockwell. HMSO – PSI licence number C 2009002278.

Douglas Hurd Memoirs, Lord Hurd of Westwell. London: Little, Brown Book Group Ltd.

East Kinabalu, Royal Society Expeditions 40th Anniversary Monograph, K. Ravi Mandalam, G. W. H. Davison and Patricia Regis, eds. Kota Kinabalu: The Sabah Society.

Emigrant Ships to Luxury Liners, Passenger Ships to Australia and New Zealand 1945 to 1999, Peter Plowman. Kenhurst: Rosenberg Publishing Pty Ltd.

Encountering Terra Australis: The Australian Voyages of Nicolas Baudin and Matthew Flinders, 1800-1803, Peter Monteath and John West-Sooby. Kent Town: Wakefield Press.

Evolution as a Process, Julian Huxley FRS, A. C. Hardy FRS, and E. B. Ford FRS. London: George Allen & Unwin Ltd.

Far Eastern File, the Intelligence War in the Far East, Peter Elphick. London: Hodder & Staughton.

Flora Malesiana, vol 17 (1), C. C. Berg and E. J. H. Corner. Leiden: National Herbarium Nederland.

From Third World to First, Lee Kuan Yew. Singapore: Times Editions.

If this should be farewell, Adrian Wood, ed. Fremantle: Fremantle Press.

In Oriente Primus: A History of the Volunteer Forces in Malaya & Singapore, Jonathan Moffatt and Paul Riches. Coventry: Jonathan Moffatt & Paul Riches

Kinabalu, Summit of Borneo (Revised and Expanded Edition), K. M. Wong and A. Phillipps, eds. Kota Kinabalu: The Sabah Society in association with Sabah Parks.

Life and Death in Changi: The War and Internment Diary of Thomas Kitching (1942-1944), Goh Eck Kheng ed. Singapore: Landmark Books.

Malayan Spymaster, Boris Hembry. Singapore: Monsoon Books.

Malaysian Fungal Diversity, Roy Watling; E. B. Gareth Jones, Kevin D. Hyde and Vikineswary Sabaratnam eds. Kuala Lumpur: Mushroom Research Centre, University of Malaya and Ministry of Natural Resources and Environment Malaysia.

Nature Conservation in Western Malaysia, 1961, J. Wyatt-Smith and P. R. Wycherley eds. Kuala Lumpur: Malaysian Nature Society.

Passenger Ships of the Orient Line, Neil McCart. Somerset: Patrick Stephens Ltd.

Proceedings of the Centenary and Bicentenary Congress of Biology 1958, R. D. Purchon ed. Kuala Lumpur: University of Malaya Press.

Portraits of Humanity under the Shadow of War, Nagoya: TV Aichi, 1985.

Rethinking Japan: Social Sciences, Ideology and Thought, Adriana Boscaro, Franco Gatti and Massimo Raveri. Sandgate: Japan Library.

Revolutionary Botany: 'Thalassiophyta' and Other Essays by A. H. Church, D. J. Mabberley, ed. Oxford: Claredon Press.

Shenton of Singapore, Governor and Prisoner of War, Brian Montgomery. London : L. Cooper in association with Secker & Warburg.

Singapore, A Guide to Buildings, Streets, Places, Norman Edwards & Peter Keys. Singapore: Times Editions.

Singapore in Sunshine and Shadow, John Bertram van Cuylenberg. Singapore: Heinemann Asia.

Singapore, the Japanese Version, Colonel Masanobu Tsuji, Margaret E. Lake, trans., H. V. Howe, ed. Sydney: Ure Smith.

Sixty Years of Science at UNESCO 1945-2005. Paris: UNESCO Publishing.

SOE Singapore 1941-1942, Richard Gough. London: Kimber.

Swettenham, Henry Sackville Barlow. Kuala Lumpur: Southdene Sdn. Bhd.

The Black Swan, Nicholas Taleb. London: Penguin Books.

The Edinburgh Journal of Botany, 64 (3): 431-437 (2007) review of *Flora Malesiana*, June 2012. Edinburgh.

The Freshwater Swamp-forest of South Johore and Singapore, E. J. H. Corner. Singapore: Singapore Botanic Gardens.

The Japanese File, Eric Robinson, Singapore: Heinemann Asia.

The Jungle is Neutral, F. Spencer Chapman. Singapore & Kuala Lumpur: Times Books International.

The Kotal Route Sketches: Royal Society Kinabalu Expedition 1964, Ravi Mandalam Kota Kinabalu: Sabah Society.

The Last Lord, Marquis Yoshichika Tokugawa. Tokyo: Kodansha Corp.

The Marquis: A Tale of Syonan-to, E.J.H. Corner. Singapore: Heinemann Asia.

The Memoirs of a Malayan Official, Victor Purcell. London: Cassell.

The Oxford Dictionary of National Biography. Oxford: Oxford University Press.

The Proceedings of the Centenary and Bicentenary Congress of Biology Singapore in 1958. Kuala Lumpur: University of Malaya Press.

The Singapore Story: Memoirs of Lee Kuan Yew, Lee Kuan Yew. Singapore: Times Editions.

Wayside Trees of Malaya, E. J. H. Corner. Kuala Lumpur: Malaysian Nature Society.